A POCKETFUL

OF PROSE

VINTAGE

SHORT FICTION

Volume II

A POCKETFUL

OF PROSE

VINTAGE

SHORT FICTION

Volume II

DAVID MADDEN

Louisiana State University

HARCOURT BRACE COLLEGE PUBLISHERS

*Fort Worth   Philadelphia   San Diego   New York   Orlando   Austin   San Antonio
Toronto   Montreal   London   Sydney   Tokyo*

PUBLISHER	*Ted Buchholz*
EDITOR IN CHIEF	*Christopher P. Klein*
EXECUTIVE EDITOR	*Michael A. Rosenberg*
ASSISTANT EDITOR	*Tina Winslow*
PROJECT EDITOR	*Laura J. Hanna*
PRODUCTION MANAGER	*Jane Tyndall Ponceti*
ART DIRECTORS	*Melinda Welch/Nick Welch*

Address for Editorial Correspondence: Harcourt Brace College Publishers, 301 Commerce Street, Suite 3700, Fort Worth, TX 76102.

Address for Orders: Harcourt Brace & Company, 6277 Sea Harbor Drive, Orlando, FL 32887-6777. 1-800-782-4479, or 1-800-433-0001 (in Florida).

Printed in the United States of America

ISBN: 0-15-502545-7

Library of Congress Catalog Card Number: 91-32546

5 6 7 8 9 0 1 2 3 4   039   10 9 8 7 6 5 4 3 2 1

A Word from the Editor to Students and Teachers

You can actually lift this book.

And you can afford it.

As with the first Vintage anthology in the Pocketful series, this selection of some of the most commonly taught short stories is aimed at satisfying the need for a concise, quality collection that students will find inexpensive and that instructors will enjoy teaching.

The reception of this series has supported our original assumption that students and teachers would welcome an innovative alternative to huge anthologies, which are rarely used entirely, tend to be too bulky to carry and to handle in class, and are, above all, expensive.

A Pocketful of Prose: Vintage, Short Fiction, Volume II contains 23 stories that research reveals to be currently among the most commonly studied in classes around the country.

The marginal notes on "Miss Brill" are intended to suggest ways to annotate the other stories, providing a basis for class discussion, papers, and review for exams.

Nine of the stories include source materials to encourage further discussion and analysis. Among these enhancements are author's comments, biographical and critical commentaries, and sections from a play and a film script for comparison of media.

The design of the text encourages students to respond to the stories as they read. You will notice that the margins are wide to allow room for notes, questions, and student commentary.

The stories are arranged according to considerations about point of view. The first three stories are examples of omniscient, first-person, and third-person, limited point-of-view techniques. The remaining stories demonstrate an increasing level of character awareness in the first-person stories and an increasing intimacy with the protagonist in the third-person stories.

At Harcourt Brace, my Acquisitions Editor, Michael Rosenberg and my Assistant Editor, Tina Winslow, shared my vision of this text and supported my desire to try new approaches to the creation of textbooks. They helped shape the collection from start to finish. Thanks also to Project Editor Laura Hanna, Art Directors Melinda Welch and Nick Welch, and Production Manager Jane Ponceti, whose talents made it possible to meet the design and production challenges of the text.

We hope that students will find the cost refreshing and that the enhancement material and annotations will help broaden their experience with the stories.

We are interested in hearing from you. To tell us your comments on how this text worked in your class, please respond in writing to Executive English Editor, Harcourt Brace, 301 Commerce Street, Suite 3700, Fort Worth, TX 76102.

David Madden
Louisiana State University

CONTENTS

Shirley Jackson, 1919–1965

The Lottery

This story first appeared in THE NEW YORKER, *1948.*

THE MORNING OF JUNE 27TH WAS CLEAR AND SUNNY, with the fresh warmth of a full-summer day; the flowers were blossoming profusely and the grass was richly green. The people of the village began to gather in the square, between the post office and the bank, around ten o'clock; in some towns there were so many people that the lottery took two days and had to be started on June 26th, but in this village, where there were only about three hundred people, the whole lottery took less than two hours, so it could begin at ten o'clock in the morning and still be through in time to allow the villagers to get home for noon dinner.

The children assembled first, of course. School was recently over for the summer, and the feeling of liberty sat uneasily on most of them; they tended to gather together quietly for a while before they broke into boisterous play, and their talk was still of the classroom and the teacher, of books and reprimands. Bobby Martin had already stuffed his pockets full of stones, and the other boys soon followed his example, selecting the smoothest and roundest stones; Bobby and Harry Jones and Dickie Delacroix—the villagers pronounced this name "Dellacroy"—eventually made a great pile of stones in one corner of the square and guarded it against the raids of the other boys. The girls stood aside, talking among themselves, looking over their shoulders at the boys, and the very small children rolled in the dust or clung to the hands of their older brothers or sisters.

Soon the men began to gather, surveying their own children, speaking of planting and rain, tractors and taxes. They stood together, away from the pile of stones in the corner, and their jokes were quiet and they smiled rather than laughed. The women, wearing faded house dresses and sweaters, came shortly after their menfolk. They greeted one another and exchanged bits of gossip as they went to join their husbands. Soon the women, standing by their husbands, began to call to their children, and the children came reluctantly, having to be called four or five times. Bobby Martin ducked under his mother's grasping hand and ran, laughing, back to the pile of stones. His father spoke up sharply, and Bobby came quickly and took his place between his father and his oldest brother.

1

The lottery was conducted—as were the square dances, the teenage club, the Halloween program—by Mr. Summers, who had time and energy to devote to civic activities. He was a roundfaced, jovial man and he ran the coal business, and people were sorry for him, because he had no children and his wife was a scold. When he arrived in the square, carrying the black wooden box, there was a murmur of conversation among the villagers and he waved and called, "Little late today, folks." The postmaster, Mr. Graves, followed him, carrying a three-legged stool, and the stool was put in the center of the square and Mr. Summers set the black box down on it. The villagers kept their distance, leaving a space between themselves and the stool, and when Mr. Summers said, "Some of you fellows want to give me a hand?" there was a hesitation before two men, Mr. Martin and his oldest son, Baxter, came forward to hold the box steady on the stool while Mr. Summers stirred up the papers inside it.

The original paraphernalia for the lottery had been lost long ago, and the black box now resting on the stool had been put into use even before Old Man Warner, the oldest man in town, was born. Mr. Summers spoke frequently to the villagers about making a new box, but no one liked to upset even as much tradition as was represented by the black box. There was a story that the present box had been made with some pieces of the box that had preceded it, the one that had been constructed when the first people settled down to make a village here. Every year, after the lottery, Mr. Summers began talking again about a new box, but every year the subject was allowed to fade off without anything's being done. The black box grew shabbier each year; by now it was no longer completely black but splintered badly along one side to show the original wood color, and in some places faded or stained.

Mr. Martin and his oldest son, Baxter, held the black box securely on the stool until Mr. Summers had stirred the papers thoroughly with his hand. Because so much of the ritual had been forgotten or discarded, Mr. Summers had been successful in having slips of paper substituted for the chips of wood that had been used for generations. Chips of wood, Mr. Summers had argued, had been all very well when the village was tiny, but now that the population was more than three hundred and likely to keep on growing, it was necessary to use something that would fit more easily into the black box. The night before the lottery, Mr. Summers and Mr. Graves made up the slips of paper and put them in the box, and it was then taken to the safe of Mr. Summers's coal company and locked up until Mr. Summers was ready to take it to the square next morning. The rest of the year, the box was put away, sometimes one place, sometimes another; it had spent one year in Mr. Graves's barn and another year underfoot in the post office, and sometimes it was set on a shelf in the Martin grocery and left there.

There was a great deal of fussing to be done before Mr. Summers declared the lottery open. There were lists to make up—of heads of families, heads of households in each family, members of each household in each family.

There was the proper swearing-in of Mr. Summers by the postmaster, as the official of the lottery; at one time, some people remembered, there had been a recital of some sort, performed by the official of the lottery, a perfunctory, tuneless chant that had been rattled off duly each year; some people believed that the official of the lottery used to stand just so when he said or sang it, others believed that he was supposed to walk among the people, but years and years ago this part of the ritual had been allowed to lapse. There had been, also, a ritual salute, which the official of the lottery had had to use in addressing each person who came up to draw from the box, but this also had changed with time, until now it was felt necessary only for the official to speak to each person approaching. Mr. Summers was very good at all this; in his clean white shirt and blue jeans, with one hand resting carelessly on the black box, he seemed very proper and important as he talked interminably to Mr. Graves and the Martins.

Just as Mr. Summers finally left off talking and turned to the assembled villagers, Mrs. Hutchinson came hurriedly along the path to the square, her sweater thrown over her shoulders, and slid into place in the back of the crowd. "Clean forgot what day it was," she said to Mrs. Delacroix, who stood next to her, and they both laughed softly. "Thought my old man was out back stacking wood," Mrs. Hutchinson went on, "and then I looked out the window and the kids were gone, and then I remembered it was the twenty-seventh and came a-running." She dried her hands on her apron, and Mrs. Delacroix said, "You're in time, though. They're still talking away up there."

Mrs. Hutchinson craned her neck to see through the crowd and found her husband and children standing near the front. She tapped Mrs. Delacroix on the arm as a farewell and began to make her way through the crowd. The people separated good-humoredly to let her through; two or three people said, in voices just loud enough to be heard across the crowd, "Here comes your Missus, Hutchinson," and "Bill, she made it after all." Mrs. Hutchinson reached her husband, and Mr. Summers, who had been waiting, said cheerfully, "Thought we were going to have to get on without you, Tessie." Mrs. Hutchinson said, grinning, "Wouldn't have me leave m'dishes in the sink, now would you, Joe?" and soft laughter ran through the crowd as the people stirred back into position after Mrs. Hutchinson's arrival.

"Well, now," Mr. Summers said soberly, "guess we better get started, get this over with, so's we can go back to work. Anybody ain't here?"

"Dunbar," several people said. "Dunbar, Dunbar."

Mr. Summers consulted his list. "Clyde Dunbar," he said. "That's right. He's broke his leg, hasn't he? Who's drawing for him?"

"Me, I guess," a woman said, and Mr. Summers turned to look at her. "Wife draws for her husband," Mr. Summers said. "Don't you have a grown boy to do it for you, Janey?" Although Mr. Summers and everyone else in the village knew the answer perfectly well, it was the business of the official of the lottery to ask such questions formally. Mr. Summers waited with an expression of polite interest while Mrs. Dunbar answered.

"Horace's not but sixteen yet," Mrs. Dunbar said regretfully. "Guess I gotta fill in for the old man this year."

"Right," Mr. Summers said. He made a note on the list he was holding. Then he asked, "Watson boy drawing this year?"

A tall boy in the crowd raised his hand. "Here," he said. "I'm drawing for m'mother and me." He blinked his eyes nervously and ducked his head as several voices in the crowd said things like "Good fellow, Jack," and "Glad to see your mother's got a man to do it."

"Well," Mr. Summers said, "guess that's everyone. Old Man Warner make it?"

"Here," a voice said, and Mr. Summers nodded.

A sudden hush fell on the crowd as Mr. Summers cleared his throat and looked at the list. "All ready?" he called. "Now, I'll read the names—heads of families first—and the men come up and take a paper out of the box. Keep the paper folded in your hand without looking at it until everyone has had a turn. Everything clear?"

The people had done it so many times that they only half listened to the directions; most of them were quiet, wetting their lips, not looking around. Then Mr. Summers raised one hand high and said, "Adams." A man disengaged himself from the crowd and came forward. "Hi, Steve," Mr. Summers said, and Mr. Adams said, "Hi, Joe." They grinned at one another humorlessly and nervously. Then Mr. Adams reached into the black box and took out a folded paper. He held it firmly by one corner as he turned and went hastily back to his place in the crowd, where he stood a little apart from his family, not looking down at his hand.

"Allen," Mr. Summers said. "Anderson. . . . Bentham."

"Seems like there's no time at all between lotteries any more," Mrs. Delacroix said to Mrs. Graves in the back row. "Seems like we got through with the last one only last week."

"Time sure goes fast," Mrs. Graves said.

"Clark. . . . Delacroix."

"There goes my old man," Mrs. Delacroix said. She held her breath while her husband went forward.

"Dunbar," Mr. Summers said, and Mrs. Dunbar went steadily to the box while one of the women said, "Go on, Janey," and another said, "There she goes."

"We're next," Mrs. Graves said. She watched while Mr. Graves came around from the side of the box, greeted Mr. Summers gravely, and selected a slip of paper from the box. By now, all through the crowd there were men holding the small folded papers in their large hands, turning them over and over nervously. Mrs. Dunbar and her two sons stood together, Mrs. Dunbar holding the slip of paper.

"Harburt. . . . Hutchinson."

"Get up there, Bill," Mrs. Hutchinson said, and the people near her laughed.

"Jones."

"They do say," Mr. Adams said to Old Man Warner, who stood next to him, "that over in the north village they're talking of giving up the lottery."

Old Man Warner snorted. "Pack of crazy fools," he said. "Listening to the young folks, nothing's good enough for *them*. Next thing you know, they'll be wanting to go back to living in caves, nobody work any more, live *that* way for a while. Used to be a saying about 'Lottery in June, corn be heavy soon.' First thing you know, we'd all be eating stewed chickweed and acorns. There's *always* been a lottery," he added petulantly. "Bad enough to see young Joe Summers up there joking with everybody."

"Some places have already quit lotteries," Mrs. Adams said.

"Nothing but trouble in *that*," Old Man Warner said stoutly. "Pack of young fools."

"Martin." And Bobby Martin watched his father go forward. "Overdyke. . . . Percy."

"I wish they'd hurry," Mrs. Dunbar said to her older son. "I wish they'd hurry."

"They're almost through," her son said.

"You get ready to run tell Dad," Mrs. Dunbar said.

Mr. Summers called his own name and then stepped forward precisely and selected a slip from the box. Then he called, "Warner."

"Seventy-seventh year I been in the lottery," Old Man Warner said as he went through the crowd. "Seventy-seventh time."

"Watson." The tall boy came awkwardly through the crowd. Someone said, "Don't be nervous, Jack," and Mr. Summers said, "Take your time, son."

"Zanini."

———

AFTER THAT, there was a long pause, a breathless pause, until Mr. Summers, holding his slip of paper in the air, said, "All right, fellows." For a minute, no one moved, and then all the slips of paper were opened. Suddenly, all women began to speak at once, saying, "Who is it?" "Who's got it?" "Is it the Dunbars?" "Is it the Watsons?" Then the voices began to say, "It's Hutchinson. It's Bill." "Bill Hutchinson's got it."

"Go tell your father," Mrs. Dunbar said to her older son.

People began to look around to see the Hutchinsons. Bill Hutchinson was standing quiet, staring down at the paper in his hand. Suddenly, Tessie Hutchinson shouted to Mr. Summers, "You didn't give him time enough to take any paper he wanted. I saw you. It wasn't fair!"

"Be a good sport, Tessie," Mrs. Delacroix called, and Mrs. Graves said, "All of us took the same chance."

"Shut up, Tessie," Bill Hutchinson said.

"Well, everyone," Mr. Summers said, "that was done pretty fast, and now we've got to be hurrying a little more to get done in time." He consulted his next list. "Bill," he said, "you draw for the Hutchinson family. You got any other households in the Hutchinsons?"

"There's Don and Eva," Mrs. Hutchinson yelled. "Make *them* take their chance!"

"Daughters draw with their husbands' families, Tessie," Mr. Summers said gently. "You know that as well as anyone else."

"It wasn't fair," Tessie said.

"I guess not, Joe," Bill Hutchinson said regretfully. "My daughter draws with her husband's family, that's only fair. And I've got no other family except the kids."

"Then, as far as drawing for families is concerned, it's you," Mr. Summers said in explanation, "and as far as drawing for households is concerned, that's you, too. Right?"

"Right," Bill Hutchinson said.

"How many kids, Bill?" Mr. Summers asked formally.

"Three," Bill Hutchinson said. "There's Bill, Jr., and Nancy, and little Dave. And Tessie and me."

"All right, then," Mr. Summers said. "Harry, you got their tickets back?"

Mr. Graves nodded and held up the slips of paper. "Put them in the box, then," Mr. Summers directed. "Take Bill's and put it in."

"I think we ought to start over," Mrs. Hutchinson said, as quietly as she could. "I tell you it wasn't *fair*. You didn't give him time enough to choose. *Every*body saw that."

Mr. Graves had selected the five slips and put them in the box, and he dropped all the papers but those onto the ground, where the breeze caught them and lifted them off.

"Listen, everybody," Mrs. Hutchinson was saying to the people around her.

"Ready, Bill?" Mr. Summers asked, and Bill Hutchinson, with one quick glance around at his wife and children, nodded.

"Remember," Mr. Summers said, "take the slips and keep them folded until each person has taken one. Harry, you help little Dave." Mr. Graves took the hand of the little boy, who came willingly with him up to the box. "Take a paper out of the box, Davy," Mr. Summers said. Davy put his hand into the box and laughed. "Take just *one* paper," Mr. Summers said. "Harry, you hold it for him." Mr. Graves took the child's hand and removed the folded paper from the tight fist and held it while little Dave stood next to him and looked up at him wonderingly.

"Nancy next," Mr. Summers said. Nancy was twelve, and her school friends breathed heavily as she went forward, switching her skirt, and took a slip daintily from the box. "Bill, Jr.," Mr. Summers said, and Billy, his face red and his feet over-large, nearly knocked the box over as he got a paper out. "Tessie," Mr. Summers said. She hesitated for a minute, looking around defiantly, and then set her lips and went up to the box. She snatched a paper out and held it behind her.

"Bill," Mr. Summers said, and Bill Hutchinson reached into the box and felt around, bringing his hand out at last with the slip of paper in it.

The crowd was quiet. A girl whispered, "I hope it's not Nancy," and the sound of the whisper reached the edges of the crowd.

"It's not the way it used to be," Old Man Warner said clearly. "People ain't the way they used to be."

"All right," Mr. Summers said. "Open the papers. Harry, you open little Dave's."

Mr. Graves opened the slip of paper and there was a general sigh through the crowd as he held it up and everyone could see that it was blank. Nancy and Bill, Jr., opened theirs at the same time, and both beamed and laughed, turning around to the crowd and holding their slips of paper above their heads.

"Tessie," Mr. Summers said. There was a pause, and then Mr. Summers looked at Bill Hutchinson, and Bill unfolded his paper and showed it. It was blank.

"It's Tessie," Mr. Summers said, and his voice was hushed. "Show us her paper, Bill."

Bill Hutchinson went over to his wife and forced the slip of paper out of her hand. It had a black spot on it, the black spot Mr. Summers had made the night before with the heavy pencil in the coal-company office. Bill Hutchinson held it up, and there was a stir in the crowd.

"All right, folks," Mr. Summers said, "let's finish quickly."

Although the villagers had forgotten the ritual and lost the original black box, they still remembered to use stones. The pile of stones the boys had made earlier was ready; there were stones on the ground with the blowing scraps of paper that had come out of the box. Mrs. Delacroix selected a stone so large she had to pick it up with both hands and turned to Mrs. Dunbar. "Come on," she said. "Hurry up."

Mrs. Dunbar had small stones in both hands, and she said, gasping for breath, "I can't run at all. You'll have to go ahead and I'll catch up with you."

The children had stones already, and someone gave little Davy Hutchinson a few pebbles.

Tessie Hutchinson was in the center of a cleared space by now, and she held her hands out desperately as the villagers moved in on her. "It isn't fair," she said. A stone hit her on the side of the head.

Old Man Warner was saying, "Come on, come on, everyone." Steve Adams was in the front of the crowd of villagers, with Mrs. Graves beside him.

"It isn't fair, it isn't right," Mrs. Hutchinson screamed, and then they were upon her.

Sherwood Anderson, 1876–1941

I'm a Fool

This story first appeared in THE DIAL, *1922.*

IT WAS A HARD JOLT FOR ME, one of the most bitterest I ever had to face. And it all came about through my own foolishness, too. Even yet sometimes, when I think of it, I want to cry or swear or kick myself. Perhaps, even now, after all this time, there will be a kind of satisfaction in making myself look cheap by telling of it.

It began at three o'clock one October afternoon as I sat in the grandstand at the fall trotting and pacing meet at Sandusky, Ohio.

To tell the truth, I felt a little foolish that I should be sitting in the grandstand at all. During the summer before, I had left my hometown with Harry Whitehead and, with a nigger named Burt, had taken a job as swipe with one of the two horses Harry was campaigning through the fall race meets that year. Mother cried and my sister Mildred, who wanted to get a job as a schoolteacher in our town that fall, stormed and scolded about the house all during the week before I left. They both thought it something disgraceful that one of our family should take a place as a swipe with race horses. I've an idea Mildred thought my taking the place would stand in the way of her getting the job she'd been working so long for.

But after all I had to work, and there was no other work to be got. A big lumbering fellow of nineteen couldn't just hang around the house and I had got too big to mow people's lawns and sell newspapers. Little chaps who could get next to people's sympathies by their sizes were always getting jobs away from me. There was one fellow who kept saying to everyone who wanted a lawn mowed or a cistern cleaned that he was saving money to work his way through college, and I used to lay awake nights thinking up ways to injure him without being found out. I kept thinking of wagons running over him and bricks falling on his head as he walked along the street. But never mind him.

I got the place with Harry and I liked Burt fine. We got along splendid together. He was a big nigger with a lazy sprawling body and soft, kind eyes, and when it came to a fight he could hit like Jack Johnson.* He had

---

Jack Johnson: world heavyweight boxing champion, 1908–1915, black.

Bucephalus, a big black pacing stallion that could do 2.09 or 2.10 if he had to, and I had a little gelding named Doctor Fritz that never lost a race all fall when Harry wanted him to win.

We set out from home late in July, in a box car with the two horses and after that, until late November, we kept moving along to the race meets and the fairs. It was a peachy time for me, I'll say that. Sometimes now I think that boys who are raised regular in houses, and never have a fine nigger like Burt for best friend, and go to high schools and college, and never steal anything, or get drunk a little, or learn to swear from fellows who know how, or come walking up in front of a grandstand in their shirt sleeves and with dirty horsy pants on when the races are going on and the grandstand is full of people all dressed up—What's the use of talking about it? Such fellows don't know nothing at all. They've never had no opportunity.

But I did. Burt taught me how to rub down a horse and put the bandages on after a race and steam a horse out and a lot of valuable things for any man to know. He could wrap a bandage on a horse's leg so smooth that if it had been the same color you would think it was his skin, and I guess he'd have been a big driver, too, and got to the top like Murphy and Walter Cox and the others if he hadn't been black.

Gee whizz! it was fun. You got to a county-seat town, maybe say on a Saturday or Sunday, and the fair began the next Tuesday and lasted until Friday afternoon. Doctor Fritz would be, say, in the 2.25 trot on Tuesday afternoon and on Thursday afternoon Bucephalus would knock 'em cold in the "free-for-all" pace. It left you a lot of time to hang around and listen to horse talk, and see Burt knock some yap cold that got too gay, and you'd find out about horses and men and pick up a lot of stuff you could use all the rest of your life, if you had some sense and salted down what you heard and felt and saw.

And then at the end of the week when the race meet was over, and Harry had run home to tend up to his livery-stable business, you and Burt hitched the two horses to carts and drove slow and steady across country, to the place for the next meeting, so as to not overheat the horses, etc., etc., you know.

Gee whizz! Gosh amighty! the nice hickory-nut and beechnut and oaks and other kinds of trees along the roads, all brown and red, and the good smells, and Burt singing a song called "Deep River," and the country girls at the windows of houses and everything. You can stick your colleges up your nose for all me. I guess I know where I got my education.

Why, one of those little burgs of towns you came to on the way, say now on a Saturday afternoon, and Burt says, "Let's lay up here." And you did.

And you took the horses to a livery stable and fed them, and you got your good clothes out of a box and put them on.

And the town was full of farmers gaping, because they could see you were racehorse people, and the kids maybe never see a nigger before and was afraid and run away when the two of us walked down their main street.

And that was before prohibition and all that foolishness, and so you went into a saloon, the two of you, and all the yaps come and stood around, and there was always some one pretended he was horsy and knew things and spoke up and began asking questions, and all you did was to lie and lie all you could about what horses you had, and I said I owned them, and then some fellow said, "Will you have a drink of whiskey?" and Burt knocked his eye out the way to could say, offhand like, "Oh, well, all right, I'm agreeable to a little nip. I'll split a quart with you." Gee whizz!

But that isn't what I want to tell my story about. We got home late in November and I promised mother I'd quit the race horses for good. There's a lot of things you've got to promise a mother because she don't know any better.

And so, there not being any work in our town any more than when I left there to go to the races, I went off to Sandusky and got a pretty good place taking care of horses for a man who owned a teaming and delivery and storage and coal and real-estate business there. It was a pretty good place with good eats, and a day off each week, and sleeping on a cot in a big barn, and mostly just shoveling in hay and oats to a lot of big good-enough skates of horses that couldn't have trotted a race with a toad. I wasn't dissatisfied and I could send money home.

And then, as I started to tell you, the fall races come to Sandusky and I got the day off and I went. I left the job at noon and had on my good clothes and my new brown derby hat I'd bought the Saturday before, and a stand-up collar.

First of all I went downtown and walked about with the dudes. I've always thought to myself, "Put up a good front," and so I did it. I had forty dollars in my pockets and so I went into the West House, a big hotel, and walked up to the cigar stand. "Give me three twenty-five cent cigars," I said. There was a lot of horsemen and strangers and dressed-up people from other towns standing around in the lobby and in the bar, and I mingled amongst them. In the bar there was a fellow with a cane and a Windsor tie on, that it made me sick to look at him. I like a man to be a man and dressed up, but not to go put on that kind of airs. So I pushed him aside, kind of rough, and had me a drink of whiskey. And then he looked at me, as though he thought maybe he'd get gay, but he changed his mind and didn't say anything. And then I had another drink of whiskey, just to show him something, and went out and had a hack out to the races, all to myself, and when I got there I bought myself the best seat I could get up in the grandstand, but didn't go in for any of these boxes. That's putting on too many airs.

And so there I was, sitting up in the grandstand as gay as you please and looking down on the swipes coming out with their horses, and with their dirty horsy pants on and the horseblankets swung over their shoulders, same as I had been doing all the year before. I liked one thing about the same as the other, sitting up there and feeling grand and being down there and looking up at the yaps and feeling grander and more important, too.

One thing's about as good as another, if you take it just right. I've often said that.

Well, right in front of me, in the grandstand that day, there was a fellow with a couple of girls and they was about my age. The young fellow was a nice guy, all right. He was the kind maybe that goes to college and then comes to be a lawyer or maybe a newspaper editor or something like that, but he wasn't stuck on himself. There are some of that kind are all right and he was one of the ones.

He had his sister with him and another girl and the sister looked around over his shoulder, accidental at first, not intending to start anything—she wasn't that kind—and her eyes and mine happened to meet.

You know how it is. Gee, she was a peach! She had on a soft dress, kind of a blue stuff and it looked carelessly made, but was well sewed and made and everything. I knew that much. I blushed when she looked right at me and so did she. She was the nicest girl I've ever seen in my life. She wasn't stuck on herself and she could talk proper grammar without being like a school-teacher or something like that. What I mean is, she was O.K. I think maybe her father was well-to-do, but not rich to make her chesty because she was his daughter, as some are. Maybe he owned a drug store or a dry-goods store in their home town, or something like that. She never told me and I never asked.

My own people are all O.K. too, when you come to that. My grandfather was Welsh and over in the old country, in Wales he was—But never mind that.

The first heat of the first race come off and the young fellow setting there with the two girls left them and went down to make a bet. I knew what he was up to, but he didn't talk big and noisy and let everyone around know he was a sport, as some do. He wasn't that kind. Well, he come back and I heard him tell the two girls what horse he'd bet on, and when the heat trotted they all half got to their feet and acted in the excited, sweaty way people do when they've got money down on a race, and the horse they bet on is up there pretty close at the end, and they think maybe he'll come on with a rush, but he never does because he hasn't got the old juice in him, come right down to it.

And then, pretty soon, the horses came out for the 2.18 pace and there was a horse in it I knew. He was a horse Bob French had in his string but Bob didn't own him. He was a horse owned by a Mr. Mathers down at Marietta, Ohio.

This Mr. Mathers had a lot of money and owned some coal mines or something and he had a swell place out in the country, and he was stuck on race horses, but was a Presbyterian or something, and I think more than likely his wife was one, too, maybe a stiffer one than himself. So he never raced his horses hisself, and the story round the Ohio race tracks was that when one of his horses got ready to go to the races he turned him over to Bob French and pretended to his wife he was sold.

So Bob had the horses and he did pretty much as he pleased and you can't blame Bob, at least, I never did. Sometimes he was out to win and sometimes he wasn't. I never cared much about that when I was swiping a horse. What

I did want to know was that my horse had the speed and could go out in front, if you wanted him to.

And, as I'm telling you, there was Bob in this race with one of Mr. Mathers's horses, was named "About Ben Ahem"* or something like that, and was fast as a streak. He was a gelding and had a mark of 2.21, but could step in .08 or .09.

Because when Burt and I were out, as I've told you, the year before, there was a nigger Burt knew, worked for Mr. Mathers and we went out there one day when we didn't have no race on at the Marietta Fair and our boss Harry was gone home.

And so everyone was gone to the fair but just this one nigger and he took us all through Mr. Mathers's swell house and he and Burt tapped a bottle of wine Mr. Mathers had hid in his bedroom, back in the closet, without his wife knowing, and he showed us this Ahem horse. Burt was always stuck on being a driver but didn't have much chance to get to the top, being a nigger, and he and the other nigger gulped the whole bottle of wine and Burt got a little lit up.

So the nigger let Burt take this About Ben Ahem and step him a mile in a track Mr. Mathers had all to himself, right there on the farm. And Mr. Mathers had one child, a daughter, kinda sick and not very good looking, and she came home and we had to hustle to get About Ben Ahem stuck back in the barn.

I'm only telling you to get everything straight. At Sandusky, that afternoon I was at the fair, this young fellow with the two girls was fussed, being with the girls and losing his bet. You know how a fellow is that way. One of them was his girl and the other his sister. I had figured that out.

"Gee whizz," I says to myself, "I'm going to give him the dope."

He was mighty nice when I touched him on the shoulder. He and the girls were nice to me right from the start and clear to the end. I'm not blaming them.

And so he leaned back and I give him the dope on About Ben Ahem. "Don't bet a cent on this first heat because he'll go like an oxen hitched to a plow, but when the first heat is over go right down and lay on your pile." That's what I told him.

Well, I never saw a fellow treat any one sweller. There was a fat man sitting beside the little girl, that had looked at me twice by this time, and I at her, and both blushing, and what did he do but have the nerve to turn and ask the fat man to get up and change places with me so I could set with his crowd.

Gee whizz, craps amighty. There I was. What a chump I was to go and get gay up there in the West House bar, and just because that dude was standing there with a cane and that kind of a necktie on, to go and get all balled up and drink that whiskey, just to show off.

---

*"About Ben Ahem": Abou Ben Adhem is the title of a well-known poem by Leigh Hunt.

Of course she would know, me setting right beside her and letting her smell of my breath. I could have kicked myself right down out of that grandstand and all around that race track and made a faster record than most of the skates of horses they had there that year.

Because that girl wasn't any mutt of a girl. What wouldn't I have give right then for a stick of chewing gum to chew, or a lozenger, or some licorice, or most anything. I was glad I had those twenty-five cent cigars in my pocket and right away I gave that fellow one and lit one myself. Then that fat man got up and we changed places and there I was, plunked right down beside her.

They introduced themselves and the fellow's best girl, he had with him, was named Miss Elinor Woodbury, and her father was a manufacturer of barrels from a placed called Tiffin, Ohio. And the fellow himself was named Wilbur Wessen and his sister was Miss Lucy Wessen.

I suppose it was their having such swell names that got me off my trolley. A fellow, just because he has been a swipe with a race horse, and works taking care of horses for a man in the teaming, delivery, and storage business isn't any better or worse than any one else. I've often thought that, and said it too.

But you know how a fellow is. There's something in that kind of nice clothes, and the kind of nice eyes she had, and the way she had looked at me, awhile before, over her brother's shoulder, and me looking back at her, and both of us blushing.

I couldn't show her up for a boob, could I?

I made a fool of myself, that's what I did. I said my name was Walter Mathers from Marietta, Ohio, and then I told all three of them the smashingest lie you ever heard. What I said was that my father owned the horse About Ben Ahem and that he had let him out to this Bob French for racing purposes, because our family was proud and had never gone into racing that way, in our own name, I mean, and Miss Lucy Wessen's eyes were shining, and I went the whole hog.

I told her about our place down at Marietta, and about the big stables and the grand brick house we had on a hill, up above the Ohio River, but I knew enough not to do it in no bragging way. What I did was to start things and then let them drag the rest out of me. I acted just as reluctant to tell as I could. Our family hasn't got any barrel factory, and since I've known us, we've always been pretty poor, but not asking anything of any one at that, and my grandfather, over in Wales—but never mind that.

We sat there talking like we had known each other for years and years, and I went and told them that my father had been expecting maybe this Bob French wasn't on the square, and had sent me up to Sandusky on the sly to find out what I could.

And I bluffed it through I had found out all about the 2.18 pace, in which About Ben Ahem was to start.

I said he would lose the first heat by pacing like a lame cow and then he would come back and skin 'em alive after that. And to back up what I said I took thirty dollars out of my pocket and handed it to Mr. Wilbur Wessen and asked him, would he mind, after the first heat, to go down and place it on About Ben Ahem for whatever odds he could get. What I said was that I didn't want Bob French to see me and none of the swipes.

Sure enough the first heat come off and About Ben Ahem went off his stride, up the back stretch, and looked like a wooden horse or a sick one, and come in to be last. Then this Wilbur Wessen went down to the betting place under the grandstand and there I was with the two girls, and when that Miss Woodbury was looking the other way once, Lucy Wessen kinda, with her shoulder you know, kinda touched me. Not just tucking down, I don't mean. You know how a woman can do. They get close, but not getting gay either. You know what they do. Gee whizz.

And then they give me a jolt. What they had done, when I didn't know, was to get together, and they had decided Wilbur Wessen would bet fifty dollars, and the two girls had gone and put in ten dollars each, of their own money, too. I was sick then, but I was sicker later.

About the gelding, About Ben Ahem, and their winning their money, I wasn't worried a lot about that. It came out O.K. Ahem stepped the next three heats like a bushel of spoiled eggs going to market before they could be found out, and Wilbur Wessen had got nine to two for the money. There was something else eating at me.

Because Wilbur come back, after he had bet the money, and after that he spent most of his time talking to that Miss Woodbury, and Lucy Wessen and I was left alone together like on a desert island. Gee, if I'd only been on the square or if there had been any way of getting myself on the square. There ain't any Walter Mathers, like I said to her and them, and there hasn't ever been one, but if there was, I bet I'd go to Marietta, Ohio, and shoot him tomorrow.

There I was, big boob that I am. Pretty soon the race was over, and Wilbur had gone down and collected our money, and we had a hack downtown, and he stood us a swell supper at the West House, and a bottle of champagne beside.

And I was with the girl and she wasn't saying much, and I wasn't saying much either. One thing I know. She wasn't stuck on me because of the lie about my father being rich and all that. There's a way you know . . . Craps amighty. There's a kind of girl you see just once in your life, and if you don't get busy and make hay, then you're gone for good and all, and might as well go jump off a bridge. They give you a look from inside of them somewhere, and it ain't no vamping, and what it means is—you want that girl to be your wife, and you want nice things around her like flowers and swell clothes, and you want her to have the kids you're going to have, and you want good music played and no ragtime. Gee whizz.

There's a place over near Sandusky, across a kind of bay, and it's called Cedar Point. And after we had supper we went over to it in a launch, all by ourselves. Wilbur and Miss Lucy and that Miss Woodbury had to catch a ten o'clock train back to Tiffin, Ohio, because, when you're out with girls like that you can't get careless and miss any trains and stay out all night, like you can with some kinds of Janes.

And Wilbur blowed himself to the launch and it cost him fifteen cold plunks, but I wouldn't never have knew if I hadn't listened. He wasn't no tin horn kind of a sport.

Over at the Cedar Point place, we didn't stay around where there was a gang of common kind of cattle at all.

There was big dance halls and dining places for yaps, and there was a beach you could walk along and get where it was dark, and we went there.

She didn't talk hardly at all and neither did I, and I was thinking how glad I was my mother was all right, and always made us kids learn to eat with a fork at the table, and not swill soup, and not be noisy and rough like a gang you see around a race track that way.

When Wilbur and his girl went away up the beach and Lucy and I sat down in a dark place, where there was some roots of old trees the water had washed up, and after that the time, till we had to go back in the launch and they had to catch their trains, wasn't nothing at all. It went like winking your eye.

Here's how it was. The place we were setting in was dark, like I said, and there was the roots from that old stump sticking up like arms, and there was a watery smell, and the night was like—as if you could put your hand out and feel it—so warm and soft and dark and sweet like an orange.

I most cried and I most swore and I most jumped up and danced, I was so mad and happy and sad.

When Wilbur come back from being alone with his girl, and she saw him coming, Lucy she says, "We got to go to the train now," and she was most crying too, but she never knew nothing I knew, and she couldn't be so all busted up. And then, before Wilbur and Miss Woodbury got up to where we was, she put her face up and kissed me quick and put her head up against me and she was all quivering and—Gee whizz.

Sometimes I hope I have cancer and die. I guess you know what I mean. We went in the launch across the bay to the train like that, and it was dark, too. She whispered and said it was like she and I could get out of the boat and walk on water, and it sounded foolish, but I knew what she meant.

And then quick we were right at the depot, and there was a big gang of yaps, the kind that goes to the fairs, and crowded and milling around like cattle, and how could I tell her? "It won't be long because you'll write and I'll write to you." That's all she said.

I got a chance like a hay barn afire. A swell chance I got.

And maybe she would write me, down at Marietta that way, and the letter would come back, and stamped on the front of it by the U.S.A. "there ain't any such guy," or something like that, whatever they stamp on a letter that way.

And me trying to pass myself off for a big-bug and a swell—to her, as decent a little body as God ever made. Craps amighty—swell chance I got!

And then the train come in, and she got on it, and Wilbur Wessen, he come and shook hands with me, and that Miss Woodbury was nice too and bowed to me, and I at her, and the train went and I busted out and cried like a kid.

Gee, I could have run after the train and made Dan Patch* look like a freight train after a wreck but, socks amighty, what was the use? Did you ever see such a fool?

I'll bet you what—if I had an arm broke right now or a train had run over my foot—I wouldn't go to no doctor at all. I'd go set down and let her hurt and hurt—that's what I'd do.

I'll bet you what—if I hadn't a drunk that booze I'd never been such a boob as to go tell such a lie—that couldn't never be made straight to a lady like her.

I wish I had that fellow right here that had on a Windsor tie and carried a cane. I'd smash him for fair. Gosh darn his eyes. He's a big fool—that's what he is.

And if I'm not another you just go find me one and I'll quit working and be a bum and give him my job. I don't care nothing for working, and earning money, and saving it for no such boob as myself.

*Dan Patch: one of the fastest harness horses in history.

Katherine Mansfield, 1888–1923

Miss Brill

This story first appeared in ATHENEUM, 1920.

ALTHOUGH IT WAS SO BRILLIANTLY FINE—the blue sky powdered with gold and great spots of light like white wine splashed over the Jardins Publiques— Miss Brill was glad that she had decided on her fur. The air was motionless, but when you opened your mouth there was just a faint chill, like a chill from a glass of iced water before you sip, and now and again a leaf came drifting—from no where, from the sky. Miss Brill put up her hand and touched her fur. Dear little thing! It was nice to feel it again. She had taken it out of its box that afternoon, shaken out the moth-powder, given it a good brush, and rubbed the life back into the dim little eyes. "What has been happening to me?" said the sad little eyes. Oh, how sweet it was to see them snap at her again from the red eiderdown! . . . But the nose, which was of some black composition, wasn't at all firm. It must have had a knock, somehow. Never mind—a little dab of black sealing-wax when the time came—when it was absolutely necessary. . . . Little rogue! Yes, she really felt like that about it. Little rogue biting its tail just by her left ear. She could have taken it off and laid it on her lap and stroked it. She felt a tingling in her hands and arms, but that came from walking, she supposed. And when she breathed, something light and sad—no, not sad, exactly—something gentle seemed to move in her bosom.

There were a number of people out this afternoon, far more than last Sunday. And the band sounded louder and gayer. That was because the Season had begun. For although the band played all the year round on Sundays, out of season it was never the same. It was like some one playing

Ironically, "Brill" means shine, sparkle, and conspicuous.

Implication: she's dressed wrong for the weather.

Delicate balance between negative & positive perception.

Process of perception.

Like a coffin.

Her point of view [third person, limited omniscience].

Applies to her: foreshadowing.

Her imagination activated.

Suggests embalming.

Where she later hears young couple ridicule her.

Implies old age.

She suppresses all negative impressions.

"Louder" implies she has come here before.

17

She identifies with "family."

She is a stranger [English-woman in France: alien].

As if she willed it—she needs to control through imagination.

They don't *need* to speak.

Brill never speaks.

Listening motif.

Vicarious participation.

Negatives before and today.

Informal style determined by using Brill's point of view.

For not being interesting.

Thus far, a familiar routine is set up.

She is like the beggar, alone.

Suggests Brill as a child.

with only the family to listen; it didn't care how it played if there weren't any strangers present. Wasn't the conductor wearing a new coat, too? She was sure it was new. He scraped with his foot and flapped his arms like a rooster about to crow, and the bandsmen sitting in the green rotunda blew out their cheeks and glared at the music. Now there came a little "flutey" bit—very pretty!—a little chain of bright drops. She was sure it would be repeated. It was; she lifted her head and smiled.

Only two people shared her "special" seat: a fine old man in a velvet coat, his hands clasped over a huge carved walking-stick, and a big old woman, sitting upright, with a roll of knitting on her embroidered apron. They did not speak. This was disappointing, for Miss Brill always looked forward to the conversation. She had become really quite expert, she thought, at listening as though she didn't listen, at sitting in other people's lives just for a minute while they talked round her.

She glanced, sideways, at the old couple. Perhaps they would go soon. Last Sunday, too, hadn't been as interesting as usual. An Englishman and his wife, he wearing a dreadful Panama hat and she button boots. And she'd gone on the whole time about how she ought to wear spectacles; she knew she needed them; but that it was no good getting any; they'd be sure to break and they'd never keep on. And he'd been so patient. He'd suggested everything—gold rims, the kind that curved round your ears, little pads inside the bridge. No, nothing would please her. "They'll always be sliding down my nose!" Miss Brill had wanted to shake her.

The old people sat on the bench, still as statues. Never mind, there was always the crowd to watch. To and fro, in front of the flower-beds and the band rotunda, the couples and groups paraded, stopped to talk, to greet, to buy a handful of flowers from the old beggar who had his tray fixed to the railings. Little children ran among them, swooping and laughing; little boys with big white silk bows under their chins, little girls, little French dolls, dressed up in velvet and lace. And sometimes a tiny staggerer came suddenly rocking into the open from under the trees, stopped, stared, as suddenly sat down "flop," until its small high-stepping mother, like a young hen, rushed scolding to its rescue. Other people sat on the benches and green chairs, but they were nearly always the same, Sunday after Sunday, and—Miss Brill had often noticed—there was something funny about nearly all of them. They were odd, silent, nearly all old, and from the way they stared they looked as though they'd just come from dark little rooms or even—even cupboards!

Behind the rotunda the slender trees with yellow leaves down drooping, and through them just a line of sea, and beyond the blue sky with gold-veined clouds.

Tum-tum-tum tiddle-um! tiddle-um! tum tiddley-um tum ta! blew the band.

Two young girls in red came by and two young soldiers in blue met them, and they laughed and paired and went off arm-in-arm. Two peasant women with funny straw hats passed, gravely, leading beautiful smoke-coloured donkeys. A cold, pale nun hurried by. A beautiful woman came along and dropped her bunch of violets, and a little boy ran after to hand them to her, and she took them and threw them away as if they'd been poisoned. Dear me! Miss Brill didn't know whether to admire that or not! And now an ermine toque and a gentleman in grey met just in front of her. He was tall, stiff, dignified, and she was wearing the ermine toque she'd bought when her hair was yellow. Now everything, her hair, her face, even her eyes, was the same colour as the shabby ermine, and her hand, in its cleaned glove, lifted to dab her lips, was a tiny yellowish paw. Oh, she was so pleased to see him—delighted! She rather thought they were going to meet that afternoon. She described where she'd been—everywhere, here, there, along by the sea. The day was so charming—didn't he agree? And wouldn't he, perhaps? . . . But he shook his head, lighted a cigarette, slowly breathed a great deep puff into her face, and, even while she was still talking and laughing, flicked the match away and walked on. The ermine toque was alone; she smiled more brightly than ever. But even the band seemed to know what she was feeling and played more softly, played tenderly, and the drum beat, "The Brute! The Brute!" over and over. What would she do? What was going

---

She stereotypes people.

Given the context, the implication is that this applies to her as well.

Implication: applies to her.

Coffin motif.

Example of Mansfield's characteristic style.

Contrast to her [dream image of herself?].

Brill is like a nun.

Juxtaposition of delicate imagery to image of insidious discord.

Pattern of clothes motifs [her fur, etc.].

She's very like Miss Brill.

Parallel to her fox fur.

Miss Brill also is pleased to see him.

Nothing in her own life gives her cause to smile.

She empathizes with the woman.

to happen now? But as Miss Brill wondered, the ermine toque turned, raised her hand as though she'd seen some one else, much nicer, just over there, and pattered away. And the band changed again and played more quickly, more gaily than ever, and the old couple on Miss Brill's seat got up and marched away, and such a funny old man with long whiskers hobbled along in time to the music and was nearly knocked over by four girls walking abreast.

Oh, how fascinating it was! How she enjoyed it! How she loved sitting here, watching it all! It was like a play. It was exactly like a play. Who could believe the sky at the back wasn't painted? But it wasn't till a little brown dog trotted on solemn and then slowly trotted off, like a little "theatre" dog, a little dog that had been drugged, that Miss Brill discovered what it was that made it so exciting. They were all on the stage. They weren't only the audience, not only looking on; they were acting. Even she had a part and came every Sunday. No doubt somebody would have noticed if she hadn't been there; she was part of the performance after all. How strange she'd never thought of it like that before! And yet it explained why she made such a point of starting from home at just the same time each week—so as not to be late for the performance—and it also explained why she had quite a queer, shy feeling at telling her English pupils how she spent her Sunday afternoons. No wonder! Miss Brill nearly laughed out loud. She was on the stage. She thought of the old invalid gentleman to whom she read the newspaper four afternoons a week while he slept in the garden. She had got quite used to the frail head on the cotton pillow, the hollowed eyes, the open mouth and the high pinched nose. If he'd been dead she mightn't have noticed for weeks; she wouldn't have minded. But suddenly he knew he was having the paper read to him by an actress! "An actress!" The old head lifted; two points of light quivered in the old eyes. "An actress—are ye?" And Miss Brill smoothed the newspaper as though it were the manuscript of her part and said gently: "Yes, I have been an actress for a long time."

The band had been having a rest. Now they started again. And what they played was warm, sunny, yet

He is a parallel to her.

Brill seems not ever to have been like these girls.

An epiphany for her, an internal revelation [contrasted later to an external revelation when the young couple ridicule her].

This is ironic later [a pattern of ironies develops throughout the story].

Others *do* laugh.

Contrast to the walk in the park.

Garden is a parallel to the park.

She imagines.

Preparation for her revelation today.

there was just a faint chill—a something, what was it?—not sadness—no, not sadness—a something that made you want to sing. The tune lifted, lifted, the light shone; and it seemed to Miss Brill that in another moment all of them, all the whole company, would begin singing. The young ones, the laughing ones who were moving together, they would begin, and the men's voices, very resolute and brave, would join them. And then she too, she too, and the others on the benches—they would come in with a kind of accompaniment—something low, that scarcely rose or fell, something so beautiful—moving. . . . And Miss Brill's eyes filled with tears and she looked smiling at all the other members of the company. Yes, we understand, we understand, she thought—though what they understood she didn't know.

> Example of effective repetition of words to give sense of the way her mind works.

> As if on her cue.

> Her repetition of words helps her to convince herself.

> Brill's sentimentality, not the author's.

Just at that moment a boy and a girl came and sat down where the old couple had been. They were beautifully dressed; they were in love. The hero and heroine, of course, just arrived from his father's yacht. And still soundlessly singing, still with that trembling smile, Miss Brill prepared to listen.

> She imagines.

> Climax of pattern of listening motifs.

"No, not now," said the girl. "Not here, I can't."

"But why? Because of that stupid old thing at the end there?" asked the boy. "Why does she come here at all—who wants her? Why doesn't she keep her silly old mug at home?"

> External revelation: she is a grotesquely comic, nonessential bit player.

> Implication: she will now.

"It's her fu-fur which is so funny," giggled the girl. "It's exactly like a fried whiting."

> Whiting is a fish.

"Ah, be off with you!" said the boy in an angry whisper. Then: "Tell me, ma petite chère—"

"No, not here," said the girl. "Not *yet.*

> Implication: see *will.*

ON HER WAY HOME she usually bought a slice of honey-cake at the baker's. It was her Sunday treat. Sometimes there was an almond in her slice, sometimes not. It made a great difference. If there was an almond it was like carrying home a tiny present—a surprise—something that might very well not have been there. She hurried on the almond Sundays and struck the match for the kettle in quite a dashing way.

> But not now.

But to-day she passed the baker's by, climbed the stairs, went into the little dark room—her room like

> Her usual ritual.

> Major change in her ritual.

Climax of pattern of
coffin motifs.

"It" is a *thing* again.

Repetition of word
"something." Implication: from
now on—herself.

a cupboard—and sat down on the red eiderdown. She sat there for a long time. The box that the fur came out of was on the bed. She unclasped the necklet quickly; quickly, without looking, laid it inside. But when she put the lid on she thought she heard something crying.

Isaac Bashevis Singer, 1904–1991

Gimpel the Fool

Translated by Saul Bellow

This story appeared in A TREASURY OF YIDDISH STORIES, *1953*.

I

I AM GIMPEL THE FOOL. I don't think myself a fool. On the contrary. But that's what folks call me. They gave me the name while I was still in school. I had seven names in all: imbecile, donkey, flax-head, dope, glump, ninny, and fool. The last name stuck. What did my foolishness consist of? I was easy to take in. They said, "Gimpel, you know the rabbi's wife has been brought to childbed?" So I skipped school. Well, it turned out to be a lie. How was I supposed to know? She hadn't had a big belly. But I never looked at her belly. Was that really so foolish? The gang laughed and hee-hawed, stomped and danced and chanted a good-night prayer. And instead of the raisins they give when a woman's lying in, they stuffed my hand full of goat turds. I was no weakling. If I slapped someone he'd see all the way to Cracow. But I'm really not a slugger by nature. I think to myself, Let it pass. So they take advantage of me.

I was coming home from school and heard a dog barking. I'm not afraid of dogs, but of course I never want to start up with them. One of them may be mad, and if he bites there's not a Tartar in the world who can help you. So I made tracks. Then I looked around and saw the whole market place wild with laughter. It was no dog at all but Wolf-Leib the thief. How was I supposed to know it was he? It sounded like a howling bitch.

When the pranksters and leg-pullers found that I was easy to fool, every one of them tried his luck with me. "Gimpel, the Czar is coming to Frampol; Gimpel, the moon fell down in Turbeen; Gimpel, little Hodel Furpiece found a treasure behind the bathhouse." And I like a *golem** believed everyone. In the first place, everything is possible, as it is written in the Wisdom of the Fathers, I've forgotten just how. Second, I had to believe when the whole

---

**golem:* simpleton. From the Hebrew: "a yet-unformed thing" (*Psalms* 139:16); a mere robot, a shapeless mass.

town came down on me! If I ever dared to say, "Ah, you're kidding!" there was trouble. People got angry. "What do you mean! You want to call every-one a liar?" What was I to do? I believed them, and I hope at least that did them some good.

I was an orphan. My grandfather who brought me up was already bent to-ward the grave. So they turned me over to a baker, and what a time they gave me there! Every woman or girl who came to bake a pan of cookies or dry a batch of noodles had to fool me at least once. "Gimpel, there's a fair in heaven; Gimpel, the rabbi gave birth to a calf in the seventh month; Gimpel, a cow flew over the roof and laid brass eggs." A student from the *yeshiva** came once to buy a roll, and he said, "You, Gimpel, while you stand here scraping with your baker's shovel the Messiah has come. The dead have arisen." "What do you mean?" I said. "I heard no one blowing the ram's horn!" He said, "Are you deaf?" And all began to cry, "We heard it, we heard!" Then in came Reitze the candle-dipper and called out in her hoarse voice, "Gimpel, your father and mother have stood up from the grave. They're looking for you."

To tell the truth, I knew very well that nothing of the sort had happened, but all the same, as folks were talking, I threw on my wool vest and went out. Maybe something had happened. What did I stand to lose by looking? Well, what a cat music went up! And then I took a vow to believe nothing more. But that was no go either. They confused me so that I didn't know the big end from the small.

I went to the rabbi to get some advice. He said, "It is written, better to be a fool all your days than for one hour to be evil. You are not a fool. They are the fools. For he who causes his neighbor to feel shame loses Paradise him-self." Nevertheless the rabbi's daughter took me in. As I left the rabbinical court she said, "Have you kissed the wall yet?" I said, "No; what for?" She an-swered, "It's a law; you've got to do it after every visit." Well, there didn't seem to be any harm in it. And she burst out laughing. It was a fine trick. She put one over on me, all right.

I wanted to go off to another town, but then everybody got busy match-making, and they were after me so they nearly tore my coat tails off. They talked at me and talked until I got water on the ear. She was no chaste maiden, but they told me she was virgin pure. She had a limp, and they said it was deliberate, from coyness. She had a bastard, and they told me the child was her little brother. I cried, "You're wasting your time. I'll never marry that whore." But they said indignantly, "What a way to talk! Aren't you ashamed of yourself? We can take you to the rabbi and have you fined for giv-ing her a bad name." I saw then that I wouldn't escape them so easily and I thought, They're set on making me their butt. But when you're married the

*yeshiva: school of theology.

husband's the master, and if that's all right with her it's agreeable to me too. Besides, you can't pass through life unscathed, nor expect to.

I went to her clay house, which was built on the sand, and the whole gang, hollering and chorusing, came after me. They acted like bearbaiters. When we came to the well they stopped all the same. They were afraid to start anything with Elka. Her mouth would open as if it were on a hinge, and she had a fierce tongue. I entered the house. Lines were strung from wall to wall and clothes were drying. Barefoot she stood by the tub, doing the wash. She was dressed in a worn hand-me-down gown of plush. She had her hair put up in braids and pinned across her head. It took my breath away, almost, the reek of it all.

Evidently she knew who I was. She took a look at me and said, "Look who's here! He's come, the drip. Grab a seat."

I told her all; I denied nothing. "Tell me the truth," I said, "are you really a virgin, and is that mischievous Yechiel actually your little brother? Don't be deceitful with me, for I'm an orphan."

"I'm an orphan myself," she answered, "and whoever tries to twist you up, may the end of his nose take a twist. But don't let them think they can take advantage of me. I want a dowry of fifty guilders, and let them take up a collection besides. Otherwise they can kiss my you-know-what." She was very plain-spoken. I said, "Don't bargain with me. Either a flat 'yes' or a flat 'no'—go back where you came from."

I thought, No bread will ever bake from *this* dough. But ours is not a poor town. They consented to everything and proceeded with the wedding. It so happened that there was a dysentery epidemic at the time. The ceremony was held at the cemetery gates, near the little corpse-washing hut. The fellows got drunk. While the marriage contract was being drawn up I heard the most pious high rabbi ask, "Is the bride a widow or a divorced woman?" And the sexton's wife answered for her, "Both a widow and divorced." It was a black moment for me. But what was I to do, run away from under the marriage canopy?

There was singing and dancing. An old granny danced opposite me, hugging a braided white *chalah*.* The master of revels made a "God 'a mercy" in memory of a bride's parents. The schoolboys threw burrs, as on *Tishe b' Av* fast day.† There were a lot of gifts after the sermon: a noodle board, a kneading trough, a bucket, brooms, ladles, household articles galore. Then I took a look and saw two strapping young men carrying a crib. "What do we need this for?" I asked. So they said, "Don't rack your brains about it. It's all right, it'll come in handy." I realized I was going to be rooked. Take it another way though, what did I stand to lose? I reflected, I'll see what comes of it. A whole town can't go altogether crazy.

---

chalah: loaf of bread glazed with egg white, a Sabbath and holiday delicacy.
†*Tishe b' Av:* day of mourning that commemorates disasters and persecutions.

II

AT NIGHT I CAME WHERE MY WIFE LAY, but she wouldn't let me in. "Say, look here, is this what they married us for?" I said. And she said, "My monthly has come." "But yesterday they took you to the ritual bath, and that's afterward, isn't it supposed to be?" "Today isn't yesterday," said she, "and yesterday's not today. You can beat it if you don't like it." In short, I waited.

Not four months later she was in childbed. The townsfolk hid their laughter with their knuckles. But what could I do? She suffered intolerable pains and clawed at the walls. "Gimpel," she cried, "I'm going. Forgive me!" The house filled with women. They were boiling pans of water. The screams rose to the welkin.

The thing to do was to go to the House of Prayer to repeat Psalms, and that was what I did.

The townsfolk liked that, all right. I stood in a corner saying Psalms and prayers, and they shook their heads at me. "Pray, pray!" they told me. "Prayer never made any woman pregnant." One of the congregation put a straw to my mouth and said, "Hay for the cows." There was something to that too, by God!

She gave birth to a boy. Friday at the synagogue the sexton stood up before the Ark, pounded on the reading table, and announced, "The wealthy Reb Gimpel invites the congregation to a feast in honor of the birth of a son." The whole House of Prayer rang with laughter. My face was flaming. But there was nothing I could do. After all, I *was* the one responsible for the circumcision honors and rituals.

Half the town came running. You couldn't wedge another soul in. Women brought peppered chick-peas, and there was a keg of beer from the tavern. I ate and drank as much as anyone, and they all congratulated me. Then there was a circumcision, and I named the boy after my father, may he rest in peace. When all were gone and I was left with my wife alone, she thrust her head through the bed-curtain and called me to her.

"Gimpel," said she, "why are you silent? Has your ship gone and sunk?"

"What shall I say?" I answered. "A fine thing you've done to me! If my mother had known of it she'd have died a second time."

She said, "Are you crazy, or what?"

"How can you make such a fool," I said, "of one who should be the lord and master?"

"What's the matter with you?" she said. "What have you taken it into your head to imagine?"

I saw that I must speak bluntly and openly. "Do you think this is the way to use an orphan?" I said. "You have borne a bastard."

She answered, "Drive this foolishness out of your head. The child is yours."

"How can he be mine?" I argued. "He was born seventeen weeks after the wedding."

She told me then that he was premature. I said, "Isn't he a little too premature?" She said she had had a grandmother who carried just as short a time and she resembled this grandmother of hers as one drop of water does another. She swore to it with such oaths that you would have believed a peasant at the fair if he had used them. To tell the plain truth, I didn't believe her; but when I talked it over the next day with the schoolmaster he told me that the very same thing had happened to Adam and Eve. Two they went up to bed, and four they descended.

"There isn't a woman in the world who is not the granddaughter of Eve," he said.

That was how it was—they argued me dumb. But then, who really knows how such things happen?

I began to forget my sorrow. I loved the child madly, and he loved me too. As soon as he saw me he'd wave his little hands and want me to pick him up, and when he was colicky I was the only one who could pacify him. I bought him a little bone teething ring and a little gilded cap. He was forever catching the evil eye from someone, and then I had to run to get one of those abracadabras for him that would get him out of it. I worked like an ox. You know how expenses go up when there's an infant in the house. I don't want to lie about it; I didn't dislike Elka either, for that matter. She swore at me and cursed, and I couldn't get enough of her. What strength she had! One of her looks could rob you of the power of speech. And her orations! Pitch and sulphur, that's what they were full of, and yet somehow also full of charm. I adored her every word. She gave me bloody wounds though.

In the evening I brought her a white loaf as well as a dark one, and also poppyseed rolls I baked myself. I thieved because of her and swiped everything I could lay hands on, macaroons, raisins, almonds, cakes. I hope I may be forgiven for stealing from the Saturday pots the women left to warm in the baker's oven. I would take out scraps of meat, a chunk of pudding, a chicken leg or head, a piece of tripe, whatever I could nip quickly. She ate and became fat and handsome.

I had to sleep away from home all during the week, at the bakery. On Friday nights when I got home she always made an excuse of some sort. Either she had heartburn, or a stitch in the side, or hiccups, or headaches. You know what women's excuses are. I had a bitter time of it. It was rough. To add to it, this little brother of hers, the bastard, was growing bigger. He'd put lumps on me, and when I wanted to hit back she'd open her mouth and curse so powerfully I saw a green haze floating before my eyes. Ten times a day she threatened to divorce me. Another man in my place would have taken French leave and disappeared. But I'm the type that bears it and says nothing. What's one to do? Shoulders are from God, and burdens too.

One night there was a calamity in the bakery; the oven burst, and we almost had a fire. There was nothing to do but go home, so I went home. Let me, I thought, also taste the joy of sleeping in bed in midweek. I didn't want to wake the sleeping mite and tiptoed into the house. Coming in, it seemed to me that I heard not the snoring of one but, as it were, a double snore, one a thin enough snore and the other like the snoring of a slaughtered ox. Oh, I didn't like that! I didn't like it at all. I went up to the bed, and things suddenly turned black. Next to Elka lay a man's form. Another in my place would have made an uproar, and enough noise to rouse the whole town, but the thought occurred to me that I might wake the child. A little thing like that—why frighten a little swallow like that, I thought. All right then, I went back to the bakery and stretched out on a sack of flour, and till morning I never shut an eye. I shivered as if I had had malaria. "Enough of being a donkey," I said to myself. "Gimpel isn't going to be a sucker all his life. There's a limit even to the foolishness of a fool like Gimpel."

In the morning I went to the rabbi to get advice, and it made a great commotion in the town. They sent the beadle for Elka right away. She came, carrying the child. And what do you think she did? She denied it, denied everything, bone and stone! "He's out of his head," she said. "I know nothing of dreams or divinations." They yelled at her, warned her, hammered on the table, but she stuck to her guns: it was a false accusation, she said.

The butchers and the horse-traders took her part. One of the lads from the slaughterhouse came by and said to me, "We've got our eye on you, you're a marked man." Meanwhile the child started to bear down and soiled itself. In the rabbinical court there was an Ark of the Covenant, and they couldn't allow that, so they sent Elka away.

I said to the rabbi, "What shall I do?"

"You must divorce her at once," said he.

"And what if she refuses?" I asked.

He said, "You must serve the divorce, that's all you'll have to do."

I said, "Well, all right, Rabbi. Let me think about it."

"There's nothing to think about," said he. "You mustn't remain under the same roof with her."

"And if I want to see the child?" I asked.

"Let her go, the harlot," said he, "and her brood of bastards with her."

The verdict he gave was that I mustn't even cross her threshold—never again, as long as I should live.

During the day it didn't bother me so much. I thought, It was bound to happen, the abscess had to burst. But at night when I stretched out upon the sacks I felt it all very bitterly. A longing took me, for her and for the child. I wanted to be angry, but that's my misfortune exactly, I don't have it in me to be really angry. In the first place—this was how my thoughts went—there's bound to be a slip sometimes. You can't live without errors. Probably that lad who was with her led her on and gave her presents and what not, and women are often long on hair and short on sense, and so he got around her. And then since she denies it so, maybe I was only seeing things? Hallucinations do happen. You see a figure or a mannikin or something, but when you come up closer it's nothing, there's not a thing there. And if that's so, I'm doing her an injustice. And when I got so far in my thoughts I started to weep. I sobbed so that I wet the flour where I lay. In the morning I went to the rabbi and told him that I had made a mistake. The rabbi wrote on with his quill, and he said that if that were so he would have to reconsider the whole case. Until he had finished I wasn't to go near my wife but I might send her bread and money by messenger.

III

NINE MONTHS PASSED BEFORE ALL THE RABBIS COULD COME TO AN AGREEMENT. Letters went back and forth. I hadn't realized that there could be so much erudition about a matter like this.

Meantime Elka gave birth to still another child, a girl this time. On the Sabbath I went to the synagogue and invoked a blessing on her. They called me up to the Torah, and I named the child for my mother-in-law, may she rest in peace. The louts and loudmouths of the town who came into the bakery gave me a going over. All Frampol refreshed its spirits because of my trouble and grief. However, I resolved that I would always believe what I was told. What's the good of *not* believing? Today it's your wife you don't believe; tomorrow it's God Himself you won't take stock in.

By an apprentice who was her neighbor I sent her daily a corn or a wheat loaf, a piece of pastry, rolls or bagels, or, when I got the chance, a slab of pudding, a slice of honeycake, or wedding strudel—whatever came my way. The apprentice was a goodhearted lad, and more than once he added something on his own. He had formerly annoyed me a lot, plucking my nose and digging me in the ribs, but when he started to be a visitor to my house he became kind and friendly. "Hey, you, Gimpel," he said to me, "you have a very decent little wife and two fine kids. You don't deserve them."

"But the things people say about her," I said.

"Well, they have long tongues," he said, "and nothing to do with them but babble. Ignore it as you ignore the cold of last winter."

One day the rabbi sent for me and said, "Are you certain, Gimpel, that you were wrong about your wife?"

I said, "I'm certain."

"Why, but look here! You yourself saw it."

"It must have been a shadow," I said.

"The shadow of what?"

"Just of one of the beams, I think."

"You can go home then. You owe thanks to the Yanover rabbi. He found an obscure reference in Maimonides* that favored you."

I seized the rabbi's hand and kissed it.

Maimonides: Jewish philosopher (1135–1204) whose *Guide for the Perplexed* (1190) attempted to reconcile Judaism and the teachings of Aristotle.

I wanted to run home immediately. It's no small thing to be separated for so long a time from wife and child. Then I reflected, I'd better go back to work now, and go home in the evening. I said nothing to anyone, although as far as my heart was concerned it was like one of the Holy Days. The women teased and twitted me as they did every day, but my thought was, Go on, with your loose talk. The truth is out, like the oil upon the water. Maimonides says it's right, and therefore it is right!

At night, when I had covered the dough to let it rise, I took my share of bread and a little sack of flour and started homeward. The moon was full and the stars were glistening, something to terrify the soul. I hurried onward, and before me darted a long shadow. It was winter and a fresh snow had fallen. I had a mind to sing, but it was growing late and I didn't want to wake the householders. Then I felt like whistling, but remembered that you don't whistle at night because it brings the demons out. So I was silent and walked as fast as I could.

Dogs in the Christian yards barked at me when I passed, but I thought, Bark your teeth out! What are you but mere dogs? Whereas I am a man, the husband of a fine wife, the father of promising children.

As I approached the house my heart started to pound as though it were the heart of a criminal. I felt no fear, but my heart went thump! thump! Well, no drawing back. I quietly lifted the latch and went in. Elka was asleep. I looked at the infant's cradle. The shutter was closed, but the moon forced its way through the cracks. I saw the newborn child's face and loved it as soon as I saw it—immediately—each tiny bone.

Then I came nearer to the bed. And what did I see but the apprentice lying there beside Elka. The moon went out all at once. It was utterly black, and I trembled. My teeth chattered. The bread fell from my hands and my wife waked and said, "Who is that, ah?"

I muttered, "It's me."

"Gimpel?" she asked. "How come you're here? I thought it was forbidden."

"The rabbi said," I answered and shook as with a fever.

"Listen to me, Gimpel," she said, "go out to the shed and see if the goat's all right. It seems she's been sick." I have forgotten to say that we had a goat. When I heard she was unwell I went into the yard. The nannygoat was a good little creature. I had a nearly human feeling for her.

With hesitant steps I went up to the shed and opened the door. The goat stood there on her four feet. I felt her everywhere, drew her by the arms, examined her udders, and found nothing wrong. She had probably eaten too much bark. "Good night, little goat," I said. "Keep well." And the little beast answered with a "Maa" as though to thank me for the good will.

I went back. The apprentice had vanished.

"Where," I asked, "is the lad?"

"What lad?" my wife answered.

"What do you mean?" I said. "The apprentice. You were sleeping with him."

"The things I have dreamed this night and the night before," she said, "may they come true and lay you low, body and soul! An evil spirit has taken root in you and dazzles your sight." She screamed out, "You hateful creature! You moon calf! You spook! You uncouth man! Get out, or I'll scream all Frampol out of bed!"

Before I could move, her brother sprang out from behind the oven and struck me a blow on the back of the head. I thought he had broken my neck. I felt that something about me was deeply wrong, and I said, "Don't make a scandal. All that's needed now is that people should accuse me of raising spooks and *dybbuks*."* For that was what she had meant. "No one will touch bread of my baking."

In short, I somehow calmed her.

"Well," she said, "that's enough. Lie down, and be shattered by wheels."

Next morning I called the apprentice aside. "Listen here, brother!" I said. And so on and so forth. "What do you say?" He stared at me as though I had dropped from the roof or something.

"I swear," he said, "you'd better go to an herb doctor or some healer. I'm afraid you have a screw loose, but I'll hush it up for you." And that's how the thing stood.

To make a long story short, I lived twenty years with my wife. She bore me six children, four daughters and two sons. All kinds of things happened, but I neither saw nor heard. I believed, and that's all. The rabbi recently said to me, "Belief in itself is beneficial. It is written that a good man lives by his faith."

Suddenly my wife took sick. It began with a trifle, a little growth upon the breast. But she evidently was not destined to live long; she had no years. I spent a fortune on her. I have forgotten to say that by this time I had a bakery of my own and in Frampol was considered to be something of a rich man. Daily the healer came, and every witch doctor in the neighborhood was brought. They decided to use leeches, and after that to try cupping. They even called a doctor from Lublin, but it was too late. Before she died she called me to her bed and said, "Forgive me, Gimpel."

I said, "What is there to forgive? You have been a good and faithful wife."

"Woe, Gimpel!" she said. "It was ugly how I deceived you all these years. I want to go clean to my Maker, and so I have to tell you that the children are not yours."

If I had been clouted on the head with a piece of wood it couldn't have bewildered me more.

"Whose are they?" I asked.

"I don't know," she said, "there were a lot. . . . But they're not yours." And as she spoke she tossed her head to the side, her eyes turned glassy, and it was all up with Elka. On her whitened lips there remained a smile.

---

dybbuks: demons, or souls of the dead, who take possession of people.

I imagined that, dead as she was, she was saying, "I deceived Gimpel. That was the meaning of my brief life."

IV

ONE NIGHT, when the period of mourning was done, as I lay dreaming on the flour sacks, there came the Spirit of Evil himself and said to me, "Gimpel, why do you sleep?"

I said, "What should I be doing? Eating *kreplach?*"*

"The whole world deceives you," he said, "and you ought to deceive the world in your turn."

"How can I deceive all the world?" I asked him.

He answered, "You might accumulate a bucket of urine every day and at night pour in into the dough. Let the sages of Frampol eat filth."

"What about judgment in the world to come?" I said.

"There is no world to come," he said. "They've sold you a bill of goods and talked you into believing you carried a cat in your belly. What nonsense!"

"Well then," I said, "and is there a God?"

He answered, "There is no God either."

"What," I said, "*is* there, then?"

"A thick mire."

He stood before my eyes with a goatish beard and horns, longtoothed, and with a tail. Hearing such words, I wanted to snatch him by the tail, but I tumbled from the flour sacks and nearly broke a rib. Then it happened that I had to answer the call of nature, and, passing, I saw the risen bread, which seemed to say to me, "Do it!" In brief, I let myself be persuaded.

At dawn the apprentice came. We kneaded the dough, scattered caraway seeds on it, and set it to bake. Then the apprentice went away, and I was left sitting in the little trench by the oven, on a pile of rags. Well, Gimpel, I thought, you've revenged yourself on them for all the shame they've put on you. Outside the frost glittered, but it was warm beside the oven. The flames heated my face. I bent my head and fell into a doze.

I saw in a dream, at once, Elka in her shroud. She called to me, "What have you done, Gimpel?"

I said to her, "It's all your fault," and started to cry.

"You fool!" she said. "You fool! Because I was false is everything false too? I never deceived anyone but myself. I'm paying for it all, Gimpel. They spare you nothing here."

I looked at her face. It was black. I was startled and waked, and remained sitting dumb. I sensed that everything hung in the balance. A false step now and I'd lose Eternal Life. But God gave me His help. I seized the long shovel

---

kreplach: a kind of dumpling containing meat, cheese, or other filling.

and took out the loaves, carried them into the yard, and started to dig a hole in the frozen earth.

My apprentice came back as I was doing it. "What are you doing, boss?" he said, and grew pale as a corpse.

"I know what I'm doing," I said, and I buried it all before his very eyes.

Then I went home, took my hoard from its hiding place, and divided it among the children. "I saw your mother tonight," I said. "She's turning black, poor thing."

They were so astounded they couldn't speak a word.

"Be well," I said, "and forget that such a one as Gimpel ever existed." I put on my short coat, a pair of boots, took the bag that held my prayer shawl in one hand, my stick in the other, and kissed the *mezzuzah*.* When people saw me in the street they were greatly surprised.

"Where are you going?" they said.

I answered. "Into the world." And so I departed from Frampol.

I wandered over the land, and good people did not neglect me. After many years I became old and white; I heard a great deal, many lies and falsehoods, but the longer I lived the more I understood that there were really no lies. Whatever doesn't really happen is dreamed at night. It happens to one if it doesn't happen to another, tomorrow if not today, or a century hence if not next year. What difference can it make? Often I heard tales of which I said, "Now this is a thing that cannot happen." But before a year had elapsed I heard that it actually had come to pass somewhere.

Going from place to place, eating at strange tables, it often happens that I spin yarns—improbable things that could never have happened—about devils, magicians, windmills, and the like. The children run after me, calling, "Grandfather, tell us a story." Sometimes they ask for particular stories, and I try to please them. A fat young boy once said to me, "Grandfather, it's the same story you told us before." The little rogue, he was right.

So it is with dreams too. It is many years since I left Frampol, but as soon as I shut my eyes I am there again. And whom do you think I see? Elka. She is standing by the washtub, as at our first encounter, but her face is shining and her eyes as radiant as the eyes of a saint, and she speaks outlandish words to me, strange things. When I wake I have forgotten it all. But while the dream lasts I am comforted. She answers all my queries, and what comes out is that all is right. I weep and implore, "Let me be with you." And she consoles me and tells me to be patient. The time is nearer than it is far. Sometimes she strokes and kisses me and weeps upon my face. When I awaken I feel her lips and taste the salt of her tears.

mezzuzah: a small oblong container, affixed near the front door of the house, which holds copies of Biblical verses (including a reminder to obey God's laws when traveling away from home).

No doubt the world is entirely an imaginary world, but it is only once removed from the true world. At the door of the hovel where I lie, there stands the plank on which the dead are taken away. The gravedigger Jew has his spade ready. The grave waits and the worms are hungry; the shrouds are prepared—I carry them in my beggar's sack. Another *shnorrer** is waiting to inherit my bed of straw. When the time comes I will go joyfully. Whatever may be there, it will be real, without complication, without ridicule, without deception. God be praised: there even Gimpel cannot be deceived.

Author's Note on His Collected Stories

It is difficult for me to comment on the choice of the forty-seven stories in this collection, selected from more than a hundred. Like some Oriental father with a harem full of women and children, I cherish them all.

In the process of creating them, I have become aware of the many dangers that lurk behind the writer of fiction. The worst of them are: 1. The idea that the writer must be a sociologist and a politician, adjusting himself to what are called social dialectics. 2. Greed for money and quick recognition. 3. Forced originality—namely, the illusion that pretentious rhetoric, precious innovations in style, and playing with artificial symbols can express the basic and ever-changing nature of human relations, or reflect the combinations and complications of heredity and environment. These verbal pitfalls of so-called "experimental" writing have done damage even to genuine talent; they have destroyed much of modern poetry by making it obscure, esoteric, and charmless. Imagination is one thing, and the distortion of what Spinoza called "the order of things" is something else entirely. Literature can very well describe the absurd, but it should never become absurd itself.

Although the short story is not in vogue nowadays, I still believe that it constitutes the utmost challenge to the creative writer. Unlike the novel, which can absorb and even forgive lengthy digressions, flashbacks, and loose construction, the short story must aim directly at its climax. It must possess uninterrupted tension and suspense. Also, brevity is its very essence. The short story must have a definite plan; it cannot be what in literary jargon is called "a slice of life." The masters of the short story, Chekhov, Maupassant, as well as the sublime scribe of the Joseph story in the Book of Genesis, knew exactly where they were going. One can read them over and over again and never get bored. Fiction in general should never become analytic. As a matter of fact, the writer of fiction should not even try to dabble in psychology and its various isms. Genuine literature informs while it entertains. It manages to be both clear and profound. It has the magical power of merging causality with purpose, doubt with faith, the

---

shnorrer: a beggar, a traveling panhandler.

passions of the flesh with the yearnings of the soul. It is unique and general, national and universal, realistic and mystical. While it tolerates commentary by others, it should never try to explain itself. These obvious truths must be emphasized, because false criticism and pseudo-originality have created a state of literary amnesia in our generation. The zeal for messages has made many writers forget that storytelling is the raison d'être of artistic prose.

For readers who would like me to say something "more personal," I quote here a few passages (though not in the order in which they were written) from a recent memoir of mine: "My isolation from everything remained the same. I had surrendered myself to melancholy and it had taken me prisoner. I had presented Creation with an ultimatum: 'Tell me your secret, or let me perish.' I had to run away from myself. But how? And where? I dreamed of a humanism and ethics the basis of which would be a refusal to justify all the evils the Almighty has sent us and is preparing to bestow upon us in the future. At its best, art can be nothing more than a means of forgetting the human disaster for a while."

I am still working hard to make this "while" worthwhile.

———————

I.B.S.

July 6, 1981

Frank O'Connor, 1903–1966

First Confession

This story first appeared in HARPER'S BAZAAR, *1939.*

ALL THE TROUBLE BEGAN WHEN MY GRANDFATHER DIED and my grandmother—my father's mother—came to live with us. Relations in the one house are a strain on the best of times, but, to make matters worse, my grandmother was a real old countrywoman and quite unsuited to the life in town. She had a fat, wrinkled old face, and, to Mother's great indignation, went round the house in bare feet—the boots had her crippled, she said. For dinner she had a jug of porter and a pot of potatoes with—sometimes—a bit of salt fish, and she poured out the potatoes on the table and ate them slowly, with great relish, using her fingers by way of a fork.

Now, girls are supposed to be fastidious, but I was the one who suffered most from this. Nora, my sister, just sucked up to the old woman for the penny she got every Friday out of the old-age pension, a thing I could not do. I was too honest, that was my trouble; and when I was playing with Bill Connell, the sergeant-major's son, and saw my grandmother steering up the path with the jug of porter sticking out from beneath her shawl I was mortified. I made excuses not to let him come into the house, because I could never be sure what she would be up to when we went in.

When Mother was at work and my grandmother made the dinner I wouldn't touch it. Nora once tried to make me, but I hid under the table from her and took the bread-knife with me for protection. Nora let on to be very indignant (she wasn't, of course, but she knew Mother saw through her, so she sided with Gran) and came after me. I lashed out at her with the bread-knife, and after that she left me alone. I stayed there till Mother came in from work and made my dinner, but when Father came in later Nora said in a shocked voice: "Oh, Dadda, do you know what Jackie did at dinnertime?" Then, of course, it all came out; Father gave me a flaking; Mother interfered, and for days after that he didn't speak to me and Mother barely spoke to Nora. And all because of that old woman! God knows, I was heart-scalded.

Then, to crown my misfortunes, I had to make my first confession and communion. It was an old woman called Ryan who prepared us for these. She was about the one age with Gran; she was well-to-do, lived in a big house on Montenotte, wore a black cloak and bonnet, and came every day to school at three o'clock when we should have been going home, and talked to us of hell. She may have mentioned the other place as well, but that could only have been by accident, for hell had the first place in her heart.

She lit a candle, took out a new half-crown, and offered it to the first boy who would hold one finger—only one finger!—in the flame for five minutes by the school clock. Being always very ambitious I was tempted to volunteer, but I thought it might look greedy. Then she asked were we afraid of holding one finger—only one finger!—in a little candle flame for five minutes and not afraid of burning all over in roasting hot furnaces for all eternity. "All eternity! Just think of that! A whole lifetime goes by and it's nothing, not even a drop in the ocean of your sufferings." The woman was really interesting about hell, but my attention was all fixed on the half-crown. At the end of the lesson she put it back in her purse. It was a great disappointment; a religious woman like that, you wouldn't think she'd bother about a thing like a half-crown.

Another day she said she knew a priest who woke one night to find a fellow he didn't recognize leaning over the end of his bed. The priest was a bit frightened—naturally enough—but he asked the fellow what he wanted, and the fellow said in a deep, husky voice that he wanted to go to confession. The priest said it was an awkward time and wouldn't it do in the morning, but the fellow said that last time he went to confession, there was one sin he kept back, being ashamed to mention it, and now it was always on his mind. Then the priest knew it was a bad case, because the fellow was after making a bad confession and committing a mortal sin. He got up to dress, and just then the cock crew in the yard outside, and—lo and behold!—when the priest looked round there was no sign of the fellow, only a smell of burning timber, and when the priest looked at his bed didn't he see the print of two hands burned in it? That was because the fellow had made a bad confession. This story made a shocking impression on me.

But the worst of all was when she showed us how to examine our conscience. Did we take the name of the Lord, our God, in vain? Did we honor our father and our mother? (I asked her did this include grandmothers and she said it did.) Did we love our neighbors as ourselves? Did we covet our neighbor's goods? (I thought of the way I felt about the penny that Nora got every Friday.) I decided that, between one thing and another, I must have broken the whole ten commandments, all on account of that old woman, and so far as I could see, so long as she remained in the house I had no hope of ever doing anything else.

I was scared to death of confession. The day the whole class went I let on to have a toothache, hoping my absence wouldn't be noticed; but at three o'clock, just as I was feeling safe, along comes a chap with a message from Mrs. Ryan that I was to go to confession myself on Saturday and be at the chapel for communion with the rest. To make it worse, Mother couldn't come with me and sent Nora instead.

Now, that girl had ways of tormenting me that Mother never knew of. She held my hand as we went down the hill, smiling sadly and saying how sorry she was for me, as if she were bringing me to the hospital for an operation.

"Oh, God help us!" she moaned. "Isn't it a terrible pity you weren't a good boy? Oh, Jackie, my heart bleeds for you! How will you ever think of all your sins? Don't forget you have to tell him about the time you kicked Gran on the shin."

"Lemme go!" I said, trying to drag myself free of her. "I don't want to go to confession at all."

"But sure, you'll have to go to confession, Jackie," she replied in the same regretful tone. "Sure, if you didn't, the parish priest would be up to the house, looking for you. 'Tisn't, God knows, that I'm not sorry for you. Do you remember the time you tried to kill me with the bread-knife under the table? And the language you used to me? I don't know what he'll do with you at all, Jackie. He might have to send you up to the bishop."

I remember thinking bitterly that she didn't know the half of what I had to tell—if I told it. I knew I couldn't tell it, and understood perfectly why the fellow in Mrs. Ryan's story made a bad confession; it seemed to me a great shame that people wouldn't stop criticizing him. I remember that steep hill down to the church, and the sunlit hillsides beyond the valley of the river, which I saw in the gaps between the houses like Adam's last glimpse of Paradise.

Then, when she had maneuvered me down the long flight of steps to the chapel yard, Nora suddenly changed her tone. She became the raging malicious devil she really was.

"There you are!" she said with a yelp of triumph, hurling me through the church door. "And I hope he'll give you the penitential psalms, you dirty little caffler."*

I knew then I was lost, given up to eternal justice. The door with the colored-glass panels swung shut behind me, the sunlight went out and gave place to deep shadow, and the wind whistled outside so that the silence within seemed to crackle like ice under my feet. Nora sat in front of me by the confession box. There were a couple of old women ahead of her, and then a miserable-looking poor devil came and wedged me in at the other side, so that I couldn't escape even if I had the courage. He joined his hands and rolled his eyes in the direction of the roof, muttering aspirations in an anguished tone, and I wondered had he a grandmother too. Only a grandmother could account for a fellow behaving in that heartbroken way, but he was better off than I, for he at least could go and confess his sins; while I would make a bad confession and then die in the night and be continually coming back and burning people's furniture.

Nora's turn came, and I heard the sound of something slamming, and then her voice as if butter wouldn't melt in her mouth, and then another slam, and

*caffler: scamp, rascal.

out she came. God, the hypocrisy of women! Her eyes were lowered, her head was bowed, and her hands were joined very low down on her stomach, and she walked up the aisle to the side altar looking like a saint. You never saw such an exhibition of devotion; and I remembered the devilish malice with which she had tormented me all the way from our door, and wondered were all religious people like that, really. It was my turn now. With the fear of damnation in my soul I went in, and the confessional door closed of itself behind me.

It was pitch-dark and I couldn't see priest or anything else. Then I really began to be frightened. In the darkness it was a matter between God and me, and He had all the odds. He knew what my intentions were before I even started; I had no chance. All I had ever been told about confession got mixed up in my mind, and I knelt to one wall and said: "Bless me, father, for I have sinned; this is my first confession." I waited for a few minutes, but nothing happened, so I tried it on the other wall. Nothing happened there either. He had me spotted all right.

It must have been then that I noticed the shelf at about one height with my head. It was really a place for grown-up people to rest their elbows, but in my distracted state I thought it was probably the place you were supposed to kneel. Of course, it was on the high side and not very deep, but I was always good at climbing and managed to get up all right. Staying up was the trouble. There was room only for my knees, and nothing you could get a grip on but a sort of wooden moulding a bit above it. I held on to the moulding and repeated the words a little louder, and this time something happened all right. A slide was slammed back; a little light entered the box, and a man's voice said: "Who's there?"

"'Tis me, father," I said for fear he mightn't see me and go away again. I couldn't see him at all. The place the voice came from was under the moulding, about level with my knees, so I took a good grip of the moulding and swung myself down till I saw the astonished face of a young priest looking up at me. He had to put his head on one side to see me, and I had to put mine on one side to see him, so we were more or less talking to one another upside-down. It struck me as a queer way of hearing confessions, but I didn't feel it my place to criticize.

"Bless me, father, for I have sinned; this is my first confession," I rattled off all in one breath, and swung myself down the least shade more to make it easier for him.

"What are you doing up there?" he shouted in an angry voice, and the strain the politeness was putting on my hold of the moulding, and the shock of being addressed in such an uncivil tone, were too much for me. I lost my grip, tumbled, and hit the door an unmerciful wallop before I found myself flat on my back in the middle of the aisle. The people who had been waiting stood up with their mouths open. The priest opened the door of the middle box and came out, pushing his biretta back from his forehead; he looked something terrible. Then Nora came scampering down the aisle.

"Oh, you dirty little caffler!" she said. "I might have known you'd do it. I might have known you'd disgrace me. I can't leave you out of my sight for one minute."

Before I could even get to my feet to defend myself she bent down and gave me a clip across the ear. This reminded me that I was so stunned I had even forgotten to cry, so that people might think I wasn't hurt at all, when in fact I was probably maimed for life. I gave a roar out of me.

"What's all this about?" the priest hissed, getting angrier than ever and pushing Nora off me. "How dare you hit the child like that, you little vixen?"

"But I can't do my penance with him, father," Nora cried, cocking an outraged eye up at him.

"Well, go and do it, or I'll give you some more to do," he said, giving me a hand up. "Was it coming to confession you were, my poor man?" he asked me.

"'Twas, father," said I with a sob.

"Oh," he said respectfully, "a big hefty fellow like you must have terrible sins. Is this your first?"

"'Tis, father," said I.

"Worse and worse," he said gloomily. "The crimes of a life-time. I don't know will I get rid of you at all today. You'd better wait now till I'm finished with these old ones. You can see by the looks of them they haven't much to tell."

"I will, father," I said with something approaching joy.

The relief of it was really enormous. Nora stuck out her tongue at me from behind his back, but I couldn't even be bothered retorting. I knew from the very moment that man opened his mouth that he was intelligent above the ordinary. When I had time to think, I saw how right I was. It only stood to reason that a fellow confessing after seven years would have more to tell than people that went every week. The crimes of a lifetime, exactly as he said. It was only what he expected, and the rest was the cackle of old women and girls with their talk of hell, the bishop, and the penitential psalms. That was all they knew. I started to make my examination of conscience, and barring the one bad business of my grandmother it didn't seem so bad.

The next time, the priest steered me into the confession box himself and left the shutter back the way I could see him get in and sit down at the further side of the grille from me.

"Well, now," he said, "what do they call you?"

"Jackie, father," said I.

"And what's a-trouble to you, Jackie?"

"Father," I said, feeling I might as well get it over while I had him in good humor, "I had it all arranged to kill my grandmother."

He seemed a bit shaken by that, all right, because he said nothing for quite a while.

"My goodness," he said at last, "that'd be a shocking thing to do. What put that into your head?"

"Father," I said, feeling very sorry for myself, "she's an awful woman."

"Is she?" he asked. "What way is she awful?"

"She takes porter, father," I said, knowing well from the way Mother talked of it that this was a mortal sin, and hoping it would make the priest take a more favorable view of my case.

"Oh my!" he said, and I could see he was impressed.

"And snuff, father," said I.

"That's a bad case, sure enough, Jackie," he said.

"And she goes round in her bare feet, father," I went on in a rush of self-pity, "and she knows I don't like her, and she gives pennies to Nora and none to me, and my da sides with her and flakes me, and one night I was so heart-scalded I made up my mind I'd have to kill her."

"And what would you do with the body?" he asked with great interest.

"I was thinking I could chop that up and carry it away in a barrow I have," I said.

"'Begor, Jackie," he said, "do you know you're a terrible child?"

"I know, father," I said, for I was just thinking the same thing myself. "I tried to kill Nora too with a bread-knife under the table, only I missed her."

"Is that the little girl that was beating you just now?" he asked.

"'Tis, father."

"Someone will go for her with a bread-knife one day, and he won't miss her," he said rather cryptically. "You must have great courage. Between our-selves, there's a lot of people I'd like to do the same to but I'd never have the nerve. Hanging is an awful death."

"Is it, father?" I asked with the deepest interest—I was always very keen on hanging. "Did you ever see a fellow hanged?"

"Dozens of them," he said solemnly. "And they all died roaring."

"Jay!" I said.

"Oh, a horrible death!" he said with great satisfaction. "Lots of the fellows I saw killed their grandmothers too, but they all said 'twas never worth it."

He had me there for a full ten minutes talking, and then walked out the chapel yard with me. I was genuinely sorry to part with him, because he was the most entertaining character I'd ever met in the religious line. Out-side, after the shadow of the church, the sunlight was like the roaring of waves on a beach; it dazzled me; and when the frozen silence melted and I heard the screech of trams on the road my heart soared. I knew now I wouldn't die in the night and come back, leaving marks on my mother's fur-niture. It would be a great worry to her, and the poor soul had enough.

Nora was sitting on the railing, waiting for me, and she put on a very sour puss when she saw the priest with me. She was mad jealous because a priest had never come out of the church with her.

"Well," she asked coldly, after he left me, "what did he give you?"

"Three Hail Marys," I said.

"Three Hail Marys," she repeatedly incredulously. "You mustn't have told him anything."

"I told him everything," I said confidently.

"About Gran and all?"

"About Gran and all."

(All she wanted was to be able to go home and say I'd made a bad confession.)

"Did you tell him you went for me with the bread-knife?" she asked with a frown.

"I did to be sure."

"And he only gave you three Hail Marys?"

"That's all."

She slowly got down from the railing with a baffled air. Clearly, this was beyond her. As we mounted the steps back to the main road she looked at me suspiciously.

"What are you sucking?" she asked.

"Bullseyes."

"Was it the priest gave them to you"

"'Twas."

"Lord God," she wailed bitterly, "some people have all the luck! 'Tis no advantage to anybody trying to be good. I might just as well be a sinner like you."

Alice Walker, 1944—

Everyday Use

This story first appeared in IN LOVE AND TROUBLE: STORIES OF BLACK WOMEN, *1973.*

for your grandmama

I WILL WAIT FOR HER IN THE YARD that Maggie and I made so clean and wavy yesterday afternoon. A yard like this is more comfortable than most people know. It is not just a yard. It is like an extended living room. When the hard clay is swept clean as a floor and the fine sand around the edges lined with tiny, irregular grooves, anyone can come and sit and look up into the elm tree and wait for the breezes that never come inside the house.

Maggie will be nervous until after her sister goes: she will stand hopelessly in corners, homely and ashamed of the burn scars down her arms and legs, eying her sister with a mixture of envy and awe. She thinks her sister has held life always in the palm of one hand, that "no" is a word the world never learned to say to her.

———————

YOU'VE NO DOUBT SEEN THOSE TV SHOWS where the child who has "made it" is confronted, as a surprise, by her own mother and father, tottering in weakly from backstage. (A pleasant surprise, of course: What would they do if parent and child came on the show only to curse out and insult each other?) On TV mother and child embrace and smile into each other's faces. Sometimes the mother and father weep, the child wraps them in her arms and leans across the table to tell how she would not have made it without their help. I have seen these programs.

Sometimes I dream a dream in which Dee and I are suddenly brought together on a TV program of this sort. Out of a dark and soft-seated limousine I am ushered into a bright room filled with many people. There I meet a smiling, gray, sporty man like Johnny Carson who shakes my hand and tells me what a fine girl I have. Then we are on the stage and Dee is embracing me with tears in her eyes. She pins on my dress a large orchid, even though she had told me once that she thinks orchids are tacky flowers.

In real life I am a large, big-boned woman with rough, man-working hands. In the winter I wear flannel nightgowns to bed and overalls during the day. I can kill and clean a hog as mercilessly as a man. My fat keeps me hot in zero weather. I can work outside all day, breaking ice to get water for washing: I can eat pork liver cooked over the open fire minutes after it comes steaming from the hog. One winter I knocked a bull calf straight in the brain between the eyes with a sledge hammer and had the meat hung up to chill before nightfall. But of course all this does not show on television. I am the way my daughter would want me to be: a hundred pounds lighter, my skin like an uncooked barley pancake. My hair glistens in the hot bright lights. Johnny Carson has much to do to keep up with my quick and witty tongue.

But that is a mistake. I know even before I wake up. Who ever knew a Johnson with a quick tongue? Who can even imagine me looking a strange white man in the eye? It seems to me I have talked to them always with one foot raised in flight, with my head turned in whichever way is farthest from them. Dee, though. She would always look anyone in the eye. Hesitation was no part of her nature.

"How do I look, Mama?" Maggie says, showing just enough of her thin body enveloped in pink skirt and red blouse for me to know she's there, almost hidden by the door.

"Come out into the yard," I say.

Have you ever seen a lame animal, perhaps a dog run over by some care-less person rich enough to own a car, sidle up to someone who is ignorant enough to be kind to him? That is the way my Maggie walks. She has been like this, chin on chest, eyes on ground, feet in shuffle, ever since the fire that burned the other house to the ground.

Dee is lighter than Maggie, with nice hair and a fuller figure. She's a woman now, though sometimes I forget. How long ago was it that the other house burned? Ten, twelve years? Sometimes I can still hear the flames and feel Maggie's arms sticking to me, her hair smoking and her dress falling off her in little black papery flakes. Her eyes seemed stretched open, blazed open by the flames reflected in them. And Dee. I see her standing off under the sweet gum tree she used to dig gum out of; a look of concentration on her face as she watched the last dingy gray board of the house fall in toward the red-hot brick chimney. Why don't you do a dance around the ashes? I'd wanted to ask her. She had hated the house that much.

I used to think she hated Maggie, too. But that was before we raised the money, the church and me, to send her to Augusta to school. She used to read to us without pity; forcing words, lies, other folks' habits, whole lives upon us two, sitting trapped and ignorant underneath her voice. She washed us in a river of make-believe, burned us with a lot of knowledge we didn't neces-sarily need to know. Pressed us to her with the serious way she read, to shove us away at just the moment, like dimwits, we seemed about to understand.

Dee wanted nice things. A yellow organdy dress to wear to her graduation from high school; black pumps to match a green suit she'd made from an old suit somebody gave me. She was determined to stare down any disaster in her efforts. Her eyelids would not flicker for minutes at a time. Often I fought off the temptation to shake her. At sixteen she had a style of her own: and knew what style was.

———————

I NEVER HAD AN EDUCATION MYSELF. After second grade the school was closed down. Don't ask me why: in 1927 colored asked fewer questions than they do now. Sometimes Maggie reads to me. She stumbles along good-naturedly but can't see well. She knows she is not bright. Like good looks and money, quickness passed her by. She will marry John Thomas (who has mossy teeth in an earnest face) and then I'll be free to sit here and I guess just sing church songs to myself. Although I never was a good singer. Never could carry a tune. I was always better at a man's job. I used to love to milk till I was hooked in the side in '49. Cows are soothing and slow and don't bother you, unless you try to milk them the wrong way.

I have deliberately turned my back on the house. It is three rooms, just like the one that burned, except the roof is tin; they don't make shingle roofs any more. There are no real windows, just some holes cut in the sides, like the portholes in a ship, but not round and not square, with rawhide holding the shutters up on the outside. This house is in a pasture, too, like the other one. No doubt when Dee sees it she will want to tear it down. She wrote me once that no matter where we "choose" to live, she will manage to come see us. But she will never bring her friends. Maggie and I thought about this and Maggie asked me, "Mama, when did Dee ever *have* any friends?"

She had a few. Furtive boys in pink shirts hanging about on washday after school. Nervous girls who never laughed. Impressed with her, they worshipped the well-turned phrase, the cute shape, the scalding humor that erupted like bubbles in lye. She read to them.

When she was courting Jimmy T she didn't have much time to pay to us, but turned all her faultfinding power on him. He *flew* to marry a cheap city girl from a family of ignorant flashy people. She hardly had time to recompose herself.

———————

WHEN SHE COMES I WILL MEET—but there they are!

Maggie attempts to make a dash for the house, in her shuffling way, but I stay her with my hand. "Come back here," I say. And she stops and tries to dig a well in the sand with her toe.

It is hard to see them clearly through the strong sun. But even the first glimpse of leg out of the car tells me it is Dee. Her feet were always neat-looking, as if God himself had shaped them with a certain style. From the other side of the car comes a short, stocky man. Hair is all over his head a foot long and hanging from his chin like a kinky mule tail. I hear Maggie suck in her breath. "Uhnnnh," is what it sounds like. Like when you see the wriggling end of a snake just in front of your foot on the road. "Uhnnnh."

Dee next. A dress down to the ground, in this hot weather. A dress so loud it hurts my eyes. There are yellows and oranges enough to throw back the light of the sun. I feel my whole face warming from the heat waves it throws out. Earrings gold, too, and hanging down to her shoulders. Bracelets dangling and making noises when she moves her arm up to shake the folds of her dress out of her armpits. The dress is loose and flows, and as she walks closer, I like it. I hear Maggie go "Uhnnnh" again. It is her sister's hair. It stands straight up like the wool on a sheep. It is black as night and around the edges are two long pigtails that rope about like small lizards disappearing behind her ears.

"Wa-su-zo-Tean-o!" she says, coming on in that gliding way the dress makes her move. The short stocky fellow with the hair to his navel is all grinning and he follows up with "Asalamalakim, my mother and sister!" He moves to hug Maggie but she falls back, right up against the back of my chair. I feel her trembling there and when I look up I see the perspiration falling off her chin.

"Don't get up," says Dee. Since I am stout it takes something of a push. You can see me trying to move a second or two before I make it. She turns, showing white heels through her sandals, and goes back to the car. Out she peeks next with a Polaroid. She stoops down quickly and lines up picture after picture of me sitting there in front of the house with Maggie cowering behind me. She never takes a shot without making sure the house is included. When a cow comes nibbling around the edge of the yard she snaps it and me and Maggie *and* the house. Then she puts the Polaroid in the backseat of the car, and comes up and kisses me on the forehead.

Meanwhile Asalamalakim is going through motions with Maggie's hand. Maggie's hand is as limp as a fish, and probably cold, despite the sweat, and she keeps trying to pull it back. It looks like Asalamalakim wants to shake hands but wants to do it fancy. Or maybe he don't know how people shake hands. Anyhow, he soon gives up on Maggie.

"Well," I say. "Dee."

"No, Mama," she says. "Not 'Dee,' Wangero Leewanika Kemanjo!"

"What happened to 'Dee'?" I wanted to know.

"She's dead," Wangero said. "I couldn't bear it any longer, being named after the people who oppress me."

"You know as well as me you was named after your aunt Dicie," I said. Dicie is my sister. She named Dee. We called her "Big Dee" after Dee was born.

"But who was *she* named after?" asked Wangero.

"I guess after Grandma Dee," I said.

"And who was she named after?" asked Wangero.

"Her mother," I said, and saw Wangero was getting tired. "That's about as far back as I can trace it," I said. Though, in fact, I probably could have carried it back beyond the Civil War through the branches.

"Well," said Asalamalakim, "there you are."

"Uhnnnh," I heard Maggie say.

"There I was not," I said, "before 'Dicie' cropped up in our family, so why should I try to trace it that far back?"

He just stood there grinning, looking down on me like somebody inspecting a Model A car. Every once in a while he and Wangero sent eye signals over my head.

"How do you pronounce this name?" I asked.

"You don't have to call me by it if you don't want to," said Wangero.

"Why shouldn't I?" I asked. "If that's what you want us to call you, we'll call you."

"I know it might sound awkward at first," said Wangero.

"I'll get used to it," I said. "Ream it out again."

Well, soon we got the name out of the way. Asalamalakim had a name twice as long and three times as hard. After I tripped over it two or three times he told me to just call him Hakim-a-barber. I wanted to ask him was he a barber, but I didn't really think he was, so I didn't ask.

"You must belong to those beef-cattle peoples down the road," I said. They said "Asalamalakim" when they met you, too, but they didn't shake hands. Always too busy: feeding the cattle, fixing the fences, putting up saltlick shelters, throwing down hay. When the white folks poisoned some of the herd the men stayed up all night with rifles in their hands. I walked a mile and a half just to see the sight.

Hakim-a-barber said, "I accept some of their doctrines, but farming and raising cattle is not my style." (They didn't tell me, and I didn't ask, whether Wangero [Dee] had really gone and married him.)

We sat down to eat and right away he said he didn't eat collards and pork was unclean. Wangero, though, went on through the chitlins and corn bread, the greens and everything else. She talked a blue streak over the sweet potatoes. Everything delighted her. Even the fact that we still used the benches her daddy made for the table when we couldn't afford to buy chairs.

"Oh, Mama!" she cried. Then turned to Hakim-a-barber. "I never knew how lovely these benches are. You can feel the rump prints," she said, running her hands underneath her and along the bench. Then she gave a sigh and her hand closed over Grandma Dee's butter dish. "That's it!" she said. "I knew there was something I wanted to ask you if I could have." She jumped up from the table and went over in the corner where the churn stood, the milk in it clabber by now. She looked at the churn and looked at it.

"This churn top is what I need," she said. "Didn't Uncle Buddy whittle it out of a tree you all used to have?"

"Yes," I said.

"Uh huh," she said happily. "And I want the dasher, too."

"Uncle Buddy whittle that, too?" asked the barber.

Dee (Wangero) looked up at me.

"Aunt Dee's first husband whittled the dash," said Maggie so low you almost couldn't hear her. "His name was Henry, but they called him Stash."

"Maggie's brain is like an elephant's," Wangero said, laughing. "I can use the churn top as a centerpiece for the alcove table," she said, sliding a plate over the churn, "and I'll think of something artistic to do with the dasher."

When she finished wrapping the dasher the handle stuck out. I took it for a moment in my hands. You didn't even have to look close to see where hands pushing the dasher up and down to make butter had left a kind of sink in the wood. In fact, there were a lot of small sinks; you could see where thumbs and fingers had sunk into the wood. It was beautiful light yellow wood, from a tree that grew in the yard where Big Dee and Stash had lived.

After dinner Dee (Wangero) went to the trunk at the foot of my bed and started rifling through it. Maggie hung back in the kitchen over the dishpan. Out came Wangero with two quilts. They had been pieced by Grandma Dee and then Big Dee and me had hung them on the quilt frames on the front porch and quilted them. One was in the Lone Star pattern. The other was Walk Around the Mountain. In both of them were scraps of dresses Grandma Dee had worn fifty and more years ago. Bits and pieces of Grandpa Jarrell's Paisley shirts. And one teeny faded blue piece, about the size of a penny matchbox, that was from Great Grandpa Ezra's uniform that he wore in the Civil War.

"Mama," Wangero said sweet as a bird. "Can I have these old quilts?"

I heard something fall in the kitchen, and a minute later the kitchen door slammed.

"Why don't you take one or two of the others?" I asked. "These old things was just done by me and Big Dee from some tops your grandma pieced before she died."

"No," said Wangero. "I don't want those. They are stitched around the borders by machine."

"That'll make them last better," I said.

"That's not the point," said Wangero. "These are all pieces of dresses Grandma used to wear. She did all this stitching by hand. Imagine!" She held the quilts securely in her arms, stroking them.

"Some of the pieces, like those lavender ones, come from old clothes her mother handed down to her," I said, moving up to touch the quilts. Dee (Wangero) moved back just enough so that I couldn't reach the quilts. They already belonged to her.

"Imagine!" she breathed again, clutching them closely to her bosom.

"The truth is," I said, "I promised to give them quilts to Maggie, for when she marries John Thomas."

She gasped like a bee had stung her.

"Maggie can't appreciate these quilts!" she said. "She'd probably be backward enough to put them to everyday use."

"I reckon she would," I said. "God knows I been saving 'em for long enough with nobody using 'em. I hope she will!" I didn't want to bring up how I had offered Dee (Wangero) a quilt when she went away to college. Then she had told me they were old-fashioned, out of style.

"But they're *priceless!*" she was saying now, furiously; for she has a temper. "Maggie would put them on the bed and in five years they'd be in rags. Less than that!"

"She can always make some more," I said. "Maggie knows how to quilt."

Dee (Wangero) looked at me with hatred. "You just will not understand. The point is these quilts, *these* quilts!"

"Well," I said, stumped. "What would *you* do with them?"

"Hang them," she said. As if that was the only thing you *could* do with quilts.

Maggie by now was standing in the door. I could almost hear the sound her feet made as they scraped over each other.

"She can have them, Mama," she said, like somebody used to never winning anything, or having anything reserved for her. "I can 'member Grandma Dee without the quilts."

I looked at her hard. She had filled her bottom lip with checkerberry snuff and it gave her face a kind of dopey, hangdog look. It was Grandma Dee and Big Dee who taught her how to quilt herself. She stood there with her scarred hands hidden in the folds of her skirt. She looked at her sister with something like fear but she wasn't mad at her. This was Maggie's portion. This was the way she knew God to work.

When I looked at her like that something hit me in the top of my head and ran down to the soles of my feet. Just like when I'm in church and the spirit of God touches me and I get happy and shout. I did something I never had done before: hugged Maggie to me, then dragged her on into the room, snatched the quilts out of Miss Wangero's hands and dumped them into Maggie's lap. Maggie just sat there on my bed with her mouth open.

"Take one or two of the others," I said to Dee.

But she turned without a word and went out to Hakim-a-barber.

"You just don't understand," she said, as Maggie and I came out to the car.

"What don't I understand?" I wanted to know.

"Your heritage," she said. And then she turned to Maggie, kissed her, and said, "You ought to try to make something of yourself, too, Maggie. It's really a new day for us. But from the way you and Mama still live you'd never know it."

She put on some sunglasses that hid everything above the tip of her nose and her chin.

Maggie smiled; maybe at the sunglasses. But a real smile, not scared. After we watched the car dust settle I asked Maggie to bring me a dip of snuff. And then the two of us sat there just enjoying, until it was time to go in the house and go to bed.

Tillie Olsen, 1912–

I Stand Here Ironing

This story first appeared in PACIFIC SPECTATOR, *1961.*

I STAND HERE IRONING, and what you asked me moves tormented back and forth with the iron.

"I wish you would manage the time to come in and talk with me about your daughter. I'm sure you can help me understand her. She's a youngster who needs help and whom I'm deeply interested in helping."

"Who needs help." . . . Even if I came, what good would it do? You think because I am her mother I have a key, or that in some way you could use me as a key? She has lived for nineteen years. There is all that life that has happened outside of me, beyond me.

And when is there time to remember, to sift, to weigh, to estimate, to total? I will start and there will be an interruption and I will have to gather it all together again. Or I will become engulfed with all I did or did not do, with what should have been and what cannot be helped.

She was a beautiful baby. The first and only one of our five that was beautiful at birth. You do not guess how new and uneasy her tenancy in her now-loveliness. You did not know her all those years she was thought homely, or see her poring over her baby pictures, making me tell her over and over how beautiful she had been—and would be, I would tell her—and was now, to the seeing eye. But the seeing eyes were few or nonexistent. Including mine.

I nursed her. They feel that's important nowadays. I nursed all the children, but with her, with all the fierce rigidity of first motherhood, I did like the books then said. Though her cries battered me to trembling and my breasts ached with swollenness, I waited till the clock decreed.

Why do I put that first? I do not even know if it matters, or if it explains anything.

She was a beautiful baby. She blew shining bubbles of sound. She loved motion, loved light, loved color and music and textures. She would lie on the floor in her blue overalls patting the surface so hard in ecstasy her hands and feet would blur. She was a miracle to me, but when she was eight months old I had to leave her daytimes with the woman downstairs to whom she was no miracle at all, for I worked or looked for work and for Emily's father, who "could no longer endure" (he wrote in his good-bye note) "sharing want with us."

I was nineteen. It was the pre-relief, pre-WPA world of the depression. I would start running as soon as I got off the streetcar, running up the stairs, the place smelling sour, and awake or asleep to startle awake, when she saw me she would break into a clogged weeping that could not be comforted, a weeping I can hear yet.

After a while I found a job hashing at night so I could be with her days, and it was better. But it came to where I had to bring her to his family and leave her.

It took a long time to raise the money for her fare back. Then she got chicken pox and I had to wait longer. When she finally came, I hardly knew her, walking quick and nervous like her father, looking like her father, thin, and dressed in a shoddy red that yellowed her skin and glared at the pockmarks. All the baby loveliness gone.

She was two. Old enough for nursery school they said, and I did not know then what I know now—the fatigue of the long day, and the lacerations of group life in the kinds of nurseries that are only parking places for children.

Except that it would have made no difference if I had known. It was the only place there was. It was the only way we could be together, the only way I could hold a job.

And even without knowing, I knew. I knew the teacher that was evil because all these years it has curdled into my memory, the little boy hunched in the corner, her rasp, "why aren't you outside, because Alvin hits you? that's no reason, go out, scaredy." I knew Emily hated it even if she did not clutch and implore "don't go Mommy" like the other children, mornings.

She always had a reason why we should stay home. Momma, you look sick. Momma, I feel sick. Momma, the teachers aren't there today, they're sick. Momma, we can't go, there was a fire there last night. Momma, it's a holiday today, no school, they told me.

But never a direct protest, never rebellion. I think of our others in their three-, four-year-oldness—the explosions, the tempers, the denunciations, the demands—and I feel suddenly ill. I put the iron down. What in me demanded that goodness in her? And what was the cost, the cost to her of such goodness?

The old man living in the back once said in his gentle way: "You should smile at Emily more when you look at her." What *was* in my face when I looked at her? I loved her. There were all the acts of love.

It was only with the others I remembered what he said, and it was the face of joy, and not of care or tightness or worry I turned to them—too late for Emily. She does not smile easily, let alone almost always as her brothers and sisters do. Her face is closed and somber, but when she wants, how fluid. You must have seen it in her pantomimes, you spoke of her rare gift for comedy on the stage that rouses laughter out of the audience so dear they applaud and applaud and do not want to let her go.

Where does it come from, that comedy? There was none of it in her when she came back to me that second time, after I had had to send her away again. She had a new daddy now to learn to love, and I think perhaps it was a better time.

Except when we left her alone nights, telling ourselves she was old enough.

"Can't you go some other time, Mommy, like tomorrow?" she would ask. "Will it be just a little while you'll be gone? Do you promise?"

The time we came back, the front door open, the clock on the floor in the hall. She rigid awake. "It wasn't just a little while. I didn't cry. Three times I called you, just three times, and then I ran downstairs to open the door so you could come faster. The clock talked loud. I threw it away, it scared me what it talked."

She said the clock talked loud again that night I went to the hospital to have Susan. She was delirious with the fever that comes from red measles, but she was fully conscious all the week I was gone and the week after we were home when she could not come near the new baby or me.

She did not get well. She stayed skeleton thin, not wanting to eat, and night after night she had nightmares. She would call for me, and I would rouse from exhaustion to sleepily call back: "You're all right, darling, go to sleep, it's just a dream," and if she still called, in a sterner voice, "now go to sleep, Emily, there's nothing to hurt you." Twice, only twice, when I had to get up for Susan anyhow, I went in to sit with her.

Now when it is too late (as if she would let me hold and comfort her like I do the others) I get up and go to her at once at her moan or restless stirring. "Are you awake, Emily? Can I get you something?" And the answer is always the same: "No, I'm all right, go back to sleep, Mother."

They persuaded me at the clinic to send her away to a convalescent home in the country where "she can have the kind of food and care you can't manage for her, and you'll be free to concentrate on the new baby." They still send children to that place. I see pictures on the society page of sleek young women planning affairs to raise money for it, or dancing at the affairs, or decorating Easter eggs or filling Christmas stockings for the children.

They never have a picture of the children so I do not know if the girls still wear those gigantic red bows and the ravaged looks on the every other Sunday when parents can come to visit "unless otherwise notified"—as we were notified the first six weeks.

Oh it is a handsome place, green lawns and tall trees and fluted flower beds. High up on the balconies of each cottage the children stand, the girls in their red bows and white dresses, the boys in white suits and giant red ties. The parents stand below shrieking up to be heard and the children shriek down to be heard, and between them the invisible wall: "Not to Be Contaminated by Parental Germs or Physical Affection."

There was a tiny girl who always stood hand in hand with Emily. Her parents never came. One visit she was gone. "They moved her to Rose Cottage," Emily shouted in explanation. "They don't like you to love anybody here."

She wrote once a week, the labored writing of a seven-year-old. "I am fine. How is the baby. If I write my leter nicly I will have a star. Love." There never was a star. We wrote every other day, letters she could never hold or keep but only hear read—once. "We simply do not have room for children to keep any personal possessions," they patiently explained when we pieced one Sunday's shrieking together to plead how much it would mean to Emily, who loved so to keep things, to be allowed to keep her letters and cards.

Each visit she looked frailer. "She isn't eating," they told us.

(They had runny eggs for breakfast or mush with lumps, Emily said later, I'd hold it in my mouth and not swallow. Nothing ever tasted good, just when they had chicken.)

It took us eight months to get her released home, and only the fact that she gained back so little of her seven lost pounds convinced the social worker.

I used to try to hold and love her after she came back, but her body would stay stiff, and after a while she'd push away. She ate little. Food sickened her, and I think much of life too. Oh she had physical lightness and brightness, twinkling by on skates, bouncing like a ball up and down up and down over the jump rope, skimming over the hill: but these were momentary.

She fretted about her appearance, thin and dark and foreign-looking at a time when every little girl was supposed to look or thought she should look a chubby blonde replica of Shirley Temple. The doorbell sometimes rang for her, but no one seemed to come and play in the house or be a best friend. Maybe because we moved so much.

There was a boy she loved painfully through two school semesters. Months later she told me how she had taken pennies from my purse to buy him candy. "Licorice was his favorite and I brought him some every day, but he still liked Jennifer better'n me. Why, Mommy?" The kind of question for which there is no answer.

School was a worry to her. She was not glib or quick in a world where glibness and quickness were easily confused with ability to learn. To her overworked and exasperated teachers she was an overconscientious "slow learner" who kept trying to catch up and was absent entirely too often.

I let her be absent, though sometimes the illness was imaginary. How different from my now-strictness about attendance with the others. I wasn't working. We had a new baby, I was home anyhow. Sometimes, after Susan grew old enough, I would keep her home from school, too, to have them all together.

Mostly Emily had asthma, and her breathing, harsh and labored, would fill the house with a curiously tranquil sound. I would bring the two old dresser mirrors and her boxes of collections to her bed. She would select beads and single earrings, bottle tops and shells, dried flowers and pebbles, old postcards and scraps, all sorts of oddments; then she and Susan would play Kingdom, setting up landscapes and furniture, peopling them with action.

Those were the only times of peaceful companionship between her and Susan. I have edged away from it, that poisonous feeling between them, that terrible balancing of hurts and needs I had to do between the two, and did so badly, those earlier years.

Oh there are conflicts between the others too, each one human, needing, demanding, hurting, taking—but only between Emily and Susan, no, Emily toward Susan that corroding resentment. It seems so obvious on the surface, yet it is not obvious. Susan, the second child, Susan, golden- and curly haired and chubby, quick and articulate and assured, everything in appearance and manner Emily was not; Susan, not able to resist Emily's precious things, losing or sometimes clumsily breaking them; Susan telling jokes and riddles to company for applause while Emily sat silent (to say to me later: that was *my* riddle, Mother, I told it to Susan); Susan, who for all the five years' difference in age was just a year behind Emily in developing physically.

I am glad for that slow physical development that widened the difference between her and her contemporaries, though she suffered over it. She was too vulnerable for that terrible world of youthful competition, of preening and parading, of constant measuring of yourself against every other, of envy, "If I had the copper hair," "If I had that skin. . . . " She tormented herself enough about not looking like the others, there was enough of the unsureness, the having to be conscious of words before you speak, the constant caring—what are they thinking of me? without having it all magnified by the merciless physical drives.

Ronnie is calling. He is wet and I change him. It is rare there is such a cry now. That time of motherhood is almost behind me when the ear is not one's own but must always be racked and listening for the child cry, the child call. We sit for a while and I hold him, looking out over the city spread in charcoal with its soft aisles of light. *"Shoogily,"* he breathes and curls closer. I carry him back to bed, asleep. *Shoogily.* A funny word, a family word, inherited from Emily, invented by her to say: *comfort.*

In this and other ways she leaves her seal, I say aloud. And startle at my saying it. What do I mean? What did I start to gather together, to try and make coherent? I was at the terrible, growing years. War years. I do not remember them well. I was working, there were four smaller ones now, there was not time for her. She had to help be a mother, and housekeeper, and shopper. She had to set her seal. Mornings of crisis and near hysteria trying to get lunches packed, hair combed, coats and shoes found, everyone to school or Child Care on time, the baby ready for transportation. And always the paper scribbled on by a smaller one, the book looked at by Susan then mislaid, the homework not done. Running out to that huge school where she was one, she was lost, she was a drop; suffering over the unpreparedness, stammering and unsure in her classes.

There was so little time left at night after the kids were bedded down. She would struggle over books, always eating (it was in those years she developed her enormous appetite that is legendary in our family) and I would be ironing, or preparing food for the next day, or writing V-mail to Bill, or tending the baby. Sometimes, to make me laugh, or out of her despair, she would imitate happenings or types at school.

I think I said once: "Why don't you do something like this in the school amateur show?" One morning she phoned me at work, hardly understandable through the weeping: "Mother, I did it. I won, I won; they gave me first prize; they clapped and clapped and wouldn't let me go."

Now suddenly she was Somebody, and as imprisoned in her difference as she had been in anonymity.

She began to be asked to perform at other high schools, even in colleges, then at city and statewide affairs. The first one we went to, I only recognized her that first moment when thin, shy, she almost drowned herself into the curtains. Then: Was this Emily? The control, the command, the convulsing and deadly clowning, the spell, then the roaring, stamping audience, unwilling to let this rare and precious laughter out of their lives.

Afterwards: You ought to do something about her with a gift like that—but without money or knowing how, what does one do? We have left it all to her, and the gift has as often eddied inside, clogged and clotted, as been used and growing.

She is coming. She runs up the stairs two at a time with her light graceful step, and I know she is happy tonight. Whatever it was that occasioned your call did not happen today.

"Aren't you ever going to finish the ironing, Mother? Whistler painted his mother in a rocker. I'd have to paint mine standing over an ironing board." This is one of her communicative nights and she tells me everything and nothing as she fixes herself a plate of food out of the icebox.

She is so lovely. Why did you want me to come in at all? Why were you concerned? She will find her way.

She starts up the stairs to bed. "Don't get me up with the rest in the morning." "But I thought you were having midterms." "Oh, those," she comes back in, kisses me, and says quite lightly, "in a couple of years when we'll all be atom-dead they won't matter a bit."

She has said it before. She *believes* it. But because I have been dredging the past, and all that compounds a human being is so heavy and meaningful in me, I cannot endure it tonight.

I will never total it all. I will never come in to say: She was a child seldom smiled at. Her father left me before she was a year old. I had to work her first six years when there was work, or I sent her home and to his relatives. There were years she had care she hated. She was dark and thin and foreign-looking in a world where the prestige went to blondeness and curly hair and dimples, she was slow where glibness was prized. She was a child of anxious, not proud, love. We were poor and could not afford for her the soil of easy growth. I was a young mother, I was a distracted mother. There were other children pushing up, demanding. Her younger sister seemed all that she was not. There were years she did not want me to touch her. She kept too much in herself, her life was such she had to keep too much in herself. My wisdom came too late. She has much to her and probably little will come of it. She is a child of her age, of depression, of war, of fear.

Let her be. So all that is in her will not bloom—but in how many does it? There is still enough left to live by. Only help her to know—help make it so there is cause for her to know—that she is more than this dress on the ironing board, helpless before the iron.

Silences: Tillie Olsen Writes About Her Difficulties as a Writer Raising Children

If I talk now quickly of my own silences—almost presumptuous after what has been told here—it is that the individual experience may add.

In the twenty years I bore and reared my children, usually had to work on a paid job as well, the simplest circumstances for creation did not exist. Nevertheless writing, the hope of it, was "the air I breathed, so long as I shall breathe at all." In that hope, there was conscious storing, snatched reading, beginnings of writing, and always "the secret rootlets of reconnaissance."

When the youngest of our four was in school, the beginnings struggled toward endings. This was a time, in Kafka's words, "like a squirrel in a cage: bliss of movement, desperation about constriction, craziness of endurance."

Bliss of movement. A full extended family life; the world of my job (transcriber in a dairy-equipment company); and the writing, which I was somehow able to carry around within me through work, through home. Time on the bus, even when I had to stand, was enough; the stolen moments at work, enough; the deep night hours for as long as I could stay awake, after the kids were in bed, after the household tasks were done, sometimes during. It is no accident that the first work I considered publishable began: "I stand here ironing, and what you asked me moves tormented back and forth with the iron."

In such snatches of time I wrote what I did in those years, but there came a time when this triple life was no longer possible. The fifteen hours of daily realities became too much distraction for the writing. I lost craziness of endurance. What might have been, I don't know; but I applied for, and was given, eight months' writing time. There was still full family life, all the household responsibilities, but I did not have to hold an eight-hour job. I had continuity, three full days, sometimes more—and it was in those months I made the mysterious turn and became a writing writer.

Then had to return to the world of work, someone else's work, nine hours, five days a week.

This was the time of festering and congestion. For a few months I was able to shield the writing with which I was so full, against the demands of jobs on which I had to be competent, through the joys and responsibilities and trials of family. For a few months. Always roused by the writing, always denied. "I could not go to write it down. It convulsed and died in me. I will pay."

My work died. What demanded to be written, did not. It seethed, bubbled, clamored, peopled me. At last moved into the hours meant for sleeping. I worked now full time on temporary jobs, a Kelly, a Western Agency girl (girl!), wandering from office to office, always hoping to manage two, three writing months ahead. Eventually there was time.

I had said: always roused by the writing, always denied. Now, like a woman made frigid, I had to learn response, to trust this possibility for fruition that had not been before. Any interruption dazed and silenced me. It took a long while of surrendering to what I was trying to write, of invoking Henry James's "passion, piety, patience," before I was able to re-establish work.

When again I had to leave the writing, I lost consciousness. A time of anesthesia. There was still an automatic noting that did not stop, but it was as if writing had never been. No fever, no congestion, no festering. I ceased being peopled, slept well and dreamlessly, took a "permanent" job. The few pieces that had been published seemed to have vanished like the not-yet-written. I wrote someone, unsent: "So long they fed each other—my life, the writing—; —the writing or hope of it, my life—; but now they begin to destroy." I knew, but did not feel the destruction.

A Ford grant in literature, awarded me on nomination by others, came almost too late. Time granted does not necessarily coincide with time that can be most fully used, as the congested time of fullness would have been. Still, it was two years.

Drowning is not so pitiful as the attempt to rise, says Emily Dickinson. I do not agree, but I know whereof she speaks. For a long time I was that emaciated survivor trembling on the beach, unable to rise and walk. Said differently, I could manage only the feeblest, shallowest growth on that devastated soil. Weeds, to be burned like weeds, or used as compost. When the habits of creation were at last rewon, one book went to the publisher, and I dared to begin my present work. It became my center, engraved on it: "Evil is whatever distracts." (By now had begun a cost to our family life, to my own participation in life as a human being.) I shall not tell the "rest, residue, and remainder" of what I was "leased, demised, and let unto" when once again I had to leave work at the flood to return to the Time-Master, to business-ese and legalese. This most harmful of all my silences has ended, but I am not yet recovered; may still be a one-book silence.

However that will be, we are in a time of more and more hidden and foreground silences, women *and* men. Denied full writing life, more may try to "nurse through night" (that part-time, part-self night) "the ethereal spark," but it seems to me there would almost have had to be "flame on flame" first; and time as needed, afterwards; and enough of the self, the capacities, undamaged for the rebeginnings on the frightful task. I would like to believe this for what has not yet been written into literature. But it cannot reconcile for what is lost by unnatural silences.

Edgar Allan Poe (1809–1849)

The Tell-Tale Heart

This story first appeared in PIONEER, *1843.*

TRUE!—NERVOUS—VERY, VERY DREADFULLY NERVOUS I had been and am; but why *will* you say that I am mad? The disease had sharpened my senses—not destroyed—not dulled them. Above all was the sense of hearing acute. I heard all things in the heaven and in the earth. I heard many things in hell. How, then, am I mad? Hearken! and observe how healthily—how calmly I can tell you the whole story.

It is impossible to say how first the idea entered my brain; but once conceived, it haunted me day and night. Object there was none. Passion there was none. I loved the old man. He had never wronged me. He had never given me insult. For his gold I had no desire. I think it was his eye! yes, it was this! One of his eyes resembled that of a vulture—a pale blue eye, with a film over it. Whenever it fell upon me, my blood ran cold; and so by degrees—very gradually—I made up my mind to take the life of the old man, and thus rid myself of the eye for ever.

Now this is the point. You fancy me mad. Madmen know nothing. But you should have seen *me.* You should have seen how wisely I proceeded—with what caution—with what foresight—with what dissimulation I went to work! I was never kinder to the old man than during the whole week before I killed him. And every night, about midnight, I turned the latch of his door and opened it—oh, so gently! And then, when I had made an opening sufficient for my head, I put in a dark lantern, all closed, closed, so that no light shone out, and then I thrust in my head. Oh, you would have laughed to see how cunningly I thrust it in! I moved it slowly—very, very slowly, so that I might not disturb the old man's sleep. It took me an hour to place my whole head within the opening so far that I could see him as he lay upon his bed. Ha!—would a madman have been so wise as this? And then, when my head was well in the room, I undid the lantern cautiously—oh, so cautiously—cautiously (for the hinges creaked)—I undid it just so much that a single thin ray fell upon the vulture eye. And this I did for seven long nights—every night just at midnight—but I found the eye always closed; and so it was impossible to do the work; for it was not the old man who vexed me, but his Evil Eye. And every morning, when the day broke, I went boldly into the chamber, and spoke courageously to him, calling him by name in a hearty tone, and inquiring how he had passed the night. So you see he would have been a very profound old man, indeed, to suspect that every night, just at twelve, I looked in upon him while he slept.

Upon the eighth night I was more than usually cautious in opening the door. A watch's minute hand moves more quickly than did mine. Never before that night had I *felt* the extent of my own powers—of my sagacity. I could scarcely contain my feelings of triumph. To think that there I was, opening the door, little by little, and he not even to dream of my secret deeds or thoughts. I fairly chuckled at the idea; and perhaps he heard me; for he moved on the bed suddenly, as if startled. Now you may think that I drew back—but no. His room was as black as pitch with the thick darkness (for the shutters were close fastened, through fear of robbers), and so I knew that he could not see the opening of the door, and I kept pushing it on steadily, steadily.

I had my head in, and was about to open the lantern, when my thumb slipped upon the tin fastening, and the old man sprang up in the bed, crying out—"Who's there?"

I kept quite still and said nothing. For a whole hour I did not move a muscle, and in the meantime I did not hear him lie down. He was still sitting up in the bed listening;—just as I have done, night after night, hearkening to the death watches* in the wall.

Presently I heard a slight groan, and I knew it was the groan of mortal terror. It was not a groan of pain or of grief—oh, no!—it was the low stifled sound that arises from the bottom of the soul when overcharged with awe. I knew the sound very well. Many a night, just at midnight, when all the world slept, it has welled up from my own bosom, deepening, with its dreadful echo, the terrors that distracted me. I say I knew it well. I knew what the old man felt, and pitied him, although I chuckled at heart. I knew that he had been lying awake ever since the first slight noise, when he had turned in the bed. His fears had been ever since growing upon him. He had been trying to fancy them causeless, but could not. He had been saying to himself—"It is nothing but the wind in the chimney—it is only a mouse crossing the floor," or "it is merely a cricket which has made a single chirp." Yes, he had been trying to comfort himself with these suppositions; but he had found all in vain. *All in vain;* because Death, in approaching him, had stalked with his black shadow before him, and enveloped the victim. And it was the mournful influence of the unperceived shadow that caused him to feel—although he neither saw nor heard—to *feel* the presence of my head within the room.

When I had waited a long time, very patiently, without hearing him lie down, I resolved to open a little—a very, very little crevice in the lantern. So I opened it—you cannot imagine how stealthily, stealthily—until, at length,

death watches: beetles that infest timbers. Their clicking sound was thought to be an omen of death.

a single dim ray, like the thread of the spider, shot from out the crevice and full upon the vulture eye.

It was open—wide, wide open—and I grew furious as I gazed upon it. I saw it with perfect distinctness—all a dull blue, with a hideous veil over it that chilled the very marrow in my bones; but I could see nothing else of the old man's face or person: for I had directed the ray as if by instinct, precisely upon the damned spot.

And now have I not told you that what you mistake for madness is but overacuteness of the senses?—now, I say, there came to my ears a low, dull, quick sound, such as a watch makes when enveloped in cotton. I knew *that* sound well too. It was the beating of the old man's heart. It increased my fury, as the beating of a drum stimulates the soldier into courage.

But even yet I refrained and kept still. I scarcely breathed. I held the lantern motionless. I tried how steadily I could maintain the ray upon the eye. Meantime the hellish tattoo of the heart increased. It grew quicker and quicker, and louder and louder every instant. The old man's terror *must* have been extreme! It grew louder, I say, louder every moment—do you mark me well? I have told you that I am nervous: so I am. And now at the dead hour of the night, amid the dreadful silence of that old house, so strange a noise as this excited me to uncontrollable terror. Yet, for some minutes longer I refrained and stood still. But the beating grew louder, louder! I thought the heart must burst. And now a new anxiety seized me—the sound would be heard by a neighbor! The old man's hour had come! With a loud yell, I threw open the lantern and leaped into the room. He shrieked once—once only. In an instant I dragged him to the floor, and pulled the heavy bed over him. I then smiled gaily, to find the deed so far done. But, for many minutes, the heart beat on with a muffled sound. This, however, did not vex me; it would not be heard through the wall. At length it ceased. The old man was dead. I removed the bed and examined the corpse. Yes, he was stone, stone dead. I placed my hand upon the heart and held it there many minutes. There was no pulsation. He was stone dead. His eye would trouble me no more.

If still you think me mad, you will think so no longer when I describe the wise precautions I took for the concealment of the body. The night waned, and I worked hastily, but in silence. First of all I dismembered the corpse. I cut off the head and the arms and the legs.

I then took up three planks from the flooring of the chamber, and deposited all between the scantlings. I then replaced the boards so cleverly, so cunningly, that no human eye—not even *his*—could have detected anything wrong. There was nothing to wash out—no stain of any kind—no bloodspot whatever. I had been too wary for that. A tub had caught all—ha! ha!

When I had made an end of these labors, it was four o'clock—still dark as midnight. As the bell sounded the hour, there came a knocking at the street door. I went down to open it with a light heart,—for what had I *now* to fear? There entered three men, who introduced themselves, with perfect suavity, as officers of the police. A shriek had been heard by a neighbor during the night; suspicion of foul play had been aroused; information had been lodged at the police office, and they (the officers) had been deputed to search the premises.

I smiled—for *what* had I to fear? I bade the gentlemen welcome. The shriek, I said, was my own in a dream. The old man, I mentioned, was absent in the country. I took my visitors all over the house. I bade them search— search *well*. I led them, at length, to *his* chamber. I showed them his treasures, secure, undisturbed. In the enthusiasm of my confidence, I brought chairs into the room, and desired them *here* to rest from their fatigues, while I myself, in the wild audacity of my perfect triumph, placed my own seat upon the very spot beneath which reposed the corpse of the victim.

The officers were satisfied. My *manner* had convinced them. I was singularly at ease. They sat, and while I answered cheerily, they chatted familiar things. But, ere long, I felt myself getting pale and wished them gone. My head ached, and I fancied a ringing in my ears: but still they sat and still chatted. The ringing became more distinct:—it continued and became more distinct: I talked more freely to get rid of the feeling: but it continued and gained definitiveness—until, at length, I found that the noise was *not* within my ears.

No doubt I now grew *very* pale:—but I talked more fluently, and with a heightened voice. Yet the sound increased—and what could I do? It was *a low, dull, quick sound—much such a sound as a watch makes when enveloped in cotton.* I gasped for breath—and yet the officers heard it not. I talked more quickly—more vehemently; but the noise steadily increased. I arose and argued about trifles, in a high key and with violent gesticulations, but the noise steadily increased. Why *would* they not be gone? I paced the floor to and fro with heavy strides, as if excited to fury by the observation of the men—but the noise steadily increased. Oh God! what *could* I do? I foamed—I raved—I swore! I swung the chair upon which I had been sitting, and grated it upon the boards, but the noise arose over all and continually increased. It grew louder—louder—*louder!* And still the men chatted pleasantly, and smiled. Was it possible they heard not? Almighty God!—no, no! They heard!—they suspected!—they *knew!*—they were making a mockery of my horror!—this I thought, and this I think. But any thing was better than this agony! Any thing was more tolerable than this derision! I could bear those hypocritical smiles no longer! I felt that I must scream or die!—and now—again!—hark! louder! louder! louder! *louder!*—

"Villains!" I shrieked, "dissemble no more! I admit the deed!—tear up the planks!—here, here!—it is the beating of his hideous heart!"

Charlotte Perkins Gilman, 1860–1935

The Yellow Wallpaper

This story first appeared in THE NEW ENGLAND MAGAZINE, *1892.*

IT IS VERY SELDOM THAT MERE ORDINARY PEOPLE like John and myself secure ancestral halls for the summer.

A colonial mansion, a hereditary estate, I would say a haunted house and reach the height of romantic felicity—but that would be asking too much of fate!

Still I will proudly declare that there is something queer about it.

Else, why should it be let so cheaply? And why have stood so long untenanted?

John laughs at me, of course, but one expects that.

John is practical in the extreme. He has no patience with faith, an intense horror of superstition, and he scoffs openly at any talk of things not to be felt and seen and put down in figures.

John is a physician, and *perhaps*—(I would not say it to a living soul, of course, but this is dead paper and a great relief to my mind)—*perhaps* that is one reason I do not get well faster.

You see, he does not believe I am sick! And what can one do?

If a physician of high standing, and one's own husband, assures friends and relatives that there is really nothing the matter with one but temporary nervous depression—a slight hysterical tendency—what is one to do?

My brother is also a physician, and also of high standing, and he says the same thing.

So I take phosphates or phosphites—whichever it is—and tonics, and air and exercise, and journeys, and am absolutely forbidden to "work" until I am well again.

Personally, I disagree with their ideas.

Personally, I believe that congenial work, with excitement and change, would do me good.

But what is one to do?

I did write for a while in spite of them; but it *does* exhaust me a good deal—having to be so sly about it, or else meet with heavy opposition.

I sometimes fancy that in my condition, if I had less opposition and more society and stimulus—but John says the very worst thing I can do is to think about my condition, and I confess it always makes me feel bad.

So I will let it alone and talk about the house.

The most beautiful place! It is quite alone, standing well back from the road, quite three miles from the village. It makes me think of English places that you read about, for there are hedges and walls and gates that lock, and lots of separate little houses for the gardeners and people.

There is a *delicious* garden! I never saw such a garden—large and shady, full of box-bordered paths, and lined with long grape-covered arbors with seats under them.

There were greenhouses, but they are all broken now.

There was some legal trouble, I believe, something about the heirs and co-heirs; anyhow, the place has been empty for years.

That spoils my ghostliness, I am afraid, but I don't care—there is something strange about the house—I can feel it.

I even said so to John one moonlight evening, but he said what I felt was a draught, and shut the window.

I get unreasonably angry with John sometimes. I'm sure I never used to be so sensitive. I think it is due to this nervous condition.

But John says if I feel so I shall neglect proper self-control; so I take pains to control myself—before him, at least, and that makes me very tired.

I don't like our room a bit. I wanted one downstairs that opened onto the piazza and had roses all over the window, and such pretty old-fashioned chintz hangings! But John would not hear of it.

He said there was only one window and not room for two beds, and no near room for him if he took another.

He is very careful and loving, and hardly lets me stir without special direction.

I have a schedule prescription for each hour in the day; he takes all care from me, and so I feel basely ungrateful not to value it more.

He said he came here solely on my account, that I was to have perfect rest and all the air I could get. "Your exercise depends on your strength, my dear," said he, "and your food somewhat on your appetite; but air you can absorb all the time." So we took the nursery at the top of the house.

It is a big, airy room, the whole floor nearly, with windows that look all ways, and air and sunshine galore. It was nursery first, and then playroom and gymnasium, I should judge, for the windows are barred for little children, and there are rings and things in the walls.

The paint and paper look as if a boys' school had used it. It is stripped off—the paper—in great patches all around the head of my bed, about as far as I can reach, and in a great place on the other side of the room low down. I never saw a worse paper in my life. One of those sprawling, flamboyant patterns committing every artistic sin.

It is dull enough to confuse the eye in following, pronounced enough constantly to irritate and provoke study, and when you follow the lame uncertain curves for a little distance they suddenly commit suicide—plunge off at outrageous angles, destroy themselves in unheard-of contradictions.

The color is repellent, almost revolting: a smoldering unclean yellow, strangely faded by the slow-turning sunlight. It is a dull yet lurid orange in some places, a sickly sulphur tint in others.

No wonder the children hated it! I should hate it myself if I had to live in this room long.

There comes John, and I must put this away—he hates to have me write a word.

———————

WE HAVE BEEN HERE TWO WEEKS, and I haven't felt like writing before, since that first day.

I am sitting by the window now, up in this atrocious nursery, and there is nothing to hinder my writing as much as I please, save lack of strength.

John is away all day, and even some nights when his cases are serious.

I am glad my case is not serious!

But these nervous troubles are dreadfully depressing.

John does not know how much I really suffer. He knows there is no reason to suffer, and that satisfies him.

Of course it is only nervousness. It does weigh on me so not to do my duty in any way!

I meant to be such a help to John, such a real rest and comfort, and here I am a comparative burden already!

Nobody would believe what an effort it is to do what little I am able—to dress and entertain, and order things.

It is fortunate Mary is so good with the baby. Such a dear baby!

And yet I *cannot* be with him, it makes me so nervous.

I suppose John never was nervous in his life. He laughs at me so about this wallpaper!

At first he meant to repaper the room, but afterward he said that I was letting it get the better of me, and that nothing was worse for a nervous patient than to give way to such fancies.

He said that after the wallpaper was changed it would be the heavy bedstead, and then the barred windows, and then that gate at the head of the stairs, and so on.

"You know the place is doing you good," he said, "and really, dear, I don't care to renovate the house just for a three months' rental."

"Then do let us go downstairs," I said. "There are such pretty rooms there."

Then he took me in his arms and called me a blessed little goose, and said he would go down cellar, if I wished, and have it whitewashed into the bargain.

But he is right enough about the beds and windows and things.

It is as airy and comfortable a room as anyone need wish, and, of course, I would not be so silly as to make him uncomfortable just for a whim.

I'm really getting fond of the big room, but all that horrid paper.

Out of one window I can see the garden—those mysterious deep-shaded arbors, the riotous old-fashioned flowers, and bushes and gnarly trees.

Out of another I get a lovely view of the bay and a little private wharf belonging to the estate. There is a beautiful shaded lane that runs down there from the house. I always fancy I see people walking in these numerous paths and arbors, but John has cautioned me not to give way to fancy in the least. He says that with my imaginative power and habit of story-making, a nervous weakness like mine is sure to lead to all manner of excited fancies, and that I ought to use my will and good sense to check the tendency. So I try.

I think sometimes that if I were only well enough to write a little it would relieve the press of ideas and rest me.

But I find I get pretty tired when I try.

It is so discouraging not to have any advice and companionship about my work. When I get really well, John says we will ask Cousin Henry and Julia down for a long visit; but he says he would as soon put fireworks in my pillow-case as to let me have those stimulating people about now.

I wish I could get well faster.

But I must not think about that. This paper looks to me as if it *knew* what a vicious influence it had!

There is a recurrent spot where the pattern lolls like a broken neck and two bulbous eyes stare at you upside down.

I get positively angry with the impertinence of it and the everlastingness. Up and down and sideways they crawl, and those absurd unblinking eyes are everywhere. There is one place where two breadths didn't match, and the eyes go all up and down the line, one a little higher than the other.

I never saw so much expression in an inanimate thing before, and we all know how much expression they have! I used to lie awake as a child and get more entertainment and terror out of blank walls and plain furniture than most children could find in a toy-store.

I remember what a kindly wink the knobs of our big old bureau used to have, and there was one chair that always seemed like a strong friend.

I used to feel that if any of the other things looked too fierce I could always hop into that chair and be safe.

The furniture in this room is no worse than inharmonious, however, for we had to bring it all from downstairs. I suppose when this was used as a playroom they had to take the nursery things out, and no wonder! I never saw such ravages as the children have made here.

The wallpaper, as I said before, is torn off in spots, and it sticketh closer than a brother—they must have had perseverance as well as hatred.

Then the floor is scratched and gouged and splintered, the plaster itself is dug out here and there, and this great heavy bed, which is all we found in the room, looks as if it had been through the wars.

But I don't mind it a bit—only the paper.

There comes John's sister. Such a dear girl as she is, and so careful of me! I must not let her find me writing.

She is a perfect and enthusiastic housekeeper, and hopes for no better profession. I verily believe she thinks it is the writing which made me sick!

But I can write when she is out, and see her a long way off from these windows.

There is one that commands the road, a lovely shaded winding road, and one that just looks off over the country. A lovely country, too, full of great elms and velvet meadows.

This wallpaper has a kind of sub-pattern in a different shade, a particularly irritating one, for you can only see it in certain lights, and not clearly then.

But in the places where it isn't faded and where the sun is just so—I can see a strange, provoking, formless sort of figure that seems to skulk about behind that silly and conspicuous front design.

There's sister on the stairs!

————————

WELL, THE FOURTH OF JULY IS OVER! The people are all gone, and I am tired out. John thought it might do me good to see a little company, so we just had Mother and Nellie and the children down for a week.

Of course I didn't do a thing. Jennie sees to everything now.

But it tired me all the same.

John says if I don't pick up faster he shall send me to Weir Mitchell in the fall.

But I don't want to go there at all. I had a friend who was in his hands once, and she says he is just like John and my brother, only more so!

Besides, it is such an undertaking to go so far.

I don't feel as if it was worthwhile to turn my hand over for anything, and I'm getting dreadfully fretful and querulous.

I cry at nothing, and cry most of the time.

Of course I don't when John is here, or anybody else, but when I am alone.

And I am alone a good deal just now. John is kept in town very often by serious cases, and Jennie is good and lets me alone when I want her to.

So I walk a little in the garden or down that lovely lane, sit on the porch under the roses, and lie down up here a good deal.

I'm getting really fond of the room in spite of the wallpaper. Perhaps *because* of the wallpaper.

It dwells in my mind so!

I lie here on this great immovable bed—it is nailed down, I believe—and follow that pattern about by the hour. It is as good as gymnastics, I assure you. I start, we'll say, at the bottom, down in the corner over there where it has not been touched, and I determine for the thousandth time that I *will* follow that pointless pattern to some sort of a conclusion.

I know a little of the principle of design, and I know this thing was not arranged on any laws of radiation, or alternation, or repetition, or symmetry, or anything else that I ever heard of.

It is repeated, of course, by the breadths, but not otherwise.

Looked at in one way, each breadth stands alone; the bloated curves and flourishes—a kind of "debased Romanesque" with delirium tremens go waddling up and down in isolated columns of fatuity.

But, on the other hand, they connect diagonally, and the sprawling outlines run off in great slanting waves of optic horror, like a lot of wallowing sea-weeds in full chase.

The whole thing goes horizontally, too, at least it seems so, and I exhaust myself trying to distinguish the order of its going in that direction.

They have used a horizontal breadth for a frieze, and that adds wonderfully to the confusion.

There is one end of the room where it is almost intact, and there, when the crosslights fade and the low sun shines directly upon it, I can almost fancy radiation after all—the interminable grotesque seems to form around a common center and rush off in headlong plunges of equal distraction.

It makes me tired to follow it. I will take a nap, I guess.

I don't know why I should write this.

I don't want to.

I don't feel able.

And I know John would think it absurd. But I *must* say what I feel and think in some way—it is such a relief!

But the effort is getting to be greater than the relief.

————————

HALF THE TIME NOW I AM AWFULLY LAZY, and lie down ever so much. John says I mustn't lose my strength, and has me take cod liver oil and lots of tonics and things, to say nothing of ale and wine and rare meat.

Dear John! He loves me very dearly, and hates to have me sick. I tried to have a real earnest reasonable talk with him the other day, and tell him how I wish he would let me go and make a visit to Cousin Henry and Julia.

But he said I wasn't able to go, nor able to stand it after I got there; and I did not make out a very good case for myself, for I was crying before I had finished.

It is getting to be a great effort for me to think straight. Just this nervous weakness, I suppose.

And dear John gathered me up in his arms, and just carried me upstairs and laid me on the bed, and sat by me and read to me till it tired my head.

He said I was his darling and his comfort and all he had, and that I must take care of myself for his sake, and keep well.

He says no one but myself can help me out of it, that I must use my will and self-control and not let any silly fancies run away with me.

There's one comfort—the baby is well and happy, and does not have to occupy this nursery with the horrid wallpaper.

If we had not used it, that blessed child would have! What a fortunate escape! Why, I wouldn't have a child of mine, an impressionable little thing, live in such a room for worlds.

I never thought of it before, but it is lucky that John kept me here after all; I can stand it so much easier than a baby, you see.

Of course I never mention it to them any more—I am too wise—but I keep watch for it all the same.

There are things in that wallpaper that nobody knows about but me, or ever will.

Behind that outside pattern the dim shapes get clearer every day.

It is always the same shape, only very numerous.

And it is like a woman stooping down and creeping about behind that pattern. I don't like it a bit. I wonder—I begin to think—I wish John would take me away from here!

It is so hard to talk with John about my case, because he is so wise, and because he loves me so.

But I tried it last night.

It was moonlight. The moon shines in all around just as the sun does.

I hate to see it sometimes, it creeps so slowly, and always comes in by one window or another.

John was asleep and I hated to waken him, so I kept still and watched the moonlight on that undulating wallpaper till I felt creepy.

The faint figure behind seemed to shake the pattern, just as if she wanted to get out.

I got up softly and went to feel and see if the paper *did* move, and when I came back John was awake.

"What is it, little girl?" he said. "Don't go walking about like that—you'll get cold."

I thought it was a good time to talk, so I told him that I really was not gaining here, and that I wished he would take me away.

"Why, darling!" said he. "Our lease will be up in three weeks, and I can't see how to leave before.

"The repairs are not done at home, and I cannot possibly leave town just now. Of course, if you were in any danger, I could and would, but you really are better, dear, whether you can see it or not. I am a doctor, dear, and I know. You are gaining flesh and color, your appetite is better, I feel really much easier about you."

"I don't weigh a bit more," said I, "nor as much; and my appetite may be better in the evening when you are here but it is worse in the morning when you are away!"

"Bless her little heart!" said he with a big hug. "She shall be as sick as she pleases! But now let's improve the shining hours by going to sleep, and talk about it in the morning!"

"And you won't go away?" I asked gloomily.

"Why, how can I, dear? It is only three weeks more and then we will take a nice little trip of a few days while Jennie is getting the house ready. Really, dear, you are better!"

"Better in body perhaps—" I began, and stopped short, for he sat up straight and looked at me with such a stern, reproachful look that I could not say another word.

"My darling," said he, "I beg of you, for my sake and for our child's sake, as well as for your own, that you will never for one instant let that idea enter your mind! There is nothing so dangerous, so fascinating, to a temperament like yours. It is a false and foolish fancy. Can you not trust me as a physician when I tell you so?"

So of course I said no more on that score, and we went to sleep before long. He thought I was asleep first, but I wasn't, and lay there for hours trying to decide whether that front pattern and the back pattern really did move together or separately.

On a pattern like this, by daylight, there is a lack of sequence, a defiance of law, that is a constant irritant to a normal mind.

The color is hideous enough, and unreliable enough, and infuriating enough, but the pattern is torturing.

You think you have mastered it, but just as you get well under way in following, it turns a back-somersault and there you are. It slaps you in the face, knocks you down, and tramples upon you. It is like a bad dream.

The outside pattern is a florid arabesque, reminding one of a fungus. If you can imagine a toadstool in joints, an interminable string of toadstools, budding and sprouting in endless convolutions—why, that is something like it.

That is, sometimes!

There is one marked peculiarity about this paper, a thing nobody seems to notice but myself, and that is that it changes as the light changes.

When the sun shoots in through the east window—I always watch for that first long, straight ray—it changes so quickly that I never can quite believe it.

That is why I watch it always.

By moonlight—the moon shines in all night where there is a moon—I wouldn't know it was the same paper.

At night in any kind of light, in twilight, candlelight, lamplight, and worst of all by moonlight, it becomes bars! The outside pattern, I mean, and the woman behind it is as plain as can be.

I didn't realize for a long time what the thing was that showed behind, that dim sub-pattern, but now I am quite sure it is a woman.

By daylight she is subdued, quiet. I fancy it is the pattern that keeps her so still. It is so puzzling. It keeps me quiet by the hour.

I lie down ever so much now. John says it is good for me, and to sleep all I can.

Indeed he started the habit by making me lie down for an hour after each meal.

It is a very bad habit, I am convinced, for you see, I don't sleep.

And that cultivates deceit, for I don't tell them I'm awake—oh, no!

The fact is I am getting a little afraid of John.

He seems very queer sometimes, and even Jennie has an inexplicable look.

It strikes me occasionally, just as a scientific hypothesis, that perhaps it is the paper!

I have watched John when he did not know I was looking, and come into the room suddenly on the most innocent excuses, and I've caught him several times *looking at the paper!* And Jennie too. I caught Jennie with her hand on it once.

She didn't know I was in the room, and when I asked her in a quiet, a very quiet voice, with the most restrained manner possible, what she was doing with the paper, she turned around as if she had been caught stealing, and looked quite angry—asked me why I should frighten her so!

Then she said that the paper stained everything it touched, that she had found yellow smooches on all my clothes and John's and she wished we would be more careful!

Did not that sound innocent? But I know she was studying that pattern, and I am determined that nobody shall find it out but myself!

———————

LIFE IS VERY MUCH MORE EXCITING NOW THAN IT USED TO BE. You see, I have something more to expect, to look forward to, to watch. I really do eat better, and am more quiet than I was.

John is so pleased to see me improve! He laughed a little the other day, and said I seemed to be flourishing in spite of my wallpaper.

I turned it off with a laugh. I had no intention of telling him it was *because* of the wallpaper—he would make fun of me. He might even want to take me away.

I don't want to leave now until I have found it out. There is a week more, and I think that will be enough.

I'm feeling so much better!

I don't sleep much at night, for it is so interesting to watch developments; but I sleep a good deal during the daytime.

In the daytime it is tiresome and perplexing.

There are always new shoots on the fungus, and new shades of yellow all over it. I cannot keep count of them, though I have tried conscientiously.

It is the strangest yellow, that wallpaper! It makes me think of all the yellow things I ever saw—not beautiful ones like buttercups, but old, foul, bad yellow things.

But there is something else about that paper—the smell! I noticed it the moment we came into the room, but with so much air and sun it was not bad. Now we have had a week of fog and rain, and whether the windows are open or not, the smell is here.

It creeps all over the house.

I find it hovering in the dining-room, skulking in the parlor, hiding in the hall, lying in wait for me on the stairs.

It gets into my hair.

Even when I go to ride, if I turn my head suddenly and surprise it—there is that smell!

Such a peculiar odor, too! I have spent hours in trying to analyze it, to find what it smelled like.

It is not bad—at first—and very gentle, but quite the subtlest, most enduring odor I ever met.

In this damp weather it is awful. I wake up in the night and find it hanging over me.

It used to disturb me at first. I thought seriously of burning the house—to reach the smell.

But now I am used to it. The only thing I can think of that it is like is the *color* of the paper! A yellow smell.

There is a very funny mark on this wall, low down, near the mopboard. A streak that runs round the room. It goes behind every piece of furniture, except the bed, a long, straight, even *smooch,* as if it had been rubbed over and over.

I wonder how it was done and who did it, and what they did it for. Round and round and round—round and round and round—it makes me dizzy!

I really have discovered something at last.

Through watching so much at night, when it changes so, I have finally found out.

The front pattern *does* move—and no wonder! The woman behind shakes it!

Sometimes I think there are a great many women behind, and sometimes only one, and she crawls around fast, and her crawling shakes it all over.

Then in the very bright spots she keeps still, and in the very shady spots she just takes hold of the bars and shakes them hard.

And she is all the time trying to climb through. But nobody could climb through that pattern—it strangles so; I think that is why it has so many heads.

They get through and then the pattern strangles them off and turns them upside down, and makes their eyes white!

If those heads were covered or taken off it would not be half so bad.

I think that woman gets out in the daytime!

And I'll tell you why—privately—I've seen her!

I can see her out of every one of my windows!

It is the same woman, I know, for she is always creeping, and most women do not creep by daylight.

I see her in that long shaded lane, creeping up and down. I see her in those dark grape arbors, creeping all around the garden.

I see her on that long road under the trees, creeping along, and when a carriage comes she hides under the blackberry vines.

I don't blame her a bit. It must be very humiliating to be caught creeping by daylight!

I always lock the door when I creep by daylight. I can't do it at night, for I know John would suspect something at once.

And John is so queer now that I don't want to irritate him. I wish he would take another room! Besides, I don't want anybody to get that woman out at night but myself.

I often wonder if I could see her out of all the windows at once.

But, turn as fast as I can, I can only see out of one at one time.

And though I always see her, she *may* be able to creep faster than I can turn! I have watched her sometimes away off in the open country, creeping as fast as a cloud shadow in a wind.

If only that top pattern could be gotten off from the under one! I mean to try it, little by little.

I have found out another funny thing, but I shan't tell it this time! It does not do to trust people too much.

There are only two more days to get this paper off, and I believe John is beginning to notice. I don't like the look in his eyes.

And I heard him ask Jennie a lot of professional questions about me. She had a very good report to give.

She said I slept a good deal in the daytime.

John knows I don't sleep very well at night, for all I'm so quiet!

He asked me all sorts of questions, too, and pretended to be very loving and kind.

As if I couldn't see through him!

Still, I don't wonder he acts so, sleeping under this paper for three months.

It only interests me, but I feel sure John and Jennie are affected by it.

———

HURRAH! This is the last day, but it is enough. John is to stay in town over night, and won't be out until this evening.

Jennie wanted to sleep with me—the sly thing; but I told her I should undoubtedly rest better for a night all alone.

That was clever, for really I wasn't alone a bit! As soon as it was moonlight and that poor thing began to crawl and shake the pattern, I got up and ran to help her.

I pulled and she shook. I shook and she pulled, and before morning we had peeled off yards of that paper.

A strip about as high as my head and half around the room.

And then when the sun came and that awful pattern began to laugh at me, I declared I would finish it today!

We go away tomorrow, and they are moving all my furniture down again to leave things as they were before.

Jennie looked at the wall in amazement, but I told her merrily that I did it out of pure spite at the vicious thing.

She laughed and said she wouldn't mind doing it herself, but I must not get tired.

How she betrayed herself that time!

But I am here, and no person touches this paper but Me—not *alive!*

She tried to get me out of the room—it was too patent! But I said it was so quiet and empty and clean now that I believed I would lie down again and sleep all I could, and not to wake me even for dinner—I would call when I woke.

So now she is gone, and the servants are gone, and the things are gone, and there is nothing left but that great bedstead nailed down, with the canvas mattress we found on it.

We shall sleep downstairs tonight, and take the boat home tomorrow.

I quite enjoy the room, now it is bare again.

How those children did tear about here!

This bedstead is fairly gnawed!

But I must get to work.

I have locked the door and thrown the key down into the front path.

I don't want to go out, and I don't want to have anybody come in, till John comes.

I want to astonish him.

I've got a rope up here that even Jennie did not find. If that woman does get out, and tries to get away, I can tie her!

But I forgot I could not reach far without anything to stand on!

This bed will *not* move!

I tried to lift and push it until I was lame, and then I got so angry I bit off a little piece of one corner—but it hurt my teeth.

Then I peeled off all the paper I could reach standing on the floor. It sticks horribly and the pattern just enjoys it! All those strangled heads and bulbous eyes and waddling fungus growths just shriek with derision!

I am getting angry enough to do something desperate. To jump out of the window would be admirable exercise, but the bars are too strong even to try.

Besides I wouldn't do it. Of course not. I know well enough that a step like that is improper and might be misconstrued.

I don't like to *look* out of the windows even—there are so many of those creeping women, and they creep so fast.

I wonder if they all come out of that wallpaper as I did?

But I am securely fastened now by my well-hidden rope—you don't get *me* out in the road there!

I suppose I shall have to get back behind the pattern when it comes night, and that is hard!

It is so pleasant to be out in this great room and creep around as I please!

I don't want to go outside. I won't, even if Jennie asks me to.

For outside you have to creep on the ground, and everything is green instead of yellow.

But here I can creep smoothly on the floor, and my shoulder just fits in that long smooch around the wall, so I cannot lose my way.

Why, there's John at the door!

It is no use, young man, you can't open it!

How he does call and pound!

Now he's crying to Jennie for an axe.

It would be a shame to break down that beautiful door!

"John, dear!" said I in the gentlest voice. "The key is down by the front steps, under a plantain leaf!"

That silenced him for a few moments.

Then he said, very quietly indeed, "Open the door, my darling!"

"I can't," said I. "The key is down by the front door under a plantain leaf!" And then I said it again, several times, very gently and slowly, and said it so often that he had to go and see, and he got it of course, and came in. He stopped short by the door.

"What is the matter?" he cried. "For God's sake, what are you doing!"

I kept on creeping just the same, but I looked at him over my shoulder.

"I've got out at last," said I, "in spite of you and Jane. And I've pulled off most of the paper, so you can't put me back!"

Now why should that man have fainted? But he did, and right across my path by the wall, so that I had to creep over him every time!

—— Linda Wagner-Martin: Example of a Short but Complete Essay on a Story

Refused by the editor of *Atlantic Monthly* because the story made him so miserable, Gilman's now classic story of a woman suffering post-partum depression, improperly treated with isolation and inactivity, was originally considered a Poe-like Gothic tale. Narratives of supernatural horror were a staple of magazines at the turn of the century, and Gilman's story—published in 1892 in *The New England Magazine,* in 1899 as a chapbook, and later reprinted by William Dean Howells in a 1920 story collection—was read without attention to the gender of the unnamed protagonist. "The Yellow Wallpaper"—revived by the Feminist Press after being out of print for 70 years—is now one of the most often read and written-about stories of feminist consciousness.

Charlotte Perkins Gilman, influential economist, lecturer, and publisher, experienced depression from the time of her first marriage to Charles Walter

Stetson, and that depression intensified after their daughter was born. Like Winifred Howells, Edith Wharton, and Jane Addams, Gilman too was sent to Dr. S. Weir Mitchell, whose "cures" for women were world famous. But Mitchell's treatment—of a rest cure which depended upon seclusion, massage, immobility, and overfeeding (some women gained 50 pounds during the six weeks of hospitalization)—had at its root complete mental inactivity. It is this stricture that bothers Gilman the most, this and the pervasive medical attitude that women's problems all stemmed from hysteria, and were womb-based.

"The Yellow Wallpaper" shows how well cared for the unnamed protagonist is, by both her authoritarian husband, John, who is conveniently a physician, and her physician brother, as well as by her stereotypical loving sister-in-law, who enjoys caring for the new baby as well as for the sick protagonist. But the woman's own views of what she would like (to see friends, to write, to read) are completely discounted, and her husband's treatment— like his language throughout the tale—is truly patriarchal. His wife is his child, and she doesn't know even the simplest things about what ails her. His use of diminutive names for her ('blessed little goose," "little girl") parallels his unresponsive replies: listening to her is the last thing on his agenda. Gilman provides several interchanges so that the self-serving qualities of his role are clear. After the woman tells him that she is no better, contrary to his reassurances, he replies, "Bless her little heart! she shall be as sick as she pleases! But now let's improve the shining hours by going to sleep, and talk about it in the morning!"

Shut off from all normal interaction and locked into what John calls a nursery but which smacks of a space used previously for incarceration, the woman fantasizes in a particularly meaningful way: she sees imprisoned women, trying to escape from the morass of crumbling yellowed wallpaper that covers all the surfaces of her prison. The diseased and stifling yellow, the meaningless patterns (of which the bored woman tries to make sense, and thereby creates the narrative of the trapped imaginary women), the omnipresence of the gloomy wall covering—and its moldy smell—would predictably augment a depressed person's malaise. The paper comes to symbolize her utter lack of power in the social construct: her husband John has the knowledge, earns the money, and makes the decisions. She has no role except to be his wife and the mother of his child; and when she rejects those roles, through the excuse of illness, he is more angry than he is concerned.

Gilman's brilliant use of the unnamed protagonist's voice, during a period when very few texts were written in any kind of first person, involves the reader in the woman's process of figuring out what is happening to her. At first, she writes with humility, sneaking out her forbidden journal carefully. She says all the expected things—her husband is understanding and knowledgeable and she is at fault for not responding to his care. But then a tone of complaint—a minor tone—enters her writing. Though she does not attack John directly, she knows at heart that her own treatment would have better results than his is having, and her impatience and frustration at his not listening to her colors her narrative.

But then her focus shifts, away from herself and her impasse with John and all the medical forces he represents, and she begins to explore her fascination with the woman (trapped, as she is herself) behind the wallpaper pattern. For the second half of the narrative, the purposely unnamed woman's attention is on seeing whether the woman behind the wallpaper can escape, and on whether she can help the woman to escape. Then, the woman becomes women and there are many trapped women trying to escape. In this transactive identification, the protagonist begins voicing her real anger at her husband and her society. She cannot express anger in her own persona because she has been convinced that what John does is best for her; so she creates a fantasy woman who is also caught in a similar imprisonment of male authority.

By the time of her taking action, crawling around the room and tearing off pieces of the hated, and imprisoning, wallpaper, the reader is firmly in the protagonist's camp. Her triumphal crawling over her shocked husband's body, when he faints at the destruction she has created in the room, and at what her behavior implies for her "recovery," seems to be a genuine triumph—until rational meaning returns to the reader. Gilman has created so much sympathy for the protagonist that the reader has accepted her mindset. Just as she sees her destruction, and her leaving the room, as triumph, so too does the reader.

The carefully modulated voice of the protagonist, writing secretly in the forbidden journal, is an amazingly effective means of telling the complicated story. This is a narrative with no simple right and wrong, no clear protagonist and antagonist (for John "loves" his wife and assumes that taking her to the country is a sure way of restoring her strength). In its writing, Gilman created a fable that explains, inductively, that women have rights, women have knowledge, and women have talents that need to be respected and employed. One of the primary themes of her book *Women and Economics* (1898), was that women need work that has value in the marketplace, and that their domestic work also needs to be given value. Otherwise, they face the plight of this fictional protagonist—nameless, faceless, characterless, a cypher in the work, and the life, of the real world.

Margaret Atwood, 1939–

Rape Fantasies

This story first appeared in DANCING GIRLS, *1977.*

THE WAY THEY'RE GOING ON ABOUT IT IN THE MAGAZINES you'd think it was just invented, and not only that but it's something terrific, like a vaccine for cancer. They put it in capital letters on the front cover, and inside they have these questionnaires like the ones they used to have about whether you were a good enough wife or an endomorph or an ectomorph, remember that? with the scoring upside down on page 73, and then these numbered do-it-yourself dealies, you know? RAPE, TEN THINGS TO DO ABOUT IT, like it was ten new hairdos or something. I mean, what's so new about it?

So at work they all have to talk about it because no matter what magazine you open, there it is, staring you right between the eyes, and they're beginning to have it on the television, too. Personally I'd prefer a June Allyson movie anytime but they don't make them any more and they don't even have them that much on the Late Show. For instance, day before yesterday, that would be Wednesday, thank god it's Friday as they say, we were sitting around in the women's lunch room—the *lunch* room, I mean you'd think you could get some peace and quiet in there—and Chrissy closes up the magazine she's been reading and says, "How about it, girls, do you have rape fantasies?"

The four of us were having our game of bridge the way we always do, and I had a bare twelve points counting the singleton with not that much of a bid in anything. So I said one club, hoping Sondra would remember about the one club convention, because the time before when I used that she thought I really meant clubs and she bids us up to three, and all I had was four little ones with nothing higher than a six, and we went down two and on top of that we were vulnerable. She is not the world's best bridge player. I mean, neither am I but there's a limit.

Darlene passed but the damage was done, Sondra's head went round like it was on ball bearings and she said, "*What* fantasies?"

"Rape fantasies," Chrissy said. She's a receptionist and she looks like one; she's pretty but cool as a cucumber, like she's been painted all over with nail polish, if you know what I mean. Varnished. "It says here all women have rape fantasies."

"For Chrissake, I'm eating an egg sandwich," I said, "and I bid one club and Darlene passed."

"You mean, like some guy jumping you in an alley or something," Sondra said. She was eating her lunch, we all eat our lunches during the game, and she bit into a piece of that celery she always brings and started to chew away on it with this thoughtful expression in her eyes and I knew we might as well pack it in as far as the game was concerned.

"Yeah, sort of like that," Chrissy said. She was blushing a little, you could see it even under her makeup.

"I don't think you should go out alone at night," Darlene said, "you put yourself in a position," and I may have been mistaken but she was looking at me. She's the oldest, she's forty-one though you wouldn't know it and neither does she, but I looked it up in the employees' file. I like to guess a person's age and then look it up to see if I'm right. I let myself have an extra pack of cigarettes if I am, though I'm trying to cut down. I figure it's harmless as long as you don't tell. I mean, not everyone has access to that file, it's more or less confidential. But it's all right if I tell you, I don't expect you'll ever meet her, though you never know, it's a small world. Anyway.

"For *heaven's* sake, it's only *Toronto,*" Greta said. She worked in Detroit for three years and she never lets you forget it, it's like she thinks she's a war hero or something, we should all admire her just for the fact that she's still walking this earth, though she was really living in Windsor the whole time, she just worked in Detroit. Which for me doesn't really count. It's where you sleep, right?

"Well, do you?" Chrissy said. She was obviously trying to tell us about hers but she wasn't about to go first, she's cautious, that one.

"I certainly don't," Darlene said, and she wrinkled up her nose, like this, and I had to laugh. "I think it's disgusting,.." She's divorced, I read that in the file too, she never talks about it. It must've been years ago anyway. She got up and went over to the coffee machine and turned her back on us as though she wasn't going to have anything more to do with it.

"Well," Greta said. I could see it was going to be between her and Chrissy. They're both blondes, I don't mean that in a bitchy way but they do try to outdress each other. Greta would like to get out of Filing, she'd like to be a receptionist too so she could meet more people. You don't meet much of anyone in Filing except other people in Filing. Me, I don't mind it so much, I have outside interests.

"Well," Greta said, "I sometimes think about, you know my apartment? It's got this little balcony, I like to sit out there in the summer and I have a few plants out there. I never both that much about locking the door to the balcony, it's one of those sliding glass ones, I'm on the eighteenth floor for heaven's sake, I've got a good view of the lake and the CN Tower and all. But I'm sitting around one night in my housecoat, watching TV with my shoes off, you know how you do, and I see this guy's feet, coming down past the window, and the next think you know he's standing on the balcony, he's let himself down by a rope with a hook on the end of it from the floor above, that's the nineteenth, and before I can even get up off the chesterfield he's inside the apartment. He's all dressed in black with black gloves on"—I knew right away what show she got the black gloves off because I saw the same one—"and then he, well, you know."

"You know what?" Chrissy said, but Greta said, "And afterwards he tells me that he goes all over the outside of the apartment building like that, from one floor to another, with his rope and his hook . . . and then he goes out to the balcony and tosses his rope, and he climbs up it and disappears."

"Just like Tarzan," I said, but nobody laughed.

"Is that all?" Chrissy said. "Don't you ever think about, well, I think about being in the bathtub, with no clothes on . . ."

"So who takes a bath in their clothes?" I said, you have to admit it's stupid when you come to think of it, but she just went on, ". . . with lots of bubbles, what I use is Vitabath, it's more expensive but it's so relaxing, and my hair pinned up, and the door opens and this fellow's standing there. . . . "

"How'd he get in?" Greta said.

"Oh, I don't know, through a window or something. Well, I can't very well get out of the bathtub, the bathroom's too small and besides he's blocking the doorway, so I just *lie* there, and he starts to very slowly take his own clothes off, and then he gets into the bathtub with me."

"Don't you scream or anything?" said Darlene. She'd come back with her cup of coffee, she was getting really interested. "I'd scream like bloody murder."

"Who'd hear me?" Chrissy said. "Besides, all the articles say it's better not to resist, that way you don't get hurt."

"Anyway you might get bubbles up your nose," I said, "from the deep breathing," and I swear all four of them looked at me like I was in bad taste, like I'd insulted the Virgin Mary or something. I mean, I don't see what's wrong with a little joke now and then. Life's too short, right?

"Listen," I said, "those aren't *rape* fantasies. I mean, you aren't getting *raped,* it's just some guy you haven't met formally who happens to be more attractive than Derek Cummins"—he's the Assistant Manager, he wears elevator shoes or at any rate they have these thick soles and he has this funny way of talking, we call him Derek Duck—"and you have a good time. Rape is when they've got a knife or something and you don't want to."

"So what about you, Estelle," Chrissy said, she was miffed because I laughed at her fantasy, she thought I was putting her down. Sondra was miffed too, by this time she'd finished her celery and she wanted to tell about hers, but she hadn't got in fast enough.

"All right, let me tell you one," I said. "I'm walking down this dark street at night and this fellow comes up and grabs my arm. Now it so happens that I have a plastic lemon in my purse, you know how it always says you should carry a plastic lemon in your purse? I don't really do it, I tried it once but the darn thing leaked all over my checkbook, but in this fantasy I have one, and

I say to him, 'You're intending to rape me, right?' and he nods, so I open my purse to get the plastic lemon, and I can't find it! My purse is full of all this junk, Kleenex and cigarettes and my change purse and my lipstick and my driver's license, you know the kind of stuff; so I ask him to hold out his hands, like this, and I pile all this junk into them and down at the bottom there's the plastic lemon, and I can't get the top off. So I hand it to him and he's very obliging, he twists the top off and hands it back to me, and I squirt him in the eye."

I hope you don't think that's too vicious. Come to think of it, it is a bit mean, especially when he was so polite and all.

"*That's* your rape fantasy?" Chrissy says. "I don't believe it."

"She's a card," Darlene says, she and I are the ones that've been here the longest and she never will forget the time I got drunk at the office party and insisted I was going to dance under the table instead of on top of it, I did a sort of Cassack number but then I hit my head on the bottom of the table— actually it was a desk—when I went to get up, and I knocked myself out cold. She's decided that's the mark of an original mind and she tells every- one new about it and I'm not sure that's fair. Though I did do it.

"I'm being totally honest," I say. I always am and they know it. There's no point in being anything else, is the way I look at it, and sooner or later the truth will get out so you might as well not waste the time, right? "You should hear the one about the Easy-Off Oven Cleaner."

But that was the end of the lunch hour, with one bridge game shot to hell, and the next day we spent most of the time arguing over whether to start a new game or play out the hands we had left over from the day before, so Son- dra never did get a chance to tell about her rape fantasy.

It started me thinking though, about my own rape fantasies. Maybe I'm abnormal or something, I mean I have fantasies about handsome strangers coming in through the window too, like Mr. Clean, I wish one would, please god somebody without flat feet and big sweat marks on his shirt, and over five feet five, believe me being tall is a handicap though it's getting better, tall guys are starting to like someone whose nose reaches higher than their belly button. But if you're being totally honest you can't count those as rape fantasies. In a real rape fantasy, what you should feel is this anxiety, like when you think about your apartment building catching on fire and whether you should use the elevator or the stairs or maybe just stick your head under a wet towel, and you try to remember everything you've read about what to do but you can't decide.

For instance, I'm walking along this dark street at night and this short, ugly fellow comes up and grabs my arm, and not only is he ugly, you know, with a sort of puffy nothing face, like those fellows you have to talk to in the bank when your account's overdrawn—of course I don't mean they're all like that—but he's absolutely covered in pimples. So he gets me pinned against the wall, he's short but he's heavy, and he starts to undo himself and the zipper gets stuck. I mean, one of the most significant moments in a girl's life, it's almost like getting married or having a baby or something, and he sticks the zipper.

So I say, kind of disgusted, "Oh for Chrissake," and he starts to cry. He tells me he's never been able to get anything right in his entire life, and this is the last straw, he's going to go jump off a bridge.

"Look," I say, I feel so sorry for him, in my rape fantasies I always end up feeling sorry for the guy, I mean there has to be something *wrong* with them, if it was Clint Eastwood it'd be different but worse luck it never is. I was the kind of little girl who buried dead robins, know what I mean? It used to drive my mother nuts, she didn't like me touching them, because of the germs I guess. So I say, "Listen, I know how you feel. You really should do something about those pimples, if you got rid of them you'd be quite good looking, honest; then you wouldn't have to go around doing stuff like this. I had them myself once," I say, to comfort him, but in fact I did, and it ends up I give him the name of my old dermatologist, the one I had in high school, that was back in Leamington, except I used to go to St. Catherines for the dermatologist. I'm telling you, I was really lonely when I first came here; I thought it was going to be such a big adventure and all, but it's a lot harder to meet people in a city. But I guess it's different for a guy.

Or I'm lying in bed with this terrible cold, my face is all swollen up, my eyes are red and my nose is dripping like a leaky tap, and this fellow comes in through the window and *he* has a terrible cold too, it's a new kind of flu that's been going around. So he says, "I'b goig do rabe you"—I hope you don't mind me holding my nose like this but that's they way I imagine it—and he lets out this terrific sneeze, which slows him down a bit, also I'm no object of beauty myself, you'd have to be some kind of pervert to want to rape someone with a cold like mine, it'd be like raping a bottle of LePage's mucilage the way my nose is running. He's looking wildly around the room, and I realize it's because he doesn't have a piece of Kleenex! "Id's ride here," I say, and I pass him the Kleenex, god know why he even bothered to get out of bed, you'd think if you were going to go around climbing in windows you'd wait till you were healthier, right? I mean, that takes a certain amount of energy. So I ask him why doesn't he let me fix him a Neo-Citran and scotch, that's what I always take, you still have the cold but you don't feel it, so I do and we end up watching the Late Show together. I mean, they aren't all sex maniacs, the rest of the time they must lead a normal life. I figure they enjoy watching the Late Show just like anybody else.

I do have a scarier one though . . . where the fellow says he's hearing angel voices that're telling him he's got to kill me, you know, you read about things like that all the time in the papers. In this one I'm not in the apartment where I live now, I'm back in my mother's house in Leamington and the fellow's been hiding in the cellar, he grabs my arm when I go downstairs to get a jar of jam and he's got hold of the axe too, out of the garage, that one is really scary. I mean, what do you say to a nut like that?

So I start to shake but after a minute I get control of myself and I say, is he sure the angel voices have got the right person, because I hear the same angel voices and they've been telling me for some time that I'm going to give birth to the reincarnation of St. Anne who in turn has the Virgin Mary and right after that comes Jesus Christ and the end of the world, and he wouldn't want to interfere with that, would he? So he gets confused and listens some more, and then he asks for a sign and I show him my vaccination mark, you can see it's sort of an odd-shaped one, it got infected because I scratched the top off, and that does it, he apologizes and climbs out the coal chute again, which is how he got in in the first place, and I say to myself there's some advantage in having been brought up a Catholic even though I haven't been to church since they changed the service into English, it just isn't the same, you might as well be a Protestant. I must write to Mother and tell her to nail up that coal chute, it always has bothered me. Funny, I couldn't tell you at all what this man looks like but I know exactly what kind of shoes he's wearing, because that's the last I see of him, his shoes going up the coal chute, and they're the old-fashioned kind that lace up the ankles, even though he's a young fellow. That's strange, isn't it?

Let me tell you though I really sweat until I see him safely out of there and I go upstairs right away and make myself a cup of tea. I don't think about that one much. My mother always said you shouldn't dwell on unpleasant things and I generally agree with that, I mean, dwelling on them doesn't make them go away. Though not dwelling on them doesn't make them go away either, when you come to think of it.

Sometimes I have these short ones where the fellow grabs my arm but I'm really a Kung-Fu expert, can you believe it, in real life I'm sure it would just be a conk on the head and that's that, like getting your tonsils out, you'd wake up and it would be all over except for the sore places, and you'd be lucky if your neck wasn't broken or something, I could never even hit the volleyball in gym and a volleyball is fairly large, you know?—and I just go *zap* with my fingers into his eyes and that's it, he falls over, or I flip him against a wall or something. But I could never really stick my fingers in anyone's eyes, could you? It would feel like hot jello and I don't even like cold jello, just thinking about it gives me the creeps. I feel a bit guilty about that one. I mean how would you like walking around knowing someone's been blinded for life because of you?

But maybe it's different for a guy.

The most touching one I have is when the fellow grabs my arm and I say, sad and kind of dignified, "You'd be raping a corpse." That pulls him up short and I explain that I've just found out I have leukemia and the doctors have only given me a few months to live. That's why I'm out pacing the streets alone at night, I need to think, you know, come to terms with myself. I don't really have leukemia but in the fantasy I do, I guess I chose that particular disease because a girl in my grade four class died of it, the whole class sent her flowers when she was in the hospital. I didn't understand then that she was going to die and I wanted to have leukemia too so I could get flowers. Kids are funny, aren't they? Well, it turns out that he has leukemia himself, and *he* only has a few months to live, that's why he's going around raping people, he's very bitter because he's so young and his life is being taken from him before he's really lived it. So we walk along gently under the street lights, it's spring and sort of misty, and we end up going for coffee, we're happy we've found the only other person in the world who can understand what we're going through, it's almost like fate, and after a while we just sort of look at each other and our hands touch, and he comes back with me and moves into my apartment and we spend our last months together before we die, we just sort of don't wake up in the morning, though I've never decided which one of us gets to die first. If it's him I have to go on and fantasize about the funeral, if it's me I don't have to worry about that, so it just about depends on how tired I am at the time. You may not believe this but sometimes I even start crying. I cry at the ends of movies, even the ones that aren't all that sad, so I guess it's the same thing. My mother's like that too.

The funny thing about these fantasies is that the man is always someone I don't know, and the statistics in the magazines, well, most of them anyway, they say it's often someone you do know, at least a little bit, like your boss or something—I mean, it wouldn't be *my* boss, he's over sixty and I'm sure he couldn't rape his way out of a paper bag, poor old thing, but it might be someone like Derek Duck, in his elevator shoes, perish the thought—or someone you just met, who invites you up for a drink, it's getting so you can hardly be sociable any more, and how are you supposed to meet people if you can't trust them even that basic amount? You can't spend your whole life in the Filing Department or cooped up in your own apartment with all the doors and windows locked and the shades down. I'm not what you would call a drinker but I like to go out now and then for a drink or two in a nice place, even if I am by myself, I'm with Women's Lib on that even though I can't agree with a lot of other things they say. Like here for instance, the waiters all know me and if anyone, you know, bothers me. . . . I don't know why I'm telling you all this, except I think it helps you get to know a person, especially at first, hearing some of the things they think about. At work they call me the office worry wart, but it isn't so much like worrying, it's more like figuring out what you should do in an emergency, like I said before.

Anyway, another thing about it is that there's a lot of conversation, in fact I spend most of my time, in the fantasy that is, wondering what I'm going to say and what he's going to say, I think it would be better if you could get a conversation going. Like, how could a fellow do that to a person he's just had a long conversation with, once you let them know you're human, you have a life too, I don't see how they could go ahead with it, right? I mean, I know it happens but I just don't understand it, that's the part I really don't understand.

Nadine Gordimer, 1923–

Once Upon a Time

This story first appeared in SALMAGUNDI, *1989.*

SOMEONE HAS WRITTEN TO ASK ME to contribute to an anthology of stories for children. I reply that I don't write children's stories; and he writes back that at a recent congress/book fair/seminar a certain novelist said every writer ought to write at least one story for children. I think of sending a postcard saying I don't accept that I "ought" to write anything.

And then last night I woke up—or rather was awakened without knowing what had roused me.

A voice in the echo-chamber of the subconscious?

A sound.

A creaking of the kind made by the weight carried by one foot after another along a wooden floor. I listened. I felt the apertures of my ears distend with concentration. Again: the creaking. I was waiting for it; waiting to hear if it indicated that feet were moving from room to room, coming up the passage—to my door. I have no burglar bars, no gun under the pillow, but I have the same fears as people who do take these precautions, and my window-panes are thin as rime, could shatter like a wineglass. A woman was murdered (how do they put it) in broad daylight in a house two blocks away, last year, and the fierce dogs who guarded an old widower and his collection of antique clocks were strangled before he was knifed by a casual laborer he had dismissed without pay.

I was staring at the door, making it out in my mind rather than seeing it, in the dark. I lay quite still—a victim already—the arrhythmia of my heart was fleeing, knocking this way and that against its body-cage. How finely tuned the senses are, just out of rest, sleep! I could never listen intently as that in the distractions of the day; I was reading every faintest sound, identifying and classifying its possible threat.

But I learned that I was to be neither threatened nor spared. There was no human weight pressing on the boards, the creaking was a buckling, an epicenter of stress. I was in it. The house that surrounds me while I sleep is built on undermined ground; far beneath my bed, the floor, the house's foundations, the stopes and passages of gold mines have hollowed the rock, and when some face trembles, detaches and falls, three thousand feet below, the whole house shifts slightly, bringing uneasy strain to the balance and

85

counterbalance of brick, cement, wood and glass that hold it as a structure around me. The misbeats of my heart tailed off like the last muffled flourishes on one of the wooden xylophones made by the Chopi and Tsonga* migrant miners who might have been down there, under me in the earth at that moment. The stope where the fall was could have been disused, dripping water from its ruptured veins; or men might now be interred there in the most profound of tombs.

I couldn't find a position in which my mind would let go of my body—release me to sleep again. So I began to tell myself a story; a bedtime story.

———

IN A HOUSE, in a suburb, in a city, there were a man and his wife who loved each other very much and were living happily ever after. They had a little boy, and they loved him very much. They had a cat and a dog that the little boy loved very much. They had a car and a caravan trailer for holidays, and a swimming-pool which was fenced so that the little boy and his playmates would not fall in and drown. They had a housemaid who was absolutely trustworthy and an itinerant gardener who was highly recommended by the neighbors. For when they began to live happily ever after they were warned, by that wise old witch, the husband's mother, not to take on anyone off the street. They were inscribed in a medical benefit society, their pet dog was licensed, they were insured against fire, flood damage and theft, and subscribed to the local Neighborhood Watch, which supplied them with a plaque for their gates lettered YOU HAVE BEEN WARNED over the silhouette of a would-be intruder. He was masked; it could not be said if he was black or white, and therefore proved the property owner was no racist.

It was not possible to insure the house, the swimming pool or the car against riot damage. There were riots, but these were outside the city, where people of another color were quartered. These people were not allowed into the suburb except as reliable housemaids and gardeners, so there was nothing to fear, the husband told the wife. Yet she was afraid that some day such people might come up the street and tear off the plaque YOU HAVE BEEN WARNED and open the gates and stream in . . . Nonsense, my dear, said the husband, there are police and soldiers and tear-gas and guns to keep them away. But to please her—for he loved her very much and buses were being burned, cars stoned, and schoolchildren shot by the police in those quarters out of sight and hearing of the suburb—he had electronically controlled gates fitted. Anyone who pulled off the sign YOU HAVE BEEN WARNED and tried to open the gates would have to announce his intentions by pressing a button and speaking into a receiver relayed to the house. The little boy was

---

Chopi and Tsonga: two peoples from Mozambique, northeast of South Africa.

fascinated by the device and used it as walkie-talkie in cops and robbers play with his small friends.

The riots were suppressed, but there were many burglaries in the suburb and somebody's trusted housemaid was tied up and shut in a cupboard by thieves while she was in charge of her employers' house. The trusted housemaid of the man and wife and little boy was so upset by this misfortune befalling a friend left, as she herself often was, with responsibility for the possessions of the man and his wife and the little boy that she implored her employers to have burglar bars attached to the doors and windows of the house, and an alarm system installed. The wife said, She is right, let us take heed of her advice. So from every window and door in the house where they were living happily ever after they now saw the trees and sky through bars, and when the little boy's pet cat tried to climb in by the fanlight to keep him company in his little bed at night, as it customarily had done, it set off the alarm keening through the house.

The alarm was often answered—it seemed—by other burglar alarms, in other houses, that had been triggered by pet cats or nibbling mice. The alarms called to one another across the gardens in shrills and bleats and wails that everyone soon became accustomed to, so that the din roused the inhabitants of the suburb no more than the croak of frogs and musical grating of cicadas' legs. Under cover of the electronic harpies' discourse intruders sawed the iron bars and broke into homes, taking away hi-fi equipment, television sets, cassette players, cameras and radios, jewelry and clothing, and sometimes were hungry enough to devour everything in the refrigerator or paused audaciously to drink the whiskey in the cabinets or patio bars. Insurance companies paid no compensation for single malt,* a loss made keener by the property owner's knowledge that the thieves wouldn't even have been able to appreciate what it was they were drinking.

Then the time came when many of the people who were not trusted housemaids and gardeners hung about the suburb because they were unemployed. Some importuned for a job: weeding or painting a roof; anything, *baas,*† madam. But the man and his wife remembered the warning about taking on anyone off the street. Some drank liquor and fouled the street with discarded bottles. Some begged, waiting for the man or his wife to drive the car out of the electronically operated gates. They sat about with their feet in the gutters, under the jacaranda trees that made a green tunnel of the street—for it was a beautiful suburb, spoilt only by their presence—and sometimes they fell asleep lying right before the gates in the midday sun. The wife could never see anyone go hungry. She sent the trusted housemaid out with bread and tea, but the trusted housemaid said these were loafers

single malt: an expensive Scotch whiskey
†*baas:* boss.

and *tsotsis,** who would come and tie her and shut her in a cupboard. The husband said, She's right. Take heed of her advice. You only encourage them with your bread and tea. They are looking for their chance . . . And he brought the little boy's tricycle from the garden into the house every night, because if the house was surely secure, once locked and with the alarm set, someone might still be able to climb over the wall or the electronically closed gates into the garden.

You are right, said the wife, then the wall should be higher. And the wise old witch, the husband's mother, paid for the extra bricks as her Christmas present to her son and his wife—the little boy got a Space Man outfit and a book of fairy tales.

But every week there were more reports of intrusion: in broad daylight and the dead of night, in the early hours of the morning, and even in the lovely summer twilight—a certain family was at dinner while the bedrooms were being ransacked upstairs. The man and his wife, talking of the latest armed robbery in the suburb, were distracted by the sight of the little boy's pet cat effortlessly arriving over the seven-foot wall, descending first with a rapid bracing of extended forepaws down on the sheer vertical surface, and then a graceful launch, landing with swishing tail within the property. The whitewashed wall was marked with the cat's comings and goings; and on the street side of the wall there were larger red-earth smudges that could have been made by the kind of broken running shoes, seen on the feet of unemployed loiterers, that had no innocent destination.

When the man and wife and little boy took the pet dog for its walk round the neighborhood streets they no longer paused to admire this show of roses or that perfect lawn; these were hidden behind an array of different varieties of security fences, walls and devices. The man, wife, little boy and dog passed a remarkable choice: there was the low-cost option of pieces of broken glass embedded in cement along the top of walls, there were iron grilles ending in lance-points, there were attempts at reconciling the aesthetics of prison architecture with the Spanish Villa style (spikes painted pink) and with the plaster urns of neoclassical façades (twelve-inch pikes finned like zigzags of lightning and painted pure white). Some walls had a small board affixed, giving the name and telephone number of the firm responsible for the installation of the devices. While the little boy and the pet dog raced ahead, the husband and wife found themselves comparing the possible effectiveness of each style against its appearance; and after several weeks when they paused before this barricade or that without needing to speak, both came out with the conclusion that only one was worth considering. It was the ugliest but the most honest in its suggestion of the pure concentration-camp style, no frills, all evident efficacy. Placed the length of walls, it consisted of a continuous coil of stiff and shining metal serrated

*tsotsis: hooligans.

into jagged blades, so that there would be no way of climbing over it and no way through its tunnel without getting entangled in its fangs. There would be no way out, only a struggle getting bloodier and bloodier, a deeper and sharper hooking and tearing of flesh. The wife shuddered to look at it. You're right, said the husband, anyone would think twice . . . And they took heed of the advice on a small board fixed to the wall: Consult DRAGON'S TEETH The People For Total Security.

Next day a gang of workmen came and stretched the razor-bladed coils all round the walls of the house where the husband and wife and little boy and pet dog and cat were living happily ever after. The sunlight flashed and slashed, off the serrations, the cornice of razor thorns encircled the home, shining. The husband said, Never mind. It will weather. The wife said, You're wrong. They guarantee it's rust-proof. And she waited until the little boy had run off to play before she said, I hope the cat will take heed . . . The husband said, Don't worry, my dear, cats always look before they leap. And it was true that from that day on the cat slept in the little boy's bed and kept to the garden, never risking a try at breaching security.

One evening, the mother read the little boy to sleep with a fairy story from the book the wise old witch had given him at Christmas. Next day he pretended to be the Prince who braves the terrible thicket of thorns to enter the palace and kiss the Sleeping Beauty back to life: he dragged a ladder to the wall, the shining coiled tunnel was just wide enough for his little body to creep in, and with the first fixing of its razor-teeth in his knees and hands and head he screamed and struggled deeper into its tangle. The trusted housemaid and the itinerant gardener, whose "day" it was, came running, the first to see and to scream with him, and the itinerant gardener tore his hands trying to get at the little boy. Then the man and his wife burst wildly into the garden and for some reason (the cat, probably) the alarm set up wailing against the screams while the bleeding mass of the little boy was hacked out of the security coil with saws, wire-cutters, choppers, and they carried it—the man, the wife, the hysterical trusted housemaid and the weeping gardener—into the house.

Herman Melville, 1819–1891

Bartleby the Scrivener
A Story of Wall Street

This story first appeared in PUTNAM'S MONTHLY MAGAZINE, *1853.*

I AM A RATHER ELDERLY MAN. The nature of my avocations for the last thirty years has brought me into more than ordinary contact with what would seem an interesting and somewhat singular set of men, of whom as yet nothing that I know of has ever been written:—I mean the law-copyists or scriveners. I have known very many of them, professionally and privately, and if I pleased, could relate divers histories, at which good-natured gentlemen might smile, and sentimental souls might weep. But I waive the biographies of all other scriveners for a few passages in the life of Bartleby, who was a scrivener and the strangest I ever saw, or heard of. While of other law-copyists I might write the complete life, of Bartleby nothing of that sort can be done. I believe that no materials exist for a full and satisfactory biography of this man. It is an irreparable loss to literature. Bartleby was one of those beings of whom nothing is ascertainable, except from the original sources, and in his case those are very small. What my own astonished eyes saw of Bartleby, *that* is all I know of him, except, indeed, one vague report which will appear in the sequel.

Ere introducing the scrivener, as he first appeared to me, it is fit I make some mention of myself, my *employés,* my business, my chambers, and general surroundings; because some such description is indispensable to an adequate understanding of the chief character about to be presented.

Imprimis. I am a man who, from his youth upward, has been filled with a profound conviction that the easiest way of life is the best. Hence, though I belong to a profession proverbially energetic and nervous, even to turbulence, at times, yet nothing of that sort have I ever suffered to invade my peace. I am one of those unambitious lawyers who never addresses a jury, or in any way draws down public applause; but in the cool tranquillity of a snug retreat, do a snug business among rich men's bonds and mortgages and title-deeds. All who know me, consider me an eminently *safe* man. The late John Jacob Astor, a personage little given to poetic enthusiasm, had no hesitation in pronouncing my first grand point to be prudence; my next, method. I do not speak it in vanity, but simply record the fact, that I was not unemployed in my profession by the late John Jacob Astor; a name which, I admit, I love to repeat, for it hath a rounded and orbicular sound to it, and rings like unto bullion. I will freely add, that I was not insensible to the late John Jacob Astor's good opinion.

Some time prior to the period at which this little history begins, my avocations had been largely increased. The good old office, now extinct in the State of New York, of a Master in Chancery, had been conferred upon me. It was not a very arduous office, but very pleasantly remunerative. I seldom lose my temper; much more seldom indulge in dangerous indignation at wrongs and outrages; but I must be permitted to be rash here and declare, that I consider the sudden and violent abrogation of the office of Master in Chancery, by the new Constitution, as a____premature act; inasmuch as I had counted upon a life-lease of the profits, whereas I only received those of a few short years. But this is by the way.

My chambers were upstairs at No.____Wall street. At one end they looked upon the white wall of the interior of a spacious skylight shaft, penetrating the building from top to bottom. This view might have been considered rather tame than otherwise, deficient in what landscape painters call "life." But if so, the view from the other end of my chambers offered, at least, a contrast, if nothing more. In that direction my windows commanded an unobstructed view of a lofty brick wall, black by age and everlasting shade; which wall required no spy-glass to bring out its lurking beauties, but for the benefit of all near-sighted spectators, was pushed up to within ten feet of my window panes. Owing to the great height of the surrounding buildings, and my chambers being on the second floor, the interval between this wall and mine not a little resembled a huge square cistern.

At the period just preceding the advent of Bartleby, I had two persons as copyists in my employment, and a promising lad as an office-boy. First, Turkey; second, Nippers; third, Ginger Nut. These may seem names, the like of which are not usually found in the Directory. In truth they were nicknames, mutually conferred upon each other by my three clerks, and were deemed expressive of their respective persons or characters. Turkey was a short, pursy Englishman of about my own age, that is, somewhere not far from sixty. In the morning, one might say, his face was of a fine florid hue, but after twelve o'clock, meridian—his dinner hour—it blazed like a grate full of Christmas coals; and continued blazing—but, as it were, with a gradual wane—till 6 o'clock P.M. or thereabouts, after which I saw no more of the proprietor of the face, which, gaining its meridian with the sun, seemed to set with it, to rise, culminate, and decline the following day, with the like regularity and undiminished glory. There are many singular coincidences I have known in the course of my life, not the least among which was the fact, that exactly when Turkey displayed his fullest beams from his red and radiant countenance, just then, too, at that critical moment, began the daily period when I considered his business capacities as seriously disturbed for the remainder of the twenty-four hours. Not that he was absolutely idle, or averse to business then; far from it. The difficulty was, he was apt to be altogether too energetic. There was a strange, inflamed, flurried, flighty recklessness of activity about him. He would be incautious in dipping his pen into his ink-stand. All his blots upon my documents, were dropped there after twelve o'clock, meridian. Indeed, not only would he be reckless and sadly given to making blots in the afternoon, but some days he went further, and was rather noisy. At such time, too, his face flamed with augmented blazonry, as if cannel coal had been heaped on anthracite. He made an unpleasant racket with his chair; spilled his sand-box; in mending his pens, impatiently split them all to pieces, and threw them on the floor in a sudden passion; stood up and leaned over his table, boxing his papers about in a most indecorous manner, very sad to behold in an elderly man like him. Nevertheless, as he was in many ways a most valuable person to me, and all the time before twelve o'clock, meridian, was the quickest, steadiest creature, too, accomplishing a great deal of work in a style not easy to be matched—for these reasons, I was willing to overlook his eccentricities, though indeed, occasionally, I remonstrated with him. I did this very gently, however, because, though the civilest, nay, the blandest and most reverential of men in the morning, yet in the afternoon he was disposed, upon provocation, to be slightly rash with his tongue, in fact, insolent. Now, valuing his morning services as I did, and resolving not to lose them—yet, at the same time, made uncomfortable by his inflamed ways after twelve o'clock; and being a man of peace, unwilling by my admonitions to call forth unseemly retorts from him—I took upon me, one Saturday noon (he was always worse on Saturdays), to hint to him, very kindly, that perhaps now that he was growing old, it might be well to abridge his labours; in short, he need not come to my chambers after twelve o'clock, but, dinner over, had best go home to his lodgings and rest himself till tea-time. But no; he insisted upon his afternoon devotions. His countenance became intolerably fervid, as he oratorically assured me—gesticulating, with a long ruler, at the other side of the room—that if his services in the morning were useful, how indispensable, then, in the afternoon?

"With submission, sir," said Turkey on this occasion, "I consider myself your right-hand man. In the morning I but marshal and deploy my columns; but in the afternoon I put myself at their head, and gallantly charge the foe, thus!"—and he made a violent thrust with the ruler.

"But the blots, Turkey," intimated I.

"True,—but, with submission, sir, behold these hairs! I am getting old. Surely, sir, a blot or two of a warm afternoon is not to be severely urged against grey hairs. Old age—even if it blot the page—is honourable. With submission, sir, we *both* are getting old."

This appeal to my fellow-feeling was hardly to be resisted. At all events, I saw that go he would not. So I made up my mind to let him stay, resolving, nevertheless, to see to it, that during the afternoon he had to do with my less important papers.

Nippers, the second on my list, was a whiskered, sallow, and, upon the whole, rather piratical-looking young man of about five and twenty. I always deemed him the victim of two evil powers—ambition and indigestion. The ambition was evinced by a certain impatience of the duties of a mere copyist—an unwarrantable usurpation of strictly professional affairs, such as the original drawing up of legal documents. The indigestion seemed betokened in an occasional nervous testiness and grinning irritability, causing the teeth to audibly grind together over mistakes committed in copying; unnecessary maledictions, hissed, rather than spoken, in the heat of business; and especially by a continual discontent with the height of the table where he worked. Though of a very ingenious mechanical turn, Nippers could never get this table to suit him. He put chips under it, blocks of various sorts, bits of pasteboard, and at last went so far as to attempt an exquisite adjustment by final pieces of folded blotting-paper. But no invention would answer. If, for the sake of easing his back, he brought the table lid at a sharp angle well up toward his chin, and wrote there like a man using the steep roof of a Dutch house for his desk—then he declared that it stopped the circulation in his arms. If now he lowered the table to his waistbands, and stooped over it in writing, then there was a sore aching in his back. In short, the truth of the matter was, Nippers knew not what he wanted. Or, if he wanted anything, it was to be rid of a scrivener's table altogether. Among the manifestations of his diseased ambition was a fondness he had for receiving visits from certain ambiguous-looking fellows in seedy coats, whom he called his clients. Indeed I was aware that not only was he, at times, considerable of a ward-politician, but he occasionally did a little business at the Justices' courts, and was not unknown on the steps of the Tombs. I have good reason to believe, however, that one individual who called upon him at my chambers, and who, with a grand air, he insisted was his client, was no other than a dun, and the alleged title-deed, a bill. But with all his failings, and the annoyances he caused me, Nippers, like his compatriot Turkey, was a very useful man to me; wrote a neat, swift hand; and, when he chose, was not deficient in a gentlemanly sort of deportment. Added to this, he always dressed in a gentlemanly sort of way; and so, incidentally, reflected credit upon my chambers. Whereas with respect to Turkey, I had much ado to keep him from being a reproach to me. His clothes were apt to look oily and smell of eating-houses. He wore his pantaloons very loose and baggy in summer. His coats were execrable; his hat not to be handled. But while the hat was a thing of indifference to me, inasmuch as his natural civility and deference, as a dependent Englishman, always led him to doff it the moment he entered the room, yet his coat was another matter. Concerning his coats, I reasoned with him; but with no effect. The truth was, I suppose, that a man with so small an income, could not afford to sport such a lustrous face and a lustrous coat at one and the same time. As Nippers once observed, Turkey's money went chiefly for red ink. One winter day I presented Turkey with a highly-respectable looking coat of my own, a padded grey coat, of a most comfortable warmth, and which buttoned straight up from the knee to the neck. I thought Turkey would appreciate the favour, and abate his rashness and obstreperousness of afternoons. But no, I verily believe that buttoning himself up in so downy and blanketlike a coat had a pernicious effect upon him; upon the same principle that too much oats are bad for horses. In fact, precisely as a rash, restive horse is said to feel his oats, so Turkey felt his coat. It made him insolent. He was a man whom prosperity harmed.

Though concerning the self-indulgent habits of Turkey I had my own private surmises, yet touching Nippers I was well persuaded that whatever might be his faults in other respects, he was, at least, a temperate young man. But, indeed, nature herself seemed to have been his vintner, and at his birth charged him so thoroughly with an irritable, brandy-like disposition, that all subsequent potations were needless. When I consider how, amid the stillness of my chambers, Nippers would sometimes impatiently rise from his seat, and stooping over his table, spread his arms wide apart, seize the whole desk, and move it, and jerk it, with a grim, grinding motion on the floor, as if the table were a perverse voluntary agent, intent on thwarting and vexing him; I plainly perceive that for Nippers, brandy and water were altogether superfluous.

It was fortunate for me that, owing to its peculiar cause—indigestion—the irritability and consequent nervousness of Nippers, were mainly observable in the morning, while in the afternoon he was comparatively mild. So that Turkey's paroxysms only coming on about twelve o'clock, I never had to do with their eccentricities at one time. Their fits relieved each other like guards. When Nippers's was on, Turkey's was off; and *vice versa*. This was a good natural arrangement under the circumstances.

Ginger Nut, the third on my list, was a lad some twelve years old. His father was a carman, ambitious of seeing his son on the bench instead of a cart, before he died. So he sent him to my office as student at law, errand boy, and cleaner and sweeper, at the rate of one dollar a week. He had a little desk to himself, but he did not use it much. Upon inspection, the drawer exhibited a great array of the shells of various sorts of nuts. Indeed, to this quick-witted youth the whole noble science of the law was contained in a nut-shell. Not the least among the employments of Ginger Nut, as well as one which he discharged with the most alacrity, was his duty as cake and apple purveyor for Turkey and Nippers. Copying law papers being proverbially a dry, husky sort of business, my two scriveners were fain to moisten their mouths very often with Spitzenbergs to be had at the numerous stalls nigh the Custom House and Post Office. Also, they sent Ginger Nut very frequently for that peculiar cake—small, flat, round, and very spicy—which he had been named by them. Of a cold morning, when business was but dull, Turkey would gobble up scores of these cakes, as if they were mere wafers—indeed they sell them at the rate of six or eight for a penny—the scrape of his pen blending with the crunching of the crisp particles in his mouth. Of all the fiery afternoon blunders and flurried rashness of Turkey, was his once moistening a ginger-cake between his lips, and clapping it on to a mortgage for a seal. I came within an ace of dismissing him then. But he mollified me by making an oriental bow and saying—"With submission, sir, it was generous of me to find you in stationery on my own account."

Now my original business—that of a conveyancer and title hunter, and drawer-up of recondite documents of all sorts—was considerably increased by receiving the master's office. There was now great work for scriveners. Not only must I push the clerks already with me, but I must have additional help. In answer to my advertisement, a motionless young man one morning stood upon my office threshold, the door being open, for it was summer. I can see that figure now—pallidly neat, pitiably respectable, incurably forlorn! It was Bartleby.

After a few words touching his qualifications, I engaged him, glad to have among my corps of copyists a man of so singularly sedate an aspect, which I thought might operate beneficially upon the flighty temper of Turkey, and the fiery one of Nippers.

I should have stated before that ground glass folding-doors divided my premises into two parts, one of which was occupied by my scriveners, the other by myself. According to my humour I threw open these doors, or closed them. I resolved to assign Bartleby a corner by the folding-doors, but on my side of them, so as to have this quiet man within easy call, in case any trifling thing was to be done. I placed his desk close up to a small side-window in that part of the room, a window which originally had afforded a lateral view of certain grimy back-yards and bricks, but which, owing to subsequent erections, commanded at present no view at all, though it gave some light. Within three feet of the panes was a wall, and the light came down from far above, between two lofty buildings, as from a very small opening in a dome. Still further to a satisfactory arrangement, I procured a high green folding screen, which might entirely isolate Bartleby from my sight, though not remove him from my voice. And thus, in a manner, privacy and society were conjoined.

At first Bartleby did an extraordinary quantity of writing. As if long famishing for something to copy, he seemed to gorge himself on my documents. There was no pause for digestion. He ran a day and night line, copying by sun-light and by candle-light. I should have been quite delighted with his application, had he been cheerfully industrious. But he wrote on silently, palely, mechanically.

It is, of course, an indispensable part of a scrivener's business to verify the accuracy of his copy, word by word. Where there are two or more scriveners in an office, they assist each other in this examination, one reading from the copy, the other holding the original. It is a very dull, wearisome, and lethargic affair. I can readily imagine that to some sanguine temperaments it would be altogether intolerable. For example, I cannot credit that the mettlesome poet Byron would have contentedly sat down with Bartleby to examine a law document of, say, five hundred pages, closely written in a crimpy hand.

Now and then, in the haste of business, it had been my habit to assist in comparing some brief document myself, calling Turkey or Nippers for this purpose. One object I had in placing Bartleby so handy to me behind the screen, was to avail myself of his services on such trivial occasions. It was on the third day, I think, of his being with me, and before any necessity had arisen for having his own writing examined, that, being much hurried to complete a small affair I had in hand, I abruptly called to Bartleby. In my haste and natural expectancy of instant compliance, I sat with my head bent over the original on my desk, and my right hand sideways, and somewhat nervously extended with the copy, so that immediately upon emerging from his retreat, Bartleby might snatch it and proceed to business without the least delay.

In this very attitude did I sit when I called to him, rapidly stating what it was I wanted him to do—namely, to examine a small paper with me. Imagine my surprise, nay, my consternation, when without moving from his privacy, Bartleby in a singularly mild, firm voice, replied, "I would prefer not to."

I sat awhile in perfect silence, rallying my stunned faculties. Immediately it occurred to me that my ears had deceived me, or Bartleby had entirely misunderstood my meaning. I repeated my request in the clearest tone I could assume. But in quite as clear a one came the previous reply, "I would prefer not to."

"Prefer not to," echoed I, rising in high excitement, and crossing the room with a stride. "What do you mean? Are you moonstruck? I want you to help me compare this sheet here—take it," and I thrust it towards him.

"I would prefer not to," said he.

I looked at him steadfastly. His face was leanly composed; his grey eye dimly calm. Not a wrinkle of agitation rippled him. Had there been the least uneasiness, anger, impatience or impertinence in his manner; in other words, had there been anything ordinarily human about him, doubtless I should have violently dismissed him from the premises. But as it was, I should have as soon thought of turning my pale plaster-of-paris bust of Cicero out of doors. I stood gazing at him awhile, as he went on with his own writing, and then reseated myself at my desk. This is very strange, thought I. What had one best do? But my business hurried me. I concluded to forget the matter for the present, reserving it for my future leisure. So calling Nippers from the other room, the paper was speedily examined.

A few days after this, Bartleby concluded four lengthy documents, being quadruplicates of a week's testimony taken before me in my High Court of Chancery. It became necessary to examine them. It was an important suit, and great accuracy was imperative. Having all things arranged, I called Turkey, Nippers and Ginger Nut from the next room, meaning to place the four copies in the hands of my four clerks, while I should read from the original. Accordingly Turkey, Nippers and Ginger Nut had taken their seats in a row, each with his document in hand, when I called to Bartleby to join this interesting group.

"Bartleby! quick, I am waiting."

I heard a slow scrape of his chair legs on the uncarpeted floor, and soon he appeared standing at the entrance of his hermitage.

"What is wanted?" said he mildly.

"The copies, the copies," said I hurriedly. "We are going to examine them. There"—and I held toward him the fourth quadruplicate.

"I would prefer not to," he said, and gently disappeared behind the screen.

For a few moments I was turned into a pillar of salt, standing at the head of my seated column of clerks. Recovering myself, I advanced toward the screen, and demanded the reason for such extraordinary conduct.

"*Why* do you refuse?"

"I would prefer not to."

With any other man I should have flown outright into a dreadful passion, scorned all further words, and thrust him ignominiously from my presence. But there was something about Bartleby that not only strangely disarmed me, but in a wonderful manner touched and disconcerted me. I began to reason with him.

"These are your own copies we are about to examine. It is labour saving to you, because one examination will answer for your four papers. It is common usage. Every copyist is bound to help examine his copy. Is it not so? Will you not speak? Answer!"

"I prefer not to," he replied in a flute-like tone. It seemed to me that while I had been addressing him, he carefully revolved every statement that I made; fully comprehended the meaning; could not gainsay the irresistible conclusion; but, at the same time, some paramount consideration prevailed with him to reply as he did.

"You are decided, then, not to comply with my request—a request made according to common usage and common sense?"

He briefly gave me to understand that on that point my judgment was sound. Yes: his decision was irreversible.

It is not seldom the case that when a man is browbeaten in some unprecedented and violently unreasonable way, he begins to stagger in his own plainest faith. He begins, as it were, vaguely to surmise that, wonderful as it may be, all the justice and all the reason are on the other side. Accordingly, if any disinterested persons are present, he turns to them for some reinforcement for his own faltering mind.

"Turkey," said I, "what do you think of this? Am I not right?"

"With submission, sir," said Turkey, with his blandest tone, "I think that you are."

"Nippers," said I, "what do *you* think of it?"

"I think I should kick him out of the office."

(The reader of nice perceptions will here perceive that, it being morning, Turkey's answer is couched in polite and tranquil terms but Nippers's reply in ill-tempered ones. Or, to repeat a previous sentence, Nippers's ugly mood was on duty, and Turkey's off.)

"Ginger Nut," said I, willing to enlist the smallest suffrage in my behalf, "what do *you* think of it?"

"I think, sir, he's a little *luny*," replied Ginger Nut, with a grin.

"You hear what they say," said I, turning towards the screen, "come forth and do your duty."

Be he vouchsafed no reply. I pondered a moment in sore perplexity. But once more business hurried me. I determined again to postpone the consideration of this dilemma to my future leisure. With a little trouble we made out to examine the papers without Bartleby, though at every page or two, Turkey deferentially dropped his opinion that this proceeding was quite out of the common; while Nippers, twitching in his chair with a dyspeptic nervousness, ground out between his set teeth occasional hissing maledictions against the stubborn oaf behind the screen. And for his (Nipper's) part, this was the first and the last time he would do another man's business without pay.

Meanwhile Bartleby sat in his hermitage, oblivious to everything but his own peculiar business there.

Some days passed, the scrivener being employed upon another lengthy work. His late remarkable conduct led me to regard his ways narrowly. I observed that he never went to dinner; indeed that he never went any where. As yet I had never of my personal knowledge known him to be outside of my office. He was a perpetual sentry in the corner. At about eleven o'clock though, in the morning, I noticed that Ginger Nut would advance towards the opening in Bartleby's screen, as if silently beckoned thither by a gesture invisible to me where I sat. The boy would then leave the office jingling a few pence, and reappear with a handful of ginger-nuts which he delivered in the hermitage, receiving two of the cakes for his trouble.

He lives, then, on ginger-nuts, thought I; never eats dinner, properly speaking; he must be a vegetarian then; but no; he never eats even vegetables, he eats nothing but ginger-nuts. My mind then ran on in reveries concerning the probable effects upon the human constitution of living entirely on ginger-nuts. Ginger-nuts are so called because they contain ginger as one of their peculiar constituents, and the final flavouring one. Now what was ginger? A hot, spicy thing. Was Bartleby hot and spicy? Not at all. Ginger, then, had no effect upon Bartleby. Probably he preferred it should have none.

Nothing so aggravates an earnest person as a passive resistance. If the individual so resisted be of a not inhumane temper, and the resisting one perfectly harmless in his passivity; then, in the better moods of the former, he will endeavour charitably to construe to his imagination what proves impossible to be solved by his judgment. Even so, for the most part, I regarded Bartleby and his ways. Poor fellow! thought I, he means no mischief; it is plain he intends no insolence; his aspect sufficiently evinces that his eccentricities are involuntary. He is useful to me. I can get along with him. If I turn him away, the chances are he will fall in with some less indulgent employer, and then he will be rudely treated, and perhaps driven forth miserably to starve. Yes. Here I can cheaply purchase a delicious self-approval. To befriend Bartleby; to humour him in his strange wilfulness, will cost me little or nothing, while I lay up in my soul what will eventually prove a sweet morsel for my conscience. But this mood was not invariable with me. The passiveness of Bartleby sometime irritated me. I felt strangely goaded on to encounter him in new opposition, to elicit some angry spark from him answerable to my own. But indeed I might as well have essayed to strike fire with my knuckles against a bit of Windsor soap. But one afternoon the evil impulse in me mastered me, and the following little scene ensued:

"Bartleby," said I, "when those papers are all copied, I will compare them with you."

"I would prefer not to."

"How? Surely you do not mean to persist in that mulish vagary?"

No answer.

I threw open the folding-doors near by, and turning upon Turkey and Nippers, exclaimed in an excited manner:

"He says, a second time, he won't examine his papers. What do you think of it, Turkey?"

It was afternoon, be it remembered. Turkey sat glowing like a brass boiler, his bald head steaming, his hands reeling among his blotted papers.

"Think of it?" roared Turkey; "I think I'll just step behind his screen, and black his eyes for him!"

So saying, Turkey rose to his feet and threw his arms into a pugilistic position. He was hurrying away to make good his promise, when I detained him, alarmed at the effect of incautiously rousing Turkey's combativeness after dinner.

"Sit down, Turkey," said I, "and hear what Nippers has to say. What do you think of it, Nippers? Would I not be justified in immediately dismissing Bartleby?"

"Excuse me, that is for you to decide, sir. I think his conduct quite unusual, and indeed unjust, as regards Turkey and myself. But it may only be a passing whim."

"Ah," exclaimed I. "You have strangely changed your mind then—you speak very gently of him now."

"All beer," cried Turkey; "gentleness is effects of beer—Nippers and I dined together to-day. You see how gentle *I* am, sir. Shall I go and black his eyes?"

"You refer to Bartleby, I suppose. No, not to-day, Turkey," I replied; "pray, put up your fists."

I closed the doors, and again advanced towards Bartleby. I felt additional incentives tempting me to my fate. I burned to be rebelled against again. I remembered that Bartleby never left the office.

"Bartleby," said I, "Ginger Nut is away; just step round to the Post Office, won't you? (it was but a three minutes' walk), and see if there is anything for me."

"I would prefer not to."

"You *will* not?"

"I *prefer* not."

I staggered to my desk, and sat there in a deep study. My blind inveteracy returned. Was there any other thing in which I could procure myself to be ignominiously repulsed by this lean, penniless wight?—my hired clerk? What added thing is there, perfectly reasonable, that he will be sure to refuse to do?

"Bartleby!"

No answer.

"Bartleby," in a louder tone.

No answer.

"Bartleby," I roared.

Like a very ghost, agreeably to the laws of magical invocation, at the third summons, he appeared at the entrance of his hermitage.

"Go to the next room, and tell Nippers to come to me."

"I prefer not to," he respectfully and slowly said, and mildly disappeared.

"Very good, Bartleby," said I, in a quiet sort of serenely severe self-possessed tone, intimating the unalterable purpose of some terrible retribution very close at hand. At the moment I half intended something of the kind. But upon the whole, as it was drawing towards my dinner-hour, I thought it best to put on my hat and walk home for the day, suffering much from perplexity and distress of mind.

Shall I acknowledge it? The conclusion of this whole business was, that it soon became a fixed fact of my chambers, that a pale young scrivener, by the name of Bartleby, had a desk there; that he copied for me at the usual rate of four cents a folio (one hundred words); but he was permanently exempt from examining the work done by him, that duty being transferred to Turkey and Nippers, out of compliment doubtless to their superior acuteness; moreover, said Bartleby was never on any account to be despatched on the most trivial errand of any sort; and that even if entreated to take upon him such a matter, it was generally understood that he would prefer not to—in other words, that he would refuse point-blank.

As days passed on, I became considerably reconciled to Bartleby. His steadiness, his freedom from all dissipation, his incessant industry (except when he chose to throw himself into a standing revery behind his screen), his great stillness, his unalterableness of demeanour under all circumstances, made him a valuable acquisition. One prime thing was this,—*he was always there;*—first in the morning, continually through the day, and the last at night. I had a singular confidence in his honesty. I felt my most precious papers perfectly safe in his hands. Sometimes to be sure I could not, for the very soul of me, avoid falling into sudden spasmodic passions with him. For it was exceeding difficult to bear in mind all the time those strange peculiarities, privileges, and unheard of exemptions, forming the tacit stipulations on Bartleby's part under which he remained in my office. Now and then, in the eagerness of despatching pressing business, I would inadvertently summon Bartleby, in a short, rapid tone, to put his finger, say, on the incipient tie of a bit of red tape with which I was about compressing some papers. Of course, from behind the screen the usual answer, "I prefer not to," was sure to come; and then, how could a human creature with the common infirmities of our nature, refrain from bitterly exclaiming upon such perverseness—such unreasonableness. However, every added repulse of this sort which I received only tended to lessen the probability of my repeating the inadvertence.

Here it must be said, that according to the custom of most legal gentlemen occupying chambers in densely-populated law buildings, there were several keys to my door. One was kept by a woman residing in the attic, which person weekly scrubbed and daily swept and dusted my apartments. Another was kept by Turkey for convenience sake. The third I sometimes carried in my own pocket. The fourth I knew not who had.

Now, one Sunday morning I happened to go to Trinity Church, to hear a celebrated preacher, and finding myself rather early on the ground, I thought I would walk round to my chambers for awhile. Luckily I had my key with me; but upon applying it to the lock, I found it resisted by something inserted from the inside. Quite surprised, I called out; when to my consternation a key was turned from within; and thrusting his lean visage at me, and holding the door ajar, the apparition of Bartleby appeared, in his shirt sleeves, and otherwise in a strangely tattered dishabille, saying quietly that he was sorry, but he was deeply engaged just then, and—preferred not admitting me at present. In a brief word or two, he moreover added, that perhaps I had better walk round the block two or three times, and by that time he would probably have concluded his affairs.

Now, the utterly unsurmised appearance of Bartleby, tenanting my law-chambers of a Sunday-morning, with his cadaverously gentlemanly *nonchalance,* yet withal firm and self-possessed, had such a strange effect upon me, that incontinently I slunk away from my own door, and did as desired. But not without sundry twinges of impotent rebellion against the mild effrontery of this unaccountable scrivener. Indeed, it was his wonderful mildness chiefly, which not only disarmed me, but unmanned me, as it were. For I consider that one, for the time, is in a way unmanned when he tranquilly permits his hired clerk to dictate to him, and order him away from his own premises. Furthermore, I was full of uneasiness as to what Bartleby could possibly be doing in my office in his shirt sleeves, and in an otherwise dismantled condition of a Sunday morning. Was anything amiss going on? Nay, that was out of the question. It was not to be thought of for a moment that Bartleby was an immoral person. But what could he be doing there—copying? Nay again, whatever might be his eccentricities, Bartleby was an eminently decorous person. He would be the last man to sit down to his desk in any state approaching to nudity. Besides, it was Sunday; and there was something about Bartleby that forbade the supposition that he would by any secular occupation violate the proprieties of the day.

Nevertheless, my mind was not pacified; and full of a restless curiosity, at last I returned to the door. Without hindrance I inserted my key, opened it, and entered. Bartleby was not to be seen. I looked around anxiously, peeped behind his screen; but it was very plain that he was gone. Upon more closely examining the place, I surmised that for an indefinite period Bartleby must have ate, dressed, and slept in my office, and that too without plate, mirror, or bed. The cushioned seat of a ricketty old sofa in one corner bore the faint impress of a lean, reclining form. Rolled away under his desk, I found a blanket; under the empty grate, a blacking box and brush; on a chair, a tin basin, with soap and a ragged towel; in a newspaper a few crumbs of ginger-nuts and a morsel of cheese. Yes, thought I, it is evident enough that Bartleby has been making his home here, keeping bachelor's hall all by himself. Immediately then the thought came sweeping across me, What miserable friendlessness and loneliness are here revealed! His poverty is great; but his solitude, how horrible! Think of it. Of a Sunday, Wall street is deserted as Petra; and every night of every day it is an emptiness. This building too, which of week-days hums with industry and life, at nightfall echoes with sheer vacancy, and all through Sunday is forlorn. And here Bartleby makes his home; sole spectator of a solitude which he has seen all populous—a sort of innocent and transformed Marius* brooding among the ruins of Carthage.[†]

For the first time in my life a feeling of overpowering stinging melancholy seized me. Before, I had never experienced aught but a not-unpleasing sadness. The bond of a common humanity now drew me irresistibly to gloom. A fraternal melancholy! For both I and Bartleby were sons of Adam. I remembered the bright silks and sparkling faces I had seen that day, in gala trim, swan-like sailing down the Mississippi of Broadway; and I contrasted them with the pallid copyist, and thought to myself, Ah, happiness courts the light, so we deem the world is gay; but misery hides aloof, so we deem that misery there is none. These sad fancyings—chimeras, doubtless, of a sick and silly brain—led on to other and more special thoughts, concerning the eccentricities of Bartleby. Presentiments of strange discoveries hovered round me. The scrivener's pale form appeared to me laid out, among uncaring strangers, in its shivering winding sheet.

Suddenly I was attracted by Bartleby's closed desk, the key in open sight left in the lock.

I mean no mischief, seek the gratification of no heartless curiosity, thought I; besides, the desk is mine, and its contents, too, so I will make bold

---

*Marius: Gaius Marius, a powerful Roman general, alive between 155(?) B.C. and 86 B.C.
†Carthage: ancient city and state on the northern coast of Africa, in the Bay of Tunis; northeast of the modern Tunis.

to look within. Everything was methodically arranged, the papers smoothly placed. The pigeon holes were deep, and, removing the files of documents, I groped into their recesses. Presently I felt something there, and dragged it out. It was an old bandana handkerchief, heavy and knotted. I opened it, and saw it was a savings' bank.

I now recalled all the quiet mysteries which I had noted in the man. I remembered that he never spoke but to answer; that though at intervals he had considerable time to himself, yet I had never seen him reading—no, not even a newspaper; that for long periods he would stand looking out, at his pale window behind the screen, upon the dead brick wall; I was quite sure he never visited any refectory or eating-house; while his pale face clearly indicated that he never drank beer like Turkey, or tea and coffee even, like other men; that he never went anywhere in particular that I could learn; never went out for a walk, unless indeed that was the case at present; that he had declined telling who he was, or whence he came, or whether he had any relatives in the world; that though so thin and pale, he never complained of ill health. And more than all, I remembered a certain unconscious air of pallid—how shall I call it?—of pallid haughtiness, say, or rather an austere reserve about him, which had positively awed me into my tame compliance with his eccentricities, when I had feared to ask him to do the slightest incidental thing for me, even though I might know, from his long-continued motionlessness, that behind his screen he must be standing in one of those dead-wall reveries of his.

Revolving all these things, and coupling them with the recently discovered fact that he made my office his constant abiding place and home, and not forgetful of his morbid moodiness; revolving all these things, a prudential feeling began to steal over me. My first emotions had been those of pure melancholy and sincerest pity; but just in proportion as the forlornness of Bartleby grew and grew to my imagination, did that same melancholy merge into fear, that pity into repulsion. So true it is, and so terrible, too, that up to a certain point the thought or sight of misery enlists our best affections; but, in certain special cases, beyond that point it does not. They err who would assert that invariably this is owing to the inherent selfishness of the human heart. It rather proceeds from a certain hopelessness of remedying excessive and organic ill. To a sensitive being, pity is not seldom pain. And when at last it is perceived that such pity cannot lead to effectual succour, common sense bids the soul be rid of it. What I saw that morning persuaded me that the scrivener was the victim of innate and incurable disorder. I might give alms to his body; but his body did not pain him; it was his soul that suffered, and his soul I could not reach.

I did not accomplish the purpose of going to Trinity Church that morning. Somehow, the things I had seen disqualified me for the time from church-going. I walked homeward, thinking what I would do with Bartleby. Finally, I resolved upon this:—I would put certain calm questions to him the next morning, touching his history, &c., and if he declined to answer them

openly and unreservedly (and I supposed he would prefer not), then to give
him a twenty dollar bill over and above whatever I might owe him, and tell
him his services were no longer required; but that if in any other way I could
assist him, I would be happy to do so, especially if he desired to return to his
native place, wherever that might be, I would willingly help to defray the expenses. Moreover, if, after reaching home, he found himself at any time in
want of aid, a letter from him would be sure of a reply.

The next morning came.

"Bartleby," said I, gently calling to him behind his screen.

No reply.

"Bartleby," said I, in a still gentler tone, "come here; I am not going to ask
you to do anything you would prefer not to do—I simply wish to speak to
you."

Upon this he noiselessly slid into view.

"Will you tell me, Bartleby, where you were born?"

"I would prefer not to."

"Will you tell me *anything* about yourself?"

"I would prefer not to."

"But what reasonable objection can you have to speak to me? I feel
friendly towards you."

He did not look at me while I spoke, but kept his glance fixed upon my
bust of Cicero, which, as I then sat, was directly behind me, some six inches
above my head.

"What is your answer, Bartleby?" said I, after waiting a considerable time
for a reply, during which his countenance remained immovable, only there
was the faintest conceivable tremor of the white attenuated mouth.

"At present I prefer to give no answer," he said, and retired into his hermitage.

It was rather weak in me I confess, but his manner on this occasion net-
tled me. Not only did there seem to lurk in it a certain calm disdain, but his
perverseness seemed ungrateful, considering the undeniable good usage
and indulgence he had received from me.

Again I sat ruminating what I should do. Mortified as I was at his behav-
iour, and resolved as I had been to dismiss him when I entered my office,
nevertheless I strangely felt something superstitious knocking at my heart,
and forbidding me to carry out my purpose, and denouncing me for a villain
if I dared to breathe one bitter word against this forlornest of mankind. At
last, familiarly drawing my chair behind his screen, I sat down and said:
"Bartleby, never mind then about revealing your history; but let me entreat
you, as a friend, to comply as far as may be with the usages of this office. Say
now you will help to examine papers to-morrow or next day: in short, say
now that in a day or two you will begin to be a little reasonable:—say so,
Bartleby."

"At present I would prefer not to be a little reasonable," was his mildly cadaverous reply.

Just then the folding-doors opened, and Nippers approached. He seemed suffering from an unusually bad night's rest, induced by severer indigestion than common. He overheard those final words of Bartleby.

"*Prefer not,* eh?" gritted Nippers—"I'd *prefer* him, if I were you, sir," addressing me—"I'd *prefer* him; I'd give him preferences, the stubborn mule! What is it, sir, pray, that he *prefers* not to do now?"

Bartleby moved not a limb.

"Mr. Nippers," said I, "I'd prefer that you would withdraw for the present."

Somehow, of late I had got into the way of involuntarily using this word "prefer" upon all sorts of not exactly suitable occasions. And I trembled to think that my contact with the scrivener had already and seriously affected me in a mental way. And what further and deeper aberration might it not yet produce? This apprehension had not been without efficacy in determining me to summary means.

As Nippers, looking very sour and sulky, was departing, Turkey blandly and deferentially approached.

"With submission, sir," said he, "yesterday I was thinking about Bartleby here, and I think that if he would but prefer to take a quart of good ale every day, it would do much towards mending him, and enabling him to assist in examining his papers."

"So you have got the word, too," said I, slightly excited.

"With submission, what word, sir," asked Turkey, respectfully crowding himself into the contracted space behind the screen, and by so doing, making me jostle the scrivener. "What word, sir?"

"I would prefer to be left alone here," said Bartleby, as if offended at being mobbed in his privacy.

"*That's* the word, Turkey," said I—"*that's* it."

"Oh, *prefer?* oh, yes—queer word. I never used it myself. But, sir, as I was saying, if he would but prefer—"

"Turkey," interrupted I, "you will please withdraw."

"Oh certainly, sir, if you prefer that I should."

As he opened the folding-door to retire, Nippers at his desk caught a glimpse of me, and asked whether I would prefer to have a certain paper copied on blue paper or white. He did not in the least roguishly accent the word prefer. It was plain that it involuntarily rolled from his tongue. I thought to myself, surely I must get rid of a demented man, who already has in some degree turned the tongues, if not the heads, of myself and clerks. But I thought it prudent not to break the dismission at once.

The next day I noticed that Bartleby did nothing but stand at his window in his dead-wall revery. Upon asking him why he did not write, he said that he had decided upon doing no more writing.

"Why, how now? what next?" exclaimed I, "do no more writing?"

"No more."

"And what is the reason?"

"Do you not see the reason for yourself?" he indifferently replied.

I looked steadfastly at him, and perceived that his eyes looked dull and glazed. Instantly it occurred to me, that his unexampled diligence in copying by his dim window for the first few weeks of his stay with me might have temporarily impaired his vision.

I was touched. I said something in condolence with him. I hinted that, of course, he did wisely in abstaining from writing for a while, and urged him to embrace that opportunity of taking wholesome exercise in the open air. This, however, he did not do. A few days after this, my other clerks being absent, and being in a great hurry to despatch certain letters by the mail, I thought that, having nothing else earthly to do, Bartleby would surely be less inflexible than usual, and carry these letters to the Post Office. But he blankly declined. So, much to my inconvenience, I went myself.

Still added days went by. Whether Bartleby's eyes improved or not, I could not say. To all appearance, I thought they did. But when I asked him if they did, he vouchsafed no answer. At all events, he would do no copying. At last, in reply to my urgings, he informed me that he had permanently given up copying.

"What!" exclaimed I; "suppose your eyes should get entirely well—better than ever before—would you not copy then?"

"I have given up copying," he answered and slid aside.

He remained, as ever, a fixture in my chamber. Nay—if that were possible—he became still more of a fixture than before. What was to be done? He would do nothing in the office: why should he stay there? In plain fact, he had now become a millstone to me, not only useless as a necklace, but afflictive to bear. Yet I was sorry for him. I speak less than truth when I say that, on his own account, he occasioned me uneasiness. If he would but have named a single relative or friend, I would instantly have written, and urged their taking the poor fellow away to some convenient retreat. But he seemed alone, absolutely alone in the universe. A bit of wreckage in the mid-Atlantic. At length, necessities connected with my business tyrannized over all other considerations. Decently as I could, I told Bartleby that in six days' time he must unconditionally leave the office. I warned him to take measures, in the interval, for procuring some other abode. I offered to assist in him this endeavour, if he himself would but take the first step towards a removal. "And when you finally quit me, Bartleby," added I, "I shall see that you go away not entirely unprovided. Six days from this hour, remember."

At the expiration of that period, I peeped behind the screen, and lo! Bartleby was there.

I buttoned up my coat, balanced myself; advanced slowly towards him, touched his shoulder, and said, "The time has come; you must quit this place; I am sorry for you; here is money; but you must go."

"I would prefer not," he replied, with his back still towards me.

"You *must*."

He remained silent.

Now I had an unbounded confidence in this man's common honesty. He had frequently restored to me sixpences and shillings carelessly dropped upon the floor, for I am apt to be very reckless in such shirt-button affairs. The proceeding then which followed will not be deemed extraordinary.

"Bartleby," said I, "I owe you twelve dollars on account; here are thirty-two; the odd twenty are yours.—Will you take it?" and I handed the bills towards him.

But he made no motion.

"I will leave them here then," putting them under a weight on the table. Then taking my hat and cane and going to the door, I tranquilly turned and added—"After you have removed your things from these offices, Bartleby, you will of course lock the door—since every one is now gone for the day but you—and if you please, slip your key underneath the mat, so that I may have it in the morning. I shall not see you again; so goodbye to you. If hereafter in your new place of abode I can be of any service to you, do not fail to advise me by letter. Good-bye, Bartleby, and fare you well."

But he answered not a word; like the last column of some ruined temple, he remained standing mute and solitary in the middle of the otherwise deserted room.

As I walked home in a pensive mood, my vanity got the better of my pity. I could not but highly plume myself on my masterly management in getting rid of Bartleby. Masterly I call it, and such it must appear to any dispassionate thinker. The beauty of my procedure seemed to consist in its perfect quietness. There was no vulgar bullying, no bravado of any sort, no choleric hectoring, no striding to and fro across the apartment, jerking out vehement commands for Bartleby to bundle himself off with his beggarly traps. Nothing of the kind. Without loudly bidding Bartleby depart—as an inferior genius might have done—I *assumed* the ground that depart he must; and upon that assumption built all I had to say. The more I thought over my procedure, the more I was charmed with it. Nevertheless, next morning, upon awakening, I had my doubts,—I had somehow slept off the fumes of vanity. One of the coolest and wisest hours a man has, is just after he awakes in the morning. My procedure seemed as sagacious as ever,—but only in theory. How it would prove in practice—there was the rub. It was truly a beautiful thought to have assumed Bartleby's departure; but, after all, that assumption was simply my own, and none of Bartleby's. The great point was, not whether I had assumed that he would quit me, but whether he would prefer so to do. He was more a man of preferences than assumptions.

After breakfast, I walked down town, arguing the probabilities *pro* and *con.* One moment I thought it would prove a miserable failure, and Bartleby would be found all alive at my office as usual; the next moment it seemed certain that I should see his chair empty. And so I kept veering about. At the corner of Broadway and Canal Street, I saw quite an excited group of people standing in earnest conversation.

"I'll take odds he doesn't," said a voice as I passed.

"Doesn't go?—done!" said I, "put up your money."

I was instinctively putting my hand in my pocket to produce my own, when I remembered that this was an election day. The words I had overheard bore no reference to Bartleby, but to the success or non-success of some candidate for the mayoralty. In my intent frame of mind, I had, as it were, imagined that all Broadway shared in my excitement, and were debating the same question with me. I passed on, very thankful that the uproar of the street screened my momentary absent-mindedness.

As I had intended, I was earlier than usual at my office door. I stood listening for a moment. All was still. He must be gone. I tried the knob. The door was locked. Yes, my procedure had worked to a charm; he indeed must be vanished. Yet a certain melancholy mixed with this: I was almost sorry for my brilliant success. I was fumbling under the door mat for the key, which Bartleby was to have left there for me, when accidentally my knee knocked against a panel, producing a summoning sound, and in response a voice came to me from within—"Not yet; I am occupied."

It was Bartleby.

I was thunderstruck. For an instant I stood like the man who, pipe in mouth, was killed one cloudless afternoon long ago in Virginia, by summer lightning; at his own warm open window he was killed, and remained leaning out there upon the dreamy afternoon, till some one touched him, and he fell.

"Not gone!" I murmured at last. But again obeying that wondrous ascendency which the inscrutable scrivener had over me—and from which ascendency, for all my chafing, I could not completely escape—I slowly went down stairs and out into the street, and while walking round the block, considered what I should next do in this unheard-of perplexity. Turn the man out by an actual thrusting I could not; to drive him away by calling him hard names would not do; calling in the police was an unpleasant idea; and yet, permit him to enjoy his cadaverous triumph over me,—this too I could not think of. What was to be done? or, if nothing could be done, was there anything further that I could *assume* in the matter? Yes, as before I had prospectively assumed that Bartleby would depart, so now I might retrospectively assume that departed he was. In the legitimate carrying out of this assumption, I might enter my office in a great hurry, and pretending not to see Bartleby at all, walk straight against him as if he were air. Such a proceeding would in a singular degree have the appearance of a home-thrust. It was hardly possible that Bartleby could withstand such an application of the doctrine of assumptions. But, upon second thought, the success of the plan seemed rather dubious. I resolved to argue the matter over with him again.

"Bartleby," said I, entering the office, with a quietly severe expression, "I am seriously displeased. I am pained, Bartleby. I had thought better of you. I had imagined you of such a gentlemanly organization, that in any delicate dilemma a slight hint would suffice—in short, an assumption; but it appears

I am deceived. Why," I added, unaffectedly starting, "you have not even touched that money yet," pointing to it, just where I had left it the evening previous.

He answered nothing.

"Will you, or will you not, quit me?" I now demanded in a sudden passion, advancing close to him.

"I would prefer *not* to quit you," he replied, gently emphasizing the *not.*

"What earthly right have you to stay here? Do you pay any rent? Do you pay my taxes? Or is this property yours?"

He answered nothing.

"Are you ready to go on and write now? Are your eyes recovered? Could you copy a small paper for me this morning? or help examine a few lines? or step round to the Post Office? In a word, will you do any thing at all, to give a colouring to your refusal to depart the premises?"

He silently retired into his hermitage.

I was now in such a state of nervous resentment that I thought it but prudent to check myself, at present, from further demonstrations. Bartleby and I were alone. I remembered the tragedy of the unfortunate Adams and the still more unfortunate Colt in the solitary office of the latter; and how poor Colt, being dreadfully incensed at Adams, and imprudently permitting himself to get wildly excited, was at unawares hurried into his fatal act—an act which certainly no man could possibly deplore more than the actor himself. Often it had occurred to me in my ponderings upon the subject, that had that altercation taken place in the public street, or at a private residence, it would not have terminated as it did. It was the circumstance of being alone in a solitary office, upstairs, of a building entirely unhallowed by humanizing domestic associations—an uncarpeted office, doubtless, of a dusty, haggard sort of appearance;—this it must have been, which greatly helped to enhance the irritable desperation of the hapless Colt.

But when this old Adam of resentment rose in me and tempted me concerning Bartleby, I grappled him and threw him. How? Why, simply by recalling the divine injunction: "A new commandment give I unto you, that ye love one another." Yes, this it was that saved me. Aside from higher considerations, charity often operates as a vastly wise and prudent principle—a great safeguard to its possessor. Men have committed murder for jealousy's sake, and anger's sake, and hatred's sake, and selfishness' sake, and spiritual pride's sake; but no man that ever I heard of, ever committed a diabolical murder for sweet charity's sake. Mere self-interest, then, if no better motive can be enlisted, should, especially with high-tempered men, prompt all beings to charity and philanthropy. At any rate, upon the occasion in question, I strove to drown my exasperated feelings towards the scrivener by benevolently construing his conduct. Poor fellow, poor fellow! thought I, he doesn't mean any thing; and besides, he has seen hard times, and ought to be indulged.

I endeavoured also immediately to occupy myself, and at the same time to comfort my despondency. I tried to fancy that in the course of the morning, at such time as might prove agreeable to him, Bartleby, of his own free accord, would emerge from his hermitage, and take up some decided line of march in the direction of the door. But no. Half-past twelve o'clock came; Turkey began to glow in the face, overturn his inkstand, and become generally obstreperous; Nippers abated down into quietude and courtesy; Ginger Nut munched his noon apple; and Bartleby remained standing at his window in one of his profoundest dead-wall reveries. Will it be credited? Ought I to acknowledge it? That afternoon I left the office without saying one further word to him.

Some days now passed, during which at leisure intervals I looked a little into "Edwards on the Will," and "Priestley on Necessity." Under the circumstances, those books induced a salutary feeling. Gradually I slid into the persuasion that these troubles of mine, touching the scrivener, had been all predestinated from eternity, and Bartleby was billeted upon me for some mysterious purpose of an all-wise Providence, which it was not for a mere mortal like me to fathom. Yes, Bartleby, stay there behind your screen, thought I; I shall persecute you no more; you are harmless and noiseless as any of these old chairs; in short, I never feel so private as when I know you are here. At least I see it, I feel it; I penetrate to the predestinated purpose of my life. I am content. Others may have loftier parts to enact; but my mission in this world, Bartleby, is to furnish you with office room for such period as you may see fit to remain.

I believe that this wise and blessed frame of mind would have continued with me had it not been for the unsolicited and uncharitable remarks obtruded upon me by my professional friends who visited the rooms. But thus it often is, that the constant friction of illiberal minds wears out at last the best resolves of the more generous. Though to be sure, when I reflected upon it, it was not strange that people entering my office should be struck by the peculiar aspect of the unaccountable Bartleby, and so be tempted to throw out some sinister observations concerning him. Sometimes an attorney having business with me, and calling at my office, and finding no one but the scrivener there, would undertake to obtain some sort of precise information from him touching my whereabouts; but without heeding his idle talk, Bartleby would remain standing immovable in the middle of the room. So, after contemplating him in that position for a time, the attorney would depart, no wiser than he came.

Also, when a Reference was going on, and the room full of lawyers and witnesses and business was driving fast, some deeply occupied legal gentleman present, seeing Bartleby wholly unemployed, would request him to run round to his (the legal gentleman's) office and fetch some papers for him. Thereupon, Bartleby would tranquilly decline, and yet remain idle as before. Then the lawyer would give a great stare, and turn to me. And what could I say? At last I was made aware that all through the circle of my professional acquaintance, a whisper of wonder was running round, having reference to the strange creature I kept at my office. This worried me very much. And as the idea came upon me of his possibly turning out a long-lived man, and keep occupying my chambers, and denying my authority; and perplexing my visitors; and scandalizing my professional reputation; and casting a general gloom over the premises; keeping soul and body together to the last upon his savings (for doubtless he spent but half a dime a day), and in the end perhaps outlive me, and claim possession of my office by right of his perpetual occupancy: as all these dark anticipations crowded upon me more and more, and my friends continually intruded their relentless remarks upon the apparition in my room, a great change was wrought in me. I resolved to gather all my faculties together, and for ever rid me of this intolerable incubus.*

Ere resolving any complicated project, however, adapted to this end, I first simply suggested to Bartleby the propriety of his permanent departure. In a calm and serious tone, I commended the idea to his careful and mature consideration. But having taken three days to meditate upon it, he apprised me that his original determination remained the same; in short, that he still preferred to abide with me.

What shall I do? I now said to myself, buttoning up my coat to the last button. What shall I do? what ought I to do? what does conscience say I *should* do with this man, or rather ghost? Rid myself of him, I must; go, he shall. But how? You will not thrust him, the poor, pale, passive mortal,—you will not thrust such a helpless creature out of your door? you will not dishonour yourself by such cruelty? No, I will not, I cannot do that. Rather would I let him live and die here, and then mason up his remains in the wall. What then will you do? For all your coaxing, he will not budge. Bribes he leaves under your own paper-weight on your table; in short, it is quite plain that he prefers to cling to you.

Then something severe, something unusual must be done. What! surely you will not have him collared by a constable, and commit his innocent pallor to the common jail? And upon what ground could you procure such a thing to be done?—a vagrant, is he? What! he a vagrant, a wanderer, who refuses to budge? It is because he will *not* be a vagrant, then, that you seek to count him *as* a vagrant. That is too absurd. No visible means of support: there I have him. Wrong again: for indubitably he *does* support himself, and that is the only unanswerable proof that any man can show of his possessing the means so to do. No more then. Since he will not quit me, I must quit him. I will change my offices; I will move elsewhere; and give him fair notice, that if I find him on my new premises I will then proceed against him as a common trespasser.

Acting accordingly, next day I thus addressed him: "I find these chambers too far from the City Hall; the air is unwholesome. In a word, I propose

incubus: something that is nightmarishly oppressive; a nightmare.

to remove my offices next week, and shall no longer require your services. I tell you this now, in order that you may seek another place."

He made no reply, and nothing more was said.

On the appointed day I engaged carts and men, proceeded to my chambers, and having but little furniture, everything was removed in a few hours. Throughout all, the scrivener remained standing behind the screen, which I directed to be removed the last thing. It was withdrawn; and being folded up like a huge folio, left him the motionless occupant of a naked room. I stood in the entry watching him a moment, while something from within me upbraided me.

I re-entered, with my hand in my pocket—and—and my heart in my mouth.

"Good-bye, Bartleby; I am going—good-bye, and God some way bless you; and take that," slipping something in his hand. But it dropped upon the floor and then—strange to say—I tore myself from him whom I had so longed to be rid of.

Established in my new quarters, for a day or two I kept the door locked, and started at every footfall in the passages. When I returned to my rooms after any little absence, I would pause at the threshold for an instant, and attentively listen, ere applying my key. But these fears were needless. Bartleby never came nigh me.

I thought all was going well, when a perturbed looking stranger visited me, inquiring whether I was the person who had recently occupied rooms at No.____Wall street.

Full of forebodings, I replied that I was.

"Then sir," said the stranger, who proved a lawyer, "you are responsible for the man you left there. He refuses to do any copying, he refuses to do anything; and he says he prefers not to; and he refuses to quit the premises."

"I am very sorry, sir," said I, with assumed tranquillity, but an inward tremor, "but, really, the man you allude to is nothing to me—he is no relation or apprentice of mine, that you should hold me responsible for him."

"In mercy's name, who is he?"

"I certainly cannot inform you. I know nothing about him. Formerly I employed him as a copyist; but he has done nothing for me now for some time past."

"I shall settle him then,—good morning, sir."

Several days passed, and I heard nothing more; and though I often felt a charitable prompting to call at the place and see poor Bartleby, yet a certain squeamishness of I know not what withheld me.

All is over with him, by this time, thought I at last, when through another week no further intelligence reached me. But coming to my room the day after, I found several persons waiting at my door in a high state of nervous excitement.

"That's the man—here he comes," cried the foremost one, whom I recognized as the lawyer who had previously called upon me alone.

"You must take him away, sir, at once," cried a portly person among them, advancing upon me, and whom I knew to be the landlord of No.____Wall street. "These gentlemen, my tenants, cannot stand it any longer; Mr. B____," pointing to the lawyer, "has turned him out of his room, and he now persists in haunting the building generally, sitting upon the banisters of the stairs by day, and sleeping in the entry by night. Everybody here is concerned; clients are leaving the offices; some fears are entertained of a mob; something you must do, and that without delay."

Aghast at this torrent, I fell back before it, and would fain have locked myself in my new quarters. In vain I persisted that Bartleby was nothing to me—no more than to any one else there. In vain:—I was the last person known to have anything to do with him, and they held me to the terrible account. Fearful then of being exposed in the papers (as one person present obscurely threatened) I considered the matter, and at length said, that if the lawyer would give me a confidential interview with the scrivener, in his (the lawyer's) own room, I would that afternoon strive my best to rid them of the nuisance they complained of.

Going up stairs to my old haunt, there was Bartleby silently sitting upon the banister at the landing.

"What are you doing here, Bartleby?" said I.

"Sitting upon the banister," he mildly replied.

I motioned him into the lawyer's room, who then left us.

"Bartleby," said I, "are you aware that you are the cause of great tribulation to me, by persisting in occupying the entry after being dismissed from the office?"

No answer.

"Now one of two things must take place. Either you must do something, or something must be done to you. Now what sort of business would you like to engage in? Would you like to re-engage in copying for some one?"

"No; I would prefer not to make any change."

"Would you like a clerkship in a dry-goods store?"

"There is too much confinement about that. No, I would not like a clerkship; but I am not particular."

"Too much confinement," I cried, "why you keep yourself confined all the time!"

"I would prefer not to take a clerkship," he rejoined, as if to settle that little item at once.

"How would a bartender's business suit you? There is no trying of the eyesight in that."

"I would not like it at all; though, as I said before, I am not particular."

His unwonted wordiness inspirited me. I returned to the charge.

"Well then, would you like to travel through the country collecting bills for the merchants? That would improve your health."

"No, I would prefer to be doing something else."

"How then would going as a companion to Europe to entertain some young gentleman with your conversation,—how would that suit you?"

"Not at all. It does not strike me that there is anything definite about that. I like to be stationary. But I am not particular."

"Stationary you shall be then," I cried, now losing all patience, and for the first time in all my exasperating connection with him fairly flying into a passion. "If you do not go away from these premises before night, I shall feel bound—indeed I *am* bound—to—to—to quit the premises myself!" I rather absurdly concluded, knowing not with what possible threat to try to frighten his immobility into compliance. Despairing of all further efforts, I was precipitately leaving him, when a final thought occurred to me—one which had not been wholly unindulged before.

"Bartleby," said I, in the kindest tone I could assume under such exciting circumstances, "will you go home with me now—not to my office, but my dwelling—and remain there till we can conclude upon some convenient arrangement for you at our leisure? Come, let us start now, right away."

"No: at present I would prefer not to make any change at all."

I answered nothing; but effectually dodging every one by the suddenness and rapidity of my flight, rushed from the building, ran up Wall street toward Broadway, and then jumping into the first omnibus was soon removed from pursuit. As soon as tranquillity returned I distinctly perceived that I had now done all that I possibly could, both in respect to the demands of the landlord and his tenants, and with regard to my own desire and sense of duty, to benefit Bartleby, and shield him from rude persecution. I now strove to be entirely care-free and quiescent; and my conscience justified me in the attempt; though indeed it was not so successful as I could have wished. So fearful was I of being again hunted out by the incensed landlord and his exasperated tenants, that, surrendering my business to Nippers, for a few days I drove about the upper part of the town and through the suburbs, in my rockaway;* crossed over to Jersey City and Hoboken, and paid fugitive visits to Manhattanville and Astoria. In fact I almost lived in my rockaway for the time.

When again I entered my office, lo, a note from the landlord lay upon the desk. I opened it with trembling hands. It informed me that the writer had sent to the police, and had Bartleby removed to the Tombs as a vagrant. Moreover, since I knew more about him than any one else, he wished me to appear at that place, and make a suitable statement of the facts. These tidings had a conflicting effect upon me. At first I was indignant; but at last almost approved. The landlord's energetic, summary disposition had led him

---

rockaway: a four-wheeled carriage with two seats and a standing top.

to adopt a procedure which I do not think I would have decided upon my-self; and yet as a last resort, under such peculiar circumstances, it seemed the only plan.

As I afterwards learned, the poor scrivener, when told that he must be conducted to the Tombs, offered not the slightest obstacle, but in his own pale, unmoving way silently acquiesced.

Some of the compassionate and curious bystanders joined the party; and headed by one of the constables, arm-in-arm with Bartleby, the silent proces-sion filed its way through all the noise, and heat, and joy of the roaring thor-oughfares at noon.

The same day I received the note I went to the Tombs, or, to speak more properly, the Halls of Justice. Seeking the right officer, I stated the purpose of my call, and was informed that the individual I described was indeed within. I then assured the functionary that Bartleby was a perfectly honest man, and greatly to be a compassionated (however unaccountable) eccen-tric. I narrated all I knew, and closed by suggesting the idea of letting him re-main in as indulgent confinement as possible till something less harsh might be done—though indeed I hardly knew what. At all events if nothing else could be decided upon, the alms-house must receive him. I then begged to have an interview.

Being under no disgraceful charge, and quite serene and harmless in all his ways, they had permitted him freely to wander about the prison, and es-pecially in the inclosed grass-platted yards thereof. And so I found him there, standing all alone in the quietest of the yards, his face toward a high wall—while all around, from the narrow slits of the jail windows, I thought I saw peering out upon him the eyes of murderers and thieves.

"Bartleby!"

"I know you," he said, without looking around,—"and I want nothing to say to you."

"It was not I that brought you here, Bartleby," said I, keenly pained at his implied suspicion. "And to you, this should not be so vile a place. Nothing re-proachful attaches to you by being here. And see, it is not so sad a place as one might think. Look, there is the sky and here is the grass."

"I know where I am," he replied, but would say nothing more, and so I left him.

As I entered the corridor again a broad, meat-like man in an apron ac-costed me, and jerking his thumb over his shoulder said—"Is that your friend?"

"Yes."

"Does he want to starve? If he does, let him live on the prison fare, that's all."

"Who are you?" asked I, not knowing what to make of such an unofficially speaking person in such a place.

"I am the grub-man. Such gentlemen as have friends here, hire me to provide them with something good to eat."

"Is this so?" said I, turning to the turnkey.

He said it was.

"Well then," said I, slipping some silver into the grub-man's hands (for so they called him), "I want you to give particular attention to my friend there: let him have the best dinner you can get. And you must be as polite to him as possible."

"Introduce me, will you?" said the grub-man, looking at me with an expression which seemed to say he was all impatience for an opportunity to give a specimen of his breeding.

Thinking it would prove of benefit to the scrivener, I acquiesced; and asking the grub-man his name, went up with him to Bartleby.

"Bartleby, this is Mr. Cutlets; you will find him very useful to you."

"Your sarvant, sir, your sarvant," said the grub-man, making a low salutation behind his apron. "Hope you find it pleasant here, sir;—spacious grounds—apartments, sir—hope you'll stay with us some time—try to make it agreeable. May Mrs. Cutlets and I have the pleasure of your company to dinner, sir, in Mrs. Cutlets' private room?"

"I prefer not to dine to-day," said Bartleby, turning away. "It would disagree with me; I am unused to dinners." So saying, he slowly moved to the other side of the enclosure and took a position fronting the dead-wall.

"How's this?" said the grub-man, addressing me with a stare of astonishment. "He's odd, ain't he?"

"I think he is a little deranged," said I, sadly.

"Deranged? deranged is it? Well now, upon my word, I thought that friend of yourn was a gentleman forger; they are always pale and genteel-like, them forgers. I can't help pity 'em—can't help it, sir. Did you know Monroe Edwards?" he added touchingly, and paused. Then, laying his hand pityingly on my shoulder, sighed, "he died of the consumption at Sing-Sing.* So you weren't acquainted with Monroe?"

"No, I was never socially acquainted with any forgers. But I cannot stop longer. Look to my friend yonder. You will not lose by it. I will see you again."

Some few days after this, I again obtained admission to the Tombs, and went through the corridors in quest of Bartleby; but without finding him.

"I saw him coming from his cell not long ago," said a turnkey, "maybe he's gone to loiter in the yards."

So I went in that direction.

---

*Sing-Sing: founded in 1825, Sing-Sing is a state prison in Ossining, New York, for men that became infamous for its harsh measures during the late 1800s.

"Are you looking for the silent man?" said another turnkey passing me. "Yonder he lies—sleeping in the yard there. 'Tis not twenty minutes since I saw him lie down."

The yard was entirely quiet. It was not accessible to the common prisoners. The surrounding walls, of amazing thickness, kept off all sounds behind them. The Egyptian character of the masonry weighed upon me with its gloom. But a soft imprisoned turf grew under foot. The heart of the eternal pyramids, it seemed, wherein by some strange magic, through the clefts grass-seed, dropped by birds, had sprung.

Strangely huddled at the base of the wall—his knees drawn up, and lying on his side, his head touching the cold stones—I saw the wasted Bartleby. But nothing stirred. I paused; then went close up to him; stooped over, and saw that his dim eyes were open; otherwise he seemed profoundly sleeping. Something prompted me to touch him. I felt his hand, when a tingling shiver ran up my arm and down my spine to my feet.

The round face of the grub-man peered upon me now. "His dinner is ready. Won't he dine to-day, either? Or does he live without dining?"

"Lives without dining," said I, and closed the eyes.

"Eh!—He's asleep, ain't he?"

"With kings and counsellors," murmured I.

There would seem little need for proceeding further in this history. Imagination will readily supply the meagre recital of poor Bartleby's interment. But ere parting with the reader, let me say, that if this little narrative has sufficiently interested him, to awaken curiosity as to who Bartleby was, and what manner of life he led prior to the present narrator's making his acquaintance, I can only reply, that in such curiosity I fully share—but am wholly unable to gratify it. Yet here I hardly know whether I should divulge one little item of rumour, which came to my ear a few months after the scrivener's decease. Upon what basis it rested, I could never ascertain; and hence, how true it is I cannot now tell. But inasmuch as this vague report has not been without a certain strange suggestive interest to me, however sad, it may prove the same with some others; and so I will briefly mention it. The report was this: that Bartleby had been a subordinate clerk in the Dead Letter Office at Washington, from which he had been suddenly removed by a change in the administration. When I think over this rumour I cannot adequately express the emotions which seize me. Dead letters! Does it not sound like dead men? Conceive a man by nature and misfortune prone to a pallid hopelessness: can any business seem more fitted to heighten it than that of continually handling these dead letters, and assorting them for the flames? For by the cartload they are annually burned. Sometimes from out the folded paper the pale clerk takes a ring:—the finger it was meant for, perhaps, moulders in the grave; a bank-note sent in swiftest charity:—he whom it would relieve, nor eats nor hungers any more; pardon for those who died despairing; hope for those who died unhoping; good tidings for those who died stifled by unrelieved calamities. On errands of life, these letters speed to death.

Ah Bartleby! Ah humanity!

Lewis Mumford Provides an Early Biographical Approach

The first biography of Herman Melville did not appear until 1921. Following Raymond Weaver's Herman Melville: Mariner and Mystic, *Lewis Mumford's biography, published in 1929, contributed to the rediscovery and reevaluation of Melville's fiction during that decade.*

"Bartleby the Scrivener" is one of Melville's longer stories; and it gains much by its juxtaposition of incongruous personalities. The story is told by a comfortable, pursy old lawyer, with an office in Wall Street; the lawyer and his copyists are hit off with a warm sense of caricature. Into this office comes a pale, bleak creature, Bartleby, to serve as a scrivener. He is quiet and industrious; but he refuses to comply with the routine of the office: he will not compare copy, even for the lawyer himself; and yet there is something in this passive self-assertion and this methodical self-obliteration which makes the lawyer humour Bartleby. With these qualities goes a mystery; and by accident, on a Sunday at church-time, the lawyer discovers, on attempting to enter his office, that Bartleby not only works for him but has quietly occupied his business premises, to eat and sleep there. In spite of this gross irregularity, the lawyer keeps Bartleby, only to have the little man quit work entirely. When the lawyer demands a reason, he answers: I would prefer not to. When the lawyer asks him to move out, he answers: I would prefer not to. There is no getting behind his silence, his dead-wall reveries, his blank self-possession.

The effect of this passive resistance upon the lawyer is upsetting. "My first emotions had been those of pure melancholy and sincerest pity; but just in proportion as the forlornness of Bartleby grew and grew to my imagination, did that same melancholy verge into fear, that pity into repulsion. So true it is, and so terrible, too, that up to a certain point the thought or sight of misery enlists our best affections; but, in certain special cases, beyond that point it does not. They err who would assert that invariably this is due to the inherent selfishness of the human heart: it rather proceeds from a certain hopelessness of remedying excessive and organic ill. To a sensitive being, pity is not seldom pain. And when at last it is perceived that such pity cannot lead to effectual succour, common sense bids the soul be rid of it. What I saw that morning convinced me that the scrivener was the victim of innate and incurable disorder. I might give alms to the body; but his body did not pain him; it was his soul that suffered, and his soul I could not reach."

The lawyer moves and Bartleby remains on the original premises; but the new tenant is not so patient and he has Bartleby arrested. When Bartleby finds himself in prison, he prefers not to eat. A kind fellow, the lawyer visits him, seeking to restore his confidence and reawaken his manhood. "Nothing reproachful attaches to you being here," he assures Bartleby. "And see, it is not so sad a place as one might think. Look, there is the sky, and here is the grass." "I know where I am," he replied.

"Bartleby" is a good story in itself: it also affords us a glimpse of Melville's own drift of mind in this miserable year: the point of the story plainly indicates Melville's present dilemma. People would admit him to their circle and give him bread and employment only if he would abandon his inner purpose: to this his answer was—I would prefer not to. By his persistence in minding his own spiritual affairs, those who might have helped him on their own terms, like Allan or his father-in-law or his Uncle Peter, inevitably became a little impatient; for in the end, they foresaw they would be obliged to throw him off, and he would find himself in prison, not in the visible prison for restraining criminals, but in the pervasive prison of dull routine and meaningless activity. When that happened there would be no use assuring him that he lived in a kindly world of blue sky and green grass. "I know where I am!" Whether or not Melville consciously projected his own intuition of his fate, there is no doubt in my mind that, as early as 1853, he was already formulating his answer. To those kind, pragmatic friends and relatives who suggested that he go into business and make a good living, or at least write the sort of books that the public would read—it amounts to pretty much the same thing—he kept on giving one stereotyped and monotonous answer: I would prefer not to. The dead-wall reverie would end in a resolution as blank and forbidding as the wall that faced him: a bleak face, a tight wounded mouth, the little blue eyes more dim, remote, and obstinate than ever: I would prefer not to!

Gabriel García Márquez, 1928–

The Handsomest Drowned Man in the World: A Tale for Children

Translated by Gregory Rabassa

This story first appeared in PLAYBOY, *1955.*

THE FIRST CHILDREN WHO SAW THE DARK AND SLINKY BULGE approaching through the sea let themselves think it was an empty ship. Then they saw it had no flags or masts and they thought it was a whale. But when it washed up on the beach, they removed the clumps of seaweed, the jellyfish tentacles, and the remains of fish and flotsam, and only then did they see that it was a drowned man.

They had been playing with him all afternoon, burying him in the sand and digging him up again, when someone chanced to see them and spread the alarm in the village. The men who carried him to the nearest house noticed that he weighed more than any dead man they had ever known, almost as much as a horse, and they said to each other that maybe he'd been floating too long and the water had got into his bones. When they laid him on the floor they said he'd been taller than all other men because there was barely enough room for him in the house, but they thought that maybe the ability to keep on growing after death was part of the nature of certain drowned men. He had the smell of the sea about him and only his shape gave one to suppose that it was the corpse of a human being, because the skin was covered with a crust of mud and scales.

They did not even have to clean off his face to know that the dead man was a stranger. The village was made up of only twenty-odd wooden houses that had stone courtyards with no flowers and which were spread about on the end of a desertlike cape. There was so little land that mothers always went about with the fear that the wind would carry off their children and the few dead that the years had caused among them had to be thrown off the cliffs. But the sea was calm and bountiful and all the men fit into seven boats. So when they found the drowned man they simply had to look at one another to see that they were all there.

That night they did not go out to work at sea. While the men went to find out if anyone was missing in neighboring villages, the women stayed behind to care for the drowned man. They took the mud off with grass swabs, they removed the underwater stones entangled in his hair, and they scraped the crust off with tools used for scaling fish. As they were doing that they noticed that the vegetation on him came from faraway oceans and deep water and that his clothes were in tatters, as if he had sailed through labyrinths of coral. They noticed too that he bore his death with pride, for he did not have the lonely look of other drowned men who came out of the sea or that haggard, needy look of men who drowned in rivers. But only when they finished cleaning him off did they become aware of the kind of man he was and it left them breathless. Not only was he the tallest strongest, most virile, and best built man they had ever seen, but even though they were looking at him there was no room for him in their imagination.

They could not find a bed in the village large enough to lay him on nor was there a table solid enough to use for his wake. The tallest men's holiday pants would not fit him, nor the fattest ones' Sunday shirts, nor the shoes of the one with the biggest feet. Fascinated by his huge size and his beauty, the women then decided to make him some pants from a large piece of sail and a shirt from some bridal Brabant linen so that he could continue through his death with dignity. As they sewed, sitting in a circle and gazing at the corpse between stitches, it seemed to them that the wind had never been so steady nor the sea so restless as on that night and they supposed that the change had something to do with the dead man. They thought that if that magnificent man had lived in the village, his house would have had the widest doors, and highest ceiling, and the strongest floor; his bedstead would have been made from a midship frame held together by iron bolts, and his wife should have been the happiest woman. They thought that he would have had so much authority that he could have drawn fish out of the sea simply by calling their names and that he would have put so much work into his land that springs would have burst forth from among the rocks so that he would have been able to plant flowers on the cliffs. They secretly compared him to their own men, thinking that for all their lives theirs were incapable of doing what he could do in one night, and they ended up dismissing them deep in their hearts as the weakest, meanest, and most useless creatures on earth. They were wandering through that maze of fantasy when the oldest women, who as the oldest had looked upon the drowned man with more compassion than passion, sighed:

"He has the face of someone called Esteban."

It was true. Most of them had only to take another look at him to see that he could not have any other name. The more stubborn among them, who were the youngest, still lived for a few hours with the illusion that when they put his clothes on and he lay among the flowers in patent leather shoes his name might be Lautaro. But it was a vain illusion. There had not been enough canvas, the poorly cut and worse sewn pants were too tight, and the hidden strength of his heart popped the buttons on his shirt. After midnight the whistling of the wind died down and the sea fell into its Wednesday drowsiness. The silence put an end to any last doubts: he was Esteban. The women who had dressed him, who had combed his hair, had cut his nails and shaved him were unable to hold back a shudder of pity when they had to resign themselves to his being dragged along the ground. It was then that they understood how unhappy he must have been with that huge body since it bothered him even after death. They could see him in life, condemned to going through doors sideways cracking his head on crossbeams, remaining on his feet during visits, not knowing what to do with his soft pink, sealion hands while the lady of the house looked for her most resistant chair and begged him, frightened to death, sit here, Esteban, please, and he, leaning against the wall, smiling, don't bother, ma'am, I'm fine where I am, his heels raw and his back toasted from having done the same thing so many times whenever he paid a visit, don't bother, ma'am, I'm fine where I am to avoid the embarrassment of breaking up the chair, and never knowing perhaps that the one who said don't go, Esteban, at least wait till the coffee's ready, were the ones who later on would whisper the big boob finally left, how nice, the handsome fool has gone. That was what the women were thinking beside the body a little before dawn. Later, when they covered his face with a handkerchief so that the light would not bother him, he looked so forever dead, so defenseless, so much like their men that the first furrows of tears opened in their hearts. It was one of the younger ones who began the weeping. The others, coming to, went from sighs to wails, and the more they sobbed the more they felt like weeping, because the drowned man was becoming all the more Esteban for them, and so they wept so much, for he was the most destitute, most peaceful, and most obliging man on earth, poor Esteban. So when the men returned with the news that the drowned man was not from the neighboring villages either, the women felt an opening of jubilation in the midst of their tears.

"Praise the Lord," they sighed, "he's ours!"

The men thought the fuss was only womanish frivolity. Fatigued because of the difficult nighttime inquiries, all they wanted was to get rid of the bother of the newcomer once and for all before the sun grew strong on that arid, windless day. They improvised a litter with the remains of foremasts and gaffs, tying it together with rigging so that it would bear the weight of the body until they reached the cliffs. They wanted to tie the anchor from a cargo ship to him so that he would sink easily into the deepest waves, where the fish are blind and divers die of nostalgia, and bad currents would not bring him back to shore, as had happened with other bodies. But the more they hurried, the more the women thought of ways to waste time. They walked about like startled hens, pecking with the sea charms on their breasts, some interfering on one side to put a scapular of the good wind on the drowned man, some on the other side to put a wrist compass on him, and after a great deal of *get away from there, woman, stay out of the way, look, you almost made me fall on top of the dead man,* the men began to feel mistrust in their livers and started grumbling about why so many main-altar decorations for a stranger, because no matter how many nails and holy-water jars he had on him, the sharks would chew him all the same, but the women kept on piling on their junk relics, running back and forth, stumbling, while they released in sighs what they did not in tears, so that the men finally exploded with *since when has there ever been such a fuss over a drifting corpse, a drowned nobody, a piece of cold Wednesday meat.* One of the women, mortified by so much lack of care, then removed the handkerchief from the dead man's face and the men were left breathless too.

He was Esteban. It was not necessary to repeat it for them to recognize him. If they had been told Sir Walter Raleigh, even they might have been impressed with his gringo accent, the macaw on his shoulder, his cannibal-killing blunderbuss, but there could be only one Esteban in the world and there he was, stretched out like a sperm whale, shoeless, wearing the pants of an undersized child, and with those stony nails that had to be cut with a knife. They had only to take the handkerchief off his face to see that he was ashamed, that it was not his fault that he was so big or so heavy or so handsome, and if he had known that this was going to happen, he would have looked for a more discreet place to drown in; seriously, I even would have tied the anchor off a galleon around my neck and staggered off a cliff like someone who doesn't like things in order not to be upsetting people now with this Wednesday dead body, as you people say, in order not to be bothering anyone with this filthy piece of cold meat that doesn't have anything to do with me. There was so much truth in his manner that even the most mistrustful men, the ones who felt the bitterness of endless nights at sea fearing that their women would tire of dreaming about them and begin to dream of drowned men, even they and others who were harder still shuddered in the marrow of their bones at Esteban's sincerity.

That was how they came to hold the most splendid funeral they could conceive of for an abandoned drowned man. Some women who had gone to get flowers in the neighboring villages returned with other women who could not believe what they had been told, and those women went back for more flowers when they saw the dead man, and they brought more and more until there were so many flowers and so many people that it was hard to walk about. At the final moment it pained them to return him to the waters as an orphan and they chose a father and mother from among the best people, and aunts and uncles and cousins, so that through him all the inhabitants of the village became kinsmen. Some sailors who heard the weeping from a distance went off course, and people heard of one who had himself tied to the mainmast, remembering ancient fables about sirens. While they fought for the privilege of carrying him on their shoulders along the steep escarpment by the cliffs, men and women became aware for the first time of the desolation of their streets, the dryness of their courtyards, the narrowness of their dreams as they faced the splendor and beauty of their drowned man. They let him go without an anchor so that he could come back if he wished and whenever he wished, and they all held their breath for the fraction of centuries the body took to fall into the abyss. They did not need to look to one another to realize that they were no longer all present, that they would never be. But they also knew that everything would be different from then on, that their houses would have wider doors, higher ceilings, and stronger floors so that Esteban's memory could go everywhere without bumping into beams and so that no one in the future would dare whisper the big boob finally died, too bad, the handsome fool has finally died, because they were going to paint their house fronts gay colors to make Esteban's memory eternal and they were going to break their backs digging for springs among the stones and planting flowers on the cliffs so that in future years at dawn the passengers on great liners would awaken, suffocated by the smell of gardens on the high seas, and the captain would have to come down from the bridge in his dress uniform, with his astrolabe, his pole star, and his row of war medals and, pointing to the promontory of roses on the horizon, he would say in fourteen languages, look there, where the wind is so peaceful now that it's gone to sleep beneath the beds, over there, where the sun's so bright that the sunflowers don't know which way to turn, yes, over there, that's Esteban's village.

Franz Kafka, 1883–1924

A Hunger Artist

Translated from the Russian by Willa and Edwin Muir

This story first appeared in A HUNGER ARTIST, *1924.*

DURING THESE LAST DECADES the interest in professional fasting has markedly diminished. It used to pay very well to stage such great performances under one's own management, but today that is quite impossible. We live in a different world now. At one time the whole town took a lively interest in the hunger artist; from day to day of his fast the excitement mounted; everybody wanted to see him at least once a day; there were people who bought season tickets for the last few days and sat from morning till night in front of his small barred cage; even in the nighttime there were visiting hours, when the whole effect was heightened by torch flares; on fine days the cage was set out in the open air, and then it was the children's special treat to see the hunger artist; for their elders he was often just a joke that happened to be in fashion, but the children stood open-mouthed, holding each other's hands for greater security, marveling at him as he sat there pallid in black tights, with his ribs sticking out so prominently, not even on a seat but down among straw on the ground, sometimes giving a courteous nod, answering questions with a constrained smile, or perhaps stretching an arm through the bars so that one might feel how thin it was, and then again withdrawing deep into himself, paying no attention to anyone or anything, not even to the all-important striking of the clock that was the only piece of furniture in his cage, but merely staring into vacancy with half-shut eyes, now and then taking a sip from a tiny glass of water to moisten his lips.

Besides casual onlookers there were also relays of permanent watchers selected by the public, usually butchers, strangely enough, and it was their task to watch the hunger artist day and night, three of them at a time, in case he should have some secret recourse to nourishment. This was nothing but a formality, instituted to reassure the masses, for the initiates knew well enough that during his fast the artist would never in any circumstances, not even under forcible compulsion, swallow the smallest morsel of food: the honor of his profession forbade it. Not every watcher, of course, was capable of understanding this, there were often groups of night watchers who were very lax in carrying out their duties and deliberately huddled together in a retired corner to play cards with great absorption, obviously intending to give the hunger artist the chance of a little

125

refreshment, which they supposed he could draw from some private hoard. Nothing annoyed the artist more than such watchers; they made him miserable; they made his fast seem unendurable; sometimes he mastered his feebleness sufficiently to sing during their watch for as long as he could keep going, to show them how unjust their suspicions were. But that was of little use; they only wondered at his cleverness in being able to fill his mouth even while singing. Much more to his taste were the watchers who sat close up to the bars, who were not content with the dim night lighting of the hall but focused him in the full glare of the electric pocket torch given them by the impresario. The harsh light did not trouble him at all, in any case he could never sleep properly, and the could always drowse a little, whatever the light, at any hour, even when the hall was thronged with noisy onlookers. He was quite happy at the prospect of spending a sleepless night with such watchers; he was ready to exchange jokes with them, to tell them stories out of his nomadic life, anything at all to keep them awake and demonstrate to them again that he had no eatables in his cage and that he was fasting as not one of them could fast. But his happiest moment was when the morning came and an enormous breakfast was brought them, at his expense, on which they flung themselves with the keen appetite of healthy men after a weary night of wakefulness. Of course there were people who argued that this breakfast was an unfair attempt to bribe the watchers, but that was going rather too far, and when they were invited to take on a night's vigil without a breakfast, merely for the sake of the cause, they made themselves scarce, although they stuck stubbornly to their suspicions.

Such suspicions, anyhow, were a necessary accompaniment to the profession of fasting. No one could possibly watch the hunger artist continuously, day and night, and so no one could produce first-hand evidence that the fast had really been rigorous and continuous; only the artist himself could know that, he was therefore bound to be the sole completely satisfied spectator of his own fast. Yet for other reasons he was never satisfied; it was not perhaps mere fasting that had brought him to such skeleton thinness that many people had regretfully to keep away from his exhibitions, because the sight of him was too much for them, perhaps it was dissatisfaction with himself that had worn him down. For he alone knew, what no other initiate knew, how easy it was to fast. It was the easiest thing in the world. He made no secret of this, yet people did not believe him, at the best they set him down as modest, most of them, however, thought he was out for publicity or else was some kind of cheat who found it easy to fast because he had discovered a way of making it easy, and then had the impudence to admit the fact, more or less. He had to put up with all that, and in the course of time had got used to it, but his inner dissatisfaction always rankled, and never yet, after any term of fasting—this must be granted to his credit—had he left the cage of his own free will. The longest period of fasting was fixed by his impresario at forty days, beyond that term he was not allowed to go, not even in great cities, and there was good reason for it, too. Experience had proved that for about forty days the interest of the public could be stimulated by a steadily increasing pressure of advertisement, but after that the town began to lose interest, sympathetic support began notably to fall off; there were of course local variations as between one town and another or one country and another, but as a general rule forty days marked the limit. So on the fortieth day the flower-bedecked cage was opened, enthusiastic spectators filled the hall, a military band played, two doctors entered the cage to measure the results of the fast, which were announced through a megaphone, and finally two young ladies appeared, blissful at having been selected for the honor, to help the hunger artist down the few steps leading to a small table on which was spread a carefully chosen invalid repast. And at this very moment the artist always turned stubborn. True, he would entrust his bony arms to the outstretched helping hands of the ladies bending over him, but stand up he would not. Why stop fasting at this particular moment, after forty days of it? He had held out for a long time, an illimitably long time; why stop now, when he was in his best fasting form, or rather, not yet quite in his best fasting form? Why should he be cheated of the fame he would get for fasting longer, for being not only the record hunger artist of all time, which presumably he was already, but for beating his own record by a performance beyond human imagination, since he felt that there were no limits to his capacity for fasting? His public pretended to admire him so much, why should it have so little patience with him; if he could endure fasting longer, why shouldn't the public endure it? Besides, he was tired, he was comfortable sitting in the straw, and now he was supposed to lift himself to his full height and go down to a meal the very thought of which gave him a nausea that only the presence of the ladies kept him from betraying, and even that with an effort. And he looked up into the eyes of the ladies who were apparently so friendly and in reality so cruel, and shook his head, which felt too heavy on its strengthless neck. But then there happened yet again what always happened. The impresario came forward, without a word—for the band made speech impossible—lifted his arms in the air above the artist, as if inviting Heaven to look down upon its creature here in the straw, this suffering martyr, which indeed he was, although in quite another sense; grasped him round the emaciated waist, with exaggerated caution, so that the frail condition he was in might be appreciated; and committed him to the care of the blenching ladies, not without secretly giving him a shaking so that his legs and body tottered and swayed. The artist now submitted completely; his head lolled on his breast as if it had landed there by chance; his body was hollowed out; his legs in a spasm of self-preservation clung close to each other at the knees, yet scraped on the ground as if it were not really solid ground, as if they were only trying to find solid ground; and the whole weight of his body, a feather-weight after all, relapsed onto one of the ladies, who, looking round for help and panting a little—this post of honor was not at all what she had expected it to be—first stretched her neck as far as she could to keep her face at least free from contact with the artist, when finding this impossible, and her more fortunate companion not coming to her aid but merely holding extended on her own trembling hand the little bunch of knucklebones that was the artist's, to the great delight of the spectators burst into tears and had to be replaced by an attendant who had long been stationed in readiness. Then came the food, a little of which the impresario managed to get between the artist's lips, while he sat in a kind of half-fainting trance, to the accompaniment of cheerful patter designed to distract the public's attention from the artist's condition; after that, a toast was drunk to the public, supposedly prompted by a whisper from the artist in the impresario's ear; the band confirmed it with a mighty flourish, the spectators melted away, and no one had any cause to be dissatisfied with the proceedings, no one except the hunger artist himself, he only, as always.

So he lived for many years, with small regular intervals of recuperation, in visible glory, honored by the world, yet in spite of that troubled in spirit, and all the more troubled because no one would take his trouble seriously. What comfort could he possibly need? What more could he possibly wish for? And if some good-natured person, feeling sorry for him, tried to console him by pointing out that his melancholy was probably caused by fasting, it could happen, especially when he had been fasting for some time, that he reacted with an outburst of fury and to the general alarm began to shake the bars of his cage like a wild animal. Yet the impresario had a way of punishing these outbreaks which he rather enjoyed putting into operation. He would apologize publicly for the artist's behavior, which was only to be excused, he admitted, because of the irritability caused by fasting; a condition hardly to be understood by well-fed people; then by natural transition he went on to mention the artist's equally incomprehensible boast that he could fast for much longer than he was doing; he praised the high ambition, the good will, the great self-denial undoubtedly implicit in such a statement; and then quite simply countered it by bringing out photographs, which were also on sale to the public, showing the artist on the fortieth day of a fast lying in bed almost dead from exhaustion. This perversion of the truth, familiar to the artist though it was, always unnerved him afresh and proved too much for him. What was a consequence of the premature ending of his fast was here presented as the cause of it! To fight against this lack of understanding, against a whole world of nonunderstanding, was impossible. Time and again in good faith he stood by the bars listening to the impresario, but as soon as the photographs appeared he always let go and sank with a groan back on to his straw, and the reassured public could once more come close and gaze at him.

A few years later when the witnesses of such scenes called them to mind, they often failed to understand themselves at all. For meanwhile the aforementioned change in public interest had set in; it seemed to happen al-most overnight; there may have been profound causes for it, but who was going to bother about that; at any rate the pampered hunger artist suddenly found himself deserted one fine day by the amusement seekers, who went streaming past him to other more favored attractions. For the last time the impresario hurried him over half of Europe to discover whether the old in-terest might still survive here and there; all in vain; everywhere, as if by se-cret agreement, a positive revulsion from professional fasting was in evidence. Of course it could not really have sprung up so suddenly as all that, and many premonitory symptoms which had not been sufficiently re-marked or suppressed during the rush and glitter of success now came ret-rospectively to mind, but it was now too late to take any countermeasures. Fasting would surely come into fashion again at some future date, yet that was no comfort for those living in the present. What, then, was the hunger artist to do? He had been applauded by thousands in his time and could hardly come down to showing himself in a street booth at village fairs, and as for adopting another profession, he was not only too old for that but too fanatically devoted to fasting. So he took leave of the impresario, his partner in an unparalleled career, and hired himself to a large circus; in order to spare his own feelings he avoided reading the conditions of his contract.

A large circus with its enormous traffic in replacing and recruiting men, animals and apparatus can always find a use for people at any time, even for a hunger artist, provided of course that he does not ask too much, and in this particular case anyhow it was not only the artist who was taken on but his famous and long-known name as well, indeed considering the peculiar na-ture of his performance, which was not impaired by advancing age, it could not be objected that here was an artist past his prime, no longer at the height of his professional skill, seeking a refuge in some quiet corner of a cir-cus; on the contrary, the hunger artist averred that he could fast as well as ever, which was entirely credible, he even alleged that if he were allowed to fast as he liked, and this was at once promised him without more ado, he could astound the world by establishing a record never yet achieved, a state-ment which certainly provoked a smile among the other professionals, since it left out of account the change in public opinion, which the hunger artist in his zeal conveniently forgot.

He had not, however, actually lost his sense of the real situation and took it as a matter of course that he and his cage should be stationed, not in the middle of the ring as a main attraction, but outside, near the animal cages, on a site that was after all easily accessible. Large and gaily painted placards made a frame for the cage and announced what was to be seen inside it. When the public came thronging out in the intervals to see the animals, they could hardly avoid passing the hunger artist's cage and stopping there for a moment, perhaps they might even have stayed longer had not those pressing behind them in the narrow gangway, who did not understand why they should be held up on their way toward the excitements of the menagerie, made it impossible for anyone to stand gazing quietly for any length of time. And that was the reason why the hunger artist, who had of course been looking forward to these visiting hours as the main achievement of his life, began instead to shrink from them. At first he could hardly wait for the intervals; it was exhilarating to watch the crowds come streaming his way, until only too soon—not even the most obstinate self-deception, clung to almost consciously, could hold out against the fact—the conviction was borne in upon him that these people, most of them, to judge from their actions, again and again, without exception, were all on their way to the menagerie. And the first sight of them from the distance remained the best. For when they reached his cage he was at once deafened by the storm of shouting and abuse that arose from the two contending factions, which renewed themselves continuously, of those who wanted to stop and stare at him—he soon began to dislike them more than the others—not out of real interest but only out of obstinate self-assertiveness, and those who wanted to go straight on to the animals. Then the first great rush was past, the stragglers came along, and these, whom nothing could have prevented from stopping to look at him as long as they had breath, raced past with long strides, hardly even glancing at him, in their haste to get to the menagerie in time. And all too rarely did it happen that he had a stroke of luck, when some father of a family fetched up before him with his children, pointed a finger at the hunger artist and explained at length what the phenomenon meant, telling stories of earlier years when he himself had watched similar but much more thrilling performances, and the children, still rather uncomprehending, since neither inside nor outside school had they been sufficiently prepared for this lesson—what did they care about fasting?—yet showed by the brightness of their intent eyes that new and better times might be coming. Perhaps, said the hunger artist to himself many a time, things would be a little better if his cage were set not quite so near the menagerie. That made it too easy for people to make their choice, to say nothing of what he suffered from the stench of the menagerie, the animals' restlessness by night, the carrying past of raw lumps of flesh for the beasts of prey, the roaring at feeding times, which depressed him continually. But he did not dare to lodge a complaint with the management; after all, he had the animals to thank for the troops of people who passed his cage, among whom there might always be one here and there to take an interest in him, and who could tell where they might seclude him if he called attention to his existence and thereby to the fact that, strictly speaking, he was only an impediment on the way to the menagerie.

A small impediment, to be sure, one that grew steadily less. People grew familiar with the strange idea that they could be expected, in times like these, to take an interest in a hunger artist, and with this familiarity the verdict went out against him. He might fast as much as he could, and he did so; but nothing could save him now, people passed him by. Just try to explain to anyone the art of fasting! Anyone who has no feeling for it cannot be made to understand it. The fine placards grew dirty and illegible, they were torn down; the little notice board telling the number of fast days achieved, which at first was changed carefully every day, had long stayed at the same figure, for after the first few weeks even this small task seemed pointless to the staff; and so the artist simply fasted on and on, as he had once dreamed of doing, and it was no trouble to him, just as he had always foretold, but no one counted the days, no one, not even the artist himself, knew what records he was already breaking, and his heart grew heavy. And when once in a time some leisurely passer-by stopped, made merry over the old figure on the board and spoke of swindling, that was in its way the stupidest lie ever invented by indifference and inborn malice, since it was not the hunger artist who was cheating; he was working honestly, but the world was cheating him of his reward.

————————

MANY MORE DAYS WENT BY, however, and that too came to an end. An overseer's eye fell on the cage one day and he asked the attendants why this perfectly good cage should be left standing there unused with dirty straw inside it; nobody knew, until one man, helped out by the notice board, remembered about the hunger artist. They poked into the straw with sticks and found him in it. "Are you still fasting?" asked the overseer. "When on earth do you mean to stop?" "Forgive me, everybody," whispered the hunger artist; only the overseer, who had his ear to the bars, understood him. "Of course," said the overseer, and tapped his forehead with a finger to let the attendants know what state the man was in, "we forgive you." "I always wanted you to admire my fasting," said the hunger artist. "We do admire it," said the overseer, affably . "But you shouldn't admire it," said the hunger artist. "Well, then we don't admire it," said the overseer, "but why shouldn't we admire it?" "Because I have to fast, I can't help it," said the hunger artist. "What a fellow you are," said the overseer, "and why can't you help it?" "Because," said the hunger artist, lifting his head a little and speaking, with his lips pursed, as if for a kiss, right into the overseer's ear, so that no syllable might be lost, "because I couldn't find the food I liked. If I had found it, believe me, I should have made no fuss and stuffed myself like you or anyone else." These were his last words, but in his dimming eyes remained the firm though no longer proud persuasion that he was still continuing to fast.

"Well, clear this out now!" said the overseer, and they buried the hunger artist, straw and all. Into the cage they put a young panther. Even the most insensitive felt it refreshing to see this wild creature leaping around the cage that had so long been dreary. The panther was all right. The food he liked was brought him without hesitation by the attendants; he seemed not even to miss his freedom; his noble body, furnished almost to the bursting point with all that it needed, seemed to carry freedom around with it too; some-where in his jaws it seemed to lurk; and the joy of life streamed with such ardent passion from his throat that for the onlookers it was not easy to stand the shock of it. But they braced themselves, crowded round the cage, and did not want ever to move away.

Stephen Crane, 1871–1900

The Bride Comes to Yellow Sky

This story first appeared in McCLURE'S MAGAZINE, *1898.*

1

THE GREAT PULLMAN WAS WHIRLING ONWARD with such dignity of motion that a glance from the window seemed simply to prove that the plains of Texas were pouring eastward. Vast flats of green grass, dull-hued spaces of mesquite and cactus, little groups of frame houses, woods of light and tender trees, all were sweeping into the east, sweeping over the horizon, a precipice.

A newly married pair had boarded this coach at San Antonio. The man's face was reddened from many days in the wind and sun, and a direct result of his new black clothes was that his brick-colored hands were constantly performing in a most conscious fashion. From time to time he looked down respectfully at his attire. He sat with a hand on each knee, like a man waiting in a barber's shop. The glances he devoted to other passengers were furtive and shy.

The bride was not pretty, nor was she very young. She wore a dress of blue cashmere, with small reservations of velvet here and there, and with steel buttons abounding. She continually twisted her head to regard her puff sleeves, very stiff, straight, and high. They embarrassed her. It was quite apparent that she had cooked, and that she expected to cook, dutifully. The blushes caused by the careless scrutiny of some passengers as she had entered the car were strange to see upon this plain, underclass countenance, which was drawn in placid, almost emotionless lines.

They were evidently very happy. "Ever been in a parlor car before?" he asked, smiling with delight.

"No," she answered, "I never was. It's fine, ain't it?"

"Great! And then after a while we'll go forward to the diner, and get a big lay-out. Finest meal in the world. Charge a dollar."

"Oh, do they?" cried the bride. "Charge a dollar? Why, that's too much—for us—ain't it, Jack?"

"Not this trip, anyhow," he answered bravely. "We're going to go the whole thing"

Later he explained to her about the trains. "You see, it's a thousand miles from one end of Texas to the other; and this train runs right across it, and never stops but four times." He had the pride of an owner. He pointed out to her the dazzling fittings of the coach; and in truth her eyes opened wider as she contemplated the sea-green figured velvet, the shining brass, silver, and glass, the wood that gleamed as darkly brilliant as the surface of a pool of oil. At one end a bronze figure sturdily held a support for a separated chamber, and at convenient places on the ceiling were frescos in olive and silver.

To the minds of the pair, their surroundings reflected the glory of their marriage that morning in San Antonio; this was the environment of their new estate; and the man's face in particular beamed with an elation that made him appear ridiculous to the Negro porter. This individual at times surveyed them from afar with an amused and superior grin. On other occasions he bullied them with skill in ways that did not make it exactly plain to them that they were being bullied. He subtly used all the manners of the most unconquerable kind of snobbery. He oppressed them; but of this oppression they had small knowledge, and they speedily forgot that infrequently a number of travelers covered them with stares of derisive enjoyment. Historically there was supposed to be something infinitely humorous in their situation.

"We are due in Yellow Sky at 3:42," he said, looking tenderly into her eyes.

"Oh, are we?" she said, as if she had not been aware of it. To evince surprise at her husband's statement was part of her wifely amiability. She took from a pocket a little silver watch; and as she held it before her, and stared at it with a frown of attention, the new husband's face shone.

"I bought it in San Anton' from a friend of mine," he told her gleefully.

"It's seventeen minutes past twelve," she said, looking up at him with a kind of shy and clumsy coquetry. A passenger, noting this play, grew excessively sardonic, and winked at himself in one of the numerous mirrors.

At last they went to the dining car. Two rows of Negro waiters, in glowing white suits, surveyed their entrance with the interest, and also the equanimity, of men who had been forewarned. The pair fell to the lot of a waiter who happened to feel pleasure in steering them through their meal. He viewed them with the manner of a fatherly pilot, his countenance radiant with benevolence. The patronage, entwined with the ordinary deference, was not plain to them. And yet, as they returned to their coach, they showed in their faces a sense of escape.

To the left, miles down a long purple slope, was a little ribbon of mist where moved the keening Rio Grande. The train was approaching it at an angle, and the apex was Yellow Sky. Presently it was apparent that, as the distance from Yellow Sky grew shorter, the husband became commensurately restless. His brick-red hands were more insistent in their prominence. Occasionally he was even rather absent-minded and faraway when the bride leaned forward and addressed him.

As a matter of truth, Jack Potter was beginning to find the shadow of a deed weigh upon him like a leaden slab. He, the town marshal of Yellow Sky, a man known, liked, and feared in his corner, a prominent person, had gone to San Antonio to meet a girl he believed he loved, and there, after the usual prayers, had actually induced her to marry him, without consulting Yellow Sky for any part of the transaction. He was now bringing his bride before an innocent and unsuspecting community.

Of course people in Yellow Sky married as it pleased them, in accordance with a general custom; but such was Potter's thought of his duty to his friends, or of their idea of his duty, or of an unspoken form which does not control men in these matters, that he felt he was heinous. He had committed an extraordinary crime. Face to face with this girl in San Antonio, and spurred by his sharp impulse, he had gone headlong over all the social hedges. At San Antonio he was like a man hidden in the dark. A knife to sever any friendly duty, any form, was easy to his hand in that remote city. But the hour of Yellow Sky—the hour of daylight—was approaching.

He knew full well that his marriage was an important thing to his town. It could only be exceeded by the burning of the new hotel. His friends could not forgive him. Frequently he had reflected on the advisability of telling them by telegraph, but a new cowardice had been upon him. He feared to do it. And now the train was hurrying him toward a scene of amazement, glee, and reproach. He glanced out of the window at the line of haze swinging slowly in toward the train.

Yellow Sky had a kind of brass band, which played painfully, to the delight of the populace. He laughed without heart as he thought of it. If the citizens could dream of his prospective arrival with his bride, they would parade the band at the station and escort them, amid cheers and laughing congratulations, to his adobe home.

He resolved that he would use all the devices of speed and plains-craft in making the journey from the station to his house. Once within that safe citadel, he could issue some sort of vocal bulletin, and then not go among the citizens until they had time to wear off a little of their enthusiasm.

The bride looked anxiously at him. "What's worrying you, Jack?"

He laughed again. "I'm not worrying, girl; I'm only thinking of Yellow Sky."

She flushed in comprehension.

A sense of mutual guilt invaded their minds and developed a finer tenderness. They looked at each other with eyes softly aglow. But Potter often laughed the same nervous laugh; the flush upon the bride's face seemed quite permanent.

The traitor to the feelings of Yellow Sky narrowly watched the speeding landscape. "We're nearly there," he said.

Presently the porter came and announced the proximity of Potter's home. He held a brush in his hand, and, with all his airy superiority gone, he brushed Potter's new clothes as the latter slowly turned this way and that way. Potter fumbled out a coin and gave it to the porter, as he had seen others do. It was a heavy and muscle-bound business, as that of a man shoeing his first horse.

The porter took their bag, and as the train began to slow they moved forward to the hooded platform of the car. Presently the two engines and their long string of coaches rushed into the station of Yellow Sky.

"They have to take water here," said Potter, from a constricted throat and in mournful cadence, as one announcing death. Before the train stopped, his eye had swept the length of the platform, and he was glad and astonished to see there was none upon it but the station agent, who, with a slightly hurried and anxious air, was walking toward the water tanks. When the train had halted, the porter alighted first, and placed in position a little temporary step.

"Come on, girl," said Potter, hoarsely. As he helped her down they each laughed on a false note. He took the bag from the Negro, and bade his wife cling to his arm. As they slunk rapidly away, his hangdog glance perceived that they were unloading the two trunks, and also that the station agent, far ahead near the baggage car, had turned and was running toward him, making gestures. He laughed, and groaned as he laughed, when he noted the first effect of his marital bliss upon Yellow Sky. He gripped his wife's arm firmly to his side, and they fled. Behind them the porter stood, chuckling fatuously.

2

THE CALIFORNIA EXPRESS ON THE SOUTHERN RAILWAY was due at Yellow Sky in twenty-one minutes. There were six men at the bar of the Weary Gentleman saloon. One was a drummer* who talked a great deal and rapidly; three were Texans who did not care to talk at that time; and two were Mexican sheep-herders, who did not talk as a general practice in the Weary Gentleman saloon. The barkeeper's dog lay on the boardwalk that crossed in front of the door. His head was on his paws, and he glanced drowsily here and there with the constant vigilance of a dog that is kicked on occasion. Across the sandy street were some vivid green grass-plots, so wonderful in appearance, amid the sands that burned near them in a blazing sun, that they caused a doubt in the mind. They exactly resembled the grass mats used to represent lawns on the stage. At the cooler end of the railway station, a man without a coat sat in a tilted chair and smoked his pipe. The fresh-cut bank of the Rio Grande circled near the town, and there could be seen beyond it a great plum-colored plain of mesquite.

Save for the busy drummer and his companions in the saloon, Yellow Sky was dozing. The newcomer leaned gracefully upon the bar, and recited many tales with the confidence of a bard who has come upon a new field.

---

*drummer: traveling salesman.

"—and at the moment that the old man fell downstairs with the bureau in his arms, the old woman was coming up with two scuttles of coal, and of course—"

The drummer's tale was interrupted by a young man who suddenly appeared in the open door. He cried: "Scratchy Wilson's drunk, and has turned loose with both hands." The two Mexicans at once set down their glasses and faded out of the rear entrance of the saloon.

The drummer, innocent and jocular, answered: "All right, old man. S'pose he has? Come in and have a drink, anyhow."

But the information had made such an obvious cleft in every skull in the room that the drummer was obliged to see its importance. All had become instantly solemn. "Say," said he, mystified, "what is this?" His three companions made the introductory gesture of eloquent speech; but the young man at the door forestalled them.

"It means, my friend," he answered, as he came into the saloon, "that for the next two hours this town won't be a health resort."

The barkeeper went to the door, and locked and barred it; reaching out of the window, he pulled in heavy wooden shutters, and barred them. Immediately a solemn, chapel-like gloom was upon the place. The drummer was looking from one to another.

"But say," he cried, "what is this anyhow? You don't mean there is going to be a gun fight?"

"Don't know whether there'll be a fight or not," answered one man, grimly, "but there'll be some shootin'—some good shootin'."

The young man who had warned them waved his hand. "Oh, there'll be a fight fast enough, if anyone wants it. Anybody can get a fight out there in the street. There's a fight just waiting."

The drummer seemed to be swayed between the interest of a foreigner and a perception of personal danger.

"What did you say his name was?" he asked.

"Scratchy Wilson," they answered in chorus.

"And will he kill anybody? What are you going to do? Does this happen often? Does he rampage around like this once a week or so? Can he break in that door?"

"No, he can't break down that door," replied the barkeeper. "He's tried it three times. But when he comes you'd better lay down on the floor, stranger. He's dead sure to shoot at it, and a bullet may come through."

Thereafter the drummer kept a strict eye upon the door. The time had not yet been called for him to hug the floor, but, as a minor precaution, he sidled near to the wall. "Will he kill anybody?" he said again.

The man laughed low and scornfully at the question.

"He's out to shoot, and he's out for trouble. Don't see any good in experimentin' with him."

"But what do you do in a case like this? What do you do?"

A man responded: "Why, he and Jack Potter—"

"But," in chorus the other men interrupted, "Jack Potter's in San Anton'."

"Well, who is he? What's he got to do with it?"

"Oh, he's the town marshal. He goes out and fights Scratchy when he gets on one of these tears."

"Wow!" said the drummer, mopping his brow. "Nice job he's got."

The voices had toned away to mere whisperings. The drummer wished to ask further questions, which were born of an increasing anxiety and bewilderment; but when he attempted them, the men merely looked at him in irritation and motioned him to remain silent. A tense waiting hush was upon them. In the deep shadows of the room their eyes shone as they listened for sounds from the street. One man made three gestures at the barkeeper; and the latter, moving like a ghost, handed him a glass and a bottle. The man poured a full glass of whisky, and set down the bottle noiselessly. He gulped the whisky in a swallow, and turned again toward the door in immovable silence. The drummer saw that the barkeeper, without a sound, had taken a Winchester from beneath the bar. Later he saw this individual beckoning to him, so he tip-toed across the room.

"You better come with me back of the bar."

"No, thanks," said the drummer, perspiring; "I'd rather be where I can make a break for the back door."

Whereupon the man of bottles made a kindly but peremptory gesture. The drummer obeyed it, and, finding himself seated on a box with his head below the level of the bar, balm was laid upon his soul at sight of various zinc and copper fittings that bore a resemblance to armor plate. The barkeeper took a seat comfortably upon an adjacent box.

"You see," he whispered, "this here Scratchy Wilson is a wonder with a gun—a perfect wonder; and when he goes on the war-trail, we hunt our holes—naturally. He's about the last one of the old gang that used to hang out along the river here. He's a terror when he's drunk. When he's sober he's all right—kind of simple—wouldn't hurt a fly—nicest fellow in town. But when he's drunk—whoo!"

There were periods of stillness. "I wish Jack Potter was back from San Anton'," said the barkeeper. "He shot Wilson up once—in the leg—and he would sail in and pull out the kinks in this thing."

Presently they heard from a distance the sound of a shot, followed by three wild yowls. It instantly removed a bond from the men in the darkened saloon. There was a shuffling to feet. They looked at each other. "Here he comes," they said.

3

A MAN IN A MAROON-COLORED FLANNEL SHIRT, which had been purchased for purposes of decoration, and made principally by some Jewish women on the east side of New York, rounded a corner and walked into the middle of the main street of Yellow Sky. In either hand the man held a long, heavy, blue-black revolver. Often he yelled, and these cries rang through a semblance of a deserted village, shrilly flying over the roofs in a volume that seemed to have no relation to the ordinary vocal strength of a man. It was as if the surrounding stillness formed the arch of a tomb over him. These cries of ferocious challenge rang against walls of silence. And his boots had red tops with gilded imprints, of the kind beloved in winter by little sledding boys on the hillsides of New England.

The man's face flamed in a rage begot of whisky. His eyes, rolling, and yet keen for ambush, hunted the still doorways and windows. He walked with the creeping movement of the midnight cat. As it occurred to him, he roared menacing information. The long revolvers in his hands were as easy as straws; they were moved with an electric swiftness. The little fingers of each hand played sometimes in a musician's way. Plain from the low collar of the shirt, the cords of his neck straightened and sank, straightened and sank, as passion moved him. The only sounds were his terrible invitations. The calm adobes preserved their demeanor at the passing of this small thing in the middle of the street.

There was no offer of fight—no offer of fight. The man called to the sky. There were no attractions. He bellowed and fumed and swayed his revolvers here and everywhere.

The dog of the barkeeper of the Weary Gentleman saloon had not appreciated the advance of events. He yet lay dozing in front of his master's door. At sight of the dog, the man paused and raised his revolver humorously. At sight of the man, the dog sprang up and walked diagonally away, with a sullen head, and growling. The man yelled, and the dog broke into a gallop. As it was about to enter an alley, there was a loud noise, a whistling, and something spat the ground directly before it. The dog screamed, and, wheeling in terror, galloped headlong in a new direction. Again there was a noise, a whistling, and sand was kicked viciously before it. Fear-stricken, the dog turned and flurried like an animal in a pen. The man stood laughing, his weapons at his hips.

Ultimately the man was attracted by the closed door of the Weary Gentleman saloon. He went to it and, hammering with a revolver, demanded drink.

The door remaining imperturbable, he picked a bit of paper from the walk, and nailed it to the framework with a knife. He then turned his back contemptuously upon this popular resort and, walking to the opposite side of the street and spinning there on his heel quickly and lithely, fired at the bit of paper. He missed it by a half-inch. He swore at himself, and went away. Later he comfortably fusilladed the windows of his most intimate friend. The man was playing with this town; it was a toy for him.

But still there was no offer of fight. The name of Jack Potter, his ancient antagonist, entered his mind, and he concluded that it would be a glad thing if he should go to Potter's house, and by bombardment induce him to come out and fight. He moved in the direction of his desire, chanting Apache scalp-music.

When he arrived at it, Potter's house presented the same still, calm front as had the other adobes. Taking up a strategic position, the man howled a challenge. But this house regarded him as might a great stone god. It gave no sign. After a decent wait, the man howled further challenges, mingling with them wonderful epithets.

Presently there came the spectacle of a man churning himself into deepest rage over the immobility of a house. He fumed at it as the winter wind attacks a prairie cabin in the North. To the distance there should have gone the sound of a tumult like the fighting of two hundred Mexicans. As necessity bade him, he paused for breath or to reload his revolvers.

4

POTTER AND HIS BRIDE WALKED SHEEPISHLY AND WITH SPEED. Sometimes they laughed together shamefacedly and low.

"Next corner, dear," he said finally.

They put forth the efforts of a pair walking bowed against a strong wind. Potter was about to raise a finger to point the first appearance of the new home when, as they circled the corner, they came face to face with a man in a maroon-colored shirt, who was feverishly pushing cartridges into a large revolver. Upon the instant the man dropped this revolver to the ground and, like lightning, whipped another from its holster. The second weapon was aimed at the bridegroom's chest.

There was a silence. Potter's mouth seemed to be merely a grave for his tongue. He exhibited an instinct to at once loosen his arm from the woman's grip, and he dropped the bag to the sand. As for the bride, her face had gone as yellow as old cloth. She was a slave to hideous rites, gazing at the apparitional snake.

The two men faced each other at a distance of three paces. He of the revolver smiled with a new and quiet ferocity.

"Tried to sneak up on me," he said. "Tried to sneak up on me!" His eyes grew more baleful. As Potter made a slight movement, the man thrust his revolver venomously forward. "No, don't you do it, Jack Potter. Don't you move a finger toward a gun just yet. Don't you move an eyelash. The time has come for me to settle with you, and I'm goin' to do it my own way, and loaf along with no interferin'. So if you don't want a gun bent on you, just mind what I tell you."

Potter looked at his enemy. "I ain't got a gun on me, Scratchy," he said. "Honest, I ain't." He was stiffening and steadying, but yet somewhere at the back of his mind a vision of the Pullman floated, the sea-green figured velvet, the shining brass, silver, and glass, the wood that gleamed as darkly brilliant as the surface of a pool of oil—all the glory of the marriage, the environment of the new estate. "You know I fight when it comes to fighting, Scratchy Wilson, but I ain't got a gun on me. You'll have to do all the shootin' yourself."

His enemy's face went livid. He stepped forward and lashed his weapon to and fro before Potter's chest. "Don't you tell me you ain't got no gun on you, you whelp. Don't tell me no lie like that. There ain't a man in Texas ever seen you without no gun. Don't take me for no kid." His eyes blazed with light, and his throat worked like a pump.

"I ain't takin' you for no kid," answered Potter. His heels had not moved an inch backward. "I'm takin' you for a damn fool. I tell you I ain't got a gun, and I ain't. If you're goin' to shoot me up, you better begin now; you'll never get a chance like this again."

So much enforced reasoning had told on Wilson's rage; he was calmer. "If you ain't got a gun, why ain't you got a gun?" he sneered. "Been to Sunday school?"

"I ain't got a gun because I've just come from San Anton' with my wife. I'm married," said Potter. "And if I'd thought there was going to be any ga-loots like you prowling around when I brought my wife home, I'd had a gun, and don't you forget it."

"Married!" said Scratchy, not at all comprehending.

"Yes, married. I'm married," said Potter, distinctly.

"Married?" said Scratchy. Seemingly for the first time, he saw the droop-ing, drowning woman at the other man's side. "No!" he said. He was like a creature allowed a glimpse of another world. He moved a pace backward, and his arm with the revolver dropped to his side. "Is this—is this the lady?" he asked.

"Yes, this is the lady," answered Potter.

There was another period of silence.

"Well," said Wilson at last, slowly, "I s'pose it's all off now."

"It's all off if you say so, Scratchy. You know I didn't make the trouble." Potter lifted his valise.

"Well, I 'low it's off Jack," said Wilson. He was looking at the ground. "Married!" He was not a student of chivalry; it was merely that in the pres-ence of this foreign condition he was a simple child of the earlier plains. He picked up his starboard revolver, and, placing both weapons in their hol-sters, he went away. His feet made funnel-shaped tracks in the heavy sand.

Alice Munro, 1931–

The Found Boat

This story first appeared in SOMETHING I'VE BEEN MEANING TO TELL YOU, *1974.*

AT THE END OF BELL STREET, McKay Street, Mayo Street, there was the Flood. It was the Wawanash River, which every spring overflowed its banks. Some springs, say one in every five, it covered the roads on that side of town and washed over the fields, creating a shallow choppy lake. Light reflected off the water made everything bright and cold, as it is in a lakeside town, and woke or revived in people certain vague hopes of disaster. Mostly during the late afternoon and early evening, there were people straggling out to look at it, and discuss whether it was still rising, and whether this time it might invade the town. In general, those under fifteen and over sixty-five were most certain that it would.

Eva and Carol rode out on their bicycles. They left the road—it was the end of Mayo Street, past any houses—and rode right into a field, over a wire fence entirely flattened by the weight of the winter's snow. They coasted a little way before the long grass stopped them, then left their bicycles lying down and went to the water.

"We have to find a log and ride on it," Eva said.

"Jesus, we'll freeze our legs off."

"Jesus, we'll freeze our legs off!" said one of the boys who were there too at the water's edge. He spoke in a sour whine, the way boys imitated girls although it was nothing like the way girls talked. These boys—there were three of them—were all in the same class as Eva and Carol at school and were known to them by name (their names being Frank, Bud and Clayton), but Eva and Carol, who had seen and recognized them from the road, had not spoken to them or looked at them or, even yet, given any sign of knowing they were there. The boys seemed to be trying to make a raft, from lumber they had salvaged from the water.

Eva and Carol took off their shoes and socks and waded in. The water was so cold it sent pain up their legs, like blue electric sparks shooting through their veins, but they went on, pulling their skirts high, tight behind and bunched so they could hold them in front.

"Look at the fat-assed ducks in wading."

"Fat-assed fucks."

Eva and Carol, of course, gave no sign of hearing this. They laid hold of a log and climbed on, taking a couple of boards floating in the water for paddles. There were always things floating around in the Flood—branches, fence-rails, logs, road signs, old lumber; sometimes boilers, washtubs, pots and pans, or even a car seat or stuffed chair, as if somewhere the Flood had got into a dump.

They paddled away from shore, heading out into the cold lake. The water was perfectly clear, they could see the brown grass swimming along the bottom. Suppose it was the sea, thought Eva. She thought of drowned cities and countries. Atlantis. Suppose they were riding in a Viking boat—Viking boats on the Atlantic were more frail and narrow than this log on the Flood—and they had miles of clear sea beneath them, then a spired city, intact as a jewel irretrievable on the ocean floor.

"This is a Viking boat," she said. "I am the carving on the front." She stuck her chest out and stretched her neck, trying to make a curve, and she made a face, putting out her tongue. Then she turned and for the first time took notice of the boys.

"Hey, you sucks!" she yelled at them."You'd be scared to come out here, this water is ten feet deep!"

"Liar," they answered without interest, and she was.

They steered the log around a row of trees, avoiding floating barbed wire, and got into a little bay created by a natural hollow of the land. Where the bay was now, there would be a pond full of frogs later in the spring, and by the middle of summer there would be no water at all, just a low tangle of reeds and bushes, green, to show that mud was still wet around their roots. Larger bushes, willows, grew around the steep bank of this pond and were still partly out of the water. Eva and Carol let the log ride in. They saw a place where something was caught.

It was a boat, or part of one. An old rowboat with most of one side ripped out, the board that had been the seat just dangling. It was pushed up among the branches, lying on what would have been its side, if it had a side, the prow caught high.

Their idea came to them without consultation, at the same time:

"You guys! Hey, you guys!"

"We found you a boat!"

"Stop building your stupid raft and come and look at the boat!"

What surprised them in the first place was that the boys really did come, scrambling overland, half running, half sliding down the bank, wanting to see.

"Hey, where?"

"Where is it, I don't see no boat."

What surprised them in the second place was that when the boys did actually see what boat was meant, this old flood-smashed wreck held up in the branches, they did not understand that they had been fooled, that a joke had been played on them. They did not show a moment's disappointment, but seemed as pleased at the discovery as if the boat had been whole and new. They were already barefoot, because they had been wading in the water to get lumber, and they waded in here without a stop, surrounding the boat and appraising it and paying no attention even of an insulting kind to Eva and Carol who bobbed up and down on their log. Eva and Carol had to call to them.

"How do you think you're going to get it off?"

"It won't float anyway."

"What makes you think it will float?"

"It'll sink. Glub-blub-blub, you'll all be drownded."

The boys did not answer, because they were too busy walking around the boat, pulling at it in a testing way to see how it could be got off with the least possible damage. Frank, who was the most literate, talkative and inept of the three, began referring to the boat as *she,* an affectation which Eva and Carol acknowledged with fish-mouths of contempt.

"She's caught two places. You got to be careful not to tear a hole in her bottom. She's heavier than you'd think."

It was Clayton who climbed up and freed the boat, and Bud, a tall fat boy, who got the weight of it on his back to turn it into the water so that they could half float, half carry it to shore. All this took some time. Eva and Carol abandoned their log and waded out of the water. They walked overland to get their shoes and socks and bicycles. They did not need to come back this way but they came. They stood at the top of the hill, leaning on their bicycles. They did not go on home, but they did not sit down and frankly watch, either. They stood more or less facing each other, but glancing down at the water and at the boys struggling with the boat, as if they had just halted for a moment out of curiosity, and staying longer than they intended, to see what came of this unpromising project.

About nine o'clock, or when it was nearly dark—dark to people inside the houses, but not quite dark outside—they all returned to town, going along Mayo Street in a sort of procession. Frank and Bud and Clayton came carrying the boat, upside-down, and Eva and Carol walked behind, wheeling their bicycles. The boys' heads were almost hidden in the darkness of the overturned boat, with its smell of soaked wood, cold swampy water. The girls could look ahead and see the street lights in their tin reflectors, a necklace of lights climbing Mayo Street, reaching all the way up to the standpipe. They turned onto Burns Street heading for Clayton's house, the nearest house belonging to any of them. This was not the way home for Eva or for Carol either, but they followed along. The boys were perhaps too busy carrying the boat to tell them to go away. Some younger children were still out playing, playing hopscotch on the sidewalk though they could hardly see. At this time of year the bare sidewalk was still such a novelty and delight. These children cleared out of the way and watched the boat go by with unwilling respect; they shouted questions after it, wanting to know where it came from and what was going to be done with it. No one answered them. Eva and Carol as well as the boys refused to answer or even look at them.

The five of them entered Clayton's yard. The boys shifted weight, as if they were going to put the boat down.

"You better take it round to the back where nobody can see it," Carol said. That was the first thing any of them had said since they came into town.

The boys said nothing but went on, following a mud path between Clayton's house and a leaning board fence. They let the boat down in the back yard.

"It's a stolen boat, you know," said Eva, mainly for the effect. "It must've belonged to somebody. You stole it."

"You was the ones who stole it then," Bud said, short of breath. "It was you seen it first."

"It was you took it."

"It was all of us then. If one of us gets in trouble then all of us does."

"Are you going to tell anybody on them?" said Carol as she and Eva rode home, along the streets which were dark between the lights now and pot-holed from winter.

"It's up to you. I won't if you won't."

"I won't if you won't."

They rode in silence, relinquishing something, but not discontented.

The board fence in Clayton's back yard had every so often a post which supported it, or tried to, and it was on these posts that Eva and Carol spent several evenings sitting, jauntily but not very comfortably. Or else they just leaned against the fence while the boys worked on the boat. During the first couple of evenings neighborhood children attracted by the sound of hammering tried to get into the yard to see what was going on, but Eva and Carol blocked their way.

"Who said you could come in here?"

"Just us can come in this yard."

These evenings were getting longer, the air milder. Skipping was starting on the sidewalks. Further along the street there was a row of hard maples that had been tapped. Children drank the sap as fast as it could drip into the buckets. The old man and woman who owned the trees, and who hoped to make syrup, came running out of the house making noises as if they were trying to scare away crows. Finally, every spring, the old man would come out on his porch and fire his shotgun into the air, and then the thieving would stop.

None of those working on the boat bothered about stealing sap, though all had done so last year.

The lumber to repair the boat was picked up here and there, along back lanes. At this time of year things were lying around—old boards and branches, sodden mitts, spoons flung out with the dishwater, lids of pudding pots that had been set in the snow to cool, all the debris that can sift through and survive winter. The tools came from Clayton's cellar—left over, presumably, from the time when his father was alive—and though they had nobody to advise them the boys seemed to figure out more or less the manner in which boats are built, or rebuilt. Frank was the one who showed up with diagrams from books and *Popular Mechanics* magazines. Clayton looked at these diagrams and listened to Frank read the instructions and then went ahead and decided in his own way what was to be done. Bud was best at sawing. Eva and Carol watched everything from the fence and offered criticism and thought up names. The names for the boat that they thought of were: Water Lily, Sea Horse, Flood Queen, and Caro-Eve, after them because they had found it. The boys did not say which, if any, of these names they found satisfactory.

The boat had to be tarred. Clayton heated up a pot of tar on the kitchen stove and brought it out and painted slowly, his thorough way, sitting astride the overturned boat. The other boys were sawing a board to make a new seat. As Clayton worked, the tar cooled and thickened so that finally he could not move the brush any more. He turned to Eva and held out the pot and said, "You can go in and heat this on the stove."

Eva took the pot and went up the back steps. The kitchen seemed black after outside, but it must be light enough to see in, because there was Clayton's mother standing at the ironing board, ironing. She did that for a living, took in wash and ironing.

"Please may I put the tar pot on the stove?" said Eva, who had been brought up to talk politely to parents, even wash-and-iron ladies, and who for some reason especially wanted to make a good impression on Clayton's mother.

"You'll have to poke up the fire then," said Clayton's mother, as if she doubted whether Eva would know how to do that. But Eva could see now, and she picked up the lid with the stove-lifter, and took the poker and poked up a flame. She stirred the tar as it softened. She felt privileged. Then and later. Before she went to sleep a picture of Clayton came to her mind; she saw him sitting astride the boat, tarpainting, with such concentration, delicacy, absorption. She thought of him speaking to her, out of his isolation, in such an ordinary peaceful taking-for-granted voice.

On the twenty-fourth of May, a school holiday in the middle of the week, the boat was carried out of town, a long way now, off the road over fields and fences that had been repaired, to where the river flowed between its normal banks. Eva and Carol, as well as the boys, took turns carrying it. It was launched in the water from a cow-trampled spot between willow bushes that were fresh out in leaf. The boys went first. They yelled with triumph when the boat did float, when it rode amazingly down the river current. The boat was painted black, and green inside, with yellow seats, and a strip of yellow all the way around the outside. There was no name on it, after all.

The boys could not imagine that it needed any name to keep it separate from the other boats in the world.

Eva and Carol ran along the bank, carrying bags full of peanut butter-and-jam sandwiches, pickles, bananas, chocolate cake, potato chips, graham crackers stuck together with corn syrup and five bottles of pop to be cooled in the river water. The bottles bumped against their legs. They yelled for a turn.

"If they don't let us they're bastards," Carol said, and they yelled together, "We found it! We found it!"

The boys did not answer, but after a while they brought the boat in, and Carol and Eva came crashing, panting down the bank.

"Does it leak?"

"It don't leak yet."

"We forgot a bailing can," wailed Carol, but nevertheless she got in, with Eva, and Frank pushed them off, crying, "Here's to a Watery Grave!"

And the thing about being in a boat was that it was not solidly bobbing, like a log, but was cupped in the water, so that riding in it was not like being on something in the water, but like being in the water itself. Soon they were all going out in the boat in mixed-up turns, two boys and a girl, two girls and a boy, a girl and a boy, until things were so confused it was impossible to tell whose turn came next, and nobody cared anyway. They went down the river—those who weren't riding, running along the bank to keep up. They passed under two bridges, one iron, one cement. Once they saw a big carp just resting, it seemed to smile at them, in the bridge-shaded water. They did not know how far they had gone on the river, but things had changed—the water had got shallower, and the land flatter. Across an open field they saw a building that looked like a house, abandoned. They dragged the boat up on the bank and tied it and set out across the field.

"That's the old station," Frank said. "That's Pedder Station." The others had heard this name but he was the one who knew, because his father was the station agent in town. He said that this was a station on a branch line that had been torn up, and that there had been a sawmill here, but a long time ago.

Inside the station it was dark, cool. All the windows were broken. Glass lay in shards and in fairly big pieces on the floor. They walked around finding the larger pieces of glass and tramping on them, smashing them, it was like cracking ice on puddles. Some partitions were still in place, you could see where the ticket window had been. There was a bench lying on its side. People had been here, it looked as if people came here all the time, though it was so far from anywhere. Beer bottles and pop bottles were lying around, also cigarette packages, gum and candy wrappers, the paper from a loaf of bread. The walls were covered with dim and fresh pencil and chalk writings and carved with knives.

I LOVE RONNIE COLES

I WANT TO FUCK

KILROY WAS HERE

RONNIE COLES IS AN ASS-HOLE

WHAT ARE YOU DOING HERE?

WAITING FOR A TRAIN

DAWNA MARY-LOU BARBARA JOANNE

It was exciting to be inside this large, dark, empty place, with the loud noise of breaking glass and their voices ringing back from the underside of the roof. They tipped the old beer bottles against their mouths. That reminded them that they were hungry and thirsty and they cleared a place in the middle of the floor and sat down and ate the lunch. They drank the pop just as it was, lukewarm. They ate everything there was and licked the smears of peanut butter and jam off the bread-paper in which the sandwiches had been wrapped.

They played Truth or Dare.

"I dare you to write on the wall, I am a Stupid Ass, and sign your name."

"Tell the truth—what is the worst lie you ever told?"

"Did you ever wet the bed?"

"Did you ever dream you were walking down the street without any clothes on?"

"I dare you to go outside and pee on the railway sign."

It was Frank who had to do that. They could not see him, even his back, but they knew he did it, they heard the hissing sound of his pee. They all sat still, amazed, unable to think of what the next dare would be.

"I dare everybody," said Frank from the doorway, "I dare—Everybody."

"What?"

"Take off all our clothes."

Eva and Carol screamed.

"Anybody who won't do it has to walk—has to *crawl*—around this floor on their hands and knees."

They were all quiet, till Eva said, almost complacently, "What first?"

"Shoes and socks."

"Then we have to go outside, there's too much glass here."

They pulled off their shoes and socks in the doorway, in the sudden blinding sun. The field before them was bright as water. They ran across where the tracks used to go.

"That's enough, that's enough," said Carol. "Watch out for thistles!"

"Tops! Everybody take off their tops!"

"I won't! We won't, will we, Eva?"

But Eva was whirling round and round in the sun where the track used to be. "I don't care, I don't care! Truth or Dare! Truth or Dare!"

She unbuttoned her blouse as she whirled, as if she didn't know what her hand was doing, she flung it off.

Carol took off hers. "I wouldn't have done it, if you hadn't!"

"Bottoms!"

Nobody said a word this time, they all bent and stripped themselves. Eva, naked first, started running across the field, and then all the others ran, all five of them running bare through the knee-high hot grass, running towards the river. Not caring now about being caught but in fact leaping and yelling to call attention to themselves, if there was anybody to hear or see. They felt as if they were going to jump off a cliff and fly. They felt that something was happening to them different from anything that had happened before, and it had to do with the boat, the water, the sunlight, the dark ruined station, and each other. They thought of each other now hardly as names or people, but as echoing shrieks, reflections, all bold and white and loud and scandalous, and as fast as arrows. They went running without a break into the cold water and when it came almost to the tops of their legs they fell on it and swam. It stopped their noise. Silence, amazement, came over them in a rush. They dipped and floated and separated, sleek as mink.

Eva stood up in the water her hair dripping, water running down her face. She was waist deep. She stood on smooth stones, her feet fairly wide apart, water flowing between her legs. About a yard away from her Clayton also stood up, and they were blinking the water out of their eyes, looking at each other. Eva did not turn or try to hide; she was quivering from the cold of the water, but also with pride, shame, boldness, and exhilaration.

Clayton shook his head violently, as if he wanted to bang something out of it, then bent over and took a mouthful of river water. He stood up with his cheeks full and made a tight hole of his mouth and shot the water at her as if it was coming out of a hose, hitting her exactly, first one breast and then the other. Water from his mouth ran down her body. He hooted to see it, a loud self-conscious sound that nobody would have expected, from him. The others looked up from wherever they were in the water and closed in to see.

Eva crouched down and slid into the water, letting her head go right under. She swam, and when she let her head out downstream, Carol was coming after her and the boys were already on the bank, already running into the grass, showing their skinny backs, their white, flat buttocks. They were laughing and saying things to each other but she couldn't hear, for the water in her ears.

"What did he do?" said Carol.

"Nothing."

They crept in to shore. "Let's stay in the bushes till they go," said Eva. "I hate them anyway. I really do. Don't you hate them?"

"Sure," said Carol, and they waited, not very long, until they heard the boys still noisy and excited coming down to the place a bit upriver where they had left the boat. They heard them jump in and start rowing.

"They've got all the hard part, going back," said Eva, hugging herself and shivering violently. "Who cares? Anyway. It never was our boat."

"What if they tell?" said Carol.

"We'll say it's all a lie."

Eva hadn't thought of this solution until she said it, but as soon as she did she felt almost light-hearted again. The ease and scornfulness of it did make them both giggle, and slapping themselves and splashing out of the water they set about developing one of those fits of laughter in which, as soon as one showed signs of exhaustion, the other would snort and start up again, and they would make helpless—soon genuinely helpless—faces at each other and bend over and grab themselves as if they had the worst pain.

Raymond Carver, 1938–1988

A Small, Good Thing

This story first appeared in PLOUGHSHARES, *1983.*

SATURDAY AFTERNOON SHE DROVE TO THE BAKERY IN THE SHOPPING CENTER. After looking through a loose-leaf binder with photographs of cakes taped onto the pages, she ordered chocolate, the child's favorite. The cake she chose was decorated with a spaceship and launching pad under a sprinkling of white stars, and a planet made of red frosting at the other end. His name, SCOTTY, would be in green letters beneath the planet. The baker, who was an older man with a thick neck, listened without saying anything when she told him the child would be eight years old next Monday. The baker wore a white apron that looked like a smock. Straps cut under his arms, went around in back and then to the front again, where they were secured under his heavy waist. He wiped his hands on his apron as he listened to her. He kept his eyes down on the photographs and let her talk. He let her take her time. He'd just come to work and he'd be there all night, baking, and he was in no real hurry.

She gave the baker her name, Ann Weiss, and her telephone number. The cake would be ready on Monday morning, just out of the oven, in plenty of time for the child's party that afternoon. The baker was not jolly. There were no pleasantries between them, just the minimum exchange of words, the necessary information. He made her feel uncomfortable, and she didn't like that. While he was bent over the counter with the pencil in his hand, she studied his coarse features and wondered if he'd ever done anything else with his life besides be a baker. She was a mother and thirty-three years old, and it seemed to her that everyone, especially someone the baker's age—a man old enough to be her father—must have children who'd gone through this special time of cakes and birthday parties. There must be that between them, she thought. But he was abrupt with her—not rude, just abrupt. She gave up trying to make friends with him. She looked into the back of the bakery and could see a long, heavy wooden table with aluminum pie pans stacked at one end; and beside the table a metal container filled with empty racks. There was an enormous oven. A radio was playing country-Western music.

The baker finished printing the information on the special order card and closed up the binder. He looked at her and said, "Monday morning." She thanked him and drove home.

ON MONDAY MORNING, the birthday boy was walking to school with another boy. They were passing a bag of potato chips back and forth and the birthday boy was trying to find out what his friend intended to give him for his birthday that afternoon. Without looking, the birthday boy stepped off the curb at an intersection and was immediately knocked down by a car. He fell on his side with his head in the gutter and his legs out in the road. His eyes were closed, but his legs moved back and forth as if he were trying to climb over something. His friend dropped the potato chips and started to cry. The car had gone a hundred feet or so and stopped in the middle of the road. The man in the driver's seat looked back over his shoulder. He waited until the boy got unsteadily to his feet. The boy wobbled a little. He looked dazed, but okay. The driver put the car into gear and drove away.

The birthday boy didn't cry, but he didn't have anything to say about anything either. He wouldn't answer when his friend asked him what it felt like to be hit by a car. He walked home, and his friend went on to school. But after the birthday boy was inside his house and was telling his mother about it—she sitting beside him on the sofa, holding his hands in her lap, saying, "Scotty, honey are you sure you feel all right, baby?" thinking she would call the doctor anyway—he suddenly lay back on the sofa, closed his eyes, and went limp. When she couldn't wake him up, she hurried to the telephone and called her husband at work. Howard told her to remain calm, remain calm, and then he called an ambulance for the child and left for the hospital himself.

Of course, the birthday party was canceled. The child was in the hospital with a mild concussion and suffering from shock. There'd been vomiting, and his lungs had taken in fluid which needed pumping out that afternoon. Now he simply seemed to be in a very deep sleep—but no coma, Dr. Francis had emphasized, no coma, when he saw the alarm in the parents' eyes. At eleven o'clock that night, when the boy seemed to be resting comfortably enough after the many X-rays and the lab work, and it was just a matter of his waking up and coming around, Howard left the hospital. He and Ann had been at the hospital with the child since that afternoon, and he was going home for a short while to bathe and change clothes. "I'll be back in an hour," he said. She nodded. "It's fine," she said. "I'll be right here." He kissed her on the forehead, and they touched hands. She sat in the chair beside the bed and looked at the child. She was waiting for him to wake up and be all right. Then she could begin to relax.

Howard drove home from the hospital. He took the wet, dark streets very fast, then caught himself and slowed down. Until now, his life had gone smoothly and to his satisfaction—college, marriage, another year of college for the advanced degree in business, a junior partnership in an investment firm. Fatherhood. He was happy and, so far, lucky—he knew that. His parents were still living, his brothers and his sister were established, his friends from college had gone out to take their places in the world. So far, he had kept away from any real harm, from those forces he knew existed and that could cripple or bring down a man if the luck went bad, if things suddenly turned. He pulled into the driveway and parked. His left leg began to tremble. He sat in the car for a minute and tried to deal with the present situation in a rational manner. Scotty had been hit by a car and was in the hospital, but he was going to be all right. Howard closed his eyes and ran his hand over his face. He got out of the car and went up to the front door. The dog was barking inside the house. The telephone rang and rang while he unlocked the door and fumbled for the light switch. He shouldn't have left the hospital, he shouldn't have. "Goddamn it!" he said. He picked up the receiver and said, "I just walked in the door!"

"There's a cake here that wasn't picked up," the voice on the other end of the line said.

"What are you saying?" Howard asked.

"A cake," the voice said. "A sixteen-dollar cake."

Howard held the receiver against his ear, trying to understand. "I don't know anything about a cake," he said. "Jesus, what are you talking about?"

"Don't hand me that," the voice said.

Howard hung up the telephone. He went into the kitchen and poured himself some whiskey. He called the hospital. But the child's condition remained the same; he was still sleeping and nothing had changed there. While water poured into the tub, Howard lathered his face and shaved. He'd just stretched out in the tub and closed his eyes when the telephone rang again. He hauled himself out, grabbed a towel, and hurried through the house, saying, "Stupid, stupid," for having left the hospital. But when he picked up the receiver and shouted, "Hello!" there was no sound at the other end of the line. Then the caller hung up.

————————

He ARRIVED BACK AT THE HOSPITAL a little after midnight. Ann still sat in the chair beside the bed. She looked up at Howard, and then she looked back at the child. The child's eyes stayed closed, the head was still wrapped in bandages. His breathing was quiet and regular. From an apparatus over the bed hung a bottle of glucose with a tube running from the bottle to the boy's arm.

"How is he?" Howard said. "What's all this?" waving at the glucose and the tube.

"Dr. Francis's orders," she said. "He needs nourishment. He needs to keep up his strength. Why doesn't he wake up, Howard? I don't understand, if he's all right."

Howard put his hand against the back of her head. He ran his fingers through her hair. "He's going to be all right. He'll wake up in a little while. Dr. Francis knows what's what."

After a time, he said, "Maybe you should go home and get some rest. I'll stay here. Just don't put up with this creep who keeps calling. Hang up right away."

"Who's calling?" she asked.

"I don't know who, just somebody with nothing better to do than call up people. You go on now."

She shook her head. "No," she said, "I'm fine."

"Really," he said. "Go home for a while, and then come back and spell me in the morning. It'll be all right. What did Dr. Francis say? He said Scotty's going to be all right. We don't have to worry. He's just sleeping now, that's all."

A nurse pushed the door open. She nodded at them as she went to the bedside. She took the left arm out from under the covers and put her fingers on the wrist, found the pulse, then consulted her watch. In a little while, she put the arm back under the covers and moved to the foot of the bed, where she wrote something on a clipboard attached to the bed.

"How is he?" Ann said. Howard's hand was a weight on her shoulder. She was aware of the pressure from his fingers.

"He's stable," the nurse said. Then she said, "Doctor will be in again shortly. Doctor's back in the hospital. He's making rounds right now."

"I was saying maybe she'd want to go home and get a little rest," Howard said. "After the doctor comes," he said.

"She could do that," the nurse said. "I think you should both feel free to do that, if you wish." The nurse was a big Scandinavian woman with blond hair. There was the trace of an accent in her speech.

"We'll see what the doctor says," Ann said. "I want to talk to the doctor. I don't think he should keep sleeping like this. I don't think that's a good sign." She brought her hand up to her eyes and let her head come forward a little. Howard's grip tightened on her shoulder, and then his hand moved up to her neck, where his fingers began to knead the muscles there.

"Dr. Francis will be here in a few minutes," the nurse said. Then she left the room.

Howard gazed at his son for a time, the small chest quietly rising and falling under the covers. For the first time since the terrible minutes after Ann's telephone call to him at his office, he felt a genuine fear starting in his limbs. He began shaking his head. Scotty was fine, but instead of sleeping at home in his own bed, he was in a hospital bed with bandages around his head and a tube in his arm. But this help was what he needed right now.

Dr. Francis came in and shook hands with Howard, though they'd just seen each other a few hours before. Ann got up from the chair. "Doctor?"

"Ann," he said and nodded. "Let's just first see how he's doing," the doctor said. He moved to the side of the bed and took the boy's pulse. He peeled back one eyelid and then the other. Howard and Ann stood beside the doctor and watched. Then the doctor turned back the covers and listened to the boy's heart and lungs with his stethoscope. He pressed his fingers here and there on the abdomen. When he was finished, he went to the end of the bed and studied the chart. He noted the time, scribbled something on the chart, and then looked at Howard and Ann.

"Doctor, how is he?" Howard said. "What's the matter with him exactly?"

"Why doesn't he wake up?" Ann said.

The doctor was a handsome, big-shouldered man with a tanned face. He wore a three-piece blue suit, a striped tie, and ivory cuff links. His gray hair was combed along the sides of his head, and he looked as if he had just come from a concert. "He's all right," the doctor said. "Nothing to shout about, he could be better, I think. But he's all right. Still, I wish he'd wake up. He should wake up pretty soon." The doctor looked at the boy again. "We'll know some more in a couple of hours, after the results of a few more tests are in. But he's all right, believe me, except for the hairline fracture of the skull. He does have that."

"Oh, no," Ann said.

"And a bit of a concussion, as I said before. Of course, you know he's in shock," the doctor said. "Sometimes you see this in shock cases. This sleeping."

"But he's out of any real danger?" Howard said. "You said before he's not in a coma. You wouldn't call this a coma, then—would you, doctor?" Howard waited. He looked at the doctor.

"No, I don't want to call it a coma," the doctor said and glanced over at the boy once more. "He's just in a very deep sleep. It's a restorative measure the body is taking on its own. He's out of any real danger, I'd say that for certain, yes. But we'll know more when he wakes up and the other tests are in," the doctor said.

"It's a coma," Ann said. "Of sorts."

"It's not a coma yet, not exactly," the doctor said. "I wouldn't want to call it coma. Not yet, anyway. He's suffered shock. In shock cases, this kind of reaction is common enough; it's a temporary reaction to bodily trauma. Coma. Well, coma is a deep, prolonged unconsciousness, something that could go on for days, or weeks even. Scotty's not in that area, not as far as we can tell. I'm certain his condition will show improvement by morning. I'm betting that it will. We'll know more when he wakes up, which shouldn't be long now. Of course, you may do as you like, stay here or go home for a time. But by all means feel free to leave the hospital for a while if you want. This is not easy, I know." The doctor gazed at the boy again, watching him, and then he turned to Ann and said, "You try not to worry, little mother. Believe me, we're doing all that can be done. It's just a question of a little more time now." He nodded at her, shook hands with Howard again, and then he left the room.

Ann put her hand over the child's forehead. "At least he doesn't have a fever," she said. Then she said, "My God, he feels so cold, though. Howard? Is he supposed to feel like this? Feel his head."

Howard touched the child's temples. His own breathing had slowed. "I think he's supposed to feel this way right now," he said. "He's in shock, remember? That's what the doctor said. The doctor was just in here. He would have said something if Scotty wasn't okay."

Ann stood there a while longer, working her lip with her teeth. Then she moved over to her chair and sat down.

Howard sat in the chair next to her chair. They looked at each other. He wanted to say something else and reassure her, but he was afraid, too. He took her hand and put it in his lap, and this made him feel better, her hand being there. He picked up her hand and squeezed it. Then he just held her hand. They sat like that for a while, watching the boy and not talking. From time to time, he squeezed her hand. Finally, she took her hand away.

"I've been praying," she said.

He nodded.

She said, "I almost thought I'd forgotten how, but it came back to me. All I had to do was close my eyes and say, 'Please God, help us—help Scotty,' and then the rest was easy. The words were right there. Maybe if you prayed, too," she said to him.

"I've already prayed," he said. "I prayed this afternoon—yesterday afternoon, I mean—after you called, while I was driving to the hospital. I've been praying," he said.

"That's good," she said. For the first time, she felt they were together in it, this trouble. She realized with a start that, until now, it had only been happening to her and to Scotty. She hadn't let Howard into it, though he was there and needed all along. She felt glad to be his wife.

The same nurse came in and took the boy's pulse again and checked the flow from the bottle hanging above the bed.

In an hour, another doctor came in. He said his name was Parsons, from Radiology. He had a bushy moustache. He was wearing loafers, a Western shirt, and a pair of jeans.

"We're going to take him downstairs for more pictures," he told them. "We need to do some more pictures, and we want to do a scan."

"What's that?" Ann said. "A scan?" She stood between this new doctor and the bed. "I thought you'd already taken all your X-rays."

"I'm afraid we need some more," he said. "Nothing to be alarmed about. We just need some more pictures, and we want to do a brain scan on him."

"My God," Ann said.

"It's perfectly normal procedure in cases like this," this new doctor said. "We just need to find out for sure why he isn't back awake yet. It's normal medical procedure, and nothing to be alarmed about. We'll be taking him down in a few minutes," this doctor said.

In a little while, two orderlies came into the room with a gurney. They were black-haired, dark-complexioned men in white uniforms, and they said a few words to each other in a foreign tongue as they unhooked the boy from the tube and moved him from his bed to the gurney. Then they wheeled him from the room. Howard and Ann got on the same elevator. Ann gazed at the child. She closed her eyes as the elevator began its descent. The orderlies stood at either end of the gurney without saying anything, though once one of the men made a comment to the other in their own language, and the other man nodded slowly in response.

Later that morning, just as the sun was beginning to lighten the windows in the waiting room outside the X-ray department, they brought the boy out and moved him back up to his room. Howard and Ann rode up on the elevator with him once more, and once more they took up their places beside the bed.

———————

THEY WAITED ALL DAY, but still the boy did not wake up. Occasionally, one of them would leave the room to go downstairs to the cafeteria to drink coffee and then, as if suddenly remembering and feeling guilty, get up from the table and hurry back to the room. Dr. Francis came again that afternoon and examined the boy once more and then left after telling them he was coming along and could wake up at any minute now. Nurses, different nurses from the night before, came in from time to time. Then a young woman from the lab knocked and entered the room. She wore white slacks and a white blouse and carried a little tray of things which she put on the stand beside the bed. Without a word to them, she took blood from the boy's arm. Howard closed his eyes as the woman found the right place on the boy's arm and pushed the needle in.

"I don't understand this," Ann said to the woman.

"Doctor's orders," the young woman said. "I do what I'm told. They say draw that one, I draw. What's wrong with him, anyway?" she said. "He's a sweetie."

"He was hit by a car," Howard said. "A hit-and-run."

The young woman shook her head and looked again at the boy. Then she took her tray and left the room.

"Why won't he wake up?" Ann said. "Howard? I want some answers from these people."

Howard didn't say anything. He sat down again in the chair and crossed one leg over the other. He rubbed his face. He looked at his son and then he settled back in the chair, closed his eyes, and went to sleep.

Ann walked to the window and looked out at the parking lot. It was night, and cars were driving into and out of the parking lot with their lights on. She stood at the window with her hands gripping the sill, and knew in her heart that they were into something now, something hard. She was afraid, and her teeth began to chatter until she tightened her jaws. She saw a big car stop in front of the hospital and someone, a woman in a long coat, get into the car. She wished she were that woman and somebody, anybody, was driving her away from here to somewhere else, a place where she would find Scotty waiting for her when she stepped out of the car, ready to say *Mom* and let her gather him in her arms.

In a little while, Howard woke up. He looked at the boy again. Then he got up from the chair, stretched, and went over to stand beside her at the window. They both stared out at the parking lot. They didn't say anything. But they seemed to feel each other's insides now, as though the worry had made them transparent in a perfectly natural way.

The door opened and Dr. Francis came in. He was wearing a different suit and tie this time. His gray hair was combed along the sides of his head, and he looked as if he had just shaved. He went straight to the bed and examined the boy. "He ought to have come around by now. There's just no good reason for this," he said. "But I can tell you we're all convinced he's out of any danger. We'll just feel better when he wakes up. There's no reason, absolutely none, why he shouldn't come around. Very soon. Oh, he'll have himself a dilly of a headache when he does, you can count on that. But all of his signs are fine. They're as normal as can be."

"It is a coma, then?" Ann said.

The doctor rubbed his smooth cheek. "We'll call it that for the time being, until he wakes up. But you must be worn out. This is hard. I know this is hard. Feel free to go out for a bite," he said. "It would do you good. I'll put a nurse in here while you're gone if you'll feel better about going. Go and have yourselves something to eat."

"I couldn't eat anything," Ann said.

"Do what you need to do, of course," the doctor said. "Anyway, I wanted to tell you that all the signs are good, the tests are negative, nothing showed up at all, and just as soon as he wakes up he'll be over the hill."

"Thank you, doctor," Howard said. He shook hands with the doctor again. The doctor patted Howard's shoulder and went out.

"I suppose one of us should go home and check on things," Howard said. "Slug needs to be fed, for one thing."

"Call one of the neighbors," Ann said. "Call the Morgans. Anyone will feed a dog if you ask them to."

"All right," Howard said. After a while, he said, "Honey why don't *you* do it? Why don't you go home and check on things, and then come back? It'll do you good. I'll be right here with him. Seriously," he said. "We need to keep up our strength on this. We'll want to be here for a while even after he wakes up."

"Why don't *you* go?" she said. "Feed Slug. Feed yourself."

"I already went," he said. "I was gone for exactly an hour and fifteen minutes. You go home for an hour and freshen up. Then come back."

She tried to think about it, but she was too tired. She closed her eyes and tried to think about it again. After a time, she said, "Maybe I *will* go home for a few minutes. Maybe if I'm not just sitting right here watching him every second, he'll wake up and be all right. You know? Maybe he'll wake up if I'm not here. I'll go home and take a bath and put on clean clothes. I'll feed Slug. Then I'll come back."

"I'll be right here," he said. "You go on home, honey. I'll keep an eye on things here." His eyes were bloodshot and small, as if he'd been drinking for a long time. His clothes were rumpled. His beard had come out again. She touched his face, and then she took her hand back. She understood he wanted to be by himself for a while, not have to talk or share his worry for a time. She picked her purse up from the nightstand, and he helped her into her coat.

"I won't be gone long," she said.

"Just sit and rest for a little while when you get home," he said. "Eat something. Take a bath. After you get out of the bath, just sit for a while and rest. It'll do you a world of good, you'll see. Then come back," he said. "Let's try not to worry. You heard what Dr. Francis said."

She stood in her coat for a minute trying to recall the doctor's exact words, looking for any nuances, any hint of something behind his words other than what he had said. She tried to remember if his expression had changed any when he bent over to examine the child. She remembered the way his features had composed themselves as he rolled back the child's eyelids and then listened to his breathing.

She went to the door, where she turned and looked back. She looked at the child, and then she looked at the father. Howard nodded. She stepped out of the room and pulled the door closed behind her.

She went past the nurses' station and down to the end of the corridor, looking for the elevator. At the end of the corridor, she turned to her right and entered a little waiting room where a Negro family sat in wicker chairs. There was a middle-aged man in a khaki shirt and pants, a baseball cap pushed back on his head. A large woman wearing a housedress and slippers was slumped in one of the chairs. A teenaged girl in jeans, hair done in dozens of little braids, lay stretched out in one of the chairs smoking a cigarette, her legs crossed at the ankles. The family swung their eyes to Ann as she entered the room. The little table was littered with hamburger wrappers and Styrofoam cups.

"Franklin," the large woman said as she roused herself. "Is it about Franklin?" Her eyes widened. "Tell me now, lady," the woman said. "Is it about Franklin?" She was trying to rise from her chair, but the man had closed his hand over her arm.

"Here, here," he said. "Evelyn."

"I'm sorry," Ann said. "I'm looking for the elevator. My son is in the hospital, and now I can't find the elevator."

"Elevator is down that way, turn left," the man said as he aimed a finger.

The girl drew on her cigarette and stared at Ann. Her eyes were narrowed to slits, and her broad lips parted slowly as she let the smoke escape. The Negro woman let her head fall on her shoulder and looked away from Ann, no longer interested.

"My son was hit by a car," Ann said to the man. She seemed to need to explain herself. "He has a concussion and a little skull fracture, but he's going to be all right. He's in shock now, but it might be some kind of coma, too. That's what really worries us, the coma part. I'm going out for a little while, but my husband is with him. Maybe he'll wake up while I'm gone."

"That's too bad," the man said and shifted in the chair. He shook his head. He looked down at the table, and then he looked back at Ann. She was still standing there. He said, "Our Franklin, he's on the operating table. Somebody cut him. Tried to kill him. There was a fight where he was at. At this party. They say he was just standing and watching. Not bothering nobody. But that don't mean nothing these days. Now he's on the operating table. We're just hoping and praying, that's all we can do now." He gazed at her steadily.

Ann looked at the girl again, who was still watching her, and at the older woman, who kept her head down, but whose eyes were now closed. Ann saw the lips moving silently, making words. She had an urge to ask what those words were. She wanted to talk more with these people who were in the same kind of waiting she was in. She was afraid, and they were afraid. They had that in common. She would have liked to have said something else about the accident, told them more about Scotty, that it had happened on the day of his birthday, Monday, and that he was still unconscious. Yet she didn't know how to begin. She stood looking at them without saying anything more.

She went down the corridor the man had indicated and found the elevator. She waited a minute in front of the closed doors, still wondering if she was doing the right thing. Then she put out her finger and touched the button.

———

SHE PULLED INTO THE DRIVEWAY AND CUT THE ENGINE. She closed her eyes and leaned her head against the wheel for a minute. She listened to the ticking sounds the engine made as it began to cool. Then she got out of the car. She could hear the dog barking inside the house. She went to the front door, which was unlocked. She went inside and turned on lights and put on a kettle of water for tea. She opened some dog food and fed Slug on the back porch. The dog ate in hungry little smacks. It kept running into the kitchen to see that she was going to stay. As she sat down on the sofa with her tea, the telephone rang.

"Yes!" she said as she answered. "Hello!"

"Mrs. Weiss," a man's voice said. It was five o'clock in the morning, and she thought she could hear machinery or equipment of some kind in the background.

"Yes, yes! What is it?" she said. "This is Mrs. Weiss. This is she. What is it, please?" She listened to whatever it was in the background. "Is it Scotty, for Christ's sake?"

"Scotty," the man's voice said. "It's about Scotty, yes. It has to do with Scotty, that problem. Have you forgotten about Scotty?" the man said. Then he hung up.

She dialed the hospital's number and asked for the third floor. She demanded information about her son from the nurse who answered the telephone. Then she asked to speak to her husband. It was, she said, an emergency.

She waited, turning the telephone cord in her fingers. She closed her eyes and felt sick at her stomach. She would have to make herself eat. Slug came in from the back porch and lay down near her feet. He wagged his tail. She pulled at his ear while he licked her fingers. Howard was on the line.

"Somebody just called here," she said. She twisted the telephone cord. "He said it was about Scotty," she cried.

"Scotty's fine," Howard told her. "I mean, he's still sleeping. There's been no change. The nurse has been in twice since you've been gone. A nurse or else a doctor. He's all right.'

"This man called. He said it was about Scotty," she told him.

"Honey, you rest for a little while, you need the rest. It must be that same caller I had. Just forget it. Come back down here after you've rested. Then we'll have breakfast or something."

"Breakfast," she said. "I don't want any breakfast."

"You know what I mean," he said. "Juice, something. I don't know. I don't know anything, Ann. Jesus, I'm not hungry, either. Ann, it's hard to talk now. I'm standing here at the desk. Dr. Francis is coming again at eight o'clock this morning. He's going to have something to tell us then, some-thing more definite. That's what one of the nurses said. She didn't know any more than that. Ann? Honey, maybe we'll know something more then. At eight o'clock. Come back here before eight. Meanwhile, I'm right here and Scotty's all right. He's still the same," he added.

"I was drinking a cup of tea," she said, "when the telephone rang. They said it was about Scotty. There was a noise in the background. Was there a noise in the background on that call you had, Howard?"

"I don't remember," he said. "Maybe the driver of the car, maybe he's a psychopath and found out about Scotty somehow. But I'm here with him. Just rest like you were going to do. Take a bath and come back by seven or so, and we'll talk to the doctor together when he gets here. It's going to be all right, honey. I'm here, and there are doctors and nurses around. They say his condition is stable."

"I'm scared to death," she said.

She ran water, undressed, and got into the tub. She washed and dried quickly, not taking the time to wash her hair. She put on clean underwear, wool slacks, and a sweater. She went into the living room, where the dog looked up at her and let its tail thump once against the floor. It was just starting to get light outside when she went out to the car.

She drove into the parking lot of the hospital and found a space close to the front door. She felt she was in some obscure way responsible for what had happened to the child. She let her thoughts move to the Negro family. She remembered the name Franklin and the table that was covered with hamburger papers, and the teenaged girl staring at her as she drew on her cigarette. "Don't have children," she told the girl's image as she entered the front door of the hospital. "For God's sake, don't."

SHE TOOK THE ELEVATOR UP TO THE THIRD FLOOR with two nurses who were just going on duty. It was Wednesday morning, a few minutes before seven. There was a page for a Dr. Madison as the elevator doors slid open on the third floor. She got off behind the nurses, who turned in the other direction and continued the conversation she had interrupted when she'd gotten into the elevator. She walked down the corridor to the little alcove where the Negro family had been waiting. They were gone now, but the chairs were scattered in such a way that it looked as if people had just jumped up from them the minute before. The tabletop was cluttered with the same cups and papers, the ashtray was filled with cigarette butts.

She stopped at the nurses' station. A nurse was standing behind the counter, brushing her hair and yawning.

"There was a Negro boy in surgery last night," Ann said. "Franklin was his name. His family was in the waiting room. I'd like to inquire about his condition."

A nurse who was sitting at a desk behind the counter looked up from a chart in front of her. The telephone buzzed and she picked up the receiver, but she kept her eyes on Ann.

"He passed away," said the nurse at the counter. The nurse held the hairbrush and kept looking at her. "Are you a friend of the family or what?"

"I met the family last night," Ann said. "My own son is in the hospital. I guess he's in shock. We don't know for sure what's wrong. I just wondered about Franklin, that's all. Thank you." She moved down the corridor. Elevator doors the same color as the walls slid open and a gaunt, bald man in white pants and white canvas shoes pulled a heavy cart off the elevator. She hadn't noticed these doors last night. The man wheeled the cart out into the corridor and stopped in front of the room nearest the elevator and consulted a clipboard. Then he reached down and slid a tray out of the cart. He rapped lightly on the door and entered the room. She could smell the unpleasant odors of warm food as she passed the cart. She hurried on without looking at any of the nurses and pushed open the door to the child's room.

Howard was standing at the window with his hands behind his back. He turned around as she came in.

"How is he?" she said. She went over to the bed. She dropped her purse on the floor beside the nightstand. It seemed to her she had been gone a long time. She touched the child's face. "Howard?"

"Dr. Francis was here a little while ago," Howard said. She looked at him closely and thought his shoulders were bunched a little.

"I thought he wasn't coming until eight o'clock this morning," she said quickly.

"There was another doctor with him. A neurologist."

"A neurologist," she said.

Howard nodded. His shoulders were bunching, she could see that. "What'd they say, Howard? For Christ's sake, what'd they say? What is it?"

"They said they're going to take him down and run more tests on him, Ann. They think they're going to operate, honey. Honey, they *are* going to operate. They can't figure out why he won't wake up. It's more than just shock or concussion, they know that much now. It's in his skull, the fracture, it has something, something to do with that, they think. So they're going to operate. I tried to call you, but I guess you'd already left the house."

"Oh, God," she said. "Oh, please, Howard, please," she said, taking his arms.

"Look!" Howard said. "Scotty! Look, Ann!" He turned her toward the bed.

The boy had opened his eyes, then closed them. He opened them again now. The eyes stared straight ahead for a minute, then moved slowly in his head until they rested on Howard and Ann, then traveled away again.

"Scotty," his mother said, moving to the bed.

"Hey, Scott," his father said. "Hey, son."

They leaned over the bed. Howard took the child's hand in his hands and began to pat and squeeze the hand. Ann bent over the boy and kissed his forehead again and again. She put her hands on either side of his face. "Scotty, honey, it's Mommy and Daddy," she said. "Scotty?"

The boy looked at them, but without any sign of recognition. Then his mouth opened, his eyes scrunched closed, and he howled until he had no more air in his lungs. His face seemed to relax and soften then. His lips parted as his last breath was puffed through his throat and exhaled gently through the clenched teeth.

THE DOCTORS CALLED IT A HIDDEN OCCLUSION and said it was a one-in-a-million circumstance. Maybe if it could have been detected somehow and surgery undertaken immediately, they could have saved him. But more than likely not. In any case, what would they have been looking for? Nothing had shown up in the tests or in the X-rays.

Dr. Francis was shaken. "I can't tell you how badly I feel. I'm so very sorry, I can't tell you," he said as he led them into the doctors' lounge. There was a doctor sitting in a chair with his legs hooked over the back of another chair, watching an early-morning TV show. He was wearing a green delivery-room outfit, loose green pants and green blouse, and a green cap that covered his hair. He looked at Howard and Ann and then looked at Dr. Francis. He got to his feet and turned off the set and went out of the room. Dr. Francis guided Ann to the sofa, sat down beside her, and began to talk in a low, consoling voice. At one point, he leaned over and embraced her. She could feel his chest rising and falling evenly against her shoulder. She kept her eyes open and let him hold her. Howard went into the bathroom, but he left the door open. After a violent fit of weeping, he ran water and washed his face. Then he came out and sat down at the little table that held a telephone. He looked at the telephone as though deciding what to do first. He made some calls. After a time, Dr. Francis used the telephone.

"Is there anything else I can do for the moment?" he asked them.

Howard shook his head. Ann stared at Dr. Francis as if unable to comprehend his words.

The doctor walked them to the hospital's front door. People were entering and leaving the hospital. It was eleven o'clock in the morning. Ann was aware of how slowly, almost reluctantly, she moved her feet. It seemed to her that Dr. Francis was making them leave when she felt they should stay, when it would be more the right thing to do to stay. She gazed out into the parking lot and then turned around and looked back at the front of the hospital. She began shaking her head. "No, no," she said. "I can't leave him here, no." She heard herself say that and thought how unfair it was that the only words that came out were the sort of words used on TV shows where people were stunned by violent or sudden deaths. She wanted her words to be her own. "No," she said, and for some reason the memory of the Negro woman's head lolling on the woman's shoulder came to her. "No," she said again.

"I'll be talking to you later in the day," the doctor was saying to Howard. "There are still some things that have to be done, things that have to be cleared up to our satisfaction. Some things that need explaining."

"An autopsy," Howard said.

Dr. Francis nodded.

"I understand," Howard said. Then he said, "Oh, Jesus. No, I don't understand, doctor. I can't, I can't. I just can't."

Dr. Francis put his arm around Howard's shoulders. "I'm sorry. God, how I'm sorry." He let go of Howard's shoulders and held out his hand. Howard looked at the hand, and then he took it. Dr. Francis put his arms around Ann once more. He seemed full of some goodness she didn't understand. She let her head rest on his shoulder, but her eyes stayed open. She kept looking at the hospital. As they drove out of the parking lot, she looked back at the hospital.

AT HOME, SHE SAT ON THE SOFA WITH HER HANDS IN HER COAT POCKETS. Howard closed the door to the child's room. He got the coffee-maker going and then he found an empty box. He had thought to pick up some of the child's things that were scattered around the living room. But instead he sat down beside her on the sofa, pushed the box to one side, and leaned forward, arms between his knees. He began to weep. She pulled his head over into her lap and patted his shoulder. "He's gone," she said. She kept patting his shoulder. Over his sobs, she could hear the coffee-maker hissing in the kitchen. "There, there," she said tenderly. "Howard, he's gone. He's gone and now we'll have to get used to that. To being alone."

In a little while, Howard got up and began moving aimlessly around the room with the box, not putting anything into it, but collecting some things together on the floor at one end of the sofa. She continued to sit with her hands in her coat pockets. Howard put the box down and brought coffee into the living room. Later, Ann made calls to relatives. After each call had been placed and the party had answered, Ann would blurt out a few words and cry for a minute. Then she would quietly explain, in a measured voice, what had happened and tell them about arrangements. Howard took the box out to the garage, where he saw the child's bicycle. He dropped the box and sat down on the pavement beside the bicycle. He took hold of the bicycle awkwardly so that it leaned against his chest. He held it, the rubber pedal sticking into his chest. He gave the wheel a turn.

Ann hung up the telephone after talking to her sister. She was looking up another number when the telephone rang. She picked it up on the first ring.

"Hello," she said, and she heard something in the background, a humming noise. "Hello!" she said. "For God's sake," she said. "Who is this? What is it you want?"

"Your Scotty, I got him ready for you," the man's voice said. "Did you forget him?"

"You evil bastard!" she shouted into the receiver. "How can you do this, you evil son of a bitch!"

"Scotty," the man said. "Have you forgotten about Scotty?" Then the man hung up on her.

Howard heard the shouting and came in to find her with her head on her arms over the table, weeping. He picked up the receiver and listened to the dial tone.

———————

MUCH LATER, JUST BEFORE MIDNIGHT, after they had dealt with many things, the telephone rang again.

"You answer it," she said. "Howard, it's him, I know." They were sitting at the kitchen table with coffee in front of them. Howard had a small glass of whiskey beside his cup. He answered on the third ring.

"Hello," he said. "Who is this? Hello! Hello!" The line went dead. "He hung up," Howard said. "Whoever it was."

"It was him," she said. "That bastard, I'd like to kill him," she said. "I'd like to shoot him and watch him kick," she said.

"Ann, my God," he said.

"Could you hear anything?" she said. "In the background? A noise, machinery, something humming?"

"Nothing, really. Nothing like that," he said. "There wasn't much time. I think there was some radio music. Yes, there was a radio going, that's all I could tell. I don't know what in God's name is going on," he said.

She shook her head "If I could, could get my hands on him." It came to her then. She knew who it was. Scotty, the cake, the telephone number. She pushed the chair away from the table and got up. "Drive me down to the shopping center," she said. "Howard."

"What are you saying?"

"The shopping center. I know who it is who's calling. I know who it is. It's the baker, the son-of-a-bitching baker, Howard. I had him bake a cake for Scotty's birthday. That's who's calling. That's who has the number and keeps calling us. To harass us about that cake. The baker, that bastard."

They drove down to the shopping center. The sky was clear and stars were out. It was cold, and they ran the heater in the car. They parked in front of the bakery. All of the shops and stores were closed, but there were cars at the far end of the lot in front of the movie theater. The bakery windows were dark, but when they looked through the glass they could see a light in the back room and, now and then, a big man in an apron moving in and out of the white, even light. Through the glass, she could see the display cases and some little tables with chairs. She tried the door. She rapped on the glass. But if the baker heard them, he gave no sign. He didn't look in their direction.

They drove around behind the bakery and parked. They got out of the car. There was a lighted window too high up for them to see inside. A sign near the back door said THE PANTRY BAKERY, SPECIAL ORDERS. She could hear faintly a radio playing inside and something creak—an oven door as it was pulled down? She knocked on the door and waited. Then she knocked again, louder. The radio was turned down and there was a scraping sound now, the distinct sound of something, a drawer, being pulled open and then closed.

Someone unlocked the door and opened it. The baker stood in the light and peered out at them. "I'm closed for business," he said. "What do you want at this hour? It's midnight. Are you drunk or something?"

She stepped into the light that fell through the open door. He blinked his heavy eyelids as he recognized her. "It's you," he said.

"It's me," she said. "Scotty's mother. This is Scotty's father. We'd like to come in."

The baker said, "I'm busy now. I have work to do."

She had stepped inside the doorway anyway. Howard came in behind her. The baker moved back. "It smells like a bakery in here. Doesn't it smell like a bakery in here, Howard?"

"What do you want?" the baker said. "Maybe you want your cake? That's it, you decided you want your cake. You ordered a cake, didn't you."

"You're pretty smart for a baker," she said. "Howard, this is the man who's been calling us." She clenched her fists. She stared at him fiercely. There was a deep burning inside her, an anger that made her feel larger than herself, larger than either of these men.

"Just a minute here," the baker said. "You want to pick up your three-day-old cake? That it? I don't want to argue with you, lady. There it sits over there, getting stale. I'll give it to you for half of what I quoted you. No. You want it? You can have it. It's no good to me, no good to anyone now. It cost me time and money to make that cake. If you want it, okay, if you don't, that's okay, too. I have to get back to work." He looked at them and rolled his tongue behind his teeth.

"More cakes," she said. She knew she was in control of it, of what was increasing in her. She was calm.

"Lady, I work sixteen hours a day in this place to earn a living," the baker said. He wiped his hands on his apron. "I work night and day in here, trying to make ends meet." A look crossed Ann's face that made the baker move back and say, "No trouble, now." He reached to the counter and picked up a rolling pin with his right hand and began to tap it against the palm of his other hand. "You want the cake or not? I have to get back to work. Bakers work at night," he said again. His eyes were small, mean-looking, she thought, nearly lost in the bristly flesh around his cheeks. His neck was thick with fat.

"I know bakers work at night," Ann said. "They make phone calls at night, too. You bastard," she said.

The baker continued to tap the rolling pin against his hand. He glanced at Howard. "Careful, careful," he said to Howard.

"My son's dead," she said with a cold, even finality. "He was hit by a car Monday morning. We've been waiting with him until he died. But, of course, you couldn't be expected to know that, could you? Bakers can't know everything—can they, Mr. Baker? But he's dead. He's dead, you bastard!" Just as suddenly as it had welled in her, the anger dwindled, gave way to something else, a dizzy feeling of nausea. She leaned against the wooden table that was sprinkled with flour, put her hands over her face, and began to cry, her shoulders rocking back and forth. "It isn't fair," she said. "It isn't, isn't fair."

Howard put his hand at the small of her back and looked at the baker. "Shame on you," Howard said to him. "Shame."

The baker put the rolling pin back on the counter. He undid his apron and threw it on the counter. He looked at them, and then he shook his head slowly. He pulled a chair out from under the card table that held papers and receipts, an adding machine, and a telephone directory. "Please sit down," he said. "Let me get you a chair," he said to Howard. "Sit down now, please." The baker went into the front of the shop and returned with two little wrought-iron chairs. "Please sit down, you people."

Ann wiped her eyes and looked at the baker. "I wanted to kill you," she said. "I wanted you dead."

The baker had cleared a space for them at the table. He shoved the adding machine to one side, along with the stacks of notepaper and receipts. He pushed the telephone directory onto the floor, where it landed with a thud. Howard and Ann sat down and pulled their chairs up to the table. The baker sat down, too.

"Let me say how sorry I am," the baker said, putting his elbows on the table. "God alone knows how sorry. Listen to me. I'm just a baker. I don't claim to be anything else. Maybe once, maybe years ago, I was a different kind of human being. I've forgotten, I don't know for sure. But I'm not any longer, if I ever was. Now I'm just a baker. That don't excuse my doing what I did, I know. But I'm deeply sorry. I'm sorry for your son, and sorry for my part in this," the baker said. He spread his hands out on the table and turned them over to reveal his palms. "I don't have any children myself, so I can only imagine what you must be feeling. All I can say to you now is that I'm sorry. Forgive me, if you can," the baker said. "I'm not an evil man, I don't think. Not evil, like you said on the phone. You got to understand what it comes down to is I don't know how to act anymore, it would seem. Please," the man said, "let me ask you if you can find it in your hearts to forgive me?"

It was warm inside the bakery. Howard stood up from the table and took off his coat. He helped Ann from her coat. The baker looked at them for a minute and then nodded and got up from the table. He went to the oven and turned off some switches. He found cups and poured coffee from an electric coffee-maker. He put a carton of cream on the table, and a bowl of sugar.

"You probably need to eat something," the baker said. "I hope you'll eat some of my hot rolls. You have to eat and keep going. Eating is a small, good thing in a time like this," he said.

He served them warm cinnamon rolls just out of the oven, the icing still runny. He put butter on the table and knives to spread the butter. Then the baker sat down at the table with them. He waited. He waited until they each took a roll from the platter and began to eat. "It's good to eat something," he said, watching them. "There's more. Eat up. Eat all you want. There's all the rolls in the world in here."

They ate rolls and drank coffee. Ann was suddenly hungry, and the rolls were warm and sweet. She ate three of them, which pleased the baker. Then he began to talk. They listened carefully. Although they were tired and in anguish, they listened to what the baker had to say. They nodded when the baker began to speak of loneliness, and of the sense of doubt and limitation that had come to him in his middle years. He told them what it was like to be childless all these years. To repeat the days with the ovens endlessly full and endlessly empty. The party food, the celebrations he'd worked over. Icing knuckle-deep. The tiny wedding couples stuck into cakes. Hundreds of them, no, thousands by now. Birthdays. Just imagine all those candles burning. He had a necessary trade. He was a baker. He was glad he wasn't a florist. It was better to be feeding people. This was a better smell anytime than flowers.

"Smell this," the baker said, breaking open a dark loaf. "It's a heavy bread, but rich." They smelled it, then he had them taste it. It had the taste of molasses and coarse grains. They listened to him. They ate what they could. They swallowed the dark bread. It was like daylight under the fluorescent trays of light. They talked on into the early morning, the high, pale cast of light in the windows, and they did not think of leaving.

Kate Chopin, 1851–1904

The Story of an Hour

This story first appeared in VOGUE, *1894.*

KNOWING THAT MRS. MALLARD WAS AFFLICTED WITH A HEART TROUBLE, great care was taken to break to her as gently as possible the news of her husband's death.

It was her sister Josephine who told her, in broken sentences, veiled hints that revealed in half concealing. Her husband's friend Richards was there, too, near her. It was he who had been in the newspaper office when intelligence of the railroad disaster was received, with Brently Mallard's name leading the list of "killed." He had only taken the time to assure himself of its truth by a second telegram, and had hastened to forestall any less careful, less tender friend in bearing the sad message.

She did not hear the story as many women have heard the same, with a paralyzed inability to accept its significance. She wept at once, with sudden, wild abandonment, in her sister's arms. When the storm of grief had spent itself she went away to her room alone. She would have no one follow her.

There stood, facing the open window, a comfortable, roomy armchair. Into this she sank, pressed down by a physical exhaustion that haunted her body and seemed to reach into her soul.

She could see in the open square before her house the tops of trees that were all aquiver with the new spring life. The delicious breath of rain was in the air. In the street below a peddler was crying his wares. The notes of a distant song which some one was singing reached her faintly, and countless sparrows were twittering in the eaves.

There were patches of blue sky showing here and there through the clouds that had met and piled one above the other in the west facing her window.

She sat with her head thrown back upon the cushion of the chair, quite motionless, except when a sob came up into her throat and shook her, as a child who has cried itself to sleep continues to sob in its dreams.

She was young, with a fair, calm face, whose lines bespoke repression and even a certain strength. But now there was a dull stare in her eyes, whose gaze was fixed away off yonder on one of those patches of blue sky. It was not a glance of reflection, but rather indicated a suspension of intelligent thought.

There was something coming to her and she was waiting for it, fearfully. What was it? She did not know; it was too subtle and elusive to name. But she felt it, creeping out of the sky, reaching toward her through the sounds, the scents, the color that filled the air.

Now her bosom rose and fell tumultuously. She was beginning to recognize this thing that was approaching to possess her, and she was striving to beat it back with her will—as powerless as her two white slender hands would have been.

When she abandoned herself a little whispered word escaped her slightly parted lips. She said it over and over under her breath: "Free, free, free!" The vacant stare and the look of terror that had followed it went from her eyes. They stayed keen and bright. Her pulses beat fast, and the coursing blood warmed and relaxed every inch of her body.

She did not stop to ask if it were not a monstrous joy that held her. A clear and exalted perception enabled her to dismiss the suggestion as trivial.

She knew that she would weep again when she saw the kind, tender hands folded in death; the face that had never looked save with love upon her, fixed and gray and dead. But she saw beyond that bitter moment a long procession of years to come that would belong to her absolutely. And she opened and spread her arms out to them in welcome.

There would be no one to live for during those coming years; she would live for herself. There would be no powerful will bending her in that blind persistence with which men and women believe they have a right to impose a private will upon a fellow creature. A kind intention or a cruel intention made the act seem no less a crime as she looked upon it in that brief moment of illumination.

And yet she had loved him—sometimes. Often she had not. What did it matter! What could love, the unsolved mystery, count for in face of this possession of self-assertion which she suddenly recognized as the strongest impulse of her being.

"Free! Body and soul free!" she kept whispering.

Josephine was kneeling before the closed door with her lips to the keyhole, imploring for admission. "Louise, open the door! I beg; open the door—you will make yourself ill. What are you doing, Louise? For heaven's sake open the door."

"Go away. I am not making myself ill." No; she was drinking in a very elixir of life through that open window.

Her fancy was running riot along those days ahead of her. Spring days, and summer days, and all sorts of days that would be her own. She breathed a quick prayer that life might be long. It was only yesterday she had thought with a shudder that life might be long.

She arose at length and opened the door to her sister's importunities. There was a feverish triumph in her eyes, and she carried herself unwittingly like a goddess of Victory. She clasped her sister's waist, and together they descended the stairs. Richards stood waiting for them at the bottom.

Some one was opening the front door with a latchkey. It was Brently Mallard who entered, a little travel-stained, composedly carrying his gripsack and umbrella. He had been far from the scene of the accident, and did not even know there had been one. He stood amazed at Josephine's piercing cry; at Richards' quick motion to screen him from the view of his wife.

But Richards was too late.

When the doctors came they said she had died of heart disease—of joy that kills.

Kate Chopin Thinks Back Through Her Mothers: Three Stories by Kate Chopin

Emily Toth

. . . "Athenaise" can be read as the story of a woman's enslavement by her own body, her submission to motherhood, and there it seems to have direct application to Kate Chopin's grandmother. In her youth, Mary Athenaise Charleville, perhaps as impractical as her fictional namesake, had also made an unfortunate marriage, nearly seventy years before Kate Chopin wrote her story. In the mid-1820s, the Catholic Mary Athenaise Charleville (whose name is sometimes given as Marie Anne Athanaise in legal documents) had married a Protestant, Wilson Faris, the well-educated son of a Virginia state representative. Although Athenaise Charleville and Wilson Faris were married in the Catholic Church, her French-speaking father never forgave her for marrying an "American."*

Faris was also an incompetent businessman whose chronic failures enraged his father-in-law, who aided his other daughters' husbands but did nothing to help Athenaise and Wilson Faris. At one point, the hapless young Faris even signed over all his worldly goods to his father-in-law, including his furniture and his horse, to repay "rent of a house and boarding."

In "Athenaise" Kate Chopin gave her heroine the chance to escape, but in life it was the husband who deserted the marriage. Like her fictional counterpart, the real-life Athenaise had found that biology was destiny and motherhood inevitable. When Wilson Faris departed, some six years before his granddaughter Kate was born, he left his wife with little money and seven children. Eliza, the eldest, was barely in her teens. Eliza was not greatly educated, but she was pretty, charming, gentle, and soft-voiced, and spoke English with a French lilt. Although her mother had been married at eighteen, and her sisters much later, Eliza Faris became a bride a little after her sixteenth birthday. On their wedding day in 1844, Thomas O'Flaherty was thirty-nine, four years older than his mother-in-law, Athenaise Faris.

*Mills, *Chauvin dit Charleville,* 51–53; Wilson, "Chopin's Family," 25–31.

In the eyes of the old French of St. Louis, including his own grandmother-in-law Mme. Charleville, who spoke only French and never could pronounce "O'Flaherty," Thomas was an upstart at a time when Irishmen were widely assumed to be drunkards and rowdies. But Thomas O'Flaherty was a self-made man, a Galway immigrant who had become a successful merchant and civic leader. He had married a young woman from a prominent "French" family, but she died young. Six months later, he married Eliza Faris. (Their daughter Kate, born in 1850, was evidently named for his first wife, Catherine.)

Whether Eliza Faris resisted marrying a man just a year younger than her father and a bare half year after the man's first wife died, is not recorded. But her reason for marrying is obvious: As the eldest child, she was providing for her family. A year after the wedding, her impecunious father died, but Eliza's marriage had solved the Farises' desperate financial need.

If Eliza ever regretted her marriage, she left no record, but her daughter Kate Chopin included more than a few hints. Chopin's fictional wives are often discontented and attracted to other men. Some yearn for the freedom of their single days, like the heroine in "Athenaise." Some, like the "Maid of Saint Phillippe," refuse to give up that freedom. Chopin may also have been thinking of her mother's marriage when she wrote *The Awakening,* for Edna, after several youthful infatuations, marries an older man who is safe, secure, and rich, thereby "closing the portals forever behind her upon the realm of romance and dreams." But it was in "The Story of an Hour" that Chopin wrote her mother's story, in the most radical revision of her female past.

By the fall of 1855, five-year-old Kate O'Flaherty had begun boarding school at the Sacred Heart Academy. Besides her half brother George, she had an older brother, Tom, and a younger sister, Jane. Eliza O'Flaherty was noted for her charm and lavish hospitality, and Thomas O'Flaherty's net financial worth qualified him as one of the "solid men of St. Louis."

Captain O'Flaherty, as he had come to be called, was on the inaugural train on November 1, 1855, for the ceremonial opening of railroad connections to Jefferson City over the new Gasconade Bridge. Among the other celebrated passengers were the ministers Artemus Bullard and John Teasdale and the banker Louis A. Benoist, the wealthiest man in St. Louis and owner of a great country estate, Oakland Plantation. (At Oakland, over a decade later, Kate O'Flaherty would meet a charming Benoist grand-nephew from Louisiana named Oscar Chopin.)

But as the ceremonial train chugged onto the Gasconade Bridge, the bridge's floor timbers suddenly gave way, and ten of the cars plunged into the river. Thirty men died, including the ministers Artemus Bullard and John Teasdale (whose granddaughter Sara would be the greatest St. Louis poet of the generation after Kate Chopin). The telegraph first brought the news to St. Louis, and then the newspapers. The Missouri *Republican* later retracted the reports of two deaths. A Mr. Moore from Cape Girardeau was injured, not killed, and a Mr. Bryan, a St. Louis lumber merchant, had not been on the train at all.

But Thomas O'Flaherty had indeed been on the train, and he was dead. Later, Eliza O'Flaherty seemed to be a pious widow, devoted to her husband's memory. Kitty Garesche, Kate's friend, recalled that Mrs. O'Flaherty was "sad and beautiful. . . . This I explain to myself by knowing that her soul must have been shrouded in grief at her dear husband's untimely death." But Eliza, only twenty-seven when her husband died, now controlled a large estate. She had four children and had already buried at least one infant. She had not married for romantic reasons, and a widow mourning the loss of her husband was always respected in society (as in Chopin's story "A Lady of Bayou St. John"). There were many reasons for a widow to remain single, and Eliza never remarried.

Meanwhile, her daughter evidently brooded over her father's death and her mother's life, for thirty-nine years after the Gasconade in "The Story of an Hour" Chopin used a husband's reported death in a train accident as a catalyst for a wife's "monstrous joy." The newly widowed Louise Mallard revels in being "free! Body and soul free!" She had loved her husband, she tells herself, but that hardly counted "in the fact of this possession of self-assertion which she suddenly recognized as the strongest impulse of her being!" But then her husband walks in, having been nowhere near the crash. The wife's weak heart fails, the doctors come, and they conclude that she died of "heart disease—of joy that kills."

Chopin called the piece "The Dream of an Hour," and it was published under that title in the December 6, 1894, issue of *Vogue.* The title was evidently changed by Per Seyersted for the *Complete Works.* The story has also been filmed twice, both versions much longer than the story: Marita Simpson and Martha Wheelock's *The Story of an Hour* (Ishtar Films) and Tina Rathbourne's *The Joy That Kills* (Cypress Films). Both versions create plots that are not in Chopin's story. Simpson and Wheelock add water imagery from *The Awakening;* Rathbourne shows the stultifying relationship between the Mallards, not unlike the marriages in Charlotte Perkins Gilman's "The Yellow Wallpaper" or Henrik Ibsen's *A Doll's House.*

Kate Chopin never wrote about her father in her surviving diaries and letters. She would scarcely have remembered him. In fact, she wrote very little about fathers, although she did write about mothers who refuse to sacrifice themselves for others, most notably in "A Pair of Silk Stockings" (1896, 1987) and *The Awakening* (1899). But in "The Story of an Hour" Chopin used a woman's solitude, as she had in "The Maid of Saint Phillippe" and "Athenaise," as a sign of the character's awakening to her own choices and her place in the universe. The maid chooses solitude, and Athenaise chooses to run away, but Mrs. Mallard is denied the new identity she has chosen.

In life, Thomas O'Flaherty did not return from the railroad crash, yet "The Story of an Hour" is more than a series of hints about what the newly widowed Eliza O'Flaherty might have thought. "Story" also contains details clearly drawn from Kate O'Flaherty's childhood memories.

As noted earlier, Chopin frequently relied on mnemonic devices and name similarities. In "The Story of an Hour," the protagonist's name is Louise, and Eliza O'Flaherty's French-speaking relatives called her "Eleeza," a name that would sound very much like Louise to a frightened eavesdropping child. Likewise, Chopin called the protagonist's sister Josephine, the name of Eliza O'Flaherty's youngest sister. For the husband's name, Brently Mallard, Chopin used a name resembling that of one of the real-life victims, Artemus Bullard, but she gave her character the same initials as Bryan and Moore, the two men falsely reported dead at the Gasconade Bridge. Through "The Story of an Hour," Chopin was openly and subtly remembering.

Like many writers, Chopin used her stories to ask and resolve questions—in her case, about marriage, motherhood, independence, passion, life, and death. Where she seems to make choices, she favors *solitude,* a word that appears some fourteen times in *The Awakening,* nearly always in positive contexts. As she came of age, Kate O'Flaherty lived in a household where her mother, grandmother, and great-grandmother were the central figures (the only males were her brother, half brother, an uncle the age of her brothers, and servants). There were no adult males and no married couples in the household until she was fifteen when her aunt Zuma and Zuma's husband, John, joined the ménage, and by then, Kate was immersed in school activities at the all-girls Sacred Heart Academy.

Until her marriage, then, Kate O'Flaherty grew up in a world of women. When she became a widow, she had numerous admirers but made the same choice her mother, grandmother, and great-grandmother had made: She would not marry again. Although she never had a room of her own until the last years of her life, Chopin always valued the nourishing solitude of her own mind. She peopled her imagination with the women before her. She looked at what they had chosen, and out of her meditations she created extraordinary stories of women in crisis and in fulfillment.

Susan Glaspell, 1882–1948

A Jury of Her Peers

This story first appeared in EVERY WEEK, *1917.*

WHEN MARTHA HALE OPENED THE STORM-DOOR and got a cut of the north wind, she ran back for her big woolen scarf. As she hurriedly wound that round her head her eye made a scandalized sweep of her kitchen. It was no ordinary thing that called her away—it was probably further from ordinary than anything that had ever happened in Dickson County. But what her eye took in was that her kitchen was in no shape for leaving: her bread all ready for mixing, half the flour sifted and half unsifted.

She hated to see things half done; but she had been at that when the team from town stopped to get Mr. Hale, and then the sheriff came running in to say his wife wished Mrs. Hale would come too—adding, with a grin, that he guessed she was getting scary and wanted another woman along. So she had dropped everything right where it was.

"Martha!" now came her husband's impatient voice. "Don't keep folks waiting out here in the cold."

She again opened the storm-door, and this time joined the three men and the one woman waiting for her in the big two-seated buggy.

After she had the robes tucked around her she took another look at the woman who sat beside her on the back seat. She had met Mrs. Peters the year before at the county fair, and the thing she remembered about her was that she didn't seem like a sheriff's wife. She was small and thin and didn't have a strong voice. Mrs. Gorman, sheriff's wife before Gorman went out and Peters came in, had a voice that somehow seemed to be backing up the law with every word. But if Mrs. Peters didn't look like a sheriff's wife, Peters made it up in looking like a sheriff. He was to a dot the kind of man who could get himself elected sheriff—a heavy man with a big voice, who was particularly genial with the law-abiding, as if to make it plain that he knew the difference between criminals and non-criminals. And right there it came into Mrs. Hale's mind, with a stab, that this man who was so pleasant and lively with all of them was going to the Wrights' now as a sheriff.

"The country's not very pleasant this time of year," Mrs. Peters at last ventured, as if she felt they ought to be talking as well as the men.

176

Mrs. Hale scarcely finished her reply, for they had gone up a little hill and could see the Wright place now, and seeing it did not make her feel like talking. It looked very lonesome this cold March morning. It had always been a lonesome-looking place. It was down in a hollow, and the poplar trees around it were lonesome-looking trees. The men were looking at it and talking about what had happened. The county attorney was bending to one side of the buggy, and kept looking steadily at the place as they drew up to it.

"I'm glad you came with me," Mrs. Peters said nervously, as the two women were about to follow the men in through the kitchen door.

Even after she had her foot on the door-step, her hand on the knob, Martha Hale had a moment of feeling she could not cross that threshold. And the reason it seemed she couldn't cross it now was simply because she hadn't crossed it before. Time and time again it had been in her mind, "I ought to go over and see Minnie Foster"—she still thought of her as Minnie Foster, though for twenty years she had been Mrs. Wright. And then there was always something to do and Minnie Foster would go from her mind. But *now* she could come.

———————

THE MEN WENT OVER TO THE STOVE. The women stood close together by the door. Young Henderson, the county attorney, turned around and said, "Come up to the fire, ladies."

Mrs. Peters took a step forward, then stopped. "I'm not—cold," she said.

And so the two women stood by the door, at first not even so much as looking around the kitchen.

The men talked for a minute about what a good thing it was the sheriff had sent his deputy out that morning to make a fire for them, and then Sheriff Peters stepped back from the stove, unbuttoned his outer coat, and leaned his hands on the kitchen table in a way that seemed to mark the beginning of official business. "Now, Mr. Hale," he said in a sort of semi-official voice, "before we move things about, you tell Mr. Henderson just what it was you saw when you came here yesterday morning."

The county attorney was looking around the kitchen.

"By the way," he said, "has anything been moved?" He turned to the sheriff. "Are things just as you left them yesterday?"

Peters looked from cupboard to sink; from that to a small worn rocker a little to one side of the kitchen table.

"It's just the same."

"Somebody should have been left here yesterday," said the county attorney.

"Oh—yesterday," returned the sheriff, with a little gesture as of yesterday having been more than he could bear to think of. "When I had to send Frank to Morris Center for that man who went crazy—let me tell you I had my hands full *yesterday*. I knew you could get back from Omaha by today, George, and as long as I went over everything here myself—"

"Well, Mr. Hale," said the county attorney, in a way of letting what was past and gone go, "tell just what happened when you came here yesterday morning."

Mrs. Hale, still leaning against the door, had that sinking feeling of the mother whose child is about to speak a piece. Lewis often wandered along and got things mixed up in a story. She hoped he would tell this straight and plain, and not say unnecessary things that would just make things harder for Minnie Foster. He didn't begin at once, and she noticed that he looked queer—as if standing in that kitchen and having to tell what he had seen there yesterday morning made him almost sick.

"Yes, Mr. Hale?" the county attorney reminded.

"Harry and I had started to town with a load of potatoes," Mrs. Hale's husband began.

Harry was Mrs. Hale's oldest boy. He wasn't with them now, for the very good reason that those potatoes never got to town yesterday and he was taking them this morning, so he hadn't been home when the sheriff stopped to say he wanted Mr. Hale to come over to the Wright place and tell the county attorney his story there, where he could point it all out. With all Mrs. Hale's other emotions came the fear now that maybe Harry wasn't dressed warm enough—they hadn't any of them realized how that north wind did bite.

"We come along this road," Hale was going on, with a motion of his hand to the road over which they had just come, "and as we got in sight of the house I says to Harry, 'I'm goin' to see if I can't get John Wright to take a telephone.' You see," he explained to Henderson, "unless I can get somebody to go in with me they won't come out this branch road except for a price *I* can't pay. I'd spoke to Wright about it once before; but he put me off, saying folks talked too much anyway, and all he asked was peace and quiet—guess you know about how much he talked himself. But I thought maybe if I went to the house and talked about it before his wife, and said all the women-folks liked the telephones, and that in this lonesome stretch of road it would be a good thing—well, I said to Harry that that was what I was going to say—though I said at the same time that I didn't know as what his wife wanted made much difference to John—"

Now there he was!—saying things he didn't need to say. Mrs. Hale tried to catch her husband's eye, but fortunately the county attorney interrupted with:

"Let's talk about that a little later, Mr. Hale. I do want to talk about that, but I'm anxious now to get along to just what happened when you got here."

When he began this time, it was very deliberately and carefully:

"I didn't see or hear anything. I knocked at the door. And still it was all quiet inside. I knew they must be up—it was past eight o'clock. So I knocked again, louder, and I thought I heard somebody say, 'Come in.' I wasn't sure—I'm not sure yet. But I opened the door—this door," jerking a hand toward the door by which the two women stood, "and there, in that rocker"—pointing to it—"sat Mrs. Wright."

Everyone in the kitchen looked at the rocker. It came into Mrs. Hale's mind that that rocker didn't look in the least like Minnie Foster—the Minnie Foster of twenty years before. It was a dingy red, with wooden rungs up the back, and the middle rung was gone, and the chair sagged to one side.

"How did she—look?" the county attorney was inquiring.

"Well," said Hale, "she looked—queer."

"How do you mean—queer?"

As he asked it he took out a note-book and pencil. Mrs. Hale did not like the sight of that pencil. She kept her eye fixed on her husband, as if to keep him from saying unnecessary things that would go into that note-book and make trouble.

Hale did speak guardedly, as if the pencil had affected him too.

"Well, as if she didn't know what she was going to do next. And kind of—done up."

"How did she seem to feel about your coming?"

"Why, I don't think she minded—one way or other. She didn't pay much attention. I said, 'Ho' do, Mrs. Wright? It's cold, ain't it?' And she said. 'Is it?'—and went on pleatin' at her apron.

"Well, I was surprised. She didn't ask me to come up to the stove, or to sit down, but just set there, not even lookin' at me. And so I said: 'I want to see John.'

"And then she—laughed. I guess you would call it a laugh.

"I thought of Harry and the team outside, so I said, a little sharp, 'Can I see John?' 'No,' says she—kind of dull like. 'Ain't he home?' says I. Then she looked at me. 'Yes,' says she, 'he's home.' 'Then why can't I see him?' I asked her, out of patience with her now. 'Cause he's dead' says she, just as quiet and dull—and fell to pleatin' her apron. 'Dead?' says I, like you do when you can't take in what you've heard.

"She just nodded her head, not getting a bit excited, but rockin' back and forth.

"'Why—where is he?' says I, not knowing *what* to say.

"She just pointed upstairs—like this"—pointing to the room above.

"I got up, with the idea of going up there myself. By this time I—didn't know what to do. I walked from there to here; then I says: 'Why, what did he die of?'

"'He died of a rope around his neck,' says she; and just went on pleatin' at her apron."

———————

HALE STOPPED SPEAKING, and stood staring at the rocker, as if he were still seeing the woman who had sat there the morning before. Nobody spoke; it was as if every one were seeing the woman who had sat there the morning before.

"And what did you do then?" the county attorney at last broke the silence.

"I went out and called Harry. I thought I might—need help. I got Harry in, and we went upstairs." His voice fell almost to a whisper. "There he was—lying over the—"

"I think I'd rather have you go into that upstairs," the county attorney interrupted, "where you can point it all out. Just go on now with the rest of the story."

"Well, my first thought was to get that rope off. It looked—"

He stopped, his face twitching.

"But Harry, he went up to him, and he said. 'No, he's dead all right, and we'd better not touch anything.' So we went downstairs.

"She was still sitting that same way. 'Has anybody been notified?' I asked. 'No,' says she, unconcerned.

"'Who did this, Mrs. Wright?' said Harry. He said it businesslike, and she stopped pleatin' at her apron. 'I don't know,' she says. 'You don't *know?*' says Harry. 'Weren't you sleepin' in the bed with him?' 'Yes,' says she, 'but I was on the inside.' 'Somebody slipped a rope round his neck and strangled him, and you didn't wake up?' says Harry. 'I didn't wake up,' she said after him.

"We may have looked as if we didn't see how that could be, for after a minute she said, 'I sleep sound.'

"Harry was going to ask her more questions, but I said maybe that weren't our business; maybe we ought to let her tell her story first to the coroner or the sheriff. So Harry went fast as he could over to High Road—the Rivers' place, where there's a telephone."

"And what did she do when she knew you had gone for the coroner?" The attorney got his pencil in his hand all ready for writing.

"She moved from that chair to this one over here"—Hale pointed to a small chair in the corner—"and just sat there with her hands held together and looking down. I got a feeling that I ought to make some conversation, so I said I had come in to see if John wanted to put in a telephone; and at that she started to laugh, and then she stopped and looked at me—scared."

At the sound of a moving pencil the man who was telling the story looked up.

"I dunno—maybe it wasn't scared," he hastened: "I wouldn't like to say it was. Soon Harry got back, and then Dr. Lloyd came, and you, Mr. Peters, and so I guess that's all I know that you don't."

He said that last with relief, and moved a little, as if relaxing. Everyone moved a little. The county attorney walked toward the stair door.

"I guess we'll go upstairs first—then out to the barn and around there."

He paused and looked around the kitchen.

"You're convinced there was nothing important here?" he asked the sheriff. "Nothing that would—point to any motive?"

The sheriff too looked all around, as if to re-convince himself.

"Nothing here but kitchen things," he said, with a little laugh for the insignificance of kitchen things.

The county attorney was looking at the cupboard—a peculiar, ungainly structure, half closet and half cupboard, the upper part of it being built in the wall, and the lower part just the old-fashioned kitchen cupboard. As if its queerness attracted him, he got a chair and opened the upper part and looked in. After a moment he drew his hand away sticky.

"Here's a nice mess," he said resentfully.

The two women had drawn nearer, and now the sheriff's wife spoke.

"Oh—her fruit," she said, looking to Mrs. Hale for sympathetic understanding. She turned back to the county attorney and explained: "She worried about that when it turned so cold last night. She said the fire would go out and her jars might burst."

Mrs. Peters' husband broke into a laugh.

"Well, can you beat the women! Held for murder, and worrying about her preserves!"

The young attorney set his lips.

"I guess before we're through with her she may have something more serious than preserves to worry about."

"Oh, well," said Mrs. Hale's husband, with good-natured superiority, "women are used to worrying over trifles."

The two women moved a little closer together. Neither of them spoke. The county attorney seemed suddenly to remember his manners—and think of his future.

"And yet," said he, with the gallantry of a young politician, "for all their worries, what would we do without the ladies?"

The women did not speak, did not unbend. He went to the sink and began washing his hands. He turned to wipe them on the roller towel—whirled it for a cleaner place.

"Dirty towels! Not much of a housekeeper, would you say, ladies?"

He kicked his foot against some dirty pans under the sink.

"There's a great deal of work to be done on a farm," said Mrs. Hale stiffly.

"To be sure. And yet"—with a little bow to her—"I know there are some Dickson County farm-houses that do not have such roller towels." He gave it a pull to expose its full length again.

"Those towels get dirty awful quick. Men's hands aren't always as clean as they might be."

"Ah, loyal to your sex, I see," he laughed. He stopped and gave her a keen look. "But you and Mrs. Wright were neighbors. I suppose you were friends, too."

Martha Hale shook her head.

"I've seen little enough of her of late years. I've not been in this house—it's more than a year."

"And why was that? You didn't like her?"

"I liked her well enough," she replied with spirit. "Farmers' wives have their hands full, Mr. Henderson. And then—" She looked around the kitchen.

"Yes?" he encouraged.

"It never seemed a very cheerful place," said she, more to herself than to him.

"No," he agreed; "I don't think anyone would call it cheerful. I shouldn't say she had the home-making instinct."

"Well, I don't know as Wright had, either," she muttered.

"You mean they didn't get on very well?" he was quick to ask.

"No; I don't mean anything," she answered, with decision. As she turned a little away from him, she added: "But I don't think a place would be any the cheerfuller for John Wright's bein' in it."

"I'd like to talk to you about that a little later, Mrs. Hale," he said. "I'm anxious to get the lay of things upstairs now."

He moved toward the stair door, followed by the two men.

"I suppose anything Mrs. Peters does'll be all right?" the sheriff inquired. "She was to take in some clothes for her, you know—and a few little things. We left in such a hurry yesterday."

The county attorney looked at the two women whom they were leaving alone there among the kitchen things.

"Yes—Mrs. Peters," he said, his glance resting on the woman who was not Mrs. Peters, the big farmer woman who stood behind the sheriff's wife. "Of course Mrs. Peters is one of us," he said, in a manner of entrusting responsibility. "And keep your eye out, Mrs. Peters, for anything that might be of use. No telling; you women might come upon a clue to the motive—and that's the thing we need."

Mr. Hale rubbed his face after the fashion of a showman getting ready for a pleasantry.

"But would the women know a clue if they did come upon it?" he said; and, having delivered himself of this, he followed the others through the stair door.

————————

THE WOMEN STOOD MOTIONLESS AND SILENT, listening to the footsteps, first upon the stairs, then in the room above them.

Then, as if releasing herself from something strange, Mrs. Hale began to arrange the dirty pans under the sink, which the county attorney's disdainful push of the foot had deranged.

"I'd hate to have men comin' into my kitchen," she said testily—"snoopin' round and criticizin'."

"Of course it's no more than their duty," said the sheriff's wife, in her manner of timid acquiescence.

"Duty's all right," replied Mrs. Hale bluffly; "but I guess that deputy sheriff that come out to make the fire might have got a little of this on." She gave the roller towel a pull. "Wish I'd thought of that sooner! Seems mean to talk about her for not having things slicked up, when she had to come away in such a hurry."

She looked around the kitchen. Certainly it was not "slicked up." Her eye was held by a bucket of sugar on a low shelf. The cover was off the wooden bucket, and beside it was a paper bag—half full.

Mrs. Hale moved toward it.

"She was putting this in there," she said to herself—slowly.

She thought of the flour in her kitchen at home—half sifted, half not sifted. She had been interrupted, and had left things half done. What had interrupted Minnie Foster? Why had that work been left half done? She made a move as if to finish it,—unfinished things always bothered her,—and then she glanced around and saw that Mrs. Peters was watching her—and she didn't want Mrs. Peters to get that feeling she had got of work begun and then—for some reason—not finished.

"It's a shame about her fruit," she said, and walked toward the cupboard that the county attorney had opened, and got on the chair, murmuring: "I wonder if it's all gone."

It was a sorry enough looking sight, but "Here's one that's all right," she said at last. She held it toward the light. "This is cherries, too." She looked again. "I declare I believe that's the only one."

With a sigh, she got down from the chair, went to the sink, and wiped off the bottle.

"She'll feel awful bad, after all her hard work in the hot weather. I remember the afternoon I put up my cherries last summer."

She set the bottle on the table, and, with another sigh, started to sit down in the rocker. But she did not sit down. Something kept her from sitting down in that chair. She straightened—stepped back, and, half turned away, stood looking at it, seeing the woman who had sat there "pleatin' at her apron."

The thin voice of the sheriff's wife broke in upon her: "I must be getting those things from the front-room closet." She opened the door into the other room, started in, stepped back. "You coming with me, Mrs. Hale?" she asked nervously. "You—you could help me get them."

They were soon back—the stark coldness of that shut-up room was not a thing to linger in.

"My!" said Mrs. Peters, dropping the things on the table and hurrying to the stove.

Mrs. Hale stood examining the clothes the woman who was being detained in town had said she wanted.

"Wright was close!"* she exclaimed, holding up a shabby black skirt that bore the marks of much making over. "I think maybe that's why she kept so much to herself. I s'pose she felt she couldn't do her part; and then, you don't enjoy things when you feel shabby. She used to wear pretty clothes and be lively—when she was Minnie Foster, one of the town girls, singing in the choir. But that—oh, that was twenty years ago."

---

* *close:* that is, frugal, tightfisted.

With a carefulness in which there was something tender, she folded the shabby clothes and piled them at one corner of the table. She looked up at Mrs. Peters, and there was something in the other woman's look that irritated her.

"She don't care," she said to herself. "Much difference it makes to her whether Minnie Foster had pretty clothes when she was a girl."

Then she looked again, and she wasn't so sure; in fact, she hadn't at any time been perfectly sure about Mrs. Peters. She had that shrinking manner, and yet her eyes looked as if they could see a long way into things.

"This all you was to take in?" asked Mrs. Hale.

"No," said the sheriff's wife; "she said she wanted an apron. Funny thing to want," she ventured in her nervous little way, "for there's not much to get you dirty in jail, goodness knows. But I suppose just to make her feel more natural. If you're used to wearing an apron—. She said they were in the bottom drawer of this cupboard. Yes—here they are. And then her little shawl that always hung on the stair door."

She took the small gray shawl from behind the door leading upstairs, and stood a minute looking at it.

Suddenly Mrs. Hale took a quick step toward the other woman.

"Mrs. Peters!"

"Yes, Mrs. Hale?"

"Do you think she—did it?"

A frightened look blurred the other thing in Mrs. Peters' eyes.

"Oh, I don't know," she said, in a voice that seemed to shrink away from the subject.

"Well, I don't think she did," affirmed Mrs. Hale stoutly. "Asking for an apron, and her little shawl. Worryin' about her fruit."

"Mr. Peters says—." Footsteps were heard in the room above; she stopped, looked up, then went on in a lowered voice: "Mr. Peters says—it looks bad for her. Mr. Henderson is awful sarcastic in a speech, and he's going to make fun of her saying she didn't—wake up."

For a moment Mrs. Hale had no answer. Then, "Well, I guess John Wright didn't wake up—when they was slippin' that rope under his neck," she muttered.

"No, it's *strange*," breathed Mrs. Peters. "They think it was such a—funny way to kill a man."

She began to laugh; at the sound of the laugh, she abruptly stopped.

"That's just what Mr. Hale said," said Mrs. Hale, in a resolutely natural voice. "There was a gun in the house. He says that's what he can't understand."

"Mr. Henderson said, coming out, that what was needed for the case was a motive. Something to show anger—or sudden feeling."

"Well, I don't see any signs of anger around here," said Mrs. Hale, "I don't—"

She stopped. It was as if her mind tripped on something. Her eye was caught by a dish-towel in the middle of the kitchen table. Slowly she moved toward the table. One half of it was wiped clean, the other half messy. Her eyes made a slow, almost unwilling turn to the bucket of sugar and the half empty bag beside it. Things begun—and not finished.

After a moment she stepped back, and said, in that manner of releasing herself:

"Wonder how they're finding things upstairs? I hope she had it a little more red up* up there. You know,"—she paused, and feeling gathered,—"it seems kind of *sneaking:* locking her up in town and coming out here to get her own house to turn against her!"

"But, Mrs. Hale," said the sheriff's wife, "the law is the law."

"I s'pose 'tis," answered Mrs. Hale shortly.

She turned to the stove, saying something about that fire not being much to brag of. She worked with it a minute, and when she straightened up she said aggressively:

"The law is the law—and a bad stove is a bad stove. How'd you like to cook on this?"—pointing with the poker to the broken lining. She opened the oven door and started to express her opinion of the oven; but she was swept into her own thoughts, thinking of what it would mean, year after year, to have that stove to wrestle with. The thought of Minnie Foster trying to bake in that oven—and the thought of her never going over to see Minnie Foster—.

She was startled by hearing Mrs. Peters say: "A person gets discouraged—and loses heart."

The sheriff's wife had looked from the stove to the sink—to the pail of water which had been carried in from outside. The two women stood there silent, above them the footsteps of the men who were looking for evidence against the woman who had worked in that kitchen. That look of seeing into things, of seeing through a thing to something else, was in the eyes of the sheriff's wife now. When Mrs. Hale next spoke to her, it was gently:

"Better loosen up your things, Mrs. Peters. We'll not feel them when we go out."

Mrs. Peters went to the back of the room to hang up the fur tippet she was wearing. A moment later she exclaimed, "Why, she was piecing a quilt," and held up a large sewing basket piled high with quilt pieces.

Mrs. Hale spread some of the blocks on the table.

"It's log-cabin pattern," she said, putting several of them together. "Pretty, isn't it?"

They were so engaged with the quilt that they did not hear the footsteps on the stairs. Just as the stair door opened Mrs. Hale was saying:

"Do you suppose she was going to quilt it or just knot it?"

The sheriff threw up his hands.

"They wonder whether she was going to quilt it or just knot it!"

*_red up:_ neat.

There was a laugh for the ways of women, a warming of hands over the stove, and then the county attorney said briskly:

"Well, let's go right out to the barn and get that cleared up."

"I don't see as there's anything so strange," Mrs. Hale said resentfully, after the outside door had closed on the three men—"our taking up our time with little things while we're waiting for them to get the evidence. I don't see as it's anything to laugh about."

"Of course they've got awful important things on their minds," said the sheriff's wife apologetically.

They returned to an inspection of the block for the quilt. Mrs. Hale was looking at the fine, even sewing, and preoccupied with thoughts of the woman who had done that sewing, when she heard the sheriff's wife say, in a queer tone:

"Why, look at this one."

She turned to take the block held out to her.

"The sewing," said Mrs. Peters, in a troubled way, "All the rest of them have been so nice and even—but—this one. Why, it looks as if she didn't know what she was about!"

Their eyes met—something flashed to life, passed between them; then, as if with an effort, they seemed to pull away from each other. A moment Mrs. Hale sat there, her hands folded over that sewing which was so unlike all the rest of the sewing. Then she had pulled a knot and drawn the threads.

"Oh, what are you doing, Mrs. Hale?" asked the sheriff's wife, startled.

"Just pulling out a stitch or two that's not sewed very good," said Mrs. Hale mildly.

"I don't think we ought to touch things," Mrs. Peters said, a little helplessly.

"I'll just finish up this end," answered Mrs. Hale, still in that mild, matter-of-fact fashion.

She threaded a needle and started to replace bad sewing with good. For a little while she sewed in silence. Then, in that thin, timid voice, she heard:

"Mrs. Hale!"

"Yes, Mrs. Peters?"

"What do you suppose she was so—nervous about?"

"Oh, *I* don't know," said Mrs. Hale, as if dismissing a thing not important enough to spend much time on. "I don't know as she was—nervous. I sew awful queer sometimes when I'm just tired."

She cut a thread, and out of the corner of her eye looked up at Mrs. Peters. The small, lean face of the sheriff's wife seemed to have tightened up. Her eyes had that look of peering into something. But next moment she moved, and said in her thin, indecisive way:

"Well, I must get those clothes wrapped. They may be through sooner than we think. I wonder where I could find a piece of paper—and string."

"In that cupboard, maybe," suggested to Mrs. Hale, after a glance around.

ONE PIECE OF THE CRAZY SEWING REMAINED UNRIPPED. Mrs. Peter's back turned, Martha Hale now scrutinized that piece, compared it with the dainty, accurate sewing of the other blocks. The difference was startling. Holding this block made her feel queer, as if the distracted thoughts of the woman who had perhaps turned to it to try and quiet herself were communicating themselves to her.

Mrs. Peters' voice roused her.

"Here's a bird-cage," she said. "Did she have a bird, Mrs. Hale?"

"Why, I don't know whether she did or not." She turned to look at the cage Mrs. Peters was holding up. "I've not been here in so long." She sighed. "There was a man round last year selling canaries cheap—but I don't know as she took one. Maybe she did. She used to sing real pretty herself."

Mrs. Peters looked around the kitchen.

"Seems kind of funny to think of a bird here." She half laughed—an attempt to put up a barrier. "But she must have had one—or why would she have a cage? I wonder what happened to it."

"I suppose maybe the cat got it," suggested Mrs. Hale, resuming her sewing.

"No; she didn't have a cat. She's got that feeling some people have about cats—being afraid of them. When they brought her to our house yesterday, my cat got in the room, and she was real upset and asked me to take it out."

"My sister Bessie was like that," laughed Mrs. Hale.

The sheriff's wife did not reply. The silence made Mrs. Hale turn round. Mrs. Peters was examining the bird-cage.

"Look at this door," she said slowly. "It's broke. One hinge has been pulled apart."

Mrs. Hale came nearer.

"Looks as if someone must have been—rough with it."

Again their eyes met—startled, questioning, apprehensive. For a moment neither spoke nor stirred. Then Mrs. Hale, turning away, said brusquely:

"If they're going to find any evidence, I wish they'd be about it. I don't like this place."

"But I'm awful glad you came with me, Mrs. Hale." Mrs. Peters put the bird-cage on the table and sat down. "It would be lonesome for me—sitting here alone."

"Yes, it would, wouldn't it?" agreed Mrs. Hale, a certain determined naturalness in her voice. She had picked up the sewing, but now it dropped in her lap, and she murmured in a different voice: "But I tell you what I *do* wish, Mrs. Peters. I wish I had come over sometimes when she was here. I wish—I had."

"But of course you were awful busy, Mrs. Hale. Your house—and your children."

"I could've come," retorted Mrs. Hale shortly. "I stayed away because it weren't cheerful—and that's why I ought to have come. I"—she looked around—"I've never liked this place. Maybe because it's down in a hollow and you don't see the road. I don't know what it is, but it's a lonesome place, and always was. I wish I had come over to see Minnie Foster sometimes. I can see now—" She did not put it into words.

"Well, you mustn't reproach yourself," counseled Mrs. Peters. "Somehow, we just don't see how it is with other folks till—something comes up."

"Not having children makes less work," mused Mrs. Hale, after a silence, "but it makes a quiet house—and Wright out to work all day—and no company when he did come in. Did you know John Wright, Mrs. Peters?"

"Not to know him. I've seen him in town. They say he was a good man."

"Yes—good," conceded John Wright's neighbor grimly. "He didn't drink, and kept his word as well as most, I guess, and paid his debts. But he was a hard man, Mrs. Peters. Just to pass the time of day with him—." She stopped, shivered a little. "Like a raw wind that gets to the bone." Her eye fell upon the cage on the table before her, and she added, almost bitterly: "I should think she would've wanted a bird!"

Suddenly she leaned forward, looking intently at the cage. "But what do you s'pose went wrong with it?"

"I don't know," returned Mrs. Peters; "unless it got sick and died."

But after she said it she reached over and swung the broken door. Both women watched it as if somehow held by it.

"You didn't know—her?" Mrs. Hale asked, a gentler note in her voice.

"Not till they brought her yesterday," said the sheriff's wife.

"She—come to think of it, she was kind of like a bird herself. Real sweet and pretty, but kind of timid and—fluttery. How—she—did—change."

That held her for a long time. Finally, as if struck with a happy thought and relieved to get back to everyday things, she exclaimed:

"Tell you what, Mrs. Peters, why don't you take the quilt in with you? It might take up her mind."

"Why, I think that's a real nice idea, Mrs. Hale," agreed the sheriff's wife, as if she too were glad to come into the atmosphere of a simple kindness. "There couldn't possibly be any objection to that, could there? Now, just what will I take? I wonder if her patches are in here—and her things?"

They turned to the sewing basket.

"Here's some red," said Mrs. Hale, bringing out a roll of cloth. Underneath that was a box. "Here, maybe her scissors are in here—and her things." She held it up. "What a pretty box! I'll warrant that was something she had a long time ago—when she was a girl."

She held it in her hand a moment; then, with a little sigh, opened it.

Instantly her hand went to her nose.

"Why—!"

Mrs. Peters drew nearer—then turned away.

"There's something wrapped up in this piece of silk," faltered Mrs. Hale.

"This isn't her scissors," said Mrs. Peters, in a shrinking voice.

Her hand not steady, Mrs. Hale raised the piece of silk. "Oh, Mrs. Peters!" she cried. "It's—"

Mrs. Peters bent closer.

"It's the bird," she whispered.

"But, Mrs. Peters!" cried Mrs. Hale. "*Look* at it! Its *neck*—look at its neck! It's all—other side *to.*"

She held the box away from her.

The sheriff's wife again bent closer.

"Somebody wrung its neck," said she, in a voice that was slow and deep.

And then again the eyes of the two women met—this time clung together in a look of dawning comprehension, of growing horror. Mrs. Peters looked from the dead bird to the broken door of the cage. Again their eyes met. And just then there was a sound at the outside door.

Mrs. Hale slipped the box under the quilt pieces in the basket, and sank into the chair before it. Mrs. Peters stood holding to the table. The county attorney and the sheriff came in from outside.

"Well, ladies," said the county attorney, as one turning from serious things to little pleasantries, "have you decided whether she was going to quilt it or knot it?"

"We think," began the sheriff's wife in a flurried voice, "that she was going to—knot it."

He was too preoccupied to notice the change that came in her voice on that last.

"Well, that's very interesting, I'm sure," he said tolerantly. He caught sight of the bird-cage. "Has the bird flown?"

"We think the cat got it," said Mrs. Hale in a voice curiously even.

He was walking up and down, as if thinking something out.

"Is there a cat?" he asked absently.

Mrs. Hale shot a look up at the sheriff's wife.

"Well, not *now,*" said Mrs. Peters. "They're superstitious, you know; they leave."

She sank into her chair.

The county attorney did not heed her. "No sign at all of anyone having come in from the outside," he said to Peters, in the manner of continuing an interrupted conversation. "Their own rope. Now let's go upstairs again and go over it, piece by piece. It would have to have been someone who knew just the—"

The stair door closed behind them and their voices were lost.

The two women sat motionless, not looking at each other, but as if peering into something and at the same time holding back. When they spoke now it was as if they were afraid of what they were saying, but as if they could not help saying it.

"She liked the bird," said Martha Hale, low and slowly. "She was going to bury it in that pretty box."

"When I was a girl," said Mrs. Peters, under her breath, "my kitten—there was a boy took a hatchet, and before my eyes—before I could get there—" She covered her face an instant. "If they hadn't held me back I would have"—she caught herself, looked upstairs where footsteps were heard, and finished weakly—"hurt him."

Then they sat without speaking or moving.

"I wonder how it would seem," Mrs. Hale at last began, as if feeling her way over strange ground—"never to have had any children around?" Her eyes made a slow sweep of the kitchen, as if seeing what that kitchen had meant through all the years. "No, Wright wouldn't like the bird," she said after that—"a thing that sang. She used to sing. He killed that too." Her voice tightened.

Mrs. Peters moved uneasily.

"Of course we don't know who killed the bird."

"I knew John Wright," was Mrs. Hale's answer.

"It was an awful thing was done in this house that night, Mrs. Hale," said the sheriff's wife. "Killing a man while he slept—slipping a thing round his neck that choked the life out of him."

Mrs. Hale's hand went out to the bird cage.

"His neck. Choked the life out of him."

"We don't *know* who killed him," whispered Mrs. Peters wildly. "We don't *know*."

Mrs. Hale had not moved. "If there had been years and years of—nothing, then a bird to sing to you, it would be awful—still—after the bird was still."

It was as if something within her not herself had spoken, and it found in Mrs. Peters something she did not know as herself.

"I know what stillness is," she said, in a queer, monotonous voice. "When we homesteaded in Dakota, and my first baby died—after he was two years old—and me with no other then—"

Mrs. Hale stirred.

"How soon do you suppose they'll be through looking for the evidence?"

"I know what stillness is," repeated Mrs. Peters, in just that same way. Then she too pulled back. "The law has got to punish crime, Mrs. Hale," she said in her tight little way.

"I wish you'd seen Minnie Foster," was the answer, "when she wore a white dress with blue ribbons, and stood up there in the choir and sang."

The picture of that girl, the fact that she had lived neighbor to that girl for twenty years, and had let her die for lack of life, was suddenly more than she could bear.

"Oh, I *wish* I'd come over here once in a while!" she cried. "That was a crime! Who's going to punish that?"

"We mustn't take on," said Mrs. Peters, with a frightened look toward the stairs.

"I might 'a' *known* she needed help! I tell you, it's *queer*, Mrs. Peters. We live close together, and we live far apart. We all go through the same things—it's all just a different kind of the same thing! If it weren't—why do you and I *understand?* Why do we *know*—what we know this minute?"

She dashed her hand across her eyes. Then, seeing the jar of fruit on the table, she reached for it and choked out:

"If I was you I wouldn't *tell* her her fruit was gone! Tell her it *ain't.* Tell her it's all right—all of it. Here—take this in to prove it to her! She—she may never know whether it was broke or not."

She turned away.

Mrs. Peters reached out for the bottle of fruit as if she were glad to take it—as if touching a familiar thing, having something to do, could keep her from something else. She got up, looked about for something to wrap the fruit in, took a petticoat from the pile of clothes she had brought from the front room, and nervously started winding that round the bottle.

"My!" she began, in a high, false voice, "it's a good thing the men couldn't hear us! Getting all stirred up over a little thing like a—dead canary." She hurried over that. "As if that could have anything to do with—with—My, wouldn't they *laugh?*"

Footsteps were heard on the stairs.

"Maybe they would," muttered Mrs. Hale—"maybe they wouldn't."

"No, Peters," said the county attorney incisively; "it's all perfectly clear, except the reason for doing it. But you know juries when it comes to women. If there was some definite thing—something to show. Something to make a story about. A thing that would connect up with this clumsy way of doing it."

In a covert way Mrs. Hale looked at Mrs. Peters. Mrs. Peters was looking at her. Quickly they looked away from each other. The outer door opened and Mr. Hale came in.

"I've got the team* round now," he said. "Pretty cold out there."

"I'm going to stay here awhile by myself," the county attorney suddenly announced. "You can send Frank out for me, can't you?" he asked the sheriff. "I want to go over everything. I'm not satisfied we can't do better."

Again, for one brief moment, the two women's eyes found one another.

The sheriff came up to the table.

"Did you want to see what Mrs. Peters was going to take in?"

The county attorney picked up the apron. He laughed.

"Oh, I guess they're not very dangerous things the ladies have picked out."

Mrs. Hale's hand was on the sewing basket in which the box was concealed. She felt that she ought to take her hand off the basket. She did not seem able to. He picked up one of the quilt blocks which she had piled on to cover the box. Her eyes felt like fire. She had a feeling that if he took up the basket she would snatch it from him.

But he did not take it up. With another little laugh, he turned away, saying:

"No; Mrs. Peters doesn't need supervising. For that matter, a sheriff's wife is married to the law. Ever think of it that way, Mrs. Peters?"

Mrs. Peters was standing beside the table. Mrs. Hale shot a look up at her; but she could not see her face. Mrs. Peters had turned away. When she spoke, her voice was muffled.

---

* *team:* team of horses pulling the buggy in which the group had come.

"Not—just that way," she said.

"Married to the law!" chuckled Mrs. Peters' husband. He moved toward the door into the front room, and said to the county attorney:

"I just want you to come in here a minute, George. We ought to take a look at these windows."

"Oh—windows," said the county attorney scoffingly.

"We'll be right out, Mr. Hale," said the sheriff to the farmer, who was still waiting by the door.

Hale went to look after the horses. The sheriff followed the county attorney into the other room. Again—for one final moment—the two women were alone in that kitchen.

Martha Hale sprang up, her hands tight together, looking at that other woman, with whom it rested. At first she could not see her eyes, for the sheriff's wife had not turned back since she turned away at that suggestion of being married to the law. But now Mrs. Hale made her turn back. Her eyes made her turn back. Slowly, unwillingly, Mrs. Peters turned her head until her eyes met the eyes of the other woman. There was a moment when they held each other in a steady, burning look in which there was no evasion nor flinching. Then Martha Hale's eyes pointed the way to the basket in which was hidden the thing that would make certain the conviction of the other woman—that woman who was not there and yet who had been there with them all through that hour.

For a moment Mrs. Peters did not move. And then she did it. With a rush forward, she threw back the quilt pieces, got the box, tried to put it in her handbag. It was too big. Desperately she opened it, started to take the bird out. But there she broke—she could not touch the bird. She stood there helpless, foolish.

There was the sound of a knob turning in the inner door. Martha Hale snatched the box from the sheriff's wife, and got it in the pocket of her big coat just as the sheriff and the county attorney came back into the kitchen.

"Well, Henry," said the county attorney facetiously, "at least we found out that she was not going to quilt it. She was going to—what is it you call it, ladies"

Mrs Hale's hand was against the pocket of her coat.

"We call it—knot it, Mr. Henderson."

Susan Glaspell's Adaptation of "A Jury of Her Peers" as a play, *Trifles*

One way to understand differences in the natures of two media is to compare the story version with the play version, both by the same writer in this instance.

The opening and the ending of *Trifles* follow:

SCENE.—*The kitchen in the now aban-doned farmhouse of* JOHN WRIGHT, *a gloomy kitchen, and left without hav-ing been put in order—unwashed pans under the sink, a loaf of bread outside the breadbox, a dish-towel on the table—other signs of incompleted work. At the rear the outer door opens and the* SHERIFF *comes in followed by the* COUNTY ATTORNEY *and* HALE. *The* SHERIFF *and* HALE *are men in middle life, the* COUNTY ATTORNEY *is a young man; all are much bundled up and go at once to the stove. They are followed by the two women—the* SHERIFF'S *wife first; she is a slight wiry woman, a thin nervous face.* MRS. HALE *is larger and would ordinarily be called more com-fortable looking, but she is disturbed now and looks fearfully about as she enters. The women have come in slowly, and stand close together near the door.*

COUNTY ATTORNEY *(rubbing his hands)*. This feels good. Come up to the fire, ladies.

MRS. PETERS *(after taking a step forward)*. I'm not—cold.

SHERIFF *(unbottoning his overcoat and stepping away from the stove as if to mark the beginning of official business)*. Now, Mr. Hale, before we move things about, you explain to Mr. Henderson just what you saw when you came here yesterday morning.

COUNTY ATTORNEY. By the way, has anything been moved? Are things just as you left them yesterday?

SHERIFF *(looking about)*. It's just the same. When it dropped below zero last night I thought I'd better send Frank out this morning to make a fire for us—no use getting pneumonia with a big case on, but I told him not to touch anything except the stove—and you know Frank.

COUNTY ATTORNEY. Somebody should have been left here yesterday.

SHERIFF. Oh—yesterday. When I had to send Frank to Morris Center for that man who went crazy—I want you to know I had my hands full yesterday. I knew you could get back from Omaha by today and as long as I went over everything here myself—

COUNTY ATTORNEY. Well, Mr. Hale, tell just what happened when you came here yesterday morning.

HALE. Harry and I had started to town with a load of potatoes. We came along the road from my place and as I got here I said, "I'm going to see if I can't get John Wright to go in with me on a party telephone." I spoke to Wright about it once before and he put me off, saying folks talked too much anyway, and all he asked was peace and quiet—I guess you know about how much he talked himself; but I thought maybe if I went to the house and talked about it before his wife, though I said to Harry that I didn't know as what his wife wanted made much difference to John—

COUNTY ATTORNEY. Let's talk about that later, Mr. Hale. I do want to talk about that, but tell now just what happened when you got to the house.

HALE. I didn't hear or see anything; I knocked at the door, and still it was all quiet inside. I knew they must be up, it was past eight o'clock. So I knocked again, and I thought I heard somebody say, "Come in." I wasn't sure, I'm not sure yet, but I opened the door—this door. *(Indicating the door by which*

the two women are still standing.)
And there in that rocker—*(pointing to it)* sat Mrs. Wright. *(They all look at the rocker.)*

COUNTY ATTORNEY. What—was she doing?

HALE. She was rockin' back and forth. She had her apron in her hand and was kind of—pleating it.

COUNTY ATTORNEY. And how did she—look?

HALE. Well, she looked queer.

COUNTY ATTORNEY. How do you mean—queer?

HALE. Well, as if she didn't know what she was going to do next. And kind of done up.

COUNTY ATTORNEY. How did she seem to feel about your coming?

HALE. Why, I don't think she minded—one way or other. She didn't pay much attention. I said, "How do, Mrs. Wright, it's cold, ain't it?" And she said, "Is it?"—and went on kind of pleating at her apron. Well, I was surprised; she didn't ask me to come up to the stove, or to set down, but just sat there, not even looking at me, so I said, "I want to see John." And then she—laughed. I guess you could call it a laugh. I thought of Harry and the team outside, so I said a little sharp: "Can't I see John?" "No," she says, kind o' dull like. "Ain't he home?" says I. "Yes," says she, "he's home." "Then why can't I see him?" I asked her, out of patience. "'Cause he's dead," says she. "*Dead?*" says I. She just nodded her head, not getting a bit excited, but rockin' back and forth. "Why—where is he?" says I, not knowing what to say. She just pointed upstairs—like that *(himself pointing to the room above).* I got up, with the idea of going up there. I walked from

there to here—then I says, "Why, what did he die of?" "He died of a rope round his neck," says she and just went on pleatin' at her apron. Well, I went out and called Harry. I thought I might—need help. We went upstairs and there he was lyin'—

COUNTY ATTORNEY. I think I'd rather have you go into that upstairs, where you can point it all out. Just go on now with the rest of the story.

HALE. Well, my first thought was to get that rope off. It looked . . . *(Stops, his face twitches.)* . . . but Harry, he went up to him, and he said, "No, he's dead all right, and we'd better not touch anything." So we went back downstairs. She was still sitting that same way. "Has anybody been notified?" I asked. "No," says she, unconcerned. "Who did this, Mrs. Wright?" said Harry. He said it businesslike—and she stopped pleatin' of her apron. "I don't know," she says. "You don't *know?*" says Harry. "No," says she. "Weren't you sleepin' in the bed with him?" says Harry. "Yes," says she, "but I was on the inside." "Somebody slipped a rope round his neck and strangled him and you didn't wake up?" says Harry. "I didn't wake up," she said after him. We must 'a' looked as if we didn't see how that could be, for after a minute she said, "I sleep sound." Harry was going to ask her more questions but I said maybe we ought to let her tell her story first to the coroner, or the sheriff, so Harry went fast as he could to Rivers' place, where there's a telephone.

COUNTY ATTORNEY. And what did Mrs. Wright do when she knew that you had gone for the coroner?

HALE. She moved from that chair to this one over here *(pointing to a small chair in the corner)* and just sat there with her hands held together and looking down. I got a feeling that I ought to make some conversation, so I said I had come in to see if John wanted to put in a telephone, and at that she started to laugh, and then she stopped and looked at me—scared. *(The* COUNTY ATTORNEY, *who has had his notebook out, makes a note.)* I dunno, maybe it wasn't scared. I wouldn't like to say it was. Soon Harry got back, and then Dr. Lloyd came, and you, Mr. Peters, and so I guess that's all I know that you don't.

COUNTY ATTORNEY *(looking around).* I guess we'll go upstairs first—and then out to the barn and around there. *(To the* SHERIFF.*)* You're convinced that there was nothing important here—nothing that would point to any motive.

SHERIFF. Nothing here but kitchen things.

(The COUNTY ATTORNEY, *after again looking around the kitchen, opens the door of a cupboard closet. He gets up on a chair and looks on a shelf. Pulls his hand away, sticky.)*

COUNTY ATTORNEY. Here's a nice mess. *(The women draw nearer.)*

MRS. PETERS *(to the other woman).* Oh, her fruit; it did freeze. *(To the* LAWYER.*)* She worried about that when it turned so cold. She said the fire'd go out and her jars would break.

SHERIFF. Well, can you beat the women! Held for murder and worryin' about her preserves.

COUNTY ATTORNEY. I guess before we're through she may have something more serious than preserves to worry about.

HALE. Well, women are used to worrying over trifles.

(The two women move a little closer together.)

COUNTY ATTORNEY *(with the gallantry of a young politician).* And yet, for all their worries, what would we do without the ladies? *(The women do not unbend. He goes to the sink, takes a dipperful of water from the pail and pouring it into a basin, washes his hands. Starts to wipe them on the roller towel, turns it for a cleaner place.)* Dirty towels! *(Kicks his foot against the pans under the sink.)* Not much of a housekeeper, would you say, ladies?

MRS. HALE *(stiffly).* There's a great deal of work to be done on a farm.

COUNTY ATTORNEY. To be sure. And yet *(with a little bow to her)* I know there are some Dickson county farmhouses which do not have such roller towels. *(He gives it a pull to expose its full length again.)*

MRS. HALE. Those towels get dirty awful quick. Men's hands aren't always as clean as they might be.

COUNTY ATTORNEY. Ah, loyal to your sex, I see. But you and Mrs. Wright were neighbors. I suppose you were friends, too.

MRS. HALE *(shaking her head).* I've not seen much of her of late years. I've not been in this house—it's more than a year.

COUNTY ATTORNEY. And why was that? You didn't like her?

MRS. HALE. I liked her all well enough. Farmers' wives have their hands full, Mr. Henderson, And then—

COUNTY ATTORNEY. Yes—?

MRS. HALE *(looking about).* It never seemed a very cheerful place.

COUNTY ATTORNEY. No—it's not cheerful. I shouldn't say she had the homemaking instinct.

MRS. HALE. Well, I don't know as Wright had, either.

COUNTY ATTORNEY. You mean that they didn't get on very well?

MRS. HALE. No, I don't mean anything. But I don't think a place'd be any cheerfuller for John Wright's being in it.

COUNTY ATTORNEY. I'd like to talk more of that a little later. I want to get the lay of things upstairs now. *(He goes to the left, where three steps lead to a stair door.)*

SHERIFF. I suppose anything Mrs. Peters does'll be all right. She was to take in some clothes for her, you know, and a few little things. We left in such a hurry yesterday.

COUNTY ATTORNEY. Yes, but I would like to see what you take, Mrs. Peters, and keep an eye out for anything that might be of use to us.

MRS. PETERS. Yes, Mr. Henderson. *(The women listen to the men's steps on the stairs, then look about the kitchen.)*

———————

COUNTY ATTORNEY *(as one turning from serious things to little pleasantries)*. Well, ladies, have you decided whether she was going to quilt it or knot it?

MRS. PETERS. We think she was going to—knot it.

COUNTY ATTORNEY. Well, that's interesting, I'm sure. *(Seeing the bird cage.)* Has the bird flown?

MRS. HALE *(putting more quilt pieces over the box)*. We think the— cat got it.

COUNTY ATTORNEY *(preoccupied)*. Is there a cat?

*(*MRS. HALE *glances in a quick covert way at* MRS. PETERS.*)*

MRS. PETERS. Well, not *now*. They're superstitious, you know. They leave.

COUNTY ATTORNEY *(to* SHERIFF PETERS, *continuing an interrupted conversation)*. No sign at all of anyone having come from the outside. Their own rope. Now let's go up again and go over it piece by piece. *(They start upstairs.)* It would have to have been someone who knew just the—

*(*MRS. PETERS *sits down. The two women sit there not looking at one another, but as if peering into something and at the same time holding back. When they talk now it is in the manner of feeling their way over strange ground, as if afraid of what they are saying, but as if they cannot help saying it.)*

MRS. HALE. She liked the bird. She was going to bury it in that pretty box.

MRS. PETERS *(in a whisper)*. When I was a girl—my kitten—there was a boy took a hatchet, and before my eyes— and before I could get there—*(Covers her face an instant.)* If they hadn't held me back I would have— *(Catches herself, looks upstairs where steps are heard, falters weakly.)*—hurt him.

MRS. HALE *(with a slow look around her)*. I wonder how it would seem never to have had any children around. *(Pause.)* No, Wright wouldn't like the bird—a thing that sang. She used to sing. He killed that, too.

MRS. PETERS *(moving uneasily)*. We don't know who killed the bird.

MRS. HALE. I knew John Wright.

MRS. PETERS. It was an awful thing was done in this house that night, Mrs. Hale. Killing a man while he slept, slipping a rope around his neck that choked the life out of him.

MRS. HALE. His neck. Choked the life out of him.

(Her hand goes out and rests on the bird-cage.)

MRS. PETERS *(with rising voice)*. We don't know who killed him. We don't *know*.

MRS. HALE *(her own feeling not interrupted)*. If there'd been years and years of nothing, then a bird to sing to you, it would be awful—still, after the bird was still.

MRS. PETERS *(something within her speaking)*. I know what stillness is. When we homesteaded in Dakota, and my first baby died—after he was two years old, and me with no other then—

MRS. HALE *(moving)*. How soon do you suppose they'll be through looking for the evidence?

MRS. PETERS. I know what stillness is. *(Pulling herself back.)* The law has got to punish crime, Mrs. Hale.

MRS. HALE *(not as if answering that)*. I wish you'd seen Minnie Foster when she wore a white dress with blue ribbons and stood up there in the choir and sang. *(A look around the room.)* Oh, I *wish* I'd come over here once in a while! That was a crime! That was a crime! Who's going to punish that?

MRS. PETERS *(looking upstairs)*. We mustn't—take on.

MRS. HALE. I might have known she needed help! I know how things can be—for women. I tell you, it's queer, Mrs. Peters. We live close together and we live far apart. We all go through the same things—it's all just a different kind of the same thing. *(Brushes her eyes, noticing the bottle of fruit, reaches out for it.)* If I was you I wouldn't tell her her fruit was gone. Tell her it *ain't*. Tell her it's all right. Take this in to prove it to her. She—

she may never know whether it was broke or not.

MRS. PETERS *(takes the bottle, looks about for something to wrap it in; takes petticoat from the clothes brought from the other room, very nervously begins winding this around the bottle. In a false voice)*. My, it's a good thing the men couldn't hear us. Wouldn't they just laugh! Getting all stirred up over a little thing like a— dead canary. As if that could have anything to do with—with—wouldn't they *laugh!*

(The men are heard coming downstairs.)

MRS. HALE *(under her breath)*. Maybe they would—maybe they wouldn't.

COUNTY ATTORNEY. No, Peters, it's all perfectly clear except a reason for doing it. But you know juries when it comes to women. If there was some definite thing. Something to show— something to make a story about—a thing that would connect up with this strange way of doing it—

(The women's eyes meet for an instant. Enter HALE from outer door.)

HALE. Well, I've got the team around. Pretty cold out there.

COUNTY ATTORNEY. I'm going to stay here a while by myself. *(To the SHERIFF.)* You can send Frank out for me, can't you? I want to go over everything. I'm not satisfied that we can't do better.

SHERIFF. Do you want to see what Mrs. Peters is going to take in?

(The LAWYER goes to the table, picks up the apron, laughs.)

COUNTY ATTORNEY. Oh, I guess they're not very dangerous things the ladies have picked out. *(Moves a few things about, disturbing the quilt pieces which cover the box. Steps back.)* No, Mrs. Peters doesn't need supervising. For that matter, a sheriff's wife is married to the law. Ever think of it that way, Mrs. Peters?

MRS. PETERS. Not—just that way.

SHERIFF *(chuckling)*. Married to the law. *(Moves toward the other room.)* I just want you to come in here a minute, George. We ought to take a look at these windows.

COUNTY ATTORNEY *(scoffingly)*. Oh, windows!

SHERIFF. We'll be right out, Mr. Hale. *(HALE goes outside. The SHERIFF follows the COUNTY ATTORNEY into the other room. Then MRS. HALE rises, hands tight together, looking intensely at MRS. PETERS, whose eyes make a slow turn, finally meeting MRS. HALE's. A moment MRS. HALE holds her, then her own eyes point the way to where the box is concealed. Suddenly MRS. PETERS throws back quilt pieces and tries to put the box in the bag she is wearing. It is too big. She opens box, starts to take bird out, cannot touch it, goes to pieces, stands there helpless. Sound of a knob turning in the other room. MRS. HALE snatches the box and puts it in the pocket of her big coat. Enter COUNTY ATORNEY and SHERIFF.)*

COUNTY ATTORNEY *(facetiously)*. Well, Henry, at least we found out that she was not going to quilt it. She was going to—what is it you call it, ladies?

MRS. HALE *(her hand against her pocket)*. We call it—knot it, Mr. Henderson.

CURTAIN

Ernest Hemingway, 1898–1961

A Clean, Well-Lighted Place

This story first appeared in SCRIBNER'S MAGAZINE, *1933.*

IT WAS LATE AND EVERY ONE HAD LEFT THE CAFÉ except an old man who sat in the shadow the leaves of the tree made against the electric light. In the day time the street was dusty, but at night the dew settled the dust and the old man liked to sit late because he was deaf and now at night it was quiet and he felt the difference. The two waiters inside the café knew that the old man was a little drunk, and while he was a good client they knew that if he became too drunk he would leave without paying, so they kept watch on him.

"Last week he tried to commit suicide," one waiter said.

"Why?"

"He was in despair."

"What about?"

"Nothing."

"How do you know it was nothing?"

"He has plenty of money."

They sat together at a table that was close against the wall near the door of the café and looked at the terrace where the tables were all empty except where the old man sat in the shadow of the leaves of the tree that moved slightly in the wind. A girl and a soldier went by in the street. The street light shone on the brass number on his collar. The girl wore no head covering and hurried beside him.

"The guard will pick him up," one waiter said.

"What does it matter if he gets what he's after?"

"He had better get off the street now. The guard will get him. They went by five minutes ago."

The old man sitting in the shadow rapped on his saucer with his glass. The younger waiter went over to him.

"What do you want?"

The old man looked at him. "Another brandy," he said.

"You'll be drunk," the waiter said. The old man looked at him. The waiter went away.

"He'll stay all night," he said to his colleague. "I'm sleepy now. I never get into bed before three o'clock. He should have killed himself last week."

The waiter took the brandy bottle and another saucer from the counter inside the café and marched out to the old man's table. He put down the saucer and poured the glass full of brandy.

"You should have killed yourself last week," he said to the deaf man. The old man motioned with his finger. "A little more," he said. The waiter poured on into the glass so that the brandy slopped over and ran down the stem into the top saucer of the pile. "Thank you," the old man said. The waiter took the bottle back inside the café. He sat down at the table with his colleague again.

"He's drunk now," he said.

"He's drunk every night."*

"What did he want to kill himself for?"

"How should I know?"

"How did he do it?"

"He hung himself with a rope."

"Who cut him down?"

"His niece."

"Why did they do it?"

"Fear for his soul."

"How much money has he got?"

"He's got plenty."

"He must be eighty years old."

"Anyway, I should say he was eighty."†

"I wish he would go home. I never get to bed before three o'clock. What kind of hour is that to go to bed?"

"He stays up because he likes it."

"He's lonely. I'm not lonely. I have a wife waiting in bed for me."

"He had a wife once too."

"A wife would be no good to him now."

"You can't tell. He might be better with a wife."

"His niece looks after him."

"I know. You said she cut him down."

"I wouldn't want to be that old. An old man is a nasty thing."

"Not always. This old man is clean. He drinks without spilling. Even now, drunk. Look at him."

"I don't want to look at him. I wish he would go home. He has no regard for those who must work."

---

*"He's drunk now," he said. "He's drunk every night": The younger waiter says both these lines. A device of Hemingway's style is sometimes to have a character pause, then speak again—as often happens in actual speech.

†"He must be eighty years old." "Anyway I should say he was eighty": Is this another instance of the same character's speaking twice? Clearly, it is the younger waiter who says the next line, "I wish he would go home."

The old man looked from his glass across the square, then over at the waiters.

"Another brandy," he said, pointing to his glass. The waiter who was in a hurry came over.

"Finished," he said, speaking with that omission of syntax stupid people employ when talking to drunken people or foreigners. "No more tonight. Close now."

"Another," said the old man.

"No. Finished." The waiter wiped the edge of the table with a towel and shook his head.

The old man stood up, slowly counted the saucers, took a leather coin purse from his pocket and paid for the drinks, leaving half a peseta tip.

The waiter watched him go down the street, a very old man walking unsteadily but with dignity.

"Why didn't you let him stay and drink?" the unhurried waiter asked. They were putting up the shutters. "It is not half-past two."

"I want to go home to bed."

"What is an hour?"

"More to me than to him."

"An hour is the same."

"You talk like an old man yourself. He can buy a bottle and drink at home."

"It's not the same."

"No, it is not," agreed the waiter with a wife. He did not wish to be unjust. He was only in a hurry.

"And you? You have no fear of going home before the usual hour?"

"Are you trying to insult me?"

"No, hombre, only to make a joke."

"No," the waiter who was in a hurry said, rising from pulling down the metal shutters. "I have confidence. I am all confidence."

"You have youth, confidence, and a job," the older waiter said. "You have everything."

"And what do you lack?"

"Everything but work."

"You have everything I have."

"No. I have never had confidence and I am not young."

"Come on. Stop talking nonsense and lock up."

"I am of those who like to stay late at the café," the older waiter said. "With all those who do not want to go to bed. With all those who need a light for the night."

"I want to go home and into bed."

"We are of two different kinds," the older waiter said. He was not dressed to go home. "It is not only a question of youth and confidence although those things are very beautiful. Each night I am reluctant to close up because there may be some one who needs the café."

"Hombre, there are bodegas* open all night long."

"You do not understand. This is a clean and pleasant café. It is well lighted. The light is very good and also, now, there are shadows of the leaves."

"Good night," said the younger waiter.

"Good night," the other said. Turning off the electric light he continued the conversation with himself. It is the light of course but it is necessary that the place be clean and pleasant. You do not want music. Certainly you do not want music. Nor can you stand before a bar with dignity although that is all that is provided for these hours. What did he fear? It was not fear or dread. It was a nothing that he knew too well. It was all a nothing and a man was nothing too. It was only that and light was all it needed and a certain cleanness and order. Some lived in it and never felt it but he knew it all was nada y pues nada y nada y pues nada.[†] Our nada who are in nada, nada be thy name thy kingdom nada thy will be nada in nada as it is in nada. Give us this nada our daily nada and nada us our nada as we nada our nadas and nada us not into nada but deliver us from nada; pues nada. Hail nothing full of nothing, nothing is with thee. He smiled and stood before a bar with a shining steam pressure coffee machine.

"What's yours?" asked the barman.

"Nada."

"Otro loco más,"[‡] said the barman and turned away.

"A little cup," said the waiter.

The barman poured it for him.

"The light is very bright and pleasant but the bar is unpolished," the waiter said.

The barman looked at him but did not answer. It was too late at night for conversation.

"You want another copita?"[§] the barman asked.

"No, thank you," said the waiter and went out. He disliked bars and bodegas. A clean, well-lighted café was a very different thing. Now, without thinking further, he would go home to his room. He would lie in the bed and finally, with daylight, he would go to sleep. After all, he said to himself, it is probably only insomnia. Many must have it.

---

*bodegas: wineshops.
†nada y pues . . . nada: nothing and then nothing and nothing and then nothing.
‡Otro loco más: another lunatic.
§copita: little cup.

— Ernest Hemingway on His Early Fiction:
Passages from His Memoir *A Moveable Feast* and the letters

It was wonderful to walk down the long flights of stairs knowing that I'd had good luck working. I always worked until I had something done and I always stopped when I knew what was going to happen next. That way I could be sure of going on the next day. But sometimes when I was starting a new story and I could not get it going, I would sit in front of the fire and squeeze the peel of the little oranges into the edge of the flame and watch the sputter of blue that they made. I would stand and look out over the roofs of Paris and think, "Do not worry. You have always written before and you will write now. All you have to do is write one true sentence. Write the truest sentence that you know." So finally I would write one true sentence, and then go on from there. It was easy then because there was always one true sentence that I knew or had seen or had heard someone say. If I started to write elaborately, or like someone introducing or presenting something, I found that I could cut that scrollwork or ornament out and throw it away and start with the first true simple declarative sentence I had written. Up in that room I decided that I would write one story about each thing that I knew about. I was trying to do this all the time I was writing, and it was good and severe discipline.

It was in that room too that I learned not to think about anything that I was writing from the time I stopped writing until I started again the next day. That way my subconscious would be working on it and at the same time I would be listening to other people and noticing everything, I hoped; learning, I hoped; and I would read so that I would not think about my work and make myself impotent to do it. Going down the stairs when I had worked well, and that needed luck as well as discipline, was a wonderful feeling and I was free then to walk anywhere in Paris. . . .

A Moveable Feast, pp. 12–13

It was a pleasant café, warm and clean and friendly, and I hung up my old waterproof on the coat rack to dry and put my worn and weathered felt hat on the rack above the bench and ordered a *café au lait.* The waiter brought it and I took out a notebook from the pocket of the coat and a pencil and started to write. I was writing about up in Michigan and since it was a wild, cold, blowing day it was that sort of day in the story. I had already seen the end of fall come through boyhood, youth and young manhood, and in one place you could write about it better than in another. That was called transplanting yourself, I thought, and it could be as necessary with people as with other sorts of growing things. But in the story the boys were drinking and this made me thirsty and I ordered a rum St. James. This tasted wonderful on the cold day and I kept on writing, feeling very well and feeling the good Martinique rum warm me all through my body and my spirit. . . .

A Moveable Feast, p. 5

When I was writing, it was necessary for me to read after I had written. If you kept thinking about it, you would lose the thing that you were writing before you could go on with it the next day. It was necessary to get exercise, to be tired in the body, and it was very good to make love with whom you loved. That was better than anything. But afterwards, when you were empty, it was necessary to read in order not to think or worry about your work until you could do it again. I had learned already never to empty the well of my writing, but always to stop when there was still something there in the deep part of the well, and let it refill at night from the springs that fed it. . . .

A Moveable Feast, pp. 25-26

[Ezra was] . . . the man who had taught me to distrust adjectives as I would later learn to distrust certain people in certain situations. . . .

A Moveable Feast, p. 134

I like to have Gertrude [Stein] bawl me out because it keeps one['s] opinion of oneself down—way down—She liked the book very much she said—But what I wanted to hear about was what she didnt like and why—She thinks the parts that fail are where I remember visually rather than make up. . . .

To F. Scott Fitzgerald, 1929,
Selected Letters, p. 310

After writing a story I was always empty and both sad and happy, as though I had made love, and I was sure this was a very good story although I would not know truly how good until I read it over the next day.

A Moveable Feast, p. 6

I sat in a corner with the afternoon light coming in over my shoulder and wrote in the notebook. The waiter brought me a *café crème* and I drank half of it when it cooled and left it on the table while I wrote. When I stopped writing I did not want to leave the river where I could see the trout in the pool, its surface pushing and swelling smooth against the resistance of the log-driven piles of the bridge. The story was about coming back from the war but there was no mention of the war in it.

A Moveable Feast, p. 76

———————

It was a very simple story called "Out of Season" and I had omitted the real end of it which was that the old man hanged himself. This was omitted on my new theory that you could omit anything if you knew that you omitted and the omitted part would strengthen the story and make people feel something more than they understood.

A Moveable Feast, p. 75

———————

If a writer of prose knows enough about what he is writing about he may omit things that he knows and the reader, if the writer is writing truly enough, will have a feeling of those things as strongly as though the writer had stated them. The dignity of movement of an ice-berg is due to only one-eighth of it being above water. A writer who omits things because he does not know them only makes hollow places in his writing.

Death in the Afternoon, p. 192

———————

Since I had started to break down all my writing and get rid of all facility and try to make instead of describe, writing had been wonderful to do. But it was very difficult, and I did not know how I would ever write anything as long as a novel. It often took me a full morning of work to write a paragraph.

A Moveable Feast, p. 156

———————

I . . . threw away about 100,000 words which was better than most of what [I] left in. It is the most cut book in the world [*To Have and Have Not*]. That may be part of what offends people. It does not have that handy family package size character you get in Dr. Dickens.

To Lillian Ross, 1948,
Selected Letters, pp. 648–649

———————

As the contract only mentions excisions it is understood of course that no alterations of words shall be made without my approval. This protects you as much as it does me as the stories are written so tight and so hard that the alteration of a word can throw an entire story out of key.

To Horace Liveright, 1925,
Selected Letters, p. 154

James Thurber, 1894–1961

The Catbird Seat

This story first appeared in A THURBER CARNIVAL, *1945.*

MR. MARTIN BOUGHT THE PACK OF CAMELS ON MONDAY NIGHT in the most crowded cigar store on Broadway. It was theater time and seven or eight men were buying cigarettes. The clerk didn't even glance at Mr. Martin, who put the pack in his overcoat pocket and went out. If any of the staff at F & S had seen him buy the cigarettes, they would have been astonished, for it was generally known that Mr. Martin did not smoke, and never had. No one saw him.

It was just a week to the day since Mr. Martin had decided to rub out Mrs. Ulgine Barrows. The term "rub out" pleased him because it suggested nothing more than the correction of an error—in this case an error of Mr. Fitweiler. Mr. Martin had spent each night of the past week working out his plan and examining it. As he walked home now he went over it again. For the hundredth time he resented the element of imprecision, the margin of guesswork that entered into the business. The project as he had worked it out was casual and bold, the risks were considerable. Something might go wrong anywhere along the line. And therein lay the cunning of his scheme. No one would ever see in it the cautious, painstaking hand of Erwin Martin, head of the filing department at F & S, of whom Mr. Fitweiler had once said, "Man is fallible but Martin isn't." No one would see his hand, that is, unless it were caught in the act.

Sitting in his apartment, drinking a glass of milk, Mr. Martin reviewed his case against Mrs. Ulgine Barrows, as he had every night for seven nights. He began at the beginning. Her quacking voice and braying laugh had first profaned the halls of F & S on March 7, 1941 (Mr. Martin had a head for dates). Old Roberts, the personnel chief, had introduced her as the newly appointed special adviser to the president of the firm, Mr. Fitweiler. The woman had appalled Mr. Martin instantly, but he hadn't shown it. He had given her his dry hand, a look of studious concentration, and a faint smile. "Well," she had said, looking at the papers on his desk, "are you lifting the oxcart out of the ditch?" As Mr. Martin recalled that moment, over his milk, he squirmed slightly. He must keep his mind on her crimes as a special adviser, not on her peccadillos as a personality. This he found difficult to do, in spite of entering an objection and sustaining it. The faults of the woman as a woman kept chattering on in his mind like an unruly witness. She had, for almost two years now, baited him. In the halls, in the elevator, even in his own office, into which she romped now and then like a circus horse, she was constantly shouting out these silly questions at him. "Are you lifting the oxcart out of the ditch? Are you tearing up the pea patch? Are you hollering down the rain barrel? Are you scraping around the bottom of the pickle barrel? Are you sitting in the catbird seat?"

It was Joey Hart, one of Mr. Martin's two assistants, who had explained what the gibberish meant. "She must be a Dodger fan*," he had said. "Red Barber announces the Dodger games over the radio and he uses those expressions—picked 'em up down South." Joey had gone on to explain one or two. "Tearing up the pea patch" meant going on a rampage; "sitting in the catbird seat" meant sitting pretty, like a batter with three balls and no strikes on him. Mr. Martin dismissed all this with an effort. It had been annoying, it had driven him near to distraction, but he was too solid a man to be moved to murder by anything so childish. It was fortunate, he reflected as he passed on to the important charges against Mrs. Barrows, that he had stood up under it so well. He had maintained always an outward appearance of polite tolerance. "Why, I even believe you like the woman," Miss Paird, his other assistant, had once said to him. He had simply smiled.

A gavel rapped in Mr. Martin's mind and the case proper was resumed. Mrs. Ulgine Barrows stood charged with willful, blatant, and persistent attempts to destroy the efficiency and system of F & S. It was competent, material, and relevant to review her advent and rise to power. Mr. Martin had got the story from Miss Paird, who seemed always able to find things out. According to her, Mrs. Barrows had met Mr. Fitweiler at a party, where she had rescued him from the embraces of a powerfully built drunken man who had mistaken the president of F & S for a famous retired Middle Western football coach. She had led him to a sofa and somehow worked upon him a monstrous magic. The aging gentleman had jumped to the conclusion there and then that this was a woman of singular attainments, equipped to bring out the best in him and in the firm. A week later he had introduced her into F & S as his special adviser. On that day confusion got its foot in the door. After Miss Tyson, Mr. Brundage, and Mr. Bartlett had been fired and Mr. Munson had taken his hat and stalked out, mailing in his resignation later, old Roberts had been emboldened to speak to Mr. Fitweiler. He mentioned that Mr. Munson's department had been "a little disrupted" and hadn't they perhaps better resume the old system there? Mr. Fitweiler had said certainly not. He had the greatest faith in Mrs. Barrows' ideas. "They require a little seasoning, a little seasoning is all," he had added. Mr. Roberts had given it up. Mr. Martin reviewed in detail all the changes wrought by Mrs. Barrows. She

---

Dodger fan: At the time of this story, the Dodgers were the Brooklyn Dodgers.

had begun chipping at the cornices of the firm's edifice and now she was swinging at the foundation stones with a pickaxe.

Mr. Martin came now, in his summing up, to the afternoon of Monday, November 2, 1942—just one week ago. On that day, at 3 P.M., Mrs. Barrows had bounced into his office. "Boo!" she had yelled. "Are you scraping around the bottom of the pickle barrel?" Mr. Martin had looked at her from under his green eyeshade, saying nothing. She had begun to wander about the office, taking it in with her great, popping eyes. "Do you really need *all* these filing cabinets?" she had demanded suddenly. Mr. Martin's heart had jumped. "Each of these files," he had said, keeping his voice even, "plays an indispensable part in the system of F & S." She had brayed at him, "Well, don't tear up the pea patch!" and gone to the door. From there she had bawled, "But you sure have got a lot of fine scrap in here!" Mr. Martin could no longer doubt that the finger was on his beloved department. Her pickaxe was on the upswing, poised for the first blow. It had not come yet; he had received no blue memo from the enchanted Mr. Fitweiler bearing nonsensical instructions deriving from the obscene woman. But there was no doubt in Mr. Martin's mind that one would be forthcoming. He must act quickly. Already a precious week had gone by. Mr. Martin stood up in his living room, still holding his milk glass. "Gentlemen of the jury," he said to himself, "I demand the death penalty for this horrible person."

———————————

THE NEXT DAY MR. MARTIN FOLLOWED HIS ROUTINE, as usual. He polished his glasses more often and once sharpened an already sharp pencil, but not even Miss Paird noticed. Only once did he catch sight of his victim; she swept past him in the hall with a patronizing "Hi!" At five-thirty he walked home, as usual, and had a glass of milk, as usual. He had never drunk anything stronger in his life—unless you could count ginger ale. The late Sam Schlosser, the S of F & S, had praised Mr. Martin at a staff meeting several years before for his temperate habits. "Our most efficient worker neither drinks nor smokes," he had said "The results speak for themselves." Mr. Fitweiler had sat by, nodding approval.

Mr. Martin was still thinking about that red-letter day as he walked over to the Schrafft's on Fifth Avenue near Forty-sixth Street. He got there, as he always did, at eight o'clock. He finished his dinner and the financial page of the *Sun* at a quarter to nine, as he always did. It was his custom after dinner to take a walk. This time he walked down Fifth Avenue at a casual pace. His gloved hands felt moist and warm, his forehead cold. He transferred the Camels from his overcoat to a jacket pocket. He wondered, as he did so, if they did not represent an unnecessary note of strain. Mrs. Barrows smoked only Luckies. It was his idea to puff a few puffs on a Camel (after the rubbing-out), stub it out in the ashtray holding her lipstick-stained Luckies, and thus drag a small red herring across the trail. Perhaps it was not a good idea. It would take time. He might even choke, too loudly.

Mr. Martin had never seen the house on West Twelfth Street where Mrs. Barrows lived, but he had a clear enough picture of it. Fortunately, she had bragged to everybody about her ducky first-floor apartment in the perfectly darling three-story redbrick. There would be no doorman or other attendants; just the tenants of the second and third floors. As he walked along, Mr. Martin realized that he would get there before nine-thirty. He had considered walking north on Fifth Avenue from Schrafft's to a point from which it would take him until ten o'clock to reach the house. At that hour people were less likely to be coming in or going out. But the procedure would have made an awkward loop in the straight thread of his casualness, and he had abandoned it. It was impossible to figure when people would be entering or leaving the house, anyway. There was a great risk at any hour. If he ran into anybody, he would simply have to place the rubbing-out of Ulgine Barrows in the inactive file forever. The same thing would hold true if there were someone in her apartment. In that case he would just say that he had been passing by, recognized her charming house and thought to drop in.

It was eighteen minutes after nine when Mr. Martin turned into Twelfth Street. A man passed him, and a man and a woman talking. There was no one within fifty paces when he came to the house, halfway down the block. He was up the steps and in the small vestibule in no time, pressing the bell under the card that said "Mrs. Ulgine Barrows." When the clicking in the lock started, he jumped forward against the door. He got inside fast, closing the door behind him. A bulb in a lantern hung from the hall ceiling on a chain seemed to give a monstrously bright light. There was nobody on the stair, which went up ahead of him along the left wall. A door opened down the hall in the wall on the right. He went toward it swiftly, on tiptoe.

"Well, for God's sake, look who's here!" bawled Mrs. Barrows, and her braying laugh rang out like the report of a shotgun. He rushed past her like a football tackle, bumping her. "Hey, quit shoving!" she said, closing the door behind them. They were in her living room, which seemed to Mr. Martin to be lighted by a hundred lamps. "What's after you?" she said. "You're as jumpy as a goat." He found he was unable to speak. His heart was wheezing in his throat. "I—yes," he finally brought out. She was jabbering and laughing as she started to help him off with his coat. "No, no," he said. "I'll put it there." He took it off and put it on a chair near the door. "Your hat and gloves, too," she said. "You're in a lady's house." He put his hat on top of the coat. Mrs. Barrows seemed larger than he had thought. He kept his gloves on. "I was passing by," he said. "I recognized—is there anyone here?" She laughed louder than ever. "No," she said, "we're all alone. You're as white as a sheet, you funny man. Whatever *has* come over you? I'll mix you a toddy." She started toward a door across the room. "Scotch-and-soda be all right? But say, you don't drink, do you?" She turned and gave him her amused look. Mr.

Martin pulled himself together. "Scotch-and-soda will be all right," he heard himself say. He could hear her laughing in the kitchen.

Mr. Martin looked quickly around the living room for the weapon. He had counted on finding one there. There were andirons and a poker and something in a corner that looked like an Indian club. None of them would do. It couldn't be that way. He began to pace around. He came to a desk. On it lay a metal knife with an ornate handle. Would it be sharp enough? He reached for it and knocked over a small brass jar. Stamps spilled out of it and it fell to the floor with a clatter. "Hey," Mrs. Barrows yelled from the kitchen, "are you tearing up the pea patch?" Mr. Martin gave a strange laugh. Picking up the knife, he tried its point against his left wrist. It was blunt. It wouldn't do.

When Mrs. Barrows reappeared, carrying two highballs, Mr. Martin, standing there with his gloves on, became acutely conscious of the fantasy he had wrought. Cigarettes in his pocket, a drink prepared for him—it was all too grossly improbable. It was more than that; it was impossible. Somewhere in the back of his mind a vague idea stirred, sprouted. "For heaven's sake, take off those gloves," said Mrs. Barrows. "I always wear them in the house," said Mr. Martin. The idea began to bloom, strange and wonderful. She put the glasses on a coffee table in front of a sofa and sat on the sofa. "Come over here, you odd little man," she said. Mr. Martin went over and sat beside her. It was difficult getting a cigarette out of the pack of Camels, but he managed it. She held a match for him, laughing. "Well," she said, handing him his drink, "this is perfectly marvelous. You with a drink and cigarette."

Mr. Martin puffed, not too awkwardly, and took a gulp of the highball. "I drink and smoke all the time," he said. He clinked his glass against hers. "Here's nuts to that old windbag, Fitweiler," he said, and gulped again. The stuff tasted awful, but he made no grimace. "Really, Mr. Martin," she said, her voice and posture changing, "you are insulting our employer." Mrs. Barrows was now all special adviser to the president. "I am preparing a bomb," said Mr. Martin, "which will blow the old goat higher than hell." He had only had a little of the drink, which was not strong. It couldn't be that. "Do you take dope or something?" Mrs. Barrows asked coldly. "Heroin," said Mr. Martin. "I'll be coked to the gills when I bump that old buzzard off." "Mr. Martin!" she shouted, getting to her feet. "That will be all of that. You must go at once." Mr. Martin took another swallow of his drink. He tapped his cigarette out in the ashtray and put the pack of Camels on the coffee table. Then he got up. She stood glaring at him. He walked over and put on his hat and coat. "Not a word about this," he said, and laid an index finger against his lips. All Mrs. Barrows could bring out was "Really!" Mr. Martin put his hand on the doorknob. "I'm sitting in the catbird seat," he said. He stuck his tongue out at her and left. Nobody saw him go.

Mr. Martin got to his apartment, walking, well before eleven. No one saw him go in. He had two glasses of milk after brushing his teeth, and he felt elated. It wasn't tipsiness, because he hadn't been tipsy. Anyway, the walk had worn off all effects of the whiskey. He got in bed and read a magazine for a while. He was asleep before midnight.

MR. MARTIN GOT TO THE OFFICE AT EIGHT-THIRTY THE NEXT MORNING, as usual. At a quarter to nine, Ulgine Barrows, who had never before arrived at work before ten, swept into his office. "I'm reporting to Mr. Fitweiler now!" she shouted. "If he turns you over to the police, it's no more than you deserve!" Mr. Martin gave her a look of shocked surprise. "I beg your pardon?" he said. Mrs. Barrows snorted and bounced out of the room, leaving Miss Paird and Joey Hart staring after her. "What's the matter with that old devil now?" asked Miss Paird. "I have no idea," said Mr. Martin, resuming his work. The other two looked at him and then at each other. Miss Paird got up and went out. She walked slowly past the closed door to Mr. Fitweiler's office. Mrs. Barrows was yelling inside, but she was not braying. Miss Paird could not hear what the woman was saying. She went back to her desk.

Forty-five minutes later, Mrs. Barrows left the president's office and went into her own, shutting the door. It wasn't until half an hour later that Mr. Fitweiler sent for Mr. Martin. The head of the filing department, neat, quiet, attentive, stood in front of the old man's desk. Mr. Fitweiler was pale and nervous. He took his glasses off and twiddled them. He made a small, bruffing sound in his throat. "Martin," he said, "you have been with us more than twenty years." "Twenty-two, sir," said Mr. Martin. "In that time," pursued the president, "your work and your—uh—manner have been exemplary." "I trust so, sir," said Mr. Martin. "I have understood, Martin," said Mr. Fitweiler, "that you have never taken a drink or smoked." "That is correct, sir," said Mr. Martin. "Ah, yes." Mr. Fitweiler polished his glasses. "You may describe what you did after leaving the office yesterday, Martin," he said. Mr. Martin allowed less than a second for his bewildered pause. "Certainly, sir," he said. "I walked home. Then I went to Schrafft's for dinner. Afterward I walked home again. I went to bed early, sir, and read a magazine for a while. I was asleep before eleven." "Ah, yes," said Mr. Fitweiler again. He was silent for a moment, searching for the proper words to say to the head of the filing department. "Mrs. Barrows," he said finally, "Mrs. Barrows has worked hard, Martin, very hard. It grieves me to report that she has suffered a severe breakdown. It has taken the form of a persecution complex accompanied by distressing hallucinations." "I am very sorry, sir," said Mr. Martin. "Mrs. Barrows is under the delusion," continued Mr. Fitweiler, "that you visited her last evening and behaved yourself in an—uh—unseemly manner." He raised his hand to silence Mr. Martin's little pained outcry. "It is the nature of these psychological diseases," Mr. Fitweiler said, "to fix upon the least likely and most innocent party as the—uh—source of persecution. These matters are not for the lay mind to grasp, Martin. I've just had my psychiatrist, Dr. Fitch, on the phone. He would not, of course, commit himself, but he made enough generalizations to substantiate my suspicions. I suggested to Mrs. Barrows when she had completed her—uh—story to me this morning, that she visit Dr. Fitch, for I suspected a condition at once. She flew, I regret to say, into a rage, and demanded—uh—requested that I call you on the carpet. You may not know, Martin, but Mrs. Barrows had planned a reorganization of your department—subject to my approval, of course, subject to my approval. This brought you, rather than anyone else, to her mind—but again that is a phenomenon for Dr. Fitch and not for us. So, Martin, I am afraid Mrs. Barrows' usefulness here is at an end." "I am dreadfully sorry, sir," said Mr. Martin.

It was at this point that the door to the office blew open with the suddenness of a gas-main explosion and Mrs. Barrows catapulted through it. "Is the little rat denying it?" she screamed. "He can't get away with that!" Mr. Martin got up and moved discreetly to a point beside Mr. Fitweiler's chair. "You drank and smoked at my apartment," she bawled at Mr. Martin, "and you know it! You called Mr. Fitweiler an old windbag and said you were going to blow him up when you got coked to the gills on your heroin!" She stopped yelling to catch her breath and a new glint came into her popping eyes. "If you weren't such a drab, ordinary little man," she said, "I'd think you'd planned it all. Sticking your tongue out, saying you were sitting in the catbird seat, because you thought no one would believe me when I told it! My God, it's really too perfect!" She brayed loudly and hysterically, and the fury was on her again. She glared at Mr. Fitweiler. "Can't you see how he has tricked us, you old fool? Can't you see his little game?" But Mr. Fitweiler had been surreptitiously pressing all the buttons under the top of his desk and employees of F & S began pouring into the room. "Stockton," said Mr. Fitweiler, "you and Fishbein will take Mrs. Barrows to her home. Mrs. Powell, you will go with them." Stockton, who had played a little football in high school, blocked Mrs. Barrows as she made for Mr. Martin. It took him and Fishbein together to force her out of the door into the hall, crowded with stenographers and office boys. She was still screaming imprecations at Mr. Martin, tangled and contradictory imprecations. The hubbub finally died out down the corridor.

"I regret that this has happened," said Mr. Fitweiler. "I shall ask you to dismiss it from your mind, Martin." "Yes, sir," said Mr. Martin, anticipating his chief's "That will be all," by moving to the door. "I will dismiss it." He went out and shut the door, and his step was light and quick in the hall. When he entered his department he had slowed down to his customary gait, and he walked quietly across the room to the W20 file, wearing a look of studious concentration.

Eudora Welty, 1909–

A Worn Path

This story first appeared in THE ATLANTIC MONTHLY, *1941.*

IT WAS DECEMBER—A BRIGHT FROZEN DAY IN THE EARLY MORNING. Far out in the country there was an old Negro woman with her head tied in a red rag, coming along a path through the pinewoods. Her name was Phoenix Jackson. She was very old and small and she walked slowly in the dark pine shadows, moving a little from side to side in her steps, with the balanced heaviness and lightness of a pendulum in a grandfather clock. She carried a thin, small cane made from an umbrella, and with this she kept tapping the frozen earth in front of her. This made a grave and persistent noise in the still air, that seemed meditative like the chirping of a solitary little bird.

She wore a dark striped dress reaching down to her shoe tops, and an equally long apron of bleached sugar sacks, with a full pocket: all neat and tidy, but every time she took a step she might have fallen over her shoelaces, which dragged from her unlaced shoes. She looked straight ahead. Her eyes were blue with age. Her skin had a pattern all its own of numberless branching wrinkles and as though a whole little tree stood in the middle of her forehead, but a golden color ran underneath, and the two knobs of her cheeks were illuminated by a yellow burning under the dark. Under the rag her hair came down on her neck in the frailest of ringlets, still black, and with an odor like copper.

Now and then there was a quivering in the thicket. Old Phoenix said, "Out of my way, all you foxes, owls, beetles, jack rabbits, coons and wild animals! . . . Keep out from under these feet, little bob-whites. . . . Keep the big wild hogs out of my path. Don't let none of those come running my direction. I got a long way." Under her small black-freckled hand her cane, limber as a buggy whip, would switch at the brush as if to rouse up any hiding things.

On she went. The woods were deep and still. The sun made the pine needles almost too bright to look at, up where the wind rocked. The cones dropped as light as feathers. Down in the hollow was the mourning dove—it was not too late for him.

The path ran up a hill. "Seem like there is chains about my feet, time I get this far," she said, in the voice of argument old people keep to use with themselves. "Something always take a hold of me on this hill—pleads I should stay."

After she got to the top she turned and gave a full, severe look behind her where she had come. "Up through pines," she said at length. "Now down through oaks."

Her eyes opened their widest, and she started down gently. But before she got to the bottom of the hill a bush caught her dress.

Her fingers were busy and intent, but her skirts were full and long, so that before she could pull them free in one place they were caught in another. It was not possible to allow the dress to tear. "I in the thorny bush," she said. "Thorns, you doing your appointed work. Never want to let folks pass, no sir. Old eyes thought you was a pretty little *green* bush."

Finally, trembling all over, she stood free, and after a moment dared to stoop for her cane.

"Sun so high!" she cried, leaning back and looking, while the thick tears went over her eyes. "The time getting all gone here."

At the foot of this hill was a place where a log was laid across the creek.

"Now comes the trial," said Phoenix.

Putting her right foot out, she mounted the log and shut her eyes. Lifting her skirt, leveling her cane fiercely before her, like a festival figure in some parade, she began to march across. Then she opened her eyes and she was safe on the other side.

"I wasn't as old as I thought," she said.

But she sat down to rest. She spread her skirts on the bank around her and folded her hands over her knees. Up above her was a tree in a pearly cloud of mistletoe. She did not dare to close her eyes, and when a little boy brought her a plate with a slice of marble-cake on it she spoke to him. "That would be acceptable," she said. But when she went to take it there was just her own hand in the air.

So she left that tree, and had to go through a barbed-wire fence. There she had to creep and crawl, spreading her knees and stretching her fingers like a baby trying to climb the steps. But she talked loudly to herself: she could not let her dress be torn now, so late in the day, and she could not pay for having her arm or leg sawed off if she got caught fast where she was.

At last she was safe through the fence and risen up out in the clearing. Big dead trees, like black men with one arm, were standing in the purple stalks of the withered cotton field. There sat a buzzard.

"Who you watching?"

In the furrow she made her way along.

"Glad this is not the season for bulls," she said, looking sideways, "and the good Lord made his snakes to curl up and sleep in the winter. A pleasure I don't see no two-headed snake coming around that tree, where it come once. It took a while to get by him, back in the summer."

She passed through the old cotton and went into a field of dead corn. It whispered and shook and was taller than her head. "Through the maze now," she said, for there was no path.

Then there was something tall, black, and skinny there, moving before her.

At first she took it for a man. It could have been a man dancing in the field. But she stood still and listened, and it did not make a sound. It was as silent as a ghost.

"Ghost," she said sharply, "who be you the ghost of? For I have heard of nary death close by."

But there was no answer—only the ragged dancing in the wind.

She shut her eyes, reached out her hand, and touched a sleeve. She found a coat and inside that an emptiness, cold as ice.

"You scarecrow," she said. Her face lighted. "I ought to be shut up for good," she said with laughter. "My senses is gone. I too old. I the oldest people I ever know. Dance, old scarecrow," she said, "while I dancing with you."

She kicked her foot over the furrow, and with mouth drawn down, shook her head once or twice in a little strutting way. Some husks blew down and whirled in steamers about her skirts.

Then she went on, parting her way from side to side with the cane, through the whispering field. At last she came to the end, to a wagon track where the silver grass blew between the red ruts. The quail were walking around like pullets, seeming all dainty and unseen.

"Walk pretty," she said. "This is the easy place. This the easy going."

She followed the track, swaying through the quiet bare fields, through the little strings of trees silver in their dead leaves, past cabins silver from weather, with the doors and windows boarded shut, all like old women under a spell sitting there. "I walking in their sleep," she said, nodding her head vigorously.

In a ravine she went where a spring was silently flowing through a hollow log. Old Phoenix bent and drank. "Sweet-gum makes the water sweet," she said, and drank more. "Nobody know who made this well, for it was here when I was born."

The track crossed a swampy part where the moss hung as white as lace from every limb. "Sleep on, alligators, and blow your bubbles." Then the track went into the road.

Deep, deep the road went down between the high green-colored banks. Overhead the live-oaks met, and it was as dark as a cave.

A black dog with a lolling tongue came up out of the weeds by the ditch. She was meditating, and not ready, and when he came at her she only hit him a little with her cane. Over she went in the ditch, like a little puff of milkweed.

Down there, her sense drifted away. A dream visited her, and she reached her hand up, but nothing reached down and gave her a pull. So she lay there and presently went to talking. "Old woman," she said to herself, "that black dog come up out of the weeds to stall you off, and now there he sitting on his fine tail smiling at you."

A white man finally came along and found her—a hunter, a young man, with his dog on a chain.

"Well, Granny!" he laughed. "What are you doing there?"

"Lying on my back like a June-bug waiting to be turned over, mister," she said, reaching up her hand.

He lifted her up, gave her a swing in the air, and set her down. "Anything broken, Granny?"

"No sir, them old dead weeds is springy enough," said Phoenix, when she had got her breath. "I thank you for your trouble."

"Where do you live, Granny?" he asked, while the two dogs were growling at each other.

"Away back yonder, sir, behind the ridge. You can't even see it from here."

"On your way home?"

"No sir, I goin to town."

"Why, that's too far! That's as far as I walk when I come out myself, and I get something for my trouble." He patted the stuffed bag he carried, and there hung down a little closed claw. It was one of the bob-whites, with its beak hooked bitterly to show it was dead. "Now you go on home, Granny!"

"I bound to go to town, mister," said Phoenix. "The time come around."

He gave another laugh, filling the whole landscape. "I know you old colored people! Wouldn't miss going to town to see Santa Claus!"

But something held old Phoenix very still. The deep lines in her face went into a fierce and different radiation. Without warning, she had seen with her own eyes a flashing nickel fall out of the man's pocket onto the ground.

"How old are you, Granny?" he was saying.

"There is no telling, mister," she said, "no telling."

Then she gave a little cry and clapped her hands and said, "Git on away from here, dog! Look! Look at that dog!" She laughed as if in admiration. "He ain't scared of nobody. He a big black dog." She whispered, "Sic him!"

"Watch me get rid of that cur," said the man. "Sic him, Pete! Sic him!"

Phoenix heard the dogs fighting, and heard the man running and throwing sticks. She even heard a gunshot. But she was slowly bending forward by that time, further and further forward, the lids stretched down over her eyes, as if she were doing this in her sleep. Her chin was lowered almost to her knees. The yellow palm of her hand came out from the fold of her apron. Her fingers slid down and along the ground under the piece of money with the grace and care they would have in lifting an egg from under a setting hen. Then she slowly straightened up, she stood erect, and the nickel was in her apron pocket. A bird flew by. Her lips moved. "God watching me the whole time I come to stealing."

The man came back, and his own dog panted about them. "Well, I scared him off that time," he said, and then he laughed and lifted his gun and pointed it at Phoenix.

She stood straight and faced him.

"Doesn't the gun scare you?" he said, still pointing it.

"No, sir. I seen plenty go off closer by, in my day, and for less than what I done," she said, holding utterly still.

He smiled, and shouldered the gun. "Well, Granny," he said, "you must be a hundred years old, and scared of nothing. I'd give you a dime if I had any money with me. But you take my advice and stay home, and nothing will happen to you."

"I bound to go on my way, mister," said Phoenix. She inclined her head in the red rag. Then they went in different directions, but she could hear the gun shooting again and again over the hill.

She walked on. The shadows hung from the oak trees to the road like curtains. Then she smelled wood-smoke, and smelled the river, and she saw a steeple and the cabins on their steep steps. Dozens of little black children whirled around her. There ahead was Natchez shining. Bells were ringing. She walked on.

In the paved city it was Christmas time. There were red and green electric lights strung and crisscrossed everywhere, and all turned on in the daytime. Old Phoenix would have been lost if she had not distrusted her eyesight and depended on her feet to know where to take her.

She paused quietly on the sidewalk where people were passing by. A lady came along in the crowd, carrying an armful of red-, green-, and silver-wrapped presents; she gave off perfume like the red roses in hot summer, and Phoenix stopped her.

"Please, missy, will you lace up my shoe?" She held up her foot.

"What do you want, Grandma?"

"See my shoe," said Phoenix. "Do all right for out in the country, but wouldn't look right to go in a big building."

"Stand still then, Grandma," said the lady. She put her packages down on the sidewalk beside her and laced and tied both shoes tightly.

"Can't lace 'em with a cane," said Phoenix. "Thank you, missy. I doesn't mind asking a nice lady to tie up my shoe, when I gets out on the street."

Moving slowly and from side to side, she went into the big building, and into a tower of steps, where she walked up and around and around until her feet knew to stop.

She entered a door, and there she saw nailed up on the wall the document that had been stamped with the gold seal and framed in the gold frame, which matched the dream that was hung up in her head.

"Here I be," she said. There was a fixed and ceremonial stiffness over her body.

"A charity case, I suppose," said an attendant who sat at the desk before her.

But Phoenix only looked above her head. There was sweat on her face, the wrinkles in her skin shone like a bright net.

"Speak up, Grandma," the woman said, "What's your name? We must have your history, you know. Have you been here before? What seems to be the trouble with you?"

Old Phoenix only gave a twitch to her face as if a fly were bothering her.

"Are you deaf?" cried the attendant.

But then the nurse came in.

"Oh, that's just old Aunt Phoenix," she said. "She doesn't come for her-self—she has a little grandson. She makes these trips just as regular as clock-work. She lives away back off the Old Natchez Trace." She bent down. "Well, Aunt Phoenix, why don't you just take a seat? We won't keep you standing after your long trip." She pointed.

The old woman sat down, bolt upright in the chair.

"Now, how is the boy?" asked the nurse.

Old Phoenix did not speak.

"I said, how is the boy?"

But Phoenix only waited and stared straight ahead, her face very solemn and withdrawn into rigidity.

"Is his throat any better?" asked the nurse. "Aunt Phoenix, don't you hear me? Is your grandson's throat any better since the last time you came for the medicine?"

With her hands on her knees, the old woman waited, silent, erect, and mo-tionless, just as if she were in armor.

"You mustn't take up our time this way, Aunt Phoenix," the nurse said. "Tell us quickly about your grandson, and get it over. He isn't dead, is he?"

At last there came a flicker and then a flame of comprehension across her face, and she spoke.

"My grandson. It was my memory had left me. There I sat and forgot why I made my long trip."

"Forgot?" the nurse frowned. "After you came so far?"

Then Phoenix was like an old woman begging a dignified forgiveness for waking up frightened in the night. "I never did go to school, I was too old at the Surrender," she said in a soft voice. "I'm an old woman without an edu-cation. It was my memory fail me. My little grandson, he is just the same, and I forgot it in the coming."

"Throat never heals, does it?" said the nurse, speaking in a loud, sure voice to old Phoenix. By now she had a card with something written on it, a little list. "Yes. Swallowed lye. When was it—January—two, three years ago—"

Phoenix spoke unasked now. "No missy, he not dead, he just the same. Every little while his throat begin to close up again, and he not able to swal-low. He not get his breath. He not able to help himself. So the time come around, and I go on another trip for the soothing medicine."

"All right. The doctor said as long as you came to get it, you could have it," said the nurse. "But it's an obstinate case."

"My little grandson, he sit up there in the house all wrapped up, waiting by himself," Phoenix went on. "We is the only two left in the world. He suffer and it don't seem to put him back at all. He got a sweet look. He going to last. He wear a little patch quilt and peep out holding his mouth open like a little bird. I remembers so plain now. I not going to forget him again, no, the whole enduring time. I could tell him from all the others in creation."

"All right." The nurse was trying to hush her now. She brought her a bottle of medicine. "Charity," she said, making a check mark in a book.

Old Phoenix held the bottle close to her eyes, and then carefully put it into her pocket.

"I thank you," she said.

"It's Christmas time, Grandma," said the attendant. "Could I give you a few pennies out of my purse?"

"Five pennies is a nickel," said Phoenix stiffly.

"Here's a nickel," said the attendant.

Phoenix rose carefully and held out her hand. She received the nickel and then fished the other nickel out of her pocket and laid it beside the new one. She stared at her palm closely, with her head on one side.

Then she gave a tap with her cane on the floor.

"This is what come to me to do," she said, "I going to the store and buy my child a little windmill they sells, made out of paper. He going to find it hard to believe there such a thing in the world. I'll march myself back where he waiting, holding it straight up in his hand."

She lifted her free hand, gave a little nod, turned around, and walked out of the doctor's office. Then her slow step began on the stairs, going down.

Excerpt from Film Script for Eudora Welty's "A Worn Path"

Bruce Schwartz

One way to understand one artistic medium is to compare it with another. Here is a passage from Bruce Schwartz's film adaptation of the passage in Miss Welty's story in which Phoenix encounters the Hunter. (The film "A Worn Path" was produced and is distributed by Harcourt Brace.)

PHOENIX

(V.O.)

Back last summer there was a two-headed snake coming around that tree.

She rounds the tree and passes through the old field of dead corn. WIND BLOWS. The dead cornstalks whisper and shake and are taller than her head.

PHOENIX

Through the maze now.

In the thick dead corn she gets lost from sight. Then as she comes out from the shifting stalks, she touches something tall and skinny and black. It keeps appearing, then disappearing.

PHOENIX

Ho! Mister . . . No, ghost. Who you be the ghost of?

She reaches out her hand, shuts her eyes, touches a sleeve.

PHOENIX'S P.O.V.

She finds an emptiness inside a black coat.

PHOENIX

You scarecrow!

ANGLE—PHOENIX

Her face lights up and she laughs, loudly, fully, her anxiety gone. She's played a joke on herself.

PHOENIX

I ought to be shut up for good. My senses is gone. I too old. I the oldest person I ever know.

She grabs the scarecrow by the arm.

PHOENIX

Dance, old scarecrow, I dancing with you.

CLOSE ON PHOENIX:

A big smile crosses her face as she swirls around once, twice, then half-dizzy, heads on, again using her cane to part the thick maze.

EXT. OPEN FIELD. DAY.

She arrives at an open area, gutted by wagon tracks. Quail are walking daintily around. Phoenix notices them.

PHOENIX

Walk pretty. This the easy place. This the easy going.

She follows the tracks through bare fields past cabins whose doors and windows are boarded shut.

EXT. RAVINE. DAY.

Coming upon a ravine she sees a spring silently flowing through a hollow log.

She bends to drink deeply from the water that's flowing out. Again, her hand trembles.

PHOENIX

This well's been here since I born. Nobody knows who made it.

EXT. SWAMPY WOODS NEAR A DITCH. DAY.

The path crosses a swampy section of woods where moss hangs white as lace from every limb.

PHOENIX

Sleep on, alligators, blow your bubbles.

Now as she moves ahead a BLACK DOG with a lolling tongue comes out of the weeds by a ditch and heads right for her. She shoos at the dog with her cane but misses him and, losing balance, falls into a shallow ditch.

In the ditch she sees the same black dog sitting by the edge, looking down on her. After a moment, a HUNTER, a young man, appears, he has a DOG on a long chain. The hunter notices her.

HUNTER

Well, Granny! What are you doing there?

PHOENIX

Lying on my back like a June-bug waiting to be turned over, mister.

She reaches up her hand and the hunter leans forward to give her his hand. He lifts her out of the ditch, then gives her a swing in the air before setting her down. Old Phoenix tries to catch her breath.

HUNTER

Anything, broken, Granny?

PHOENIX

No, sir, them old dead weeds is springy enough. I thank you for your trouble.

HUNTER

Where do you live, Granny?

PHOENIX

Away back yonder, sir, behind the ridge. You can't even see it from here.

The two dogs are beginning to growl at one another.

HUNTER

On your way home?

PHOENIX

No sir, I'm going to town.

HUNTER

Why, that's too far! That's as far as I walk when I come out myself, and I get something for my trouble.

He pats the stuffed bag he carries. Peaking out of one corner is the dead beak of a bob-white.

HUNTER

Now you go home, Granny!

PHOENIX

I bound to go to town. The times come around.

He gives her a loud laugh.

HUNTER

I know you colored people! Wouldn't miss going to town to see Santa Claus!

The hunter draws out a handkerchief to blow his nose and as he does a flashing nickel falls out of his pocket.

ANGLE—NICKEL

Phoenix sees it, glinting silver in the sunlight.

ANGLE—PHOENIX AND THE HUNTER

The hunter hasn't noticed what he's dropped. He turns to look back at her.

HUNTER

How old are you, Granny?

PHOENIX

There is no telling mister. No telling.

The big black dog begins to sniff around the other dog in earnest.

PHOENIX

Git on away from here, dog! Look! Look at that dog! He ain't scared of no-body. He a big black dog. Sic him!

HUNTER

Watch me get rid of that cur. Sic him, Pete. Sic him!

The dogs begin to fight and the man follows them, throwing sticks.

CLOSER ANGLE—PHOENIX:

As she now eyes the nickel. We TILT with her as she slowly bends down, her chin lowered nearly to her knees. The yellow palm of her hand comes out from the fold of her apron and she quickly slides the coin into her apron pocket.

Then she slowly straightens up. She glances up at a bird that flies by in the sky. She shakes her hand sadly.

PHOENIX

God watching me the whole time I come to stealing.

She glanced over at the hunter who has broken up the fighting dogs and is now returning. The hunter's dog is panting about them.

HUNTER

Well, I scared him off that time.

He laughs and lifts his gun and points it at Phoenix.

HUNTER

Don't that gun scare you none?

PHOENIX

No, sir, I seen plenty go off closer by, in my day, and for less than what I done.

She holds utterly still. After a moment, he smiles and shoulders the gun.

HUNTER

Well, Granny, you must be a hundred years old, and scared of nothing. I'd give you a dime if I had any money with me. But you take my advice and stay home, and nothing will happen to you.

PHOENIX

I bound to go my way, mister.

EXTERIOR. CITY OF NATCHEZ. DAY.

Phoenix reaches a paved road in 1940s Natchez.

William Faulkner, 1897–1962

Barn Burning

This story first appeared in HARPER'S MONTHLY, *1939.*

THE STORE IN WHICH THE JUSTICE OF THE PEACE'S COURT WAS SITTING SMELLED OF CHEESE. The boy, crouched on his nail keg at the back of the crowded room, knew he smelled cheese, and more: from where he sat he could see the ranked shelves close-packed with the solid, squat, dynamic shapes of tin cans whose labels his stomach read, not from the lettering which meant nothing to his mind but from the scarlet devils and the silver curve of fish—this, the cheese which he knew he smelled and the hermetic meat which his intestines believed he smelled coming in intermittent gusts momentary and brief between the other constant one, the smell and sense just a little of fear because mostly of despair and grief, the old fierce pull of blood. He could not see the table where the Justice sat and before which his father and his father's enemy (*our enemy* he thought in that despair; *ourn! mine and hisn both! He's my father!*) stood, but he could hear them, the two of them that is, because his father had said no word yet:

"But what proof have you, Mr. Harris?"

"I told you. The hog got into my corn. I caught it up and sent it back to him. He had no fence that would hold it. I told him so, warned him. The next time I put the hog in my pen. When he came to get it I gave him enough wire to patch up his pen. The next time I put the hog up and kept it. I rode down to his house and saw the wire I gave him still rolled on to the spool in his yard. I told him he could have the hog when he paid me a dollar pound fee. That evening a nigger came with the dollar and got the hog. He was a strange nigger. He said, 'He say to tell you wood and hay kin burn.' I said, 'What?' 'That whut he say to tell you,' the nigger said. 'Wood and hay kin burn.' That night my barn burned. I got the stock out but I lost the barn."

"Where is the nigger? Have you got him?"

"He was a strange nigger, I tell you. I don't know what became of him."

"But that's not proof. Don't you see that's not proof?"

"Get that boy up here. He knows." For a moment the boy thought too that the man meant his older brother until Harris said, "Not him. The little one. The boy," and, crouching, small for his age, small and wiry like his father, in patched and faded jeans even too small for him, with straight, uncombed, brown hair and eyes gray and wild as storm scud, he saw the men between himself and the table part and become a lane of grim faces, at the end of which he saw the Justice, a shabby, collarless, graying man in spectacles, beckoning him. He felt no floor under his bare feet; he seemed to walk beneath the palpable weight of the grim turning faces. His father, stiff in his black Sunday coat donned not for the trial but for the moving, did not even look at him. *He aims for me to lie,* he thought, again with that frantic grief and despair. *And I will have to do hit.*

"What's your name, boy?" the Justice said.

"Colonel Sartoris Snopes," the boy whispered.

"Hey?" the Justice said. "Talk louder. Colonel Sartoris? I reckon anybody named for Colonel Sartoris in this country can't help but tell the truth, can they?" The boy said nothing. *Enemy! Enemy!* he thought; for a moment he could not even see, could not see that the Justice's face was kindly nor discern that his voice was troubled when he spoke to the man named Harris: "Do you want me to question this boy?" But he could hear, and during those subsequent long seconds while there was absolutely no sound in the crowded little room save that of quiet and intent breathing it was as if he had swung outward at the end of a grape vine, over a ravine, and at the top of the swing had been caught in a prolonged instant of mesmerized gravity, weightless in time.

"No!" Harris said violently, explosively. "Damnation! Send him out of here!" Now time, the fluid world, rushed beneath him again, the voices coming to him again through the smell of cheese and sealed meat, the fear and despair and the old grief of blood:

"This case is closed. I can't find against you, Snopes, but I can give you advice. Leave this country and don't come back to it."

His father spoke for the first time, his voice cold and harsh, level, without emphasis: "I aim to. I don't figure to stay in a country among people who . . ." he said something unprintable and vile, addressed to no one.

"That'll do," the Justice said. "Take your wagon and get out of this country before dark. Case dismissed."

His father turned, and he followed the stiff black coat, the wiry figure walking a little stiffly from where a Confederate provost's man's* musket ball had taken him in the heel on a stolen horse thirty years ago, followed the two backs now, since his older brother had appeared from somewhere in the crowd, no taller than the father but thicker, chewing tobacco steadily, between the two lines of grim-faced men and out of the store and across the worn gallery and down the sagging steps and among the dogs and half-grown boys in the mild May dust where as he passed a voice hissed:

"Barn burner!"

Again he could not see, whirling; there was a face in a red haze, moonlike, bigger than the full moon, the owner of it half again his size, he leaping

provost's man: a military policeman.

in the red haze toward the face, feeling no blow, feeling no shock when his head struck the earth, scrabbling up and leaping again, feeling no blow this time either and tasting no blood, scrabbling up to see the other boy in full flight and himself already leaping into pursuit as his father's hand jerked him back, the harsh, cold voice speaking above him: "Go get in the wagon."

It stood in a grove of locusts and mulberries across the road. His two hulking sisters in their Sunday dresses and his mother and her sister in calico and sunbonnets were already in it, sitting on and among the sorry residue of the dozen and more movings which even the boy could remember—the battered stove, the broken beds and chairs, the clock inlaid with mother-of-pearl, which would not run, stopped at some fourteen minutes past two o'clock of a dead and forgotten day and time, which had been his mother's dowry. She was crying, though when she saw him she drew her sleeve across her face and began to descend from the wagon. "Get back," the father said.

"He's hurt. I got to get some water and wash his . . ."

"Get back in the wagon," his father said. He got in too, over the tailgate. His father mounted to the seat where the older brother already sat and struck the gaunt mules two savage blows with the peeled willow, but without heat. It was not even sadistic; it was exactly that same quality which in later years would cause his descendants to overrun the engine before putting a motor car into motion, striking and reining back in the same movement. The wagon went on, the store with its quiet crowd of grimly watching men dropped behind; a curve in the road hid it. *Forever* he thought. *Maybe he's done satisfied now, now that he has* . . . stopping himself, not to say it aloud even to himself. His mother's hand touched his shoulder.

"Does hit hurt?" she said.

"Naw," he said. "Hit don't hurt. Lemme be."

"Can't you wipe some of the blood off before hit dries?"

"I'll wash to-night," he said. "Lemme be, I tell you."

The wagon went on. He did not know where they were going. None of them ever did or ever asked, because it was always somewhere, always a house of sorts waiting for them a day or two days or even three days away. Likely his father had already arranged to make a crop on another farm before he . . . Again he had to stop himself. He (the father) always did. There was something about his wolf-like independence and even courage when the advantage was at least neutral which impressed strangers, as if they got from his latent ravening ferocity not so much a sense of dependability as a feeling that his ferocious conviction in the rightness of his own actions would be of advantage to all whose interest lay with his.

That night they camped, in a grove of oaks and beeches where a spring ran. The nights were still cool and they had a fire against it, of a rail lifted from a nearby fence and cut into lengths—a small fire, neat, niggard almost, a shrewd fire; such fires were his father's habit and custom always, even in freezing weather. Older, the boy might have remarked this and wondered why not a big one; why should not a man who had not only seen the waste and extravagance of war, but who had in his blood an inherent voracious prodigality with material not his own, have burned everything in sight? Then he might have gone a step farther and thought that that was the reason: that niggard blaze was the living fruit of nights passed during those four years in the woods hiding from all men, blue or gray, with his strings of horses (captured horses, he called them). And older still, he might have divined the true reason: that the element of fire spoke to some deep mainspring of his father's being, as the element of steel or of powder spoke to other men, as the one weapon for the preservation of integrity, else breath were not worth the breathing, and hence to be regarded with respect and used with discretion.

But he did not think this now and he had seen those same niggard blazes all his life. He merely ate his supper beside it and was already half asleep over his iron plate when his father called him, and once more he followed the stiff back, the stiff and ruthless limp, up the slope and on to the starlit road where, turning, he could see his father against the stars but without face or depth—a shape black, flat, and bloodless as though cut from tin in the iron folds of the frockcoat which had not been made for him, the voice harsh like tin and without heat like tin:

"You were fixing to tell them. You would have told him." He didn't answer. His father struck him with the flat of his hand on the side of the head, hard but without heat, exactly as he had struck the two mules at the store, exactly as he would strike either of them with any stick in order to kill a horse fly, his voice still without fear or anger: "You're getting to be a man. You got to learn. You got to learn to stick to your own blood or you ain't going to have any blood to stick to you. Do you think either of them, any man there this morning, would? Don't you know all they wanted was a chance to get at me because they knew I had them beat? Eh?" Later, twenty years later, he was to tell himself, "If I had said they wanted only truth, justice, he would have hit me again." But now he said nothing. He was not crying. He just stood there. "Answer me," his father said.

"Yes," he whispered. His father turned.

"Get on to bed. We'll be there tomorrow."

Tomorrow they were there. In the early afternoon the wagon stopped before a paintless two-room house identical almost with the dozen others it had stopped before even in the boy's ten years, and again, as on the other dozen occasions, his mother and aunt got down and began to unload the wagon, although his two sisters and his father and brother had not moved.

"Likely hit ain't fitten for hawgs," one of the sisters said.

"Nevertheless, fit it will and you'll hog it and like it," his father said. "Get out of them chairs and help your Ma unload."

The two sisters got down, big, bovine, in a flutter of cheap ribbons; one of them drew from the jumbled wagon bed a battered lantern, the other a worn broom. His father handed the reins to the older son and began to climb stiffly over the wheel. "When they get unloaded, take the team to the barn and feed them." Then he said, and at first the boy thought he was still speaking to his brother: "Come with me."

"Me?" he said.

"Yes," his father said. "You."

"Abner," his mother said. His father paused and looked back—the harsh level stare beneath the shaggy, graying, irascible brows.

"I reckon I'll have a word with the man that aims to begin tomorrow owning me body and soul for the next eight months."

They went back up the road. A week ago—or before last night, that is—he would have asked where they were going, but not now. His father had struck him before last night but never before had he paused afterward to explain why; it was as if the blow and the following calm, outrageous voice still rang, repercussed, divulging nothing to him save the terrible handicap of being young, the light weight of his few years, just heavy enough to prevent his soaring free of the world as it seemed to be ordered but not heavy enough to keep him footed solid in it, to resist it and try to change the course of its events.

Presently he could see the grove of oaks and cedars and the other flowering trees and shrubs, where the house would be, though not the house yet. They walked beside a fence massed with honeysuckle and Cherokee roses and came to a gate swinging open between two brick pillars, and now, beyond a sweep of drive, he saw the house for the first time and at that instant he forgot his father and the terror and despair both, and even when he remembered his father again (who had not stopped) the terror and despair did not return. Because, for all the twelve movings, they had sojourned until now in a poor country, a land of small farms and fields and houses, and he had never seen a house like this before. *Hit's big as a courthouse* he thought quietly, with a surge of peace and joy whose reason he could not have thought into words, being too young for that: *They are safe from him. People whose lives are a part of this peace and dignity are beyond his touch, he no more to them than a buzzing wasp: capable of stinging for a little moment but that's all; the spell of this peace and dignity rendering even the barns and stable and cribs which belong to it impervious to the puny flames he might contrive* . . . this, the peace and joy, ebbing for an instant as he looked again at the stiff black back, the stiff and implacable limp of the figure which was not dwarfed by the house, for the reason that it had never looked big anywhere and which now, against the serene columned backdrop, had more than ever that impervious quality of something cut ruthlessly from tin, depthless, as though, sidewise to the sun, it would cast no shadow. Watching him, the boy remarked the absolutely undeviating course which his father held and saw the stiff foot come squarely down in a pile of fresh droppings where a horse had stood in the drive and which his father could have avoided by a simple change of stride. But it ebbed only for a moment, though he could not have thought this into words either, walking on in the spell of the house, which he could even want but without envy, without sorrow, certainly never with that ravening and jealous rage which unknown to him walked in the ironlike black coat before him: *Maybe he will feel it too. Maybe it will even change him now from what maybe he couldn't help but be.*

They crossed the portico. Now he could hear his father's stiff foot as it came down on the boards with clocklike finality, a sound out of all proportion to the displacement of the body it bore and which was not dwarfed either by the white door before it, as though it had attained to a sort of vicious and ravening minimum not to be dwarfed by anything—the flat, wide, black hat, the formal coat of broadcloth which had once been black but which had now that friction-glazed greenish cast of the bodies of old house flies, the lifted sleeve which was too large, the lifted hand like a curled claw. The door opened so promptly that the boy knew the Negro must have been watching them all the time, an old man with neat grizzled hair, in a linen jacket, who stood barring the door with his body, saying, "Wipe yo foots, white man, fo you come in here. Major ain't home nohow."

"Get out of my way, nigger," his father said, without heat too, flinging the door back and the Negro also and entering, his hat still on his head. And now the boy saw the prints of the stiff foot on the doorjamb and saw them appear on the pale rug behind the machinelike deliberation of the foot which seemed to bear (or transmit) twice the weight which the body compassed. The Negro was shouting "Miss Lula! Miss Lula!" somewhere behind them, then the boy, deluged as though by a warm wave by a suave turn of carpeted stair and a pendant glitter of chandeliers and a mute gleam of gold frames, heard the swift feet and saw her too, a lady—perhaps he had never seen her like before either—in a gray, smooth gown with lace at the throat and an apron tied at the waist and the sleeves turned back, wiping cake or biscuit dough from her hands with a towel as she came up the hall, looking not at his father at all but at the tracks on the blond rug with an expression of incredulous amazement.

"I tried," the Negro cried. "I tole him to . . ."

"Will you please go away?" she said in a shaking voice. "Major de Spain is not at home. Will you please go away?"

His father had not spoken again. He did not speak again. He did not even look at her. He just stood stiff in the center of the rug, in his hat, the shaggy iron-gray brows twitching slightly above the pebble-colored eyes as he appeared to examine the house with brief deliberation. Then with the same deliberation he turned; the boy watched him pivot on the good leg and saw the stiff foot drag round the arc of the turning, leaving a final long and fading smear. His father never looked at it, he never once looked down at the rug. The Negro held the door. It closed behind them, upon the hysteric and indistinguishable woman-wail. His father stopped at the top of the steps and scraped his boot clean on the edge of it. At the gate he stopped again. He stood for a moment, planted stiffly on the stiff foot, looking back at the house. "Pretty and white, ain't it?" he said. "That's sweat. Nigger sweat. Maybe it ain't white enough yet to suit him. Maybe he wants to mix some white sweat with it."

Two hours later the boy was chopping wood behind the house within which his mother and aunt and the two sisters (the mother and aunt, not the two girls, he knew that; even at this distance and muffled by walls the flat loud voices of the two girls emanated an incorrigible idle inertia) were setting up the stove to prepare a meal, when he heard the hooves and saw the linen-clad man on a fine sorrel mare, whom he recognized even before he saw the rolled rug in front of the Negro youth following on a fat bay carriage horse—a suffused, angry face vanishing, still at full gallop, beyond the corner of the house where his father and brother were sitting in the two tilted chairs; and a moment later, almost before he could have put the axe down, he heard the hooves again and watched the sorrel mare go back out of the yard, already galloping again. Then his father began to shout one of the sisters' names, who presently emerged backward from the kitchen door dragging the rolled rug along the ground by one end while the other sister walked behind it.

"If you ain't going to tote, go on and set up the wash pot," the first said.

"You, Sarty!" the second shouted. "Set up the wash pot!" His father appeared at the door, framed against that shabbiness, as he had been against that other bland perfection, impervious to either, the mother's anxious face at his shoulder.

"Go on," the father said. "Pick it up." The two sisters stooped, broad, lethargic; stooping, they presented an incredible expanse of pale cloth and a flutter of tawdry ribbons.

"If I thought enough of a rug to have to git hit all the way from France I wouldn't keep hit where folks coming in would have to tromp on hit," the first said. They raised the rug.

"Abner," the mother said. "Let me do it."

"You go back and git dinner," his father said. "I'll tend to this."

From the woodpile through the rest of the afternoon the boy watched them, the rug spread flat in the dust beside the bubbling wash-pot, the two sisters stooping over it with that profound and lethargic reluctance, while the father stood over them in turn, implacable and grim, driving them though never raising his voice again. He could smell the harsh homemade lye they were using; he saw his mother come to the door once and look toward them with an expression not anxious now but very like despair; he saw his father turn, and he fell to with the axe and saw from the corner of his eye his father raise from the ground a flattish fragment of field stone and examine it and return to the pot, and this time his mother actually spoke: "Abner. Abner. Please don't. Please, Abner."

Then he was done too. It was dusk; the whippoorwills had already begun. He could smell coffee from the room where they would presently eat the cold food remaining from the mid-afternoon meal, though when he entered the house he realized they were having coffee again probably because there was a fire on the hearth, before which the rug now lay spread over the backs of the two chairs. The tracks of his father's foot were gone. Where they had been were now long, water-cloudy scoriations resembling the sporadic course of a Lilliputian mowing machine.

It still hung there while they ate the cold food and then went to bed, scattered without order or claim up and down the two rooms, his mother in one bed, where his father would later lie, the older brother in the other, himself, the aunt, and the two sisters on pallets on the floor. But his father was not in bed yet. The last thing the boy remembered was the depthless, harsh silhouette of the hat and coat bending over the rug and it seemed to him that he had not even closed his eyes when the silhouette was standing over him, the fire almost dead behind it, the stiff foot prodding him awake. "Catch up the mule," his father said.

When he returned with the mule his father was standing in the black door, the rolled rug over his shoulder. "Ain't you going to ride?" he said.

"No. Give me your foot."

He bent his knee into his father's hand, the wiry, surprising power flowed smoothly, rising, he rising with it, on to the mule's bare back (they had owned a saddle once; the boy could remember it though not when or where) and with the same effortlessness his father swung the rug up in front of him. Now in the starlight they retraced the afternoon's path, up the dusty road rife with honeysuckle, through the gate and up the black tunnel to the drive to the lightless house, where he sat on the mule and felt the rough warp of the rug drag across his thighs and vanish.

"Don't you want me to help?" he whispered. His father did not answer and now he heard again that stiff foot striking the hollow portico with that wooden and clocklike deliberation, that outrageous overstatement of the weight it carried. The rug, hunched, not flung (the boy could tell that even in the darkness) from his father's shoulder struck the angle of wall and floor with a sound unbelievably loud, thunderous, then the foot again, unhurried and enormous; a light came on in the house and the boy sat, tense, breathing steadily and quietly and just a little fast, though the foot itself did not increase its beat at all, descending the steps now; now the boy could see him.

"Don't you want to ride now?" he whispered. "We kin both ride now," the light within the house altering now, flaring up and sinking. *He's coming down the stairs now,* he thought. He had already ridden the mule up beside the horse block; presently his father was up behind him and he doubled the reins over and slashed the mule across the neck, but before the animal could begin to trot the hard, thin arm came round him, the hard, knotted hand jerking the mule back to a walk.

In the first red rays of the sun they were in the lot, putting plow gear on the mules. This time the sorrel mare was in the lot before he heard it at all, the rider collarless and even bareheaded, trembling, speaking in a shaking voice as the woman in the house had done, his father merely looking up once before stooping again to the hame he was buckling, so that the man on the mare spoke to his stooping back:

"You must realize you have ruined that rug. Wasn't there anybody here, any of your women . . ." he ceased, shaking, the boy watching him, the older brother leaning now in the stable door, chewing, blinking slowly and steadily at nothing apparently. "It cost a hundred dollars. But you never had a hundred dollars. You never will. So I'm going to charge you twenty bushels of corn against your crop. I'll add it in your contract and when you come to the commissary you can sign it. That won't keep Mrs. de Spain quiet but maybe it will teach you to wipe your feet off before you enter her house again."

Then he was gone. The boy looked at his father, who still had not spoken or even looked up again, who was now adjusting the logger-head in the hame.

"Pap," he said. His father looked at him—the inscrutable face, the shaggy brows beneath which the gray eyes glinted coldly. Suddenly the boy went toward him, fast, stopping as suddenly. "You done the best you could!" he cried. "If he wanted hit done different why didn't he wait and tell you how? He won't git no twenty bushels! He won't git none! We'll gether hit and hide hit! I kin watch . . ."

"Did you put the cutter back in that straight stock like I told you?"

"No, sir," he said.

"Then go do it."

That was Wednesday. During the rest of that week he worked steadily, at what was within his scope and some which was beyond it, with an industry that did not need to be driven nor even commanded twice; he had this from his mother, with the difference that some at least of what he did he liked to do, such as splitting wood with the half-size axe which his mother and aunt had earned, or saved money somehow, to present him with at Christmas. In company with the two older women (and on one afternoon, even one of the sisters), he built pens for the shoat and the cow which were a part of his father's contract with the landlord, and one afternoon, his father being absent, gone somewhere on one of the mules, he went to the field.

They were running a middle buster now, his brother holding the plow straight while he handled the reins, and walking beside the straining mule, the rich black soil shearing cool and damp against his bare ankles, he thought *Maybe this is the end of it. Maybe even that twenty bushels that seems hard to have to pay for just a rug will be a cheap price for him to stop forever and always from being what he used to be;* thinking, dreaming now, so that his brother had to speak sharply to him to mind the mule: *Maybe he even won't collect the twenty bushels. Maybe it will all add up*

*and balance and vanish—corn, rug, fire; the terror and grief, the being
pulled two ways like between two teams of horses—gone, done with for
ever and ever.*

Then it was Saturday; he looked up from beneath the mule he was har-
nessing and saw his father in the black coat and hat. "Not that," his father
said. "The wagon gear." And then, two hours later, sitting in the wagon bed
behind his father and brother on the seat, the wagon accomplished a final
curve, and he saw the weathered paintless store with its tattered tobacco- and
patent-medicine posters and the tethered wagons and saddle animals below
the gallery. He mounted the gnawed steps behind his father and brother, and
there again was the lane of quiet, watching faces for the three of them to
walk through. He saw the man in spectacles sitting at the plank table and he
did not need to be told this was a Justice of the Peace; he sent one glare of
fierce, exultant, partisan defiance at the man in collar and cravat now, whom
he had seen but twice before in his life, and that on a galloping horse, who
now wore on his face an expression not of rage but of amazed unbelief which
the boy could not have known was at the incredible circumstance of being
sued by one of his own tenants, and came and stood against his father and
cried at the Justice: "He ain't done it! He ain't burnt . . ."

"Go back to the wagon," his father said.

"Burnt?" the Justice said. "Do I understand this rug was burned too?"

"Does anybody here claim it was?" his father said. "Go back to the wagon."
But he did not, he merely retreated to the rear of the room, crowded as that
other had been, not to sit down this time, instead, to stand pressing among
the motionless bodies, listening to the voices:

"And you claim twenty bushels of corn is too high for the damage you did
to the rug?"

"He brought the rug to me and said he wanted the tracks washed out of it.
I washed the tracks out and took the rug back to him."

"But you didn't carry the rug back to him in the same condition it was in
before you made the tracks on it."

His father did not answer, and now for perhaps half a minute there was no
sound at all save that of breathing, the faint, steady suspiration of complete
and intent listening.

"You decline to answer that, Mr. Snopes?" Again his father did not answer.
"I'm going to find against you, Mr. Snopes. I'm going to find that you were
responsible for the injury to Major de Spain's rug and hold you liable for it.
But twenty bushels of corn seems a little high for a man in your circumstances to have to pay. Major de Spain claims it cost a hundred dollars. October corn will be worth about fifty cents. I figure that if Major de Spain can
stand a ninety-five dollar loss on something he paid cash for, you can stand a
five-dollar loss you haven't earned yet. I hold you in damages to Major de
Spain to the amount of ten bushels of corn over and above your contract
with him, to be paid to him out of your crop at gathering time. Court ad-
journed."

It had taken no time hardly, the morning was but half begun. He thought they would return home and perhaps back to the field, since they were late, far behind all other farmers. But instead his father passed on behind the wagon, merely indicating with his hand for the older brother to follow with it, and crossed the road toward the blacksmith shop opposite, pressing on after his father, overtaking him, speaking, whispering up at the harsh, calm face beneath the weathered hat: "He won't git no ten bushels neither. He won't git one. We'll . . ." until his father glanced for an instant down at him, the face absolutely calm, the grizzled eyebrows tangled above the cold eyes, the voice almost pleasant, almost gentle:

"You think so? Well, we'll wait till October anyway."

The matter of the wagon—the setting of a spoke or two and the tightening of the tires—did not take long either, the business of the tires accomplished by driving the wagon into the spring branch behind the shop and letting it stand there, the mules muzzling into the water from time to time, and the boy on the seat with the idle reins, looking up the slope and through the sooty tunnel of the shed where the slow hammer rang and where his father sat on an upended cypress bolt, easily, either talking or listening, still sitting there when the boy brought the dripping wagon up out of the branch and halted it before the door.

"Take them on to the shade and hitch," his father said. He did so and returned. His father and the smith and a third man squatting on his heels inside the door were talking, about crops and animals; the boy, squatting too in the ammoniac dust and hoof-parings and scales of rust, heard his father tell a long and unhurried story out of the time before the birth of the older brother even when he had been a professional horsetrader. And then his father came up beside him where he stood before a tattered last year's circus poster on the other side of the store, gazing rapt and quiet at the scarlet horses, the incredible poisings and convolutions of tulle and tights and the painted leers of comedians, and said, "It's time to eat."

But not at home. Squatting beside his brother against the front wall, he watched his father emerge from the store and produce from a paper sack a segment of cheese and divide it carefully and deliberately into three with his pocket knife and produce crackers from the same sack. They all three squatted on the gallery and ate, slowly, without talking; then in the store again, they drank from a tin dipper tepid water smelling of the cedar bucket and of living beech trees. And still they did not go home. It was a horse lot this time, a tall rail fence upon and along which men stood and sat and out of which one by one horses were led, to be walked and trotted and then cantered back and forth along the road while the slow swapping and buying went on and the sun began to slant westward, they—the three of them—watching and listening, the older brother with his muddy eyes and his steady, inevitable tobacco, the father commenting now and then on certain of the animals, to no one in particular.

It was after sundown when they reached home. They ate supper by lamp-light, then, sitting on the doorstep, the boy watched the night fully accomplish, listening to the whippoorwills and the frogs, when he heard his mother's voice: "Abner! No! No! Oh, God. Oh, God. Abner!" and he rose, whirled, and saw the altered light through the door where a candle stub now burned in a bottle neck on the table and his father, still in the hat and coat, at once formal and burlesque as though dressed carefully for some shabby and ceremonial violence, emptying the reservoir of the lamp back into the five-gallon kerosene can from which it had been filled, while the mother tugged at his arm until he shifted the lamp to the other hand and flung her back, not savagely or viciously, just hard, into the wall, her hands flung out against the wall for balance, her mouth open and in her face the same quality of hopeless despair as had been in her voice. Then his father saw him standing in the door.

"Go to the barn and get that can of oil we were oiling the wagon with," he said. The boy did not move. Then he could speak.

"What . . ." he cried. "What are you . . ."

"Go get that oil," his father said. "Go."

Then he was moving, running, outside the house, toward the stable: this the old habit, the old blood which he had not been permitted to choose for himself, which had been bequeathed him willy nilly and which had run for so long (and who knew where, battening on what of outrage and savagery and lust) before it came to him. *I could keep on,* he thought. *I could run on and on and never look back, never need to see his face again. Only I can't. I can't,* the rusted can in his hand now, the liquid sploshing in it as he ran back to the house and into it, into the sound of his mother's weeping in the next room, and handed the can to his father.

"Ain't you going to even send a nigger?" he cried. "At least you sent a nigger before!"

This time his father didn't strike him. The hand came even faster than the blow had, the same hand which had set the can on the table with almost excruciating care flashing from the can toward him too quick for him to follow it, gripping him by the back of his shirt and on to tiptoe before he had seen it quit the can, the face stooping at him in breathless and frozen ferocity, the cold, dead voice speaking over him to the older brother who leaned against the table, chewing with that steady, curious, sidewise motion of cows:

"Empty the can into the big one and go on. I'll catch up with you."

"Better tie him up to the bedpost," the brother said.

"Do like I told you," the father said. Then the boy was moving, his bunched shirt and the hard, bony hand between his shoulder-blades, his toes just touching the floor, across the room and into the other one, past the sisters sitting with spread heavy thighs in the two chairs over the cold hearth, and to where his mother and aunt sat side by side on the bed, the aunt's arms about his mother's shoulders.

"Hold him," the father said. The aunt made a startled movement. "Not you," the father said. "Lennie. Take hold of him. I want to see you do it." His mother took him by the wrist. "You'll hold him better than that. If he gets loose don't you know what he is going to do? He will go up yonder." He jerked his head toward the road. "Maybe I'd better tie him."

"I'll hold him," his mother whispered.

"See you do then." Then his father was gone, the stiff foot heavy and measured upon the boards, ceasing at last.

Then he began to struggle. His mother caught him in both arms, he jerking and wrenching at them. He would be stronger in the end, he knew that. But he had no time to wait for it. "Lemme go!" he cried. "I don't want to have to hit you!"

"Let him go!" the aunt said. "If he don't go, before God, I am going up there myself!"

"Don't you see I can't?" his mother cried. "Sarty! Sarty! No! No! Help me, Lizzie!"

Then he was free. His aunt grasped at him but it was too late. He whirled, running, his mother stumbled forward on to her knees behind him, crying to the nearer sister: "Catch him, Net! Catch him!" But that was too late too, the sister (the sisters were twins, born at the same time, yet either of them now gave the impression of being, encompassing as much living meat and volume and weight as any other two of the family) not yet having begun to rise from the chair, her head, face, alone merely turned, presenting to him in the flying instant an astonishing expanse of young female features untroubled by any surprise even, wearing only an expression of bovine interest. Then he was out of the room, out of the house, in the mild dust of the starlit road and the heavy rifeness of honeysuckle, the pale ribbon unspooling with terrific slowness under his running feet, reaching the gate at last and turning in, running, his heart and lungs drumming, on up the drive toward the lighted house, the lighted door. He did not knock, he burst in, sobbing for breath, incapable for the moment of speech; he saw the astonished face of the Negro in the linen jacket without knowing when the Negro had appeared.

"De Spain!" he cried, panted. "Where's . . ." then he saw the white man too emerging from a white door down the hall. "Barn!" he cried. "Barn!"

"What?" the white man said "Barn?"

"Yes!" the boy cried. "Barn!"

"Catch him!" the white man shouted.

But it was too late this time too. The Negro grasped his shirt, but the entire sleeve, rotten with washing, carried away, and he was out that door too and in the drive again, and had actually never ceased to run even while he was screaming into the white man's face.

Behind him the white man was shouting. "My horse! Fetch my horse!" and he thought for an instant of cutting across the park and climbing the fence into the road, but he did not know the park nor how high the vine-massed fence might be and he dared not risk it. So he ran on down the drive, blood and breath roaring; presently he was in the road again though he could not see it. He could not hear either: the galloping mare was almost upon him before he heard her, and even then he held his course, as if the very urgency of his wild grief and need must in a moment more find him wings, waiting until the ultimate instant to hurl himself aside and into the weed-choked roadside ditch as the horse thundered past and on, for an instant in furious silhouette against the stars, the tranquil early summer night sky which, even before the shape of the horse and rider vanished, stained abruptly and violently upward: a long, swirling roar incredible and soundless, blotting the stars, and he springing up and into the road again, running again, knowing it was too late yet still running even after he heard the shot and, an instant later, two shots, pausing now without knowing he had ceased to run, crying "Pap! Pap!", running again before he knew he had begun to run, stumbling, tripping over something and scrabbling up again without ceasing to run, looking backward over his shoulder at the glare as he got up, running on among the invisible trees, panting, sobbing, "Father! Father!"

At midnight he was sitting on the crest of a hill. He did not know it was midnight and he did not know how far he had come. But there was no glare behind him now and he sat now, his back toward what he had called home for four days anyhow, his face toward the dark woods which he would enter when breath was strong again, small, shaking steadily in the chill darkness, hugging himself into the remainder of his thin, rotten shirt, the grief and despair now no longer terror and fear but just grief and despair. *Father. My father,* he thought. "He was brave!" he cried suddenly, aloud but not loud, no more than a whisper: "He was! He was in the war! He was in Colonel Sartoris' cav'ry!" not knowing that his father had gone to that war a private in the fine old European sense, wearing no uniform, admitting the authority of and giving fidelity to no man or army or flag, going to war as Malbrouck himself did: for booty—it meant nothing and less than nothing to him if it were enemy booty or his own.

The slow constellations wheeled on. It would be dawn and then sun-up after a while and he would be hungry. But that would be tomorrow and now he was only cold, and walking would cure that. His breathing was easier now and he decided to get up and go on, and then he found that he had been asleep because he knew it was almost dawn, the night almost over. He could tell that from the whippoorwills. They were everywhere now among the dark trees below him, constant and inflectioned and ceaseless, so that, as the instant for giving over to the day birds drew nearer and nearer, there was no interval at all between them. He got up. He was a little stiff, but walking would cure that too as it would the cold, and soon there would be the sun. He went on down the hill, toward the dark woods within which the liquid silver voices of the birds called unceasing—the rapid and urgent beating of the urgent and quiring heart of the late spring night. He did not look back.

Katherine Anne Porter, 1890–1980

The Jilting of Granny Weatherall

This story first appeared in TRANSITION, *1929.*

SHE FLICKED HER WRIST NEATLY out of Doctor Harry's pudgy careful fingers and pulled the sheet up to her chin. The brat ought to be in knee breeches. Doctoring around the country with spectacles on his nose! "Get along now, take your schoolbooks and go. There's nothing wrong with me."

Doctor Harry spread a warm paw like a cushion on her forehead where the forked green vein danced and made her eyelids twitch. "Now, now, be a good girl, and we'll have you up in no time."

"That's no way to speak to a woman nearly eighty years old just because she's down. I'd have you respect your elders, young man."

"Well, Missy, excuse me." Doctor Harry patted her cheek. "But I've got to warn you, haven't I? You're a marvel, but you must be careful or you're going to be good and sorry."

"Don't tell me what I'm going to be. I'm on my feet now, morally speaking. It's Cornelia. I had to go to bed to get rid of her."

Her bones felt loose, and floated around in her skin, and Doctor Harry floated like a balloon around the foot of the bed. He floated and pulled down his waistcoat and swung his glasses on a cord. "Well, stay where you are, it certainly can't hurt you."

"Get along and doctor your sick," said Granny Weatherall. "Leave a well woman alone. I'll call for you when I want you. . . . Where were you forty years ago when I pulled through milk leg and double pneumonia? You weren't even born. Don't let Cornelia lead you on," she shouted, because Doctor Harry appeared to float up to the ceiling and out. "I pay my own bills, and I don't throw my money away on nonsense!"

She meant to wave good-by, but it was too much trouble. Her eyes closed of themselves, it was like a dark curtain drawn around the bed. The pillow rose and floated under her, pleasant as a hammock in a light wind. She listened to the leaves rustling outside the window. No, somebody was swishing newspapers: no, Cornelia and Doctor Harry were whispering together. She leaped broad awake, thinking they whispered in her ear.

"She was never like this, *never* like this!" "Well, what can we expect?" "Yes, eighty years old. . . . "

Well, and what if she was? She still had ears. It was like Cornelia to whisper around doors. She always kept things secret in such a public way. She was always being tactful and kind. Cornelia was dutiful; that was the trouble with her." Dutiful and good: "So good and dutiful," said Granny, "that I'd like to spank her." She saw herself spanking Cornelia and making a fine job of it.

"What'd you say, Mother?"

Granny felt her face tying up in hard knots.

"Can't a body think, I'd like to know?"

"I thought you might want something."

"I do. I want a lot of things. First off, go away and don't whisper."

She lay and drowsed, hoping in her sleep that the children would keep out and let her rest a minute. It had been a long day. Not that she was tired. It was always pleasant to snatch a minute now and then. There was always so much to be done, let me see: tomorrow.

Tomorrow was far away and there was nothing to trouble about. Things were finished somehow when the time came; thank God there was always a little margin over for peace: then a person could spread out the plan of life and tuck in the edges orderly. It was good to have everything clean and folded away, with the hair brushes and tonic bottles sitting straight on the white embroidered linen: the day started without fuss and the pantry shelves laid out with rows of jelly glasses and brown jugs and white stone-china jars with blue whirligigs and words painted on them: coffee, tea, sugar, ginger, cinnamon, allspice: and the bronze clock with the lion on top nicely dusted off. The dust that lion could collect in twenty-four hours! The box in the attic with all those letters tied up, well, she'd have to go through that tomorrow. All those letters—George's letters and John's letters and her letters to them both—lying around for the children to find afterwards made her uneasy. Yes, that would be tomorrow's business. No use to let them know how silly she had been once.

While she was rummaging around she found death in her mind and it felt clammy and unfamiliar. She had spent so much time preparing for death there was no need for bringing it up again. Let it take care of itself now. When she was sixty she had felt very old, finished, and went around making farewell trips to see her children and grandchildren, with a secret in her mind: This is the very last of your mother, children! Then she made her will and came down with a long fever. That was all just a notion like a lot of other things, but it was lucky too, for she had once for all got over the idea of dying for a long time. Now she couldn't be worried. She hoped she had better sense now. Her father had lived to be one hundred and two years old and had drunk a noggin of strong hot toddy on his last birthday. He told the reporters it was his daily habit, and he owed his long life to it. He had made quite a scandal and was very pleased about it. She believed she'd just plague Cornelia a little.

"Cornelia! Cornelia!" No footsteps, but a sudden hand on her cheek. "Bless you, where have you been?"

"Here, Mother."

"Well, Cornelia, I want a noggin of hot toddy."

"Are you cold, darling?"

"I'm chilly, Cornelia. Lying in bed stops the circulation. I must have told you that a thousand times."

Well, she could just hear Cornelia telling her husband that Mother was getting a little childish and they'd have to humor her. The thing that most annoyed her was that Cornelia thought she was deaf, dumb, and blind. Little hasty glances and tiny gestures tossed around her and over her head saying, "Don't cross her, let her have her way, she's eighty years old," and she sitting there as if she lived in a thin glass cage. Sometimes Granny almost made up her mind to pack up and move back to her own house where nobody could remind her every minute that she was old. Wait, wait, Cornelia, till your own children whisper behind your back!

In her day she had kept a better house and had got more work done. She wasn't too old yet for Lydia to be driving eighty miles for advice when one of the children jumped the track, and Jimmy still dropped in and talked things over: "Now, Mammy, you've a good business head, I want to know what you think of this? . . ." Old. Cornelia couldn't change the furniture around without asking. Little things, little things! They had been so sweet when they were little. Granny wished the old days were back again with the children young and everything to be done over. It had been a hard pull, but not too much for her. When she thought of all the food she had cooked, and all the clothes she had cut and sewed, and all the gardens she had made—well, the children showed it. There they were, made out of her, and they couldn't get away from that. Sometimes she wanted to see John again and point to them and say, Well, I didn't do so badly, did I? But that would have to wait. That was for tomorrow. She used to think of him as a man, but now all the children were older than their father, and he would be a child beside her if she saw him now. It seemed strange and there was something wrong in the idea. Why, he couldn't possibly recognize her. She had fenced in a hundred acres once, digging the post holes herself and clamping the wires with just a negro boy to help. That changed a woman. John would be looking for a young woman with the peaked Spanish comb in her hair and the painted fan. Digging post holes changed a woman. Riding country roads in the winter when women had their babies was another thing: sitting up nights with sick horses and sick negroes and sick children and hardly ever losing one. John, I hardly ever lost one of them! John would see that in a minute, that would be something he could understand, she wouldn't have to explain anything!

It made her feel like rolling up her sleeves and putting the whole place to rights again. No matter if Cornelia was determined to be everywhere at once, there were a great many things left undone on this place. She would start tomorrow and do them. It was good to be strong enough for every-thing, even if all you made melted and changed and slipped under your hands, so that by the time you finished you almost forgot what you were working for. What was it I set out to do? she asked herself intently, but she could not remember. A fog rose over the valley, she saw it marching across the creek swallowing the trees and moving up the hill like an army of ghosts. Soon it would be at the near edge of the orchard, and then it was time to go in and light the lamps. Come in, children, don't stay out in the night air.

Lighting the lamps had been beautiful. The children huddled up to her and breathed like little calves waiting at the bars in the twilight. Their eyes followed the match and watched the flame rise and settle in a blue curve, then they moved away from her. The lamp was lit, they didn't have to be scared and hang on to mother any more. Never, never, never more. God, for all my life I thank Thee. Without Thee, my God, I could never have done it. Hail, Mary, full of grace.

I want you to pick all the fruit this year and see that nothing is wasted. There's always someone who can use it. Don't let good things rot for want of using. You waste life when you waste good food. Don't let things get lost. It's bitter to lose things. Now, don't let me get to thinking, not when I am tired and taking a little nap before supper. . . .

The pillow rose about her shoulders and pressed against her heart and the memory was being squeezed out of it: oh, push down the pillow, somebody: it would smother her if she tried to hold it. Such a fresh breeze blowing and such a green day with no threats in it. But he had not come, just the same. What does a woman do when she has put on the white veil and set out the white cake for a man and he doesn't come? She tried to remember. No, I swear he never harmed me but in that. He never harmed me but in that . . . and what if he did? There was the day, the day, but a whirl of dark smoke rose and covered it, crept up and over into the bright field where everything was planted so carefully in orderly rows. That was hell, she knew hell when she saw it. For sixty years she had prayed against remembering him and against losing her soul in the deep pit of hell, and now the two things were mingled in one and the thought of him was a smoky cloud from hell that moved and crept in her head when she had just got rid of Doctor Harry and was trying to rest a minute. Wounded vanity, Ellen, said a sharp voice in the top of her mind. Don't let your wounded vanity get the upper hand of you. Plenty of girls get jilted. You were jilted, weren't you? Then stand up to it. Her eyelids wavered and let in streamers of blue-gray light like tissue paper over her eyes. She must get up and pull the shades down or she'd never sleep. She was in bed again and the shades were not down. How could that happen? Better turn over, hide from the light, sleeping in the light gave you nightmares. "Mother, how do you feel now?" and a stinging wetness on her forehead. But I don't like having my face washed in cold water!

Hapsy? George? Lydia? Jimmy? No, Cornelia, and her features were swollen and full of little puddles. "They're coming, darling, they'll all be here soon." Go wash your face, child, you look funny.

Instead of obeying, Cornelia knelt down and put her head on the pillow. She seemed to be talking but there was no sound. "Well, are you tongue-tied? Whose birthday is it? Are you going to give a party?"

Cornelia's mouth moved urgently in strange shapes. "Don't do that, you bother me, daughter."

"O, no, Mother. Oh, no. . . . "

Nonsense. It was strange about children. They disputed your every word. "No what, Cornelia?"

"Here's Doctor Harry."

"I won't see that boy again. He just left three minutes ago."

"That was this morning, Mother. It's night now. Here's the nurse."

"This is Doctor Harry, Mrs. Weatherall. I never saw you look so young and happy!"

"Ah, I'll never be young again—but I'd be happy if they'd let me lie in peace and get rested."

She thought she spoke up loudly, but no one answered. A warm weight on her forehead, a warm bracelet on her wrist, and a breeze went on whispering, trying to tell her something. A shuffle of leaves in the everlasting hand of God. He blew on them and they danced and rattled. "Mother, don't mind, we're going to give you a little hypodermic." "Look here, daughter, how do ants get in this bed? I saw sugar ants yesterday." Did you send for Hapsy too?

It was Hapsy she really wanted. She had to go a long way back through a great many rooms to find Hapsy standing with a baby on her arm. She seemed to herself to be Hapsy also, and the baby on Hapsy's arm was Hapsy and himself and herself, all at once, and there was no surprise in the meeting. Then Hapsy melted from within and turned flimsy as gray gauze and the baby was a gauzy shadow, and Hapsy came up close and said, "I thought you'd never come," and looked at her very searchingly and said, "You haven't changed a bit!" They leaned forward to kiss, when Cornelia began whispering from a long way off, "Oh, is there anything you want to tell me? Is there anything I can do for you?"

Yes, she had changed her mind after sixty years and she would like to see George. I want you to find George. Find him and be sure to tell him I forgot him. I want him to know I had my husband just the same and my children and my house like any other woman. A good house too and a good husband that I loved and fine children out of him. Better than I hoped for even. Tell him I was given back everything he took away and more. Oh, no, oh, God, no, there was something else besides the house and the man and the children. Oh, surely they were not all? What was it? Something not given back . . . Her breath crowded down under her ribs and grew into a monstrous frightening

shape with cutting edges; it bored up into her head, and the agony was unbe-
lievable: Yes, John, get the Doctor now, no more talk, my time has come.

When this one was born it should be the last. The last. It should have
been born first, for it was the one she had truly wanted. Everything came in
good time. Nothing left out, left over. She was strong, in three days she
would be as well as ever. Better. A woman needed milk in her to have her
full health.

"Mother, do you hear me?"

"I've been telling you—"

"Mother, Father Connolly's here."

"I went to Holy Communion only last week. Tell him I'm not so sinful as
all that."

"Father just wants to speak to you."

He could speak as much as he pleased. It was like him to drop in and inquire about her soul as if it were a teething baby, and then stay for a cup of
tea and a round of cards and gossip. He always had a funny story of some
sort, usually about an Irishman who made his little mistakes and confessed
them, and the point lay in some absurd thing he would blurt out in the confessional showing his struggles between native piety and original sin.
Granny felt easy about her soul. Cornelia, where are your manners? Give Father Connolly a chair. She had her secret comfortable understanding with a
few favorite saints who cleared a straight road to God for her. All as surely
signed and sealed as the papers for the new Forty Acres. Forever . . . heirs
and assigns forever. Since the day the wedding cake was not cut, but thrown
out and wasted. The whole bottom dropped out of the world, and there she
was blind and sweating with nothing under her feet and walls falling away.
His hand had caught her under the breast, she had not fallen, there was the
freshly polished floor with the green rug on it, just as before. He had cursed
like a sailor's parrot and said, "I'll kill him for you." Don't lay a hand on him,
for my sake leave something to God. "Now, Ellen, you must believe what I
tell you. . . . "

So there was nothing, nothing to worry about any more, except sometimes in the night one of the children screamed in a nightmare, and they
both hustled out shaking and hunting for the matches and calling, "There,
wait a minute, here we are!" John, get the doctor now, Hapsy's time has
come. But there was Hapsy standing by the bed in a white cap. "Cornelia,
tell Hapsy to take off her cap. I can't see her plain."

Her eyes opened very wide and the room stood out like a picture she had
seen somewhere. Dark colors with the shadows rising towards the ceiling in
long angles. The tall black dresser gleamed with nothing on it but John's picture, enlarged from a little one, with John's eyes very black when they
should have been blue. You never saw him, so how do you know how he
looked? But the man insisted the copy was perfect, it was very rich and
handsome. For a picture, yes, but it's not my husband. The table by the bed

had a linen cover and a candle and a crucifix. The light was blue from Cornelia's silk lampshades. No sort of light at all, just frippery. You had to live forty years with kerosene lamps to appreciate honest electricity. She felt very strong and she saw Doctor Harry with a rosy nimbus around him.

"You look like a saint, Doctor Harry, and I vow that's as near as you'll ever come to it."

"She's saying something."

"I heard you, Cornelia. What's all this carrying-on?"

"Father Connolly's saying—"

Cornelia's voice staggered and bumped like a cart in a bad road. It rounded corners and turned back again and arrived nowhere. Granny stepped up in the cart very lightly and reached for the reins, but a man sat beside her and she knew him by his hands, driving the cart. She did not look in his face, for she knew without seeing, but looked instead down the road where the trees leaned over and bowed to each other and a thousand birds were singing a Mass. She felt like singing too, but she put her hand in the bosom of her dress and pulled out a rosary, and Father Connolly murmured Latin in a very solemn voice and tickled her feet. My God, will you stop that nonsense? I'm a married woman. What if he did run away and leave me to face the priest by myself? I found another a whole world better. I wouldn't have exchanged my husband for anybody except St. Michael himself, and you may tell him that for me with a thank you in the bargain.

Light flashed on her closed eyelids, and a deep roaring shook her. Cornelia, is that lightning? I hear thunder. There's going to be a storm. Close all the windows. Call the children in. . . . "Mother, here we are, all of us." "Is that you, Hapsy?" "Oh, no, I'm Lydia. We drove as fast as we could." Their faces drifted above her, drifted away. The rosary fell out of her hands and Lydia put it back. Jimmy tried to help, their hands fumbled together, and Granny closed two fingers around Jimmy's thumb. Beads wouldn't do, it must be something alive. She was so amazed her thoughts ran round and round. So, my dear Lord, this is my death and I wasn't even thinking about it. My children have come to see me die. But I can't, it's not time. Oh, I always hated surprises. I wanted to give Cornelia the amethyst set—Cornelia, you're to have the amethyst set, but Hapsy's to wear it when she wants, and, Doctor Harry, do shut up. Nobody sent for you. Oh, my dear Lord, do wait a minute. I meant to do something about the Forty Acres, Jimmy doesn't need it and Lydia will later on, with that worthless husband of hers. I meant to finish the altar cloth and send six bottles of wine to Sister Borgia for her dyspepsia. I want to send six bottles of wine to Sister Borgia, Father Connolly, now don't let me forget.

Cornelia's voice made short turns and tilted over and crashed, "Oh, Mother, oh, Mother, oh, Mother. . . . "

"I'm not going, Cornelia. I'm taken by surprise. I can't go."

You'll see Hapsy again. What about her? "I thought you'd never come." Granny made a long journey outward, looking for Hapsy. What if I don't find her? What then? Her heart sank down and down, there was no bottom to death, she couldn't come to the end of it. The blue light from Cornelia's lampshade drew into a tiny point in the center of her brain, it flickered and winked like an eye, quietly it fluttered and dwindled. Granny lay curled down within herself, amazed and watchful, staring at the point of light that was herself; her body was now only a deeper mass of shadow in an endless darkness and this darkness would curl around the light and swallow it up. God, give a sign!

For the second time there was no sign. Again no bridegroom and the priest in the house. She could not remember any other sorrow because this grief wiped them all away. Oh, no, there's nothing more cruel than this—I'll never forgive it. She stretched herself with a deep breath and blew out the light.

—— Joan Givner Provides a Biographical Context ——————

Two stories written at this time were published. These were "Magic" and "The Jilting of Granny Weatherall," and their completion was a significant achievement because they show that she was at last finding her own subject matter and establishing some control over it.

———————

In the . . . story, "The Jilting of Granny Weatherall," Porter described again a strong female character surrounded by unreliable men. Ellen Weatherall's first lover jilts her at the altar; her husband dies and leaves her to manage the land and raise the children by herself; and finally an inconsiderate God calls her to an untimely death before she is quite ready. Granny's personal weakness is that when her first lover jilts her she does not give way honestly and naturally to her anger, but suppresses it so that it undermines her whole life.

Porter said she drew on several "Granny" figures for her story, but the central matriarchal character which finally emerges owes more to her own grandmother than any other. Like Aunt Cat, Granny is totally effective in managing her life without men. She runs the farm, raises her young children, and dominates their lives when they are grown. The sorrow of her life is the loss of her favorite daughter, who dies in childbirth, and her hope for her life after death is that she will be reunited with that daughter. The strength of the story is the power of the "felt experience," which is present always when Porter draws on her own past and her familiar childhood world of central Texas.

———————

In 1956, Katherine Anne Porter wrote: "I believe, I hope I shall have my place in the story of American literature; even at this point how could they write it and leave me out?" Her reputation gained very little from the novel or from the stories that appeared subsequently, but it was already assured, as she had guessed, by the short fiction written in the first half of her life.

For years these stories were the standard fare offered to college freshmen in literary anthologies. Generations of students were nurtured on "The Grave," "The Jilting of Granny Weatherall," "Flowering Judas," and "Noon Wine." Lately her stories have been displaced, not by better stories but by more current favorites. Porter does not deserve to be dislodged by the whims of fashion. As her fame was once exaggerated by her theatrical stage presence, so the present decline in her popularity is an error of judgment.

Porter's work, moreover, has woven itself into the fabric of American literature by its influence on other writers. Many have expressed their debt to Porter. Among the earliest to do so were Eudora Welty and Kay Boyle. Besides a host of Texas writers, Carson McCullers and Truman Capote at one time idolized her. Tillie Olsen revered her and that reverence is evident in *Tell Me a Riddle.* Flannery O'Connor professed an influence which Porter claimed not to see, but which is apparent when "The Displaced Person" is compared with "Noon Wine."

She did face it herself, and her best fictions are full of instances of her artistic courage—her portrayal of sexual terror in "The Grave," of Granny Weatherall's never-ending humiliation, of Frau Rittersdorf's terrifying ambush by her childhood memories, of Mrs. Treadwell's reaction to the brutalities of a lifetime. These are the real toads in Porter's imaginary gardens.

Is it any wonder that the production of her fiction through the exploration of its sources was a slow, agonizing process, a kind of self-torture, or that her tendency to procrastinate was legendary? But in spite of the almost superhuman effort it required, she never abandoned her battle to "wangle the sprawling mess of . . . existence in this bloody world into some kind of shape." It was a lonely, desperate battle, costly to herself and to the people she sacrificed in her determination to be somebody and to create something lasting, beautiful, and orderly. But who can deny that it was a valiant effort, a most brave voyage?

Considerations as You Read

The purpose of the *study* of fiction is to develop an ability to respond as fully as possible to every aspect of a story. Remember, the writer had to struggle through the revision process to create the story you are reading. The act of reading that story is also a part of the creative process.

If you become confused, mystified, or disoriented at any point in reading (or, more usefully, *re*-reading) a story, review the following list of considerations. These considerations suggest what you might mark in your text for later discussion and writing review.

1. Every element in a story—character, conflict, plot, theme—is controlled by the way writers handle the *point of view* they have chosen (first person, third person–limited omniscient).

2. The writer's *style*—the conscious choice of words, the phrasing—is determined by the point of view he or she employs.

3. Beginning with the first crucial paragraph, the writer uses words to create a *context,* which evolves from paragraph to paragraph to the crucial final paragraph.

4. The literal statements work within the overall context, and within the immediate context of any given paragraph, to enable the writer to *imply* what is not explicitly stated.

5. What is implied (or evoked or conveyed indirectly) in a story usually has a more powerful effect than what is obviously stated because *implication* stimulates the reader's own emotions, imagination, and intellect.

6. The reason why writers use various *technical devices* is to create contexts and implications or to stimulate some specific response from the reader; as the reader becomes involved, the reader's experiences become richer and more complex, and the effects are deeper and more lasting.

7. *Contrast* and *comparison* are simple devices that enable the writer to call your attention to the use of symbols and irony, among other things.

8. To respond to the writer's use of a *symbol,* an *allusion,* or to *irony,* a reader must be intimately, intricately, and actively involved in the process of reading and responding; the result is a much richer experience than if the reader were only passively reacting to literal statements.

9. With considerations 1 through 8 in mind, a person who is studying the nature and effect of fiction, as opposed simply to reading it as one usually does, may more fully respond to all the experiences the writer has imagined for the reader.

10. Is the story written in a specific genre? If so, does it depart from the limited elements of that genre? Or does the story draw on aspects of several genres?

Review Questions That Apply to Most Fiction

Each question one may ask about each story read in introductory courses may be restated in general terms and applied to most (but not all) stories. The questions provide a review of some of the major points for reading, discussion, and writing.

1. Who is the *protagonist?*

2. When and where is the *setting?*

3. What is the *story or plot?*

4. What is the *conflict?*

5. What is the *point of view?*

6. What are the characteristics of the style that derive from the *point of view?*

7. What is the *external context?* What is the *general context?* What are some of the most significant *immediate contexts?*

8. What *other techniques* or *devices* does the author use?

    Comparison and Contrast

    Symbolism

    Allusion

    Irony

9. To what *genre* does the story belong (if relevant)?

10. How do the preceding considerations suggest *theme* or *meaning?*

Other Fiction by These Writers

SHIRLEY JACKSON. Stories: *The Lottery: Or, The Adventures of James Harris,* 1949; *Come Along with Me,* 1968. Novels: *The Road Through the Wall,* 1948; *Hangsaman,* 1951; *The Bird's Nest,* 1954; *The Haunting of Hill House,* 1959; *We Have Always Lived in the Castle,* 1962.

SHERWOOD ANDERSON. Stories: *Winesburg, Ohio,* 1919; *The Triumph of the Egg,* 1921; *Horses and Men,* 1923; *Death in the Woods,* 1933. Novels: *Windy McPherson's Son,* 1916; *Poor White,* 1920. Essays: *Puzzled America,* 1935. Autobiography: *A Story Teller's Story,* 1924.

KATHERINE MANSFIELD. Stories: *In a German Pension,* 1911; *Bliss,* 1920; *The Garden Party,* 1922; *The Dove's Nest,* 1923.

ISAAC BASHEVIS SINGER. Stories: *Gimpel the Fool,* 1957; *The Spinoza of Market Street,* 1961; *Short Friday,* 1967; *The Séance,* 1968; *A Friend of Kafka,* 1970; *A Crown of Feathers,* 1973; *Passions,* 1976; *The Collected Stories,* 1982. Novels: *The Family Moskat,* 1950; *The Slave,* 1962; *The Manor,* 1967; *Enemies: A Love Story,* 1972; *Shosha,* 1978.

FRANK O'CONNOR. Stories: *Guests of the Nation,* 1931; *Selected Stories,* 1946; *Stories of Frank O'Connor,* 1952; *More Stories by Frank O'Connor,* 1954; *Domestic Relations,* 1957. Criticism: *The Mirror in the Roadway,* 1956; *The Lonely Voice,* 1963. Autobiography: *My Father's Son,* 1968. Also a playwright, author of two novels.

ALICE WALKER. Stories: *In Love and Trouble: Stories of Black Women,* 1973; *You Can't Keep a Good Woman Down,* 1981. Novels: *The Third Life of Grange Copeland,* 1970; *Meridian,* 1976; *The Temple of My Familiar,* 1989; *Possessing the Secret of Joy,* 1992.

TILLIE OLSEN. Stories: *Tell Me a Riddle.* Novels: *Yonnondio: From the Thirties,* 1974. Essays: *Silences,* 1978.

CHARLOTTE PERKINS GILMAN. Novel: *Herland,* 1915. *The Charlotte Perkins Gilman Reader,* ed. Ann J. Lane, 1980.

MARGARET ATWOOD. Stories: *Blue Beard's Egg,* 1983. Novels: *The Edible Women,* 1969; *Surfacing,* 1972; *Life Before Man,* 1979; *Bodily Harm,* 1981; *A Handmaid's Tale,* 1986; *Cat's Eye,* 1989.

NADINE GORDIMER. Stories: *Face to Face,* 1949; *The Soft Voice of the Serpent,* 1952; *Six Feet of the Country,* 1956; *Friday's Footprints,* 1960; *Not for Publication,* 1965; *Livingston's Companions,* 1971; *Selected Stories,* 1976; *A Soldier's Embrace,* 1980. Novels: *The Lying Days,* 1953; *A World of Strangers,* 1958; *Occasion for Loving,* 1963; *The Late Bourgeois World,* 1966; *A Guest of Honour,* 1971; *The Conservationist,* 1975; *Burger's Daughter,* 1980; *July's People,* 1981.

HERMAN MELVILLE. Stories: *Piazza Tales,* 1856. Novels: *Typee,* 1846; *Omoo* 1847; *Mardi,* 1849; *Redburn,* 1849; *White Jacket,* 1850; *Moby Dick,* 1851; *Pierre,* 1852; *Israel Potter,* 1855; *The Confidence Man,* 1857; *Billy Budd, Foretopman,* 1924.

GABRIEL GARCÍA MÁRQUEZ. Stories: *No One Writes to the Colonel and Other Stories,* 1962; *Leaf Storm and Other Stories,* 1972; *Innocent Erendia and Other Stories,* 1972, 1978. Novels: *One Hundred Years of Solitude,* 1967; *The Autumn of the Patriarch,* 1975; *Chronicle of a Death Foretold,* 1981.

FRANZ KAFKA. Stories: *Franz Kafka, The Complete Stories,* 1971. Novels: *The Trial,* 1925; *The Castle,* 1926; *Amerika,* 1927.

STEPHEN CRANE. Stories: *The Little Regiment and Other Episodes of the American Civil War,* 1896; *The Open Boat and Other Tales of Adventure,* 1898; *The Monster and Other Stories,* 1899; *Whilomville Stories,* 1900; *Wounds in the Rain: War Stories,* 1900. Novels: *Maggie: A Girl of the Streets,* 1893; *The Red Badge of Courage: An Episode of the American Civil War,* 1895; *George's Mother,* 1896; *Third Violet,* 1897; *Active Service,* 1899.

ALICE MUNRO. Stories: *Dance of the Happy Shades,* 1968; *Something I've Been Meaning to Tell You,* 1978; *Who Do You Think You Are?,* 1978; *The Beggar Maid,* 1979; *The Moons of Jupiter,* 1983; *The Progress of Love,* 1986; *Friend of My Youth,* 1990. Novel: *Lives of Girls and Women,* 1971.

RAYMOND CARVER. Stories: *Will You Please Be Quiet, Please,* 1976; *What We Talk About When We Talk About Love,* 1981; *Cathedral,* 1982; *Where I'm Calling From, New and Selected Stories,* 1988.

KATE CHOPIN. Stories: *Bayou Folk,* 1894; *A Night in Acadia,* 1897. Novels: *At Fault,* 1890; *The Awakening,* 1899.

SUSAN GLASPELL. Novels: *The Glory of the Conquered,* 1909; *The Visioning,* 1911; *Fidelity,* 1915; *Brook Evans,* 1928; *Fugitive's Return,* 1929; *Ambrose Holt and Family,* 1931; *The Morning Is Near Us,* 1940; *Norma Ashe,* 1942; *Judd Rankin's Daughter,* 1945. Plays: *"Trifles",* 1917; *Alison's House,* 1930.

ERNEST HEMINGWAY. Stories: *In Our Time,* 1924–1925; *Men Without Women,* 1927; *Winner Take Nothing,* 1933; *The Fifth Column,* 1938. Novels: *The Sun Also Rises,* 1926; *A Farewell to Arms,* 1929; *For Whom the Bell Tolls,* 1940; *The Old Man and the Sea,* 1952. Nonfiction: *Death in the Afternoon,* 1932. Memoir: *A Moveable Feast,* 1964.

JAMES THURBER. Stories: *Is Sex Necessary,* 1929; *The Seal in the Bedroom and Other Predicaments,* 1932; *My Life and Hard Times,* 1933; *The Middle-aged Man on the Flying Trapeze,* 1935; *My World—And Welcome to It!,* 1942; *Men, Women and Dogs,* 1943; *The Thurber Carnival,* 1945; *Thurber Country,* 1953.

EUDORA WELTY. Stories: *A Curtain of Green,* 1941; *The Wide Net,* 1943; *The Golden Apples,* 1949; *The Bride of Innisfallen,* 1955; *Thirteen Stories,* 1965; *A Sweet Devouring,* 1969; *The Collected Stories,* 1980. Novels: *Delta Wedding,* 1946; *The Ponder Heart,* 1954; *Losing Battles,* 1970; *The Optimist's Daughter,* 1972. Nonfiction: *Place in Fiction,* 1957.

WILLIAM FAULKNER. Stories: *Collected Short Stories of William Faulkner,* 1950; *Big Woods,* 1955. Novels: *Sartoris,* 1929; *The Sound and the Fury,* 1929; *As I Lay Dying,* 1930; *Sanctuary,* 1931; *Light in August,* 1932; *Absalom, Absalom!,* 1936; *A Fable,* 1954; *The Reivers,* 1961. Poetry: *The Marble Faun,* 1924; *The Green Bough,* 1933.

KATHERINE ANNE PORTER. Stories: *Flowering Judas,* 1930; *Noon Wine,* 1937; *Pale Horse, Pale Rider,* 1938; *The Leaning Tower,* 1944; *The Collected Stories,* 1965. Novel: *Ship of Fools,* 1962. Essays: *The Collected Essays and Occasional Writings of Katherine Anne Porter,* 1970.

Credits

Praise for THE Myth OF Excellence

"A startlingly sensible analysis."   *—Miami Herald*

"This crisply written book provides an insight into consumer behavior that will prove of great use to business leaders."   *—Pittsburgh Gazette*

"Tired of business drivel? If you are ready to step beyond platitudinous mission statements and strategies cooked up in distant boardrooms that have no connection to the trenches where business battles are actually being fought, this is the book for you. It is grounded, readable, and honest—just like your business should be."   —PACO UNDERHILL, *Why We Buy: The Science of Shopping*

"*The Myth of Excellence* stands apart from the deluge of business books on the market with its candor and readability. For the brand-marketing executive, the book provides some especially revealing insights into underlying consumer values. Even more refreshing is the authors' approach to imparting business lessons through real research and first-hand case studies."
                              —C. MANLY MOLPUS, Chairman and CEO,
                                     The Grocery Manufacturers of America

"Everyone in business thinks they really know their customers and what they want. But, in *The Myth of Excellence,* Fred Crawford and Ryan Mathews have given me new and useful insights into the startling changes taking place before our very eyes. When they tell us, for example, that 'human values are the contemporary currency of commerce,' they are not just offering another new business platitude but rather a new lens through which to view the consumer—a lens very few people understand. *The Myth of Excellence* is both a big idea and a blueprint for action. A true must-read."
                              —MICHAEL BURANDT, President,
                  North American Consumer Products, Georgia-Pacific Corporation

"Today's customers are leading a revolution against business as usual: They are demanding that companies recognize them as individuals and conduct business on their terms. In *The Myth of Excellence,* Crawford and Mathews provide proven strategies for meeting the demands of today's empowered customers, who are crying out to be treated with respect, dignity, and courtesy."
                  —THOMAS M. SIEBEL, Chairman and CEO, Siebel Systems, Inc.

Also by Ryan Mathews

The Deviant's Advantage

(coauthor Watts Wacker)

THE Myth
OF Excellence

Why **Great** Companies
Never Try to Be the Best at Everything

Fred Crawford and
Ryan Mathews

 THREE RIVERS PRESS • NEW YORK

For Chris and Luke (I love you guys—sorry I've missed so many evenings) and our families—Fred, Margaret, Ron, Debbie, Ray, Ryan, John, Jeanette, Johnnie, and Michael.

—Fred Crawford

For Sierra and Gabriel, who grew into the two most amazing people it's been my pleasure to meet, mostly when I wasn't smart enough to be watching.

—Ryan Mathews

Published by Three Rivers Press, New York, New York.
Member of the Crown Publishing Group, a division of Random House, Inc.
www.randomhouse.com

THREE RIVERS PRESS and the Tugboat design are registered trademarks of Random House, Inc.

Originally published in hardcover by Crown Business, a division of Random House, Inc., in 2001.

Printed in the United States of America

DESIGN BY LYNNE AMFT

Library of Congress Cataloging-in-Publication Data
Crawford, Fred.
    The myth of excellence : why great companies never try to be the best at everything/
Fred Crawford and Ryan Mathews.—1st ed.
    Includes bibliographical references and index.
    1. Marketing research—Case studies.   2. Consumer behavior—Case studies.
    3. Shopping—Case studies.   I. Mathews, Ryan.   II. Title.
    HF5415.2 .C76 2001
    658.8'34—dc21   2001017344

ISBN 0-609-81001-4

10 9 8 7 6 5 4 3 2 1

First Paperback Edition

Contents

113884

Acknowledgments

WE WOULD BOTH LIKE to thank our publishing team: agent extraordinaire Raphael Sagalyn of The Sagalyn Agency, who gave us our first, sometimes hard, lessons in publishing; John Mahaney, the spiritual leader of the Crown Publishing Group, whose editorial guidance helped shape both our thinking and final product; Jonathan Slonim, editorial assistant, for his liaison work on our behalf; and Will Weisser, Debbie Koenig, and the rest of the Crown promotional and advertising team.

Special recognition needs to be given to three individuals, each of whom placed an indelible stamp on this project. Without their efforts this book literally would not have been possible. Marcella Mosier brought a remarkable and tireless faith to this effort—even when our direction was unclear—and contributed content, provided insight, delivered against project goals, and in the process helped shape what became Consumer Relevancy. Priscilla Donegan contributed her insights, thoughts, and discipline; forced this manuscript into readability through tireless editing; made us act like adults; broke the ties; and donated hours to this project nobody should have given or been asked for. Finally, to Rebecca Sue River, thanks for everything—and we do mean everything.

A special mention also goes to Susan Buddenbaum, whose insights and early contributions provided the momentum for what today has become Consumer Relevancy. And thanks also to Bob Stanojev, who put us together in the first place. Other important early contributors included Bernie Thiel and Syed Hoda.

The Myth of Excellence simply wouldn't have been written without the cooperation and support of several individuals and companies. Feargal Quinn charmed himself to the top of this list by providing great access into his own company, providing invitations into other companies, and once again proving himself to be one of the best hosts and friends to be found anywhere in this world. We recommend that any reader finding herself or himself in Ireland stop by to visit Superquinn, and please buy something while you're there.

Thanks also go to our other Irish friends: Patrick Campbell, Donal O'Brien, and Paul O'Toole of Campbell-Bewley Group, and Derek McDonagh and Edward Stephenson of Jurys Doyle Hotel Group. Staying on the international note, special thanks to Bill Keon and the entire Pueblo family in San Juan.

Returning stateside we want to thank: Catherine Baum of Stanley Martin; Janet Kraus at Circles; Claudia Kotchka at Tremor; Craig Schnuck, his family, and the staff at Schnuck Markets; Ross Roeder and the staff at Smart & Final; Ron Pearson and his staff at Hy-Vee; John Gottfried, Ned Visser, and Andrew Arons at Gourmet Garage; Mike Himes and the other good vibrations at Record Time; Bob Carpenter and the team at Dollar General.

Five other companies assisted us in our early work, helping Consumer Relevancy take on its initial shape: Domino's Pizza, Ames, Eddie Bauer, Southwest Airlines, and Midwest Express.

Special thanks also go out to Wesley Wright, Jimmy Wright, Roger Kidd, and the rest of the team at Diversified Retail Solutions. Thanks also to Don Dufek for his efforts in initially helping shape Consumer Relevancy. The following companies and associations were kind enough to give us support, encouragement, resources, and, most important, platforms: Georgia-Pacific, Procter & Gamble, the Grocery Manufacturers of America, Kellogg, Unilever Bestfoods, C&A, British American Tobacco, and Royal Dutch Ahold.

Fred extends thanks to the Cap Gemini Ernst & Young family for putting up with all of the trials and tribulations of this project. To Terry Ozan, Dale Wartluft, Bob McIlhattan, Berend Brix, and Geoff Unwin, thanks very much for your support. Also, a special thanks to Stephanie Shern at Ernst & Young LLP, who got me focused on this in the first place. To Doug Dickson and Stella Goulet, thanks for all your hard work and support. To Charlie Gottdiener, who took the concept of Consumer Relevancy and helped shape it into something tangible, thanks a lot. To all of the CPRD team around the globe, thanks for all your hard work and dedication to our practice and to the concept of Consumer Relevancy. And while we said it together, to Rebecca and Marcie, an encore thanks!

To Bake, Burke, Bow, MTV, Spiro, Heath, and the crew, rock on.

And again to the home team, Chris and Luke, who make it all worthwhile.

Ryan would also like to thank the FirstMatter team: Watts Wacker, futuring's cosmic cowboy and my comrade-in-arms, for the sage publishing advice, creative counsel, patience, and friendship; Mary DeVito, whose great organizational skills, logistical expertise, and attention to large and small details both professional and personal were invaluable in the completion of this manuscript; Darrell Stewart, the special librarian with the big heart and a constant friend through several vocational incarnations; and last but not least Michael Strother, who managed to keep the hardware, software, and wetware running in sync, no small task given my admitted technological limitations.

I would also like to thank Tara, Mark, Rochelle, Liz, and the other Motor City friends and neighbors whose qualitative responses helped confirm our original quantitative findings; the Wacker family—Betsy, Cal, and Lee—who provided food, shelter, and a true home away from home; Syed Hoda, for the exciting car rides in Puerto Rico and the interest in this project as it developed; friends, especially Mark Baum, Mike Maurer, Russ Hockin, Joe Finegan, Craig MacDonald, and John Gray, each of whom made a unique contribution to both this book and all the activities surrounding its creation. Encore thanks to Priscilla, Rebecca Sue, and Marcie. And a special thanks goes out to Rick Jackson, whose intuitive understanding of the principles in this book allows him to operate the finest shoe shine stand in Detroit's Metro Airport, for the friendship and good conversation that brightened many a morning and confirmed that what we are saying here is right.

Again for Gabe and Sierra, who have helped me in ways they may not fully understand or appreciate for decades to come. And finally, a wink and a nod to WTB and PTH, because without at least a little magic, life wouldn't be half as much fun.

Introduction to the Paperback Edition

In June 2001, when Crown Business released *The Myth of Excellence,* we thought we had come to the end of a long, sometimes frustrating, and often rewarding journey. *Myth* was the product of almost three years of writing, research, and field experience, and we assumed it would have its moment in the sun and move on. Happily, we were wrong. Its essential message—that human values have superceded commercial value as the primary currency of contemporary commerce—has been reinforced significantly. The tragic events of September 11th have caused the nation, and the world, to rethink what life is about and how perishable all institutions can be. The scandals that rocked former pillars of corporate respectability such as Global Crossing, Enron, WorldCom, and Arthur Andersen have underscored and deepened what we first diagnosed as a growing crisis of consumer confidence. The gulf separating the consumer from the enterprises that serve him has widened, not closed.

Some have argued that nothing is the same since September 11th. The actions of terrorists have stripped away our ability to even feign naivety. We have tested that hypothesis in the only way we know, by rerunning our original research in the wake of the attacks on the World Trade Center and the Pentagon. We found that our conclusions were still valid. In fact, the emphasis on human values was somewhat more marked in our post–September 11th research.

A general decline in the economy during the first years of the Bush Administration also seemed to strengthen our initial findings. Consumer confidence has consistently been down; stock prices have declined; layoffs are now far more commonplace; and, as we write this on the advent of the 2002 holiday season, most businesses are more bearish than bullish about the prospects of a near-term recovery, despite the kinds of discounting we generally associate with the post-, rather than the pre-, holiday period. This overall sense of economic insecurity is mirrored by the general population, many of whom have seen stock portfolios devalued and their 401(k) plans evaporate. If we had been desperate for security, connection, honesty, and values in a universe where we tried to buffer our needs with things, how much greater does our need become in a world where things are increasingly out of reach?

Since the initial publication of *Myth,* we have expanded our research globally. Research conducted with 6,000 consumers in nine European nations found no significant difference between the attitude of European shoppers and the values orientation we discovered among their U.S. peers. This came as a bit of a surprise. We had anticipated a significant difference between, say, the French and the Germans or, at the very least, a significant difference between European and American shopping attitudes. Yet, the number one responses in all five commercial attribute categories (access, experience, price, product, and service) were identical in Europe and America. Interestingly, in contrast to the conventional wisdom that European businesses generally command more consumer loyalty than their American peers, the majority of European consumers were hard-pressed to identify favorite stores in many retail channels. In fact, retailers in general proved fairly undifferentiated in the minds of their customers in terms of their value propositions.

Unlike the United States, however, demography seemed a bit more important in Europe. Throughout most of the nine countries, women were much more likely than men to rate the factors related to shopping satisfaction as extremely important, while younger consumers (15–34) were less apt to do so than older shoppers. This demographic variation hasn't been seen in the United States.

We also wanted to see if our theories could be extended to the realm of consumer goods and branding. Additional research, conducted in association with *Chain Store Age* magazine, identified an enormous gap between what consumers are looking for and what they believe branded manufacturers are delivering. For example, 83 percent of shoppers surveyed said they strongly agreed that it was important that the products they purchase perform according to advertised claims, and 75 percent said it was important that the advertised claims they see are true. Yet a mere 16 percent said they "believe that manufacturers' claims and communications about their products are generally true." These findings point to a gap in fundamental credibility and trust. This suggests that advertising, marketing, and merchandising strategies need to be immediately rethought. We may have simply oversaturated the market. The American Academy of Pediatrics has estimated that the average American child is exposed to more than 20,000 advertising messages a year, which may help explain why some people see technology such as TiVo and Replay TV as the tip of an ad-free future.

The study, which polled 7,000 consumers, discovered that when it comes to the basic attributes of a commercial transaction the communication gap we had previously uncovered between consumers and those selling them goods and services also separated consumers and manufacturers. Our research found that a product's features and functions are no longer enough to capture the imagination—not to mention the wallet and loyalty—of today's demanding consumer and that consumers respond best to makers of consumer products that incorporate basic human values into their offerings. In addition, we found hard evidence that consumer-product companies that understand what consumers really want from brands have an opportunity to strengthen thier competitive position, drive top-line and bottom-line growth, and build brand loyalty.

For years, most consumer-products manufacturers have relied almost entirely on the *content* of their products—that is, functionality, quality, usage information, lowest price—to build their brands. But this approach is no longer sufficient. As manufacturers look to differentiate their brands in a crowded marketplace with increasingly demanding consumers, they must move into territory foreign to many of them—the world of context, or the way in which they deliver their products. Context, which lies at the heart of what we call the Consumer Relevancy methodology, offers an entirely new approach for a consumer-products manufacturer to build and strengthen the relationship of its brands with consumers, drive growth and new product development, and improve its competitive position. It also provides manufacturers with an opportunity to equalize the balance of power between themselves and their retail partners.

This is especially important in light of today's channel-blurring phenomenon. Our research found clear evidence of consumers' indifference to the notion of "channels" as traditionally defined by the retail trade, a finding with significant ramifications for consumer-products companies. When consumers were asked, for instance, to name the department store in which they shopped most often, they were more likely to cite discounters such as Wal-Mart and Target than they were to point to traditional operators like Nordstrom, Filene's, Kaufmann's, Sears, or J.C. Penney. And in the case of drugstores, consumers rated Wal-Mart more highly than traditional channel players such as Walgreens, CVS, Rite Aid, and Eckerd. Once manufacturers understand that consumers don't care where they buy a product they can begin to adopt new approaches that don't discriminate by channel, but rather by the type of consumer served and by the fit of the retailer's value proposition with that of their own brand. This might signal a move away from the notion that ubiquitous distribution is the best distribution and open the door to creating value through limiting distribution.

What is the functional difference between content and context in the consumer-products business? Here's how each applies to the five key attributes we describe in *Myth*. In the case of *access,* content focuses on retail distribution points, while context emphasizes consumer needs' satisfaction. The issue is not how easy it is to locate a place offering a good or service, but rather whether that location presents the offering in a way that resonates with the customer. The ability to modify context acts as a differentiator in a world where so many commercial offerings tend to appear to be commodities. After all, anyone can offer a Sony Walkman for sale, presumably at the same price. But, despite the commodity-like nature of the personal electronics world, retailers still find ways to differentiate the shopping experience. When it comes to *experience,* content is about consumer use of a brand; context is about consumer identity with that brand. For *price,* content comes down to low list, while context is about consistent value. In the case of *product,* content focuses on features and functions, while context puts the emphasis on inspiration. And for *service,* content is all about reacting and responding uniformly; context focuses on a proactive and customized approach. While content is the basis of all commerce, context gives manufacturers a competitive edge they can leverage to build their brands.

Since consumers rarely deal directly with manufacturers—except possibly to rectify a performance problem after purchase—their insights regarding brands, as we uncovered in our research are particularly instructive. The strength of their answers comes through in the consistently high scores for basic human values people expect from the makers of consumer products. The critical role played by values is among the key principles forming the foundation of Consumer Relevancy. Our research makes it clear that consumers will respond to and reward consumer-products companies that offer reinforcement of values such as trust, honesty, respect, dignity, and fairness.

Consumers are looking for products that are inspirational, empowering and that reinforce or improve their self-image. Manufacturers, on the other hand, are still by and large lost in the land of efficacy. Responding to a list of 44 statements about products, consumers rated matters of respect, trust, honest pricing, easy communications, performance-as-promised and responsive service at the head of the list. Following were the top responses to the consumer products survey:

- It's important that a manufacturer's service representative treats me with respect (84 percent said they "strongly agree").
- It's important that the products I purchase perform according to advertised claims (83 percent).
- It's important to me that products are priced honestly, consistently, and are not artificially increased (80 percent).
- When I call a manufacturer, it's important that I am quickly put in touch with a person (77 percent).
- It's important to me that the ad claims I see are true (75 percent).
- It's important to me that I can trust the manufacturers from whom I buy products (74 percent).

In short, the case for human values we made when *Myth* was first released has never been stronger or more broadly applicable to all businesses.

As Irish Senator Feargal Quinn, founder of the Superquinn grocery chain profiled in Chapter 4, told us this year when we asked him how his company was doing, "We are as committed as ever to the belief that in a competitive market, the customer becomes even more important. Customer service at Superquinn is the bedrock of our continued success and even more so when the economy faces the challenge of a possible downturn." Feargal Quinn is not alone. In the months following the initial publication of *Myth*, Record Time, the two-unit independent music retailer profiled in Chapter 6, has seen its largest regional-chain competitor close its doors while Record Time survives through rededication to keeping faith with the consumer. Since *Myth* first appeared in 2001, its principles have been adopted in full or in part by organizations as diverse as FedEx, Borders, Best Buy, and the Christian Booksellers Association.

As with any book, buyers have a right to know why they should read it. Our answer: In good economic times, the material these pages contain was helpful for businesses targeting growth; today, as companies battle daily for survival, it's nothing short of imperative. If you are rereading *Myth*, we urge you to do so with a new mindset. If you've picked it up for the first time, we suggest you read it with a sense of urgency. The need for businesses to address fundamental human values has never been more pronounced.

FRED CRAWFORD   RYAN MATHEWS
New York   *Detroit*

Preface

"It's not what you don't know that hurts you, it's what you know that ain't so."
—Mark Twain

Mark Twain couldn't have been more right, especially when it comes to modern business strategy and execution. Over the past three years, we've conducted research that jolted us out of our personal smug assumptions about the nature of business. What we "knew" about business was keeping us from seeing the changing realities of commerce. Perhaps like you, we had ample reason to believe that we had a handle on the nature of business, a deep understanding of what customers wanted from the companies that served them, and a better than average insight into what makes commerce tick. We believed that when customers talked about price, they naturally meant they wanted the lowest price available. We were wrong. We also believed that—given a choice—customers would naturally always prefer the highest product quality. Again, we were wrong. And, perhaps most significant of all, we believed that all businesses should strive to be the best they can be at everything they do. Frankly, we discovered we couldn't have been more wrong about this, and we hope our experience sets off some alarm bells in your head.

What we discovered was that, across the globe and across all industries, businesses are spending billions of dollars sending poorly aimed—and in some cases offensive—messages to their customers and leaving literally billions more on the table each day. Instead of talking to customers in a language they can understand and find meaningful, most businesses are actually demonstrating—through advertising, marketing, merchandising, product assortment and selection, transactional terms, and service levels—that they don't respect or even know whom they are doing business with. To paraphrase the G. B. Shaw aphorism about the British and the Americans, businesses and customers are increasingly separated by a common language. The words used by both are the same, but the meanings are entirely different.

Companies large and small are offering customers everything except what those customers really want. Every business day, thousands of businesses spend millions of dollars on focus groups, surveys, and processing call-center reports, all to limited avail. In almost every trade sector, all businesses—including market leaders—live in the shadow of unforeseen competitive threats. Just consider how many local businesses, from supermarkets and sporting-goods stores to jewelry and hardware stores, spent years confident that they knew their customers and what those customers valued. Imagine how comfortable they felt and how secure they thought their businesses were, until Wal-Mart opened up in their towns and—armed with a superior understanding of customers and what they wanted—summarily put them out of business. Or imagine how confident IBM and, yes, even Xerox were that they understood the needs of the computer user, until their market dominance was usurped by "upstarts" such as Microsoft, Dell, Gateway, and Apple. Think about how Apple itself fell prey to the same trap. The bottom line: Global business—and perhaps more important to you, your business—is inexorably, and unknowingly, marching toward a crisis point.

The bad news: Today's market leaders across all commercial sectors are in jeopardy. We are poised on the brink of a customer revolution, a revolution whose demands could not be more clearly articulated: Recognize and respect me as an individual and start doing business my way. The good news: Not only can the worst-case scenario be prevented, but also companies that pay attention to the lessons we've learned can avoid disaster and take advantage of an unprecedented growth opportunity.

It's true that the demand for new business practices is edging many businesses close to crisis, but it's also true that in a world of increasingly ubiquitous product quality, increasingly similar market offerings, standardized service levels, and relatively normalized if not standardized pricing, companies that crack the customer code and break from traditional business practices stand to gain disproportionate advantage over their competition. Our mission in *The Myth of Excellence* is both to describe the parameters of the threat to *your* business as well as map out a plan for *your* future success.

No matter how robust or poor the economy appears, and no matter how much sales and profits increase or decrease, commercial prosperity bears a frightening resemblance to a house of cards, because customers are deeply resentful and personally dissatisfied with their commercial experiences. For the first time in history, businesses are being asked to do something other than engage in commerce. Customers increasingly frustrated with the experience of their lives want reinforcement of personal—not just commercial—values. The terms of commercial engagement have changed, and changed forever; businesses that don't find ways to engage on the new terms will fail.

As a result of misunderstanding what customers really want and how best to serve those wants, even the world's most successful businesses have bought into what we have termed the myth of excellence—the false belief that a company ought to try to be good at everything it does. Misdiagnose the problem and you almost inevitably misdiagnose the solution. Because businesses focus on increasing transactional value rather than nurturing sustaining relationships, and increasing the value of a transaction rather than worrying about the values surrounding the transaction, they almost intuitively adopt strategies aimed at becoming the best at every aspect of a transaction, an approach that leads to a lack of enterprise focus, which in turns confuses and alienates customers.

We interviewed dozens of world-class business leaders, and time after time we heard how their companies offered customers the highest-quality products at the lowest prices, providing the easiest access to sales environments that were fun and characterized by the best service available. They had spent literal fortunes customizing their products and services based on what they "heard" their customers saying, but they consistently failed to "listen" to what those same customers were really saying. When we talked to their customers, we were told a much different story.

We heard CEOs boast of how well they customized their products and services against target markets only to watch their sales slide over the next few months. We interviewed companies in the course of researching this book that went bankrupt before the final draft was completed. And over and over again, we found companies overspending against any plausible hope of a return. Their experiences form the foundation of this book. Business isn't a Greek tragedy: Learning from the mistakes of others can help you change your fate.

For the purposes of our analysis, we have divided all commercial transactions into five elements or attributes: price, product, access, service, and experience. We identified these five attributes because they are present in every commercial transaction—business-to-consumer or business-to-business. We assigned a numerical value to each of these attributes, with 5 indicating market domination on an attribute, 4 indicating differentiation around an attribute, and 3 indicating that you've effectively met—but not exceeded—market competition on an attribute. We've termed the ability to see business through the customer's eyes and conduct business on terms that customers find meaningful on a personal level Consumer Relevancy. And we've found that you can profitably conduct business on these terms. Looking at the world through the lens of Consumer Relevancy, we found that the best companies have a strategy for *dominating* (i.e., being world-class) on *one* of the five attributes of product, price, access, experience, and service, *differentiating* on a second, and being at *industry par* (i.e., average) on the remaining three. On a 1-to-5 scale, where 5 is world-class, 3 is industry par, and 1 is unacceptable, a perfect score is 5, 4, 3, 3, 3. Two additional "rules" apply: There is a "no-man's-land" or "consumer underworld" into which no company should travel. As a result, you can't be below industry par on any one attribute. At the same time, you shouldn't attempt to be a 5 on more than one attribute and a 4 on more than one. If a business is below par on any attribute, it cannot be viable for very long, as consumers will reject its value proposition over time. If a business is a 5 on more than one attribute and a 4 on more than one, it has created needless differentiation and is leaving money on the table.

There is a growing gap between the content of a business transaction (the value of a product or service) and the context (the values surrounding doing business). We found business after business simply missing the point and believing that value was an effective commercial substitute for values and that transactions were an acceptable alternative to the relationships customers want. In companies trying to be great at everything, this misunderstanding created substantial value leakage. In companies that weren't so great, it was the first step toward disaster. Customers are looking for deeper levels of personal recognition and a clear statement of values, but their pleas are going largely unheeded by the businesses that serve them. The *context* in which your business engages consumers (in Wal-Mart's case, the absolute trust of an honest low price) has grown in importance, eclipsing the *content* of your product or service. Most businesses have been improving their product offering since opening their doors, yet the context surrounding the transaction has been an afterthought, a necessary evil in the mindless dash for differentiation. *Human values*, not commercial value, have become the contemporary currency of commerce.

Let's briefly go back to Wal-Mart and try and put some flesh on the bones. Wal-Mart is known as the price leader, but its prices are not always lowest. It dominates (earns a 5 rating) on price because consumers trust that its "everyday low prices" philosophy will provide them with an honest price in the low-price range, a price with no hidden gimmicks, and in all product categories. Wal-Mart's honesty and true understanding of what consumers value is reflected in Wal-Mart's values and how the company treats customers. Wal-Mart differentiates itself on product (earns a 4 rating). Product quality is high but not as high as key competitor Target. And on service, access, and experience, Wal-Mart is industry par, i.e., average (earns a 3 rating) in each of these attributes.

We don't believe all businesses are the same; in fact, we don't really believe any two businesses are identical. But we do believe we've found a process and methodology that can be customized and applied to any business from the corner barbershop to Microsoft with proportionately equal benefit. It begins by mapping out how all the stakeholders of a business really see that business; moves to an analysis of competitive factors; and, finally, allows you to create a future blueprint for your business. We'll also describe the great "white space" opportunity that lies just beyond your current grasp—the opportunity to both reduce operating costs and, more important, increase top-line sales and profits.

And, of course, there's another reason to read. Business is a two-way street, and everyone from Bill Gates to the Queen of England is somebody's customer. *The Myth of Excellence* helps bring understanding to both sides of the transaction, allowing businesses to see through the eyes of their customers—and vice versa.

CHAPTER 1

Field Notes from the Commercial Wilderness

THIS BOOK IS REALLY the diary of a journey—field notes from an expedition into the commercial wilderness, if you will. Our trek began with a survey, fairly modest in conception although broad in scope. After all, we thought we knew how consumers felt. Understanding consumer dynamics, analyzing marketplaces and market spaces, anticipating the impact of technological change on businesses and consumers, and looking into the future are all significant elements of our day-to-day business and personal lives. In retrospect, it is incredible how naive we really were—naive, but not unlike a lot of other businesspeople. Since we knew what we were looking for, we wanted the data to provide verification of our brilliant insights. Like a company polling its customers and rationalizing any negative comments, we expected the survey results to support our entrenched assumptions.

We assumed, for example, that consumers wanted the absolute lowest prices, the very best products, and lots of value-added services. We also expected them to tell us that they wanted shopping to be fun and entertaining. We were in for a shock.

Our real journey started when the data came back. We were sitting in the conference room of a restored Victorian home in Westport,

Connecticut, marveling at how it was possible for 5,000 Americans to be so wrong. Our initial research included more than 4,000 consumer telephone surveys and 1,000 additional Internet polls, covering a wide range of questions about various facets of the consumer/business relationship and the "average" shopping experience, followed up by hundreds of additional one-on-one conversations with consumers.

We had asked consumers some basic questions about relatively simple business transactions, or so we thought, and they'd blown it. They didn't get it. What had gotten into them? Slowly, the grim truth began to dawn on us: They weren't wrong. *We* were.

The survey results told us that consumers are looking for values, not just value. They wanted recognition as individual human beings, not just a 30 percent discount. While we had started asking questions about retail, we quickly began to see retail as a metaphor for something much broader. Life apparently wasn't too satisfying, and our initial respondents expected somebody or something—apparently business—to set things right.

We began to totally reevaluate our work. The survey tool we had developed was an excellent diagnostic, applicable to any business. But what did the results mean? We had thought about the notion of business simply in terms of the successful transfer of goods and services—basic buying and selling. Yet suddenly we felt more like social workers, wrestling with intangible issues like respect and trust. Like teenagers out for a joyride in a Ferrari Testarossa, we found ourselves behind the wheel of a vehicle whose power was much greater than we had initially anticipated. So we eased the clutch down, gingerly downshifted, and gently applied the brakes. We concentrated on understanding the tool, fine-tuned it and ran limited tests in real companies until we were sure the new insights that kept pouring in were correct. Then we spent a year focusing on in-depth analysis, conferring with our colleagues, conducting thousands of one-on-one consumer interviews and dozens of interviews with business leaders.

Gradually things became clearer. Over and over again, the responses of our pilot 5,000 respondents kept echoing back to us. The critical elements of a transaction, business-to-consumer or business-to-business, weren't capital, goods, and services—they were the human qualities of the people or companies exchanging those elements. It didn't seem to matter what business we were talking about. The lessons we first learned in the retail sector applied to any and all of the businesses we looked at, whether it was airlines, banks, auto companies, high-tech, insurance, or entertainment. Consumers' expectations had changed and changed radically. Unfortunately, not enough people in business had noticed. Some had, of course—the successful always do.

But even the most successful companies are often overspending and only partially achieving their aims. What led us to that conclusion? Our research caused us to see that every business transaction—from the simplest sale of goods to the most complex service offering—can be broken down to five attributes: price, service, access, experience, and product. We found that many companies tried to be "excellent" in all of these areas. This misguided strategy, which we've come to term the myth of excellence, had several failings: First, it's impossible for one company to be great at everything. Even Wal-Mart, arguably the most successful retailer in history, doesn't dominate its competitors on every attribute.

Second, even assuming a company could excel in all five areas, it would have difficulty communicating a clear value proposition to consumers. Imagine the confusion if Tiffany suddenly began advertising deep discount prices on emeralds, or McDonald's began offering free-range chicken and tofu. In selecting the attribute that defines their primary field of competition (the one on which a company seeks to dominate), the most successful consumer businesses hone the one that their target consumers value the most.

This seems simple enough, but it's surprising how often companies try to be the best at something their consumers don't want. Several years ago, for example, Kmart embarked on a campaign to make its line of clothing more upscale. As part of that campaign, the retailer began offering higher-priced Gitano designer jeans. The move, not surprisingly, was a resounding flop—the retailer's customers didn't believe designer clothes could be sold at Kmart prices. At the same time, Gitano hurt itself on the other end of its business, because upscale shoppers didn't believe that any brand sold by Kmart could still carry sufficient high-fashion cachet. On the other hand, the Martha Stewart line has been a great success, apparently because Kmart consumers believe that somebody who can make a candelabra out of wild gourds shares a sense of values with them. High fashion put the shoppers off. High craft seemed a bit more accessible. It wasn't that the Gitano jeans weren't a good value, it's that Kmart shoppers said to themselves that *low cost, high fashion* must somehow also mean *low quality*.

Finally, we found that even the most successful companies tended to be right for the wrong reasons—they weren't paying enough attention to what we came to recognize as a desperate cry for basic human values. It became increasingly clear to us that this was at the heart of the myth of excellence.

But if universal commercial excellence was a myth, what was the reality? We found the answer inside our original consumer data. There was, in fact, a way for businesses to answer consumers' demand for values on terms that the consumers could recognize, a way of speaking to customers in their own language. We call this Consumer Relevancy, a way of appropriately framing an offering that enhances its value to a customer. Again, we stopped. If we were right, how could we explain the longest uninterrupted period of prosperity in human history? What could be wrong? The answer, we found, is, Plenty.

The Eye of the Storm: The Forces Driving Change in Consumer Values

Something is wrong in industrialized societies across the globe—really, really wrong. Measured in historical terms, these are truly still the best of times. Yet despite all the material prosperity that surrounds us, we are living in some of the worst of personal times. There is a huge difference between economic and psychic well-being, between being able to afford physical comforts and feeling whole, between living in affluent surroundings and having a sense of connectedness. We're living our lives and running our businesses in the shadows of satisfaction. We look around at everything we have accomplished, everything we have built, and everything we own, but they somehow don't mean exactly what we thought they would.

Self-styled culture jammer and "adbuster" Kalle Lasn looks at our problem this way: "Take stock of your life. Look around at what you drive, wear, eat, smoke, read. Are these things *you*? Would an anthropologist, given a pile of all your material possessions, be able to assemble an accurate portrait of your personality? Would that portrait reflect a true original or a 'type'?"[1] There's something—some fundamental element—missing in our lives. We feel it every day, and so do you. Most of the time we blame the food, the schedule, or the stress, but intuitively we feel something is wrong that can't be fixed by a better diet, a few days off, or some hours in the gym. The hows and whys of what we're feeling take some explaining, but start by asking yourself a few simple questions:

- How frequently do you miss key life events (birthdays, anniversaries, even soccer games), and what toll is it taking on your family?
- How did it feel to watch the peace of the suburban American Dream shattered by the gunfire of Columbine, guns in the hands of affluent sixteen-year-olds from good homes?
- Do you ever wonder how we moved so quickly from a time when Gary Hart couldn't run for office to a time when Bill Clinton couldn't be removed?
- How often do you spend a day completely unplugged—no e-mail, voice mail, or pager?
- How do you verify that anything you read, see, or hear is true? Are margarine, red wine, aspirin, and eggs good or bad for you?

It's clear that on a macro level, things are changing, and not for the better. But what about on a micro level? What's going on every day in your life?

- Do you look forward to flying on any commercial airplane, and when was the last time you really enjoyed a flight?
- Is holiday shopping fun or just another duty eating away at your free time?

- Are you tired of standing in line at the supermarket or bank only to deal with someone who can't make eye contact or say hello?
- Do you fully understand how your health insurance works?

So, you're more affluent than your parents ever dreamed of being, but is your life *really* as good as theirs? The answer to this question is increasingly "no." But why?

Historically, we have looked to our social institutions to reinforce our personal values. Yet, as we have already hinted at and will document more fully in a moment, these institutions are chronically and repeatedly failing us. The search for values, like nature, abhors a vacuum. The fact that our social institutions no longer can be counted on as consistent sources of personal value or fulfillment doesn't mean our individual search for those qualities gets set aside. This creates a unique opportunity for businesses to fill this values gap, assuming they recognize it and move quickly. It's an opportunity that we as consumers do not explicitly request but will both appreciate and pay a premium for. It's an opportunity that provides businesses with a chance to simultaneously build their brand and increase market share and margin, a troika that does not present itself often.

Before we go any further, we'd like you to answer a few basic questions about your customers and your business:

- Do you really know why your customers behave as they do? What makes them buy from you, and what could you do that would lose their business?
- Do you know how a new—or existing—competitor could steal your business?
- What is the one thing you're not providing your customers today that they are secretly begging for?
- What are two things about your business that you cannot—under any circumstances—afford to change?

If you think you've got good answers to all these questions, we suggest you close this book, mix yourself a large martini, and enjoy the fruits of your labor. If, on the other hand, you have at least some niggling little doubts about your answers, we encourage you to keep reading. We suspect you're an expert in your business, but that doesn't offer much protection against becoming a victim of your own assumptions and past experience. In many respects, we are all experts on the nature and impact of commerce—not just as businesspeople, but because we all buy something every day. Things are changing, however, and if you're honest with yourself, you have to admit it's getting harder and harder just to stay even. We live in a world that is more stressful, less accommodating, moving faster, and, frankly speaking, tough to deal with. At the same time, much of the support infrastructure that has fortified and sustained us is breaking down. So what do we want?

The Perpetual Scavenger Hunt for Values

Human values—trust, respect, honesty, dignity, courtesy, ease—are the building blocks of any free, advanced society. Yet those very things are gradually but systematically being stripped away from our daily lives. We cannot enjoy product or service provision in an environment devoid of human values—values that are harder and harder to find in society. To understand exactly how this values gap impacts us, we first need to analyze our personal and social circumstances: What is changing around us that gives rise to a shift in our desires as consumers? Three key changes—societal devolution, personal time compression, and the proliferation of information and communication technologies—all occurring at once, are driving us to crave something different. Actually, it's less something different than it is a change in the relative weighting we assign to the context of a transaction. Let's examine these three factors:

1. **Societal devolution.** All human beings look to put themselves in situations where they recognize and relate to the values being portrayed around them. This obvious and fundamental truth explains why there are biker bars and martini bars, churches and synagogues, Republican and Democratic political parties, chat rooms on virtu-

ally every subject, and, while we may never understand why, Britney Spears fan clubs. But all of these different splinters are anchored by a core set of fundamental values. Everyone wants to be respected, to be treated well, not to be taken advantage of, to be recognized and valued: in short, to be validated as an individual. Historically, that responsibility hasn't fallen very heavily on goods and services providers. People were able to find such reinforcement in many places: family, government, their marriages, school, social-club membership, church. Each made a contribution, some more than others, to validating and reinforcing the value of the individual, the worth of their society, and the sanctity of their place in it.

But today much of this is changing. We're not suggesting that the world is coming to an end, but in dozens of small ways the edges of the social fabric are slowly unraveling. Some of these ways make us mildly, but unidentifiably, uncomfortable. Some cause us stress, and some make us question ideas and institutions that we were trained since birth to accept. One by one, the institutions that have historically safeguarded our values have begun to fail us. Our trust in government leaders is slowly eroding. In April 1966, with the Vietnam War raging, 66 percent of Americans *rejected* the view that "people running the country don't really care what happens to you." In December 1997, in the midst of the longest period of peace and prosperity in more than two generations, 57 percent of Americans *endorsed* that same view.[2] This is manifesting itself in voter turnout. Since 1960, the turnout for the U.S. presidential election has steadily declined, dropping below the 50 percent mark in 1988.

Families, too, have changed dramatically over the past four decades. According to a 2000 YMCA survey, more than 60 percent of the respondents believed communication with their children had deteriorated dramatically in the 1990s. American fathers spoke with their children 45 minutes a day on average in the 1960s. Today that "quality time" has shrunk to about six minutes. And as Swedish academics Kjell Nordström and Jonas Ridderstråle note in their book *Funky Business: Talent Makes Capital Dance,* "When the Norwegian furniture company Stokke launched its Tripp Trapp children's chair in France there was a disappointing response. Then it discovered why. Families did not sit down for meals together anymore. Even in France, home of gastronomy and convivial meals, families eat at different times. There simply wasn't a need for a chair that allowed children to sit comfortably at the same height as adults. So, a Norwegian company had to set about reeducating the French to eat meals with their kids."

Organized religion, once both the font and final preserve of aggregate human values, has lost its historic monopoly on the moral high ground. By 1996, only 38 percent of people in the United States worshiped each week,[3] while in the United Kingdom the number of people attending the Church of England each week dipped below the 1 million mark in 2000 for the first time since Henry VIII set up the Church.[4] Ambivalence has riddled the American Roman Catholic Church since the days of Vatican II. Protestants have seen their fundamentalist wing evolve into a decidedly more secular faction increasingly concerned with impacting elections rather than individual lives. In Israel, Orthodox and Reform Jews wrestle not only for control of the government but also of society, while Jews of Arab descent complain of being second-class citizens. Japan, which is both the world's most literate nation and Asia's most industrialized state, has birthed more than 500 new religions since the end of World War II.[5] Church attendance is down, while New Age religions from born-again Buddhism to Gaia flourish, as, in a search for values and meaning, more and more people try to create their own spiritual templates outside the context of traditional organized religion.

The same pattern holds true in education. At graduation, American high school students are behind students in 96 percent of the countries in the developed world in terms of math, reading, and science proficiency.[6] Not only have American schools consistently failed to educate—and therefore to communicate values—but also, from Columbine to Cleveland, they have come to embody *la vida loca* more than *in loco parentis*.

The upshot of all this is that traditional institutions have become less able to adequately reflect fundamental human values. As individuals, we unconsciously seek out reinforcement and ratification of our personal values and consciously reward those commercial institutions smart enough to build values into their offerings. This simple fact came across loud and clear in our research. While there are countless examples of this in our interviews, the following excerpt from our interview with Sandra, a working mother, sums it up well:

> There's one store that treats me, and most other moms, with respect and dignity. While most stores have a children's area, this store goes those others one better. It has a VCR, with a variety of movies, games, and a picnic table. The mothers now routinely come in and have a cup of coffee. They put their kids in the play area and bring their friends. They've developed relationships and discuss decorating their houses together. It's not unusual for them to be there an hour on average, but it's also not unusual for someone to be there two or three hours.

2. **Increased inability to keep pace with daily life.** Everywhere we turned during our research for this book, we heard it: "I simply can't keep up." From white-collar professionals we heard complaints of e-mail, voice mail, pager, cell phone, fax machine, and computer overload. The great experiment of the Information Age is claiming its early victims. From blue-collar professionals we heard complaints about technology-driven productivity expectations concurrent with staffing reductions, of the need to work two or even three jobs per family to maintain a standard of living or just get by, of the difficulty in getting adequate health insurance. U.S. Census Bureau data indicated that 16 percent of all Americans, or about 44 million people, do not have health insurance.[7] The situation is particularly pronounced in lower-income families. Nearly a third of Americans with

income levels below the poverty line, or about 11 million people, have no health insurance. And the gap between the haves and the have-nots is growing. According to Congressional Budget Office data, the after-tax income of the top one-fifth of America's population rose 43 percent between 1977 and 1999, compared with a decline of 9 percent for the bottom one-fifth. And from everybody we heard complaints of not enough time . . . to be a good father or mother, son or daughter, brother or sister, employee, coach, volunteer.

It is clear that expectations are rising and we are falling further behind. There are plenty of facts to support this claim. Here are a few:

- **Time pressure starts with too much work.** U.S. citizens work almost 2,000 hours a year on average, more than the Japanese, and nine workweeks more than the average European. "The Economic Policy Institute . . . has found that, together, parents in middle-class families work 3,335 hours per year on average, up from 3,200 (in the 1980s) and just over 3,000 (in the 1970s)."[8]

- **Stress is getting to us all—everywhere in the world.** A recent survey by the United Kingdom's Institute of Management found all of the survey respondents agreeing that stress had increased dramatically since 1993.[9]

- **Depression will soon hit almost as many of us as heart disease.** By the year 2020, the World Health Organization (WHO) estimates that depression will be the second leading cause of "lost years of healthy life" worldwide—behind only ischemic heart disease.[10] A recent University of Wisconsin study showed a 50 percent increase in the number of students going to campus counselors for depression, with nearly one-third taking mood-altering medication.[11] Sales of the antidepressants Prozac, Zoloft, and Paxil exceed $4 billion annually.

- **Suicide rates have risen globally.** "Since the mid-1950s, global suicide rates have jumped by 60 percent. This year, the WHO estimates
1 million people will die by their own hand. . . . In the United
States, the suicide rate tops the homicide rate by 50 percent. Every
day four Finns will commit suicide. And China, which makes up
about 22 percent of the world's population, accounts for 44 percent
of the world's suicides."[12]

3. **Proliferation of increasingly intrusive information and communication technologies.** Concurrent with the first two factors, there has
been an explosion in the amount and availability of information in
our lives. It may not be good or accurate information, but that is
largely left for each of us to decipher. It is coming from everywhere:
the Internet, cable television, billboards, radio, the backs of buses,
and your broker. We live in an era where things are moving so fast,
and breakthroughs (technical, medical, and otherwise) are coming
so quickly that we don't know whom or what to believe.

    This proliferation comes at us from all directions:

- The adoption rate of the Internet, PCs, and cell phones is phenomenal in historic terms. While it took television fifty-five years
to reach 50 percent of the U.S. population, it's taken the Internet
only thirty-two years; PCs, twenty-five years; and cell phones,
twenty-four years. By July 2000, the number of households in
the United Kingdom with Internet access increased from one in
ten to one in four.

- Cable television penetration continues to grow. More than 70
percent of U.S. households have access to cable. The number of
available cable channels ranges from fifty at the low end to more
than five hundred at the high end.

- Advertising spending continues to soar. Spending on advertising
overall is growing at a 6 percent to 8 percent rate annually—to
a total of $353 billion worldwide.[13] Internet advertising has grown
at a more rapid pace, reaching $7 billion worldwide in 1999.[14]

The impact of this media explosion is compounded by a growing granularity of media coverage. The Columbine tapes have been released as a commercial product; we followed O. J. Simpson down the L.A. freeway; we were treated to testimony about our president's extramarital sexual activity. The global media now have the ability to bring horror into our living room in real time, whether it is the image of a bomb making its lethal descent down a chimney in Iraq or of Elián González being grabbed by a flak-jacketed, helmeted government agent armed with an automatic rifle. The line of appropriate and acceptable coverage is gradually moving. And this expanded media coverage is increasingly being paid for by what *Advertising Age* columnist Bob Garfield calls "advertrocities"—Benetton's dying AIDS patients and dead Bosnian soldiers and the heroin chic of Calvin Klein ads. We know more, we see more. As cultural critic Kalle Lasn notes:

> I think these ads are operating on a deeper level than even the advertisers themselves know or understand. Their cumulative effect is to erode our ability to empathize, to take social issues seriously, to be moved by atrocity. They inure us to the suffering (or joy) of other people. They engender an attitude of malaise toward the things that make us most human. We pretend not to care as advertisers excavate the most sacred parts of ourselves, and we end up actually not caring.[15]

Faced with this onslaught of information and commercial imagery—much of it of questionable validity and taste—what are we to do? Simply put, we tune out. We are simultaneously better "informed" but less aware. We are becoming both cynical and confused. As media critic Neil Postman, author of *Amusing Ourselves to Death: Public Discourse in the Age of Show Business,* notes:

> Information has become a form of garbage. It comes indiscriminately—directed at no one in particular, disconnected from usefulness, we are swamped by information, have no control over it and do not know what to do with it. And the reason we don't is that we no longer have a coherent conception of ourselves, our universe and

our relation to one another and our world. Our defenses against the information glut have broken down; our information immune system is inoperable.[16]

What do consumers want in this environment of information overload? *Clarity, ease, certainty,* and *trust.* We need someone we can trust and rely on to clarify our options, to simplify our choices, to allow us to feel satisfaction with our decisions. Once again, this presents an opportunity for businesses to redefine value by recognizing the importance of values, to change the game for the mutual benefit of their customers and themselves.

The pursuit of commercial excellence is difficult even in settled times. Today's environment, with its radical time compression, increasing personal pressures, stress, ever-intrusive media, nonstop parade of technological and communication innovations, and lack of clearly communicated institutional values, has birthed a new consumer, a consumer we call the "instavidual." Instaviduals define value in direct relationship to a moment of personal need. Their need sets vary from day to day and even from hour to hour. Instaviduals demand that businesses be relevant to them, but their attribute preferences change as frequently as the weather. Catch this consumer at 7 A.M. and an acceptable product may take the form of an Egg McMuffin. But catch that same instavidual at 7 P.M. and an acceptable meal looks like a filet mignon and a double extra-dry martini at Morton's of Chicago. While most businesses insist on putting customers into traditional boxes suitable for longitudinal studies, instaviduals either defy definition or meet multiple definitions.

The convergence of these myriad forces has also created a new market in its wake, a market characterized by the emergence of a new consumer need set—one never seen by business and therefore consistently not addressed. We're not arguing the need to address the social issues raised in this discussion. These issues have been identified and potential remedies covered exhaustively in books such as Robert Putnam's *Bowling Alone: The Collapse and Revival of American Community* or Robert William Fogel's *The Fourth Great Awakening and the Future of Egalitarianism.* The purpose of this book is to define and articulate a coherent strategy for creating enhanced consumer value, and to put forth a methodology for implementing operational changes to allow that new strategy to come to life.

As we see it, the situation can be summarized as follows:

SOCIETAL SITUATION	HUMAN CONDITION	HUMAN NEED
Societal devolution	Inability of traditional institutions to adequately reflect fundamental human values	"Fortify, reinforce, ratify my personal values"
Increasing inability to keep pace with daily life	Increase in stress, guilt, anxiety	"Help me survive psychologically and emotionally"
Proliferation of information and communication technologies	Informed and aware, but cynical and confused consumers	"Clarify my options, allow me to feel satisfied with my choices"

Because consumers' personal needs and values are not being fully addressed, they are potential defectors who will take their business to competitors quickly and often. How else can we explain the initial consumer attraction to companies like Yahoo!, Amazon.com, eBay, and Dell Computer Corp.? They created a business model more in tune with what customers want and need: "Make it easy for me to find what I want, save me time, provide reasonable price value, deliver it where I ask, give me the opportunity to interact if (and only if) I want to, allow me to shop exactly when I want to, show me that you pay attention, and learn more and more about my tastes and preferences as you do business with me."

These companies teach us an important lesson, one that ought to frighten traditional consumer businesses. Of course, this is both an opportunity and a threat. But for many businesses that have been operating against a different consumer need set for years, the cost of switching, in terms of dislocation and risk, is quite high. It is always difficult to abandon a business model that has been successful. But, as we've shown, times have changed. And for those companies that move fast and early, an opportunity exists to drive new business into the white space created by this shift.

The solution to meeting the new need set of today's consumer is embodied in our construct of Consumer Relevancy, which can be defined simply as driving top-line growth by aligning the commercial context with realized human values. Consumer Relevancy is based upon three foundations:

1. **Human values are the contemporary currency of commerce.** In an environment where fundamental human needs are being met less and less elsewhere, businesses that address these needs are well-positioned to take shares from their competitors. Amazon, for instance, moved rapidly into a white-space opportunity by creating a technology-enabled business model that overcame the time and space constraints inherent to traditional book retailing.

2. **Human values determine commercial value.** Historically, product features and functions were the primary determinants of value in business. Build a better mousetrap, and the world will beat a path to your door. Today, product quality is table stakes, the ante in a high-stakes game of poker. While inferior quality will not be tolerated by today's consumer, product quality alone is not enough. Most cars run today, and do so consistently. Refrigerators keep food cold, stereos sound good, detergents get clothes clean, hotel rooms are clean and quiet. Consumers in mature economies expect products to perform at a given level of quality. Today, it is the human values that are displayed during the provision of goods and services that provide the opportunity for extreme differentiation, branding, and building loyalty.

    For example, Tom's of Maine's product offering parallels its target consumer's values. None of the products are tested on animals, the external packaging is all from recycled materials, and the majority of the ingredients are organic. Each tube of Tom's of Maine toothpaste is packaged with a customer story. The cost of printing and marketing these consumer messages, direct testimonials reinforcing the values of the target market, are treated as a production cost. The values of the company's customers appear as an ingredient cost on the balance sheet, just like wintergreen and spearmint.

3. *Values* **are more important than value in the eyes of today's consumer.** There was a time when most people derived their sense of self from traditional institutions. When things were less hectic, when we weren't as well-informed (or overloaded), the worth of a commercial transaction was defined largely by the product or service itself. Of course, it mattered how it was delivered, but that paled in comparison to the attributes of the product or service. This is no longer true. Today, differentiation is found in the manner in which the product or service is rendered, viewed through the lens of human values.

These three foundations give rise to the central argument that anchors the concept of Consumer Relevancy, and is the reason this book is critically important to business and business leaders. Right here and right now, the convergence we have described has fundamentally changed the definition of value when consumers search for providers of goods and services. Context has overtaken content as the primary driver of consumer value. It is within the context of any commercial transaction that the representation of human values can be found. Consumer Relevancy defines the new competitive battleground and offers a blueprint for future success.

In the course of writing this book, we found many examples of how Consumer Relevancy can translate first into strategy and later into tactical execution. But moving from theory to strategy requires that a company listen to its customers, its potential customers, its management team, its line managers, and even its suppliers to understand where it—and its competitors—are in a market. Once that assessment has been completed, a company needs to decide on which attribute it will dominate and which it will use as a differentiator. Trying to be all things to all people, or at least marketing "excellence" across all five attribute areas, is one of the most persistent and chronic ills affecting modern business. This impulse—and all its attendant symptoms—is at the heart of the myth of excellence. Great companies intuitively understand the seductive dangers of the myth and go to great lengths to define their competitive position by clearly selecting one of the attributes and then demonstrating how they dominate on that attribute even when there is little actual difference in the physical characteristics of the products and services themselves.

Gateway and Dell computers, for example, are essentially the same machines. But Dell chooses to dominate on service, while Gateway has focused on enhancing the customer's experience. Wal-Mart and Target compete in the same channel, but where Wal-Mart dominates on price, Target chooses to dominate on product. Northwest and Southwest Airlines both fly from Detroit to Chicago, but Southwest successfully competes against Northwest by stressing price and experience against Northwest's more frequent flight schedule and increased access. Morton's of Chicago and McDonald's both sell beef, but Morton's does it by stressing the product and experience while McDonald's leverages access. Sony and Bose both make audio components and dominate on product. But where Sony differentiates in the access arena, Bose chooses to differentiate on experience. Each of these companies has assessed its market, analyzed its values, and selected what it believes are the most effective attributes to dominate and differentiate itself in the minds of its customers. Endgame never occurs, because customer values are a perpetually moving target. Even the most effective attribute domination and differentiation strategy today needs to be rigorously reexamined tomorrow.

So how does a company construct a values-based market offering? The first step is to look past the offering (the product or service) it is selling and to begin thinking on a customer's terms. Saturn, for example, understood that buying an automobile was relatively simple compared with finding an automobile company and dealer you could trust. Understanding that most people placed an increasingly high value on honesty, fairness, directness, and accurate descriptions allowed Saturn to essentially "reverse engineer" from a values platform to a market offering.

We can't swear to it, but we bet somebody at Southwest Airlines had spent more than one afternoon watching the faces of passengers marching past the relative comfort of the first-class cabin into the more utilitarian confines of coach. The customer's need to be respected and treated as an equal became a platform of the external face of Southwest. When a customer gets on one of their planes she knows that her seat is no better or worse than any other seat on the plane.

And perhaps the greatest example of values-based marketing occurred when Johnson & Johnson voluntarily recalled every box of Tylenol from retail sale in the wake of a tampering scare. The company understood the value of "walking the talk" of trust and concern for the customer.

Finding out what values you ought to embody is relatively easy: You just have to talk to your customers in their language and be open to what they're saying. And once you've got the message, it must form the cornerstone of everything you do that touches the customer—no exceptions, no sacrifices to a clever marketing idea du jour, no panic when sales drop in a quarter. Saturn always sells trust, concern, and respect. Southwest always sells respect, equality, and fun. And Johnson & Johnson has come to stand for the ultimate in respect and integrity no matter what the cost. But knowing what your customers' values are and building them into your offering is not enough. They need to be reinforced internally as well as externally every business day. To build values-based offerings, you must first build a values-based culture. And that is much easier said than done, especially in highly competitive industries.

The incorporation of values is the cornerstone of Consumer Relevancy, and in the next chapter, we'll take an in-depth look at the Consumer Relevancy model and see how you can apply the concept in your company.

CHAPTER 2

The New Model for Consumer Relevancy

SO WHAT DOES SUCCESSFUL Consumer Relevancy look like in action? Consider this story. When we were working on this book, Ryan was walking through the aisles of a Superquinn supermarket, just outside Dublin. Here's what happened:

Executives in several industries had told us that Superquinn might just be the best example of a service-centric company in the world, and so I found myself in Ireland walking through one of their stores. I wasn't pushing a cart, or carrying a basket, or being escorted by a company official. I was just one more male shopper wandering through the store with the kind of lost-sheep look so common to men who find themselves in a supermarket. "American?" the young clerk stocking the cheese case asked as I passed her. "Yes, but how did you know?" I answered. "It's the shoes," she said. "The shoes always give you away.

"So, what's your name?" she asked, introducing herself, "and what brings you to our store?" Trying to keep my research at least quasi-objective, I told her I was in Ireland on business and had wanted to see as much of the country, and how people lived, as I could. "Do you like Irish cheese?" she asked. I said that I had only had a few Irish cheeses, and those were generally well-aged. "Well, Ryan, tell me, what kind of cheeses do you like?" she asked. "Bleu cheeses," I found myself responding. "Have you ever tried a Cashell Bleu?" she asked. "No," I said, "at least not a fresh one." Without hesitation, she reached into the case, grabbed a cheese, brought out a knife, and cut open the package so I could sample the contents. "Now, if you like a little sharper bleu, there's this," she said, grabbing a second cheese from the case. The second cheese was joined by a third and a fourth and a fifth. Our conversation was drawing a small crowd, as good conversations often do in Ireland.

"This is Ryan from America, here to do business and learn about our cheeses," the clerk said to any and all in earshot. "I've given him a bit of this one and that. Here, go ahead and try a bit yourself." Soon, there we were, a community of cheese eaters. No strangers here. We all knew each other's names and what we did for a living. I learned about their relatives in America, and they learned about the Irish branches of my family. It wasn't the cheeses or the store that brought us together, although they were important elements. It wasn't even the (justifiably) legendary sense of Irish hospitality. It was the ability of a retail clerk stocking a cheese case to notice something about me as an individual and parlay that observation into the beginning of a personalized relationship, reinforced by the presence of some of the best bleu cheese on earth.

This would be a good story if it stopped there, but it didn't. Later that week, Ryan sat with Patrick Campbell, chairman of Campbell Bewley Group, an Irish-based manufacturer of quality teas and coffees and an operator of a variety of foodservice outlets from full-line restaurants to coffee bars and kiosks. They were discussing Campbell's marketing strategy for his teas and coffees. "We're careful where we sell," he told Ryan. "That's why we're so pleased that Superquinn carries our goods. We think it says something about us that we're sold through their stores." We know exactly what

he meant. Superquinn clearly dominates on service and just as clearly differentiates itself on product. Superquinn unconsciously embodies the principles of Consumer Relevancy. What our visits to Ireland, the Netherlands,
Belgium, England, the Caribbean, and France confirmed was that
Consumer Relevancy has global and not just U.S. application.

Why? Well, from the seller's point of view, the relationships between
consumers and businesses haven't changed all that radically from the days
of the nineteenth-century country store and its urban equivalent to the
twenty-first century's cybersouk. After all, the country-store operator had
perfect knowledge of his or her customers, often sold without the exchange
of hard currency, and in many cases delivered—essentially the same goals
of today's cybercapitalists. So if things haven't changed that much, why do
consumers seem so upset? Part of the answer is that while the essential
transactional infrastructure (the five basic attributes of commerce—access,
experience, price, product, and service) appears the same over time, the
covering of that infrastructure (the specific meaning of those attributes at
any given point) has been radically transformed.

Let's look at what this means for each of the five attributes.

1. **The mythology of price: Business brags about cheap, but people
   value honest.** One of the reasons we initially thought the survey
   respondents must be wrong ought to serve as a wake-up call for all
   companies. Time and time again, in our phone surveys and face-to-
   face interviews, consumers—regardless of income level, geographic
   location, and/or education—told us they were less concerned with
   getting the lowest price than they were with getting a fair and honest price. What does that mean? It means they want a price that is
   consistent and that doesn't appear to have been artificially increased
   or decreased at the expense of other things they want to buy. We've
   found whole industries guilty of practicing Consumer Irrelevancy in
   their pricing practices. Exhibit A: the American telephone industry.
   Consumers want some assurance that they've selected a fair and honest rate plan. Instead, they're bombarded with dueling verbiage
   about minutes, caller networks, multistate plans, and meaningless

features and options. Most customers don't care that they can get the lowest price available for calling their great-aunt Sadie on Sundays after midnight provided they call Sadie from Ohio when she's in Alaska on the fourth Sunday of any month starting with "J"—they just want to be able to understand their phone bill.

2. **Setting the service bar: Walk your talk.** Time after time, we have seen companies falling over themselves to provide "value-added" services for consumers in one area, while failing to provide basic service in others. Perhaps it's the hotel that offers weary business travelers discounted weekend family packages but gives away guaranteed rooms or loses reservations. Or consider the do-it-yourself store that offers classes in Renaissance parquetry but won't let you return a wrong-sized washer. All those special services mean little if a company can't successfully serve customers' basic, everyday requests. No matter how much you try to pad an offer, any customer knows one size never fits all. They don't want to be buried under a pile of bells and whistles. They want to be recognized as individuals and know that the company they're doing business with is willing to customize its offerings to their individual needs. Options don't mean much if you can't find the basic service you want.

3. **Access: It ain't just location anymore.** Yesterday, access meant a right-hand turn into a bank's parking lot or having gas stations on all four corners of a busy intersection. Today, consumers care more about navigation—physical and psychological—than mere geographic location. They don't want to be confused or slowed down by clever and elaborate layouts or trapped by forced traffic patterns into a human imitation of sheep in a slaughter chute. Getting to a business is far less important than getting what they want once they've arrived. Offer too much in the way of selection or distraction, and you run the risk of making the most important aspect of access— the customer's ability to actually locate and buy—too high a hurdle. This helps explain the success of e-ticket machines in airports and

the growing popularity of "Fast Pass" systems at parks like Disney World.

4. **The real meaning of experience: Intimacy matters.** One of the assumptions we made—and, we believe, one that is made by many others—was to equate "experience" with "entertainment." However, consumers across the globe told us they were looking for something quite different from business. According to these consumers, entertainment doesn't even make the top 15 on the list of important issues. What *do* they want? They want respect, to be treated like a human being, and to be offered unique products or services. We believe this is the strength of high-tech manufacturers like Gateway, which routinely sells products configured to specific customer needs rather than pushing only the most expensive computer system available. This approach of treating customers like human beings rather than as human purchase orders stands in stark contrast to the proverbial and stereotypical car salesman who tries to trick people into buying far more car than they need.

5. **Product: Your best just isn't good enough.** There's bad news here for branders—especially mid-range branders. Just because you believe your products are the best doesn't necessarily mean they dominate a customer's consciousness. Despite our initial misguided belief about how consumers view price, we thought we understood what they wanted out of product. Naturally, we assumed everyone would want "the best" (recognizing that "best" is relative, subjective, and personal)—or, at the very least, something approximating the highest quality. Once again, we were wrong. While a few consumers—notably Internet shoppers—said they buy only the best they can find, the vast majority of consumers indicated that consistently good product was more desirable than a single best offering. A number of our direct interviews said they were unlikely to spend the extra money on top-of-the-line products if they perceived that a less expensive item is likely to be "good enough." The overriding

sentiment is that, at any given price point, there is a "band of accept-ability"—i.e., the quality of products or services must fall within a certain range to be acceptable to consumers.

It Doesn't Have to Be That Way: A Hierarchy of Interaction

Consumers are sending a clear message: "If you give me what I need (honesty, respect, and trust), I will give you what you desire from me (my loyal patronage)." Explain it using any sociological or psychological theory that makes you comfortable, but the simple fact is that people are so hungry for basic human values, values they're not experiencing in their day-to-day lives, that they will flock to a company that provides them. This need for trust is so strong that it transcends the boundaries of the physical store, the pages of a catalog, and the bandwidth of the Internet. It is fundamental to any successful consumer business, from the largest online bookstore to a local coffeehouse, from an airline to a bank, from a mom-and-pop restaurant in Brooklyn to a national health-care carrier.

A consumer's interaction with sellers operates at one of three potential levels: accept, prefer, and seek (Table 2.1). There is also a negative level—one "below ground"—an area of deep distrust and loss of credibility, a space in which no company wants to operate. Ask consumers and they will tell you of those times when they suffered the disrespect, dehumanization, and lack of accommodation at the hands of companies—even entire industries. Where a company falls in this "hierarchy of interaction" depends on how well it listens to its consumers, truly understands what they are looking for, and satisfies their needs.

How does a company solidify a relationship with its consumers and work its way up the hierarchy of interaction? Most of all, it requires a new way of thinking—in short, a new concept of Consumer Relevancy, one that allows for differentiation, without attempting to do everything at world-class levels. Understanding Consumer Relevancy begins with an understanding of the interaction that exists among consumer behavior, business strategy, and the resulting relationship at each of the three levels.

TABLE **2.1**

Hierarchy of Interaction:
What Consumers Are *Really* Saying About How
They Want to Interact with Companies

Attributes

LEVEL	ACCESS	EXPERIENCE	PRICE	PRODUCT	SERVICE
III: Consumer Seeks the Company (Dominate)	Give me a **solution;** help me out in a bind.	Establish **intimacy** with me by doing something no one else can.	Be my **agent;** let me trust you to make my purchases.	**Inspire** me with an assortment of great products I didn't know about.	**Customize** the product or service to fit my needs.
II: Consumer Prefers the Company (Differentiate)	Make the interaction **convenient** for me.	**Care** about my needs and me.	Be fair and **consistent** in your pricing. I'm not necessarily after the lowest price.	Be **dependable** in your selection and in-stock position, so I can rely on you when I'm in a bind.	**Educate** me when I encounter a product or a situation I don't understand.
I: Consumer Accepts the Company (Operate at Par)	Make it **easy** for me to find what I need, get in and out in a hurry.	**Respect** me; treat me like a human being.	Keep the prices **honest;** don't jack them up or offer big savings when there are none.	Be **credible** in your product and service offerings.	**Accommodate** me; bend over backward sometimes to show me you care.
Consumer Underworld	Block my way, hassle me, keep me waiting, make it hard for me to get in and out.	Dehumanize me; disrespect me; ignore my needs.	Be inconsistent, unclear, or misleading in your pricing.	Offer me poor-quality merchandise and services that I can't use.	Give me an experience I'd just as soon forget; give me a reason to tell my friends and relatives to stay away.

Level I is the threshold at which the customer says, *"I accept you. I trust you enough to buy your products and services and to consider coming back."* A basic level of *acceptance*—representing *par* for a particular market or business—needs to be established in customers' minds before they even consider a company as a default choice. If they find honest pricing, credible products, accommodating service, easy access, and the respect they believe they deserve, chances are that an opportunity exists for you to establish a comfortable interaction with a consumer, one that can lead to stronger ties and some degree of loyalty. Sounds obvious, until you remember the bank branch that never seems to have fewer than twenty-five people in line, or the website that seems to take days to move from page to page, or the thousands of stores across the country that are happy to sell you something but make you feel invisible if you try to bring it back. We could go on, but—based on your own experience—you probably get the picture.

In a Level I relationship, consumers are willing to make their *routine purchases* from the company. At this level, the relationship is transactional: The consumer needs something, the company carries an acceptable offering, and the exchange of cash for goods or services is made. This level conveys little sense of loyalty either way. The consumers may never buy from that company again, and the company doesn't necessarily care.

At *Level II,* you have an opportunity to serve the consumer, who says, *"I prefer your store, products, and services, and—all things being equal—I will probably make my purchases there."* Once the door is opened to doing business with a consumer, the next hurdle is to get that customer to *prefer* doing business with you. In the vocabulary of the instaviduai, what can be done to encourage the consumer to drive the additional half-mile through heavy traffic to your store, wait patiently in line to be served by employees he or she has come to know and like, and look to your company as providing consistently good values and fair prices? At Level II, consumers actually prefer one store or brand over another. This happens when the company makes access to its facilities, product, or website convenient, shows respect on a personal level, clearly presents consistent prices, offers reliable, good-quality products, and is able to educate a consumer on how a product or service works.

To hit Level II, you must find ways to *differentiate* yourself from your competitors. Think for a minute about how you view your own suppliers or how you, as a consumer, relate to the companies competing for your business. Now try to see consumers as purchasing agents for their own lives, and think about how you could become one of the two or three "preferred vendors." What would your criteria look like? How would you bid a household's needs? There are plenty of options: Consider Blockbuster Video's promise to never let a customer go home disappointed because she wasn't able to find the video she came to rent. Or it may be a pledge like Burger King's to let customers have a Whopper any way they choose. That pledge was so compelling that it forced McDonald's to eventually follow suit by offering custom-built Big Macs. Or it could take a form such as AT&T's introduction of the Digital One program, which broke new ground in the cellular-phone industry by being the first to offer flat-rate pricing with no long-distance or "roaming" charges. Or think about Sears' commitment to buyers of Craftsman tools to unconditionally guarantee the products for the life of the tool, even if that exceeds the life of generations of owners.

Level II companies have distinguished themselves from market competitors and built a degree of trust sufficient to cause consumers to prefer doing business with them. There is an *affinity* between consumer and company that causes the consumer to recall the company's name or products at his moment of need. The consumer may also think of two or three other companies offering similar or even identical products, but they're rejected as quickly as they're recalled.

At *Level III,* the consumer says to the company, *"I trust you so completely that I will not only seek you out among all the other options, but I will also give you the authority to edit my options for me."* This is the ideal state, in which the consumer not only prefers one company over another but also will actively *seek* out the company of choice. At this level, consumers will gladly wait six months for delivery of the new-model BMW, will refuse to buy kitchen gadgets at any store but Williams-Sonoma, or won't drink coffee not brewed by Starbucks.

Of course, all consumer businesses want to find some way to differentiate themselves from their competition. That's more or less the first commandment of business: Unless thou hast something better or different to offer, keep it to thyself. The most successful companies, though, don't stop at just differentiating themselves. They find ways to *dominate,* to further separate themselves from the pack, causing them to be the one choice that pops into the consumer's mind at the moment of need. Successfully transforming differentiation into market domination, these companies become the definitive source of goods and services. For example, by offering easy access to a range of products and services that no other bookseller had before, Amazon became, in the minds of millions of consumers, the default retailer of books on the Internet. The Home Depot has grown to be the largest home-center retailer in the United States, providing an impressive array of products backed by a strong service orientation.

It is at this level that a company has the opportunity to move consumers to *lifestyle* relationships. Level III companies capture consumers' imagination so completely that those shoppers no longer even think about other options. In Level III relationships, the company becomes the source that customers appoint to make all the right decisions in light of their unique lifestyles.

Getting to Level III doesn't just happen. Companies achieve this degree of authority only through constant monitoring of consumer interactions at a level of detail that other companies find too granular. Of course, a number have done it, including Wal-Mart, America Online, Southwest Airlines, Lexus, Eddie Bauer, Citibank, eBay, Nokia, and Dell. These companies understand the new definitions of consumer value.

Naturally, the goal for any consumer business interested in long-term growth and profitability is to move up the levels as much as is practical and desirable. Few companies turn away the occasional shopper, but a company can't rely on "accidental" customers to increase market share over the long haul. Even at the preference level, where a particular business is one of a few options a consumer would consider, there's the risk that the company won't be chosen most of the time. While being a "preferred vendor" gives you a leg up, it doesn't guarantee growth.

The only way to ensure the strength and viability of your company for the foreseeable future is to fully dominate your market and build a lifestyle relationship with consumers who seek you out. If you sell "business casual" clothing, such as Eddie Bauer, you want to be the only place consumers go for slacks, blazers, and sweaters. If you are a purveyor of fine automobiles, like BMW, you want to capture all of your target consumers' vehicle purchases over the course of their lives. And if you're a provider of cellular-phone services, like AT&T, you want there to be no other options for cell-phone users—ever. At this level, you want your brand and products to be so closely defined with how consumers live their lives that the individuals wouldn't be caught dead wearing, driving, eating, drinking, or using anything else.

Creating a Consumer-Relevant Company

So how do you find the road to this commercial Promised Land? It starts with being seen as relevant by the consumer on his or her own terms and ends only when that relevancy translates into a lifestyle relationship. As we stated in Chapter 1, perhaps the most significant insight to come out of our research concerns the myth of excellence. Truly consumer-relevant companies don't attempt to dominate in every customer-centric category— price, service, access, experience, and service. Great companies learn to overcome the constant temptation to strive for universal excellence. You must decide on which attribute you want to compete.

In addition to choosing a primary attribute, companies that are highly relevant to consumers select a second attribute that serves as a strong complement and helps them further differentiate themselves from competitors. This kind of pairing explains how Target has been able to successfully coexist with Wal-Mart.

Finally, the most successful consumer businesses recognize that regardless of how well they perform on their primary and secondary attributes, they cannot fall below industry par on the other three. Many companies often overlook this critically important point. For instance, a retailer that has the best service and a broad selection of products will ultimately fail if its operating hours are too short, its stores are too hard to locate, or its prices are too high. Similarly, a restaurant where "everybody knows your name" and does a good job of satisfying special dietary preferences will struggle if its food quality is not up to snuff. Catalog retailer Lands' End has fallen into this trap. One of the most successful apparel merchants through the 1980s because of its superior service and ability to offer honest, consistent pricing, the company has fallen on hard times recently because of its "unexciting inventory" and "unattractive merchandise."[1]

The overriding message here is that successful companies understand that value, in consumers' minds, is the intangible "sum total" of a business's performance on all five attributes. There is an aggregate minimum threshold that every company must meet across the board to be successful. This threshold, though, is not the same for all companies. In mature markets or industries, the value threshold is much higher than in emerging industries or among companies with innovative business models.

The traditional retail grocery business, for example, is one of the most mature industries in the country. Because of their years of experience in shopping at supermarkets, consumers have high expectations for grocers in all areas of operations and have little tolerance for slippage. They expect competitive prices, ease of shopping and checkout, a wide selection of fresh products, friendly service, and a pleasant shopping experience. But that doesn't mean that grocery retailers must excel in all five areas; rather, it means that the bar for what constitutes the minimum acceptable performance in those areas is significantly higher than it is for, say, online booksellers. In this emerging market, consumers are more apt to give merchants some leeway in their performance because they recognize that the novelty of the business model carries some inherent challenges that will take time to address. This helps explain why the same consumers that do not tolerate inattentive or surly grocery-store employees put up with less-than-stellar customer service from their favorite online retailers.

But no honeymoon lasts forever, and even online companies have learned that ecstatic abandon has left the love affair that consumers initially had with Web retailing. The holiday shopping season of 1999 will be remembered as the beginning of the end for many Internet companies that—literally—couldn't fulfill their promises to customers. Thousands of consumers were furious when the presents they ordered from online merchants failed to make it under the tree by Christmas morning. Many of those who did receive their orders and found that they weren't quite what they wanted faced a daunting task in returning the merchandise to retailers that lacked a clear and easy-to-follow return policy. The point is that while consumers could overlook shortcomings in service among Web merchants in the early days, they now believe companies have had enough time to shake the bugs out of the system.

The Attribute Value Matrix

To illustrate the interplay among the five value attributes, and to demonstrate how a successful company can use these attributes to create unquestioned value for its target consumer, we have assigned a numerical value to each of the attributes. These values represent a company's allocation of resources and operational efforts to achieve either a threshold level of acceptance at which it seeks to meet market competition on an attribute (a 3), a level of differentiation where the company hopes to use an attribute to persuade consumers to prefer its products or services (a 4), or a level of market dominance where the consumer refuses to buy anywhere else (a 5).

When applying the model, there are four simple rules to keep in mind:

1. A perfect score across the five attributes is 5 (domination) on one attribute, 4 (differentiation) on a second attribute, and 3 (acceptable) on the remaining three.

2. Anything less than a 3 on any attribute is not sustainable and will cause brand damage.

3. Domination or differentiation on more than one attribute is excessive and is not economically optimal, resulting in companies leaving money on the table.

4. The definition of a 3 (acceptable) as it relates to any of the attributes can continually change, as consumer expectations change. Failure to keep pace and perform to the level of these changing expectations can cause the score to drop below 3.

Let's look at some real-world examples of how successful companies have used various combinations of the value attributes to compete in very different ways. We constructed a table (Table 2.2) in which the primary attribute is located on the horizontal axis and the secondary attribute on the vertical axis. We have placed leading consumer companies and brands at intersections in the grid to paint a picture of the competitive landscape. In actual client work, we've found that some of the most enlightening discussions occur when a company's executives sit together and try to place themselves and their competition on a blank version of this chart. In our experience, it almost always raises some interesting executive-alignment issues.

We've also asked groups of employees (executive office, middle management, and front-line troops) to perform this same exercise independently of one another, and then we've compared the results. Invariably, we've found that they appear to be working for several different companies and competing across several different markets—a signal that the company has critical internal communication and policy issues.

The point of the grid is not to be definitive about a particular company's strategy; it is to show how the pairing of certain primary and secondary attributes can give a company a commanding lead over its competitors. These placements represent values consumers believe the companies are offering (which *should* correspond with what the companies think they provide). By the way, whether we're right about all of our placements, and whether you agree with those placements, is not the issue. In fact, we may be wrong about some of them. The crucial point is that the people who matter—customers and consumers—have definite opinions, and our work to date tells us that many executives are ignorant of how their companies are perceived, how their competition is perceived, and what to do to create needed differentiation in a crowded, competitive field.

Wal-Mart, for example, was seen by most consumers in our survey as a retailer that primarily offers consistently low prices, a quality mirrored by the company's longstanding marketing slogan, "Always low prices. Always." Secondarily, the company prides itself on carrying a wide assortment of brand-name products—not necessarily the best products available,

TABLE 2.2

Primary and Secondary Attributes of Selected Companies and Brands

		PRIMARY ATTRIBUTE				
		PRICE	SERVICE	PRODUCT	EXPERIENCE	ACCESS
SECONDARY ATTRIBUTE	PRICE		Geico, Lands' End, Dell, Gold's Gym	Target, Staples, Kohl's, Dixons, Mazda, Honda (car), Maytag	Chuck E. Cheese, Ikea, Club Med, Gateway, Southwest Airlines, Gourmet Garage	Avon, E* Trade, Tide
	SERVICE	AutoZone, Tesco, Craftsman tools, Saturn		The Home Depot, Ferragamo, Gucci, Record Time	Four Seasons, Kraft, Peapod, Canyon Ranch	McDonald's, Webvan, Progressive Corp., Circles, Gerber
	PRODUCT	Wal-Mart, Ames, Costco, Red Roof Inns, Zara, Suave	Circuit City, Citibank, Allstate, Boots, Superquinn, Chevy Trucks, Continental Airlines		REI, Midwest Express, Nike Stores, The Disney Store, Harrods, Bewley's, BMW, Rolex	Amway, Walgreens, Yahoo!, Amazon.com, Coke, Kodak, CNN, Gatorade
	EXPERIENCE	Honda Goldwing motorcycles	Nordstrom, Singapore Airways, Hong Kong Suits	Williams-Sonoma, Best Buy, Pier 1, Tumi, Tylenol, Bose		AOL, Hallmark
	ACCESS	Dollar General, Family Dollar, Charles Schwab, Priceline, Visa, Carrefour, Casio	Dell Computer, American Express, M&M Mars (online)	Sony, Frito-Lay, 3M, Eddie Bauer, Chase Bank, Whirlpool, Lowe's	iVillage.com, Starbucks, Marlboro	

but ones that consumers consider desirable and important. On the rest of the attributes, Wal-Mart performs as people would expect any mass merchandiser to perform.

Recognizing it would have a difficult time competing directly against Wal-Mart, discounter Target—which operates in approximately the same arena—has chosen to do something a little different. One of the few companies that has managed to stand up to the challenge of the Arkansas juggernaut, Target, like Wal-Mart, emphasizes the same two attributes—price and product—but Target focuses primarily on product and secondarily on price. Yes, Target's prices tend to be lower than specialty stores, but they aren't as low as Wal-Mart's. However, its product assortment tends to be much more trendy than that of Wal-Mart, attracting a shopper who's a bit more stylish and fashion-conscious.

According to Robyn Waters, vice president of trend merchandising at Target, the company's ability to combine "hip design with value pricing" is what sets the retailer apart from others. "We are very focused on making the budget dress or the budget glass the best it could be—in its style, quality, merchandising, and marketing—or we don't bother," she noted. Added Roger Goddu, a former Target executive, "It all comes back to trend merchandising. [Target] is viewed as a vogue place to shop for fashion at value prices. Their customers are more into fashion trends than Wal-Mart's, and they can coexist with Wal-Mart on this basis."[2]

A similar contrast exists in the do-it-yourself home-center arena, where The Home Depot is the reigning champ and Lowe's the strong challenger. Early in the game, The Home Depot staked out its competitive ground by focusing primarily on a broad assortment of nearly every type of hardware, lumber, and gardening product one could need, and secondarily on offering superior service. While initial advertising promoted low prices, The Home Depot quickly set the bar for service in this segment, with its hiring of associates who actually knew something about the products sold (or training them well if they didn't); its policy that any shopper asking for the location of an item should be led, not pointed, to the spot by the associate; and the offering of in-store seminars and workshops for customers on myriad home-improvement topics.

Lowe's, on the other hand, has chosen to emphasize access over service, while maintaining the same primary focus on products. The product assortment at a Lowe's store is similar to that at The Home Depot. But the company stresses the fact that it is easy to find those items, thanks to clear, visible pricing and wide aisles—the key characteristics of access.

Striking the Balance

Finding the right combination of access, experience, price, product, and service is not only critical, but it's also extremely difficult to achieve. However, as we explore later in the book, many successful businesses, such as Gourmet Garage, Dollar General, Best Buy, and Irish grocery chain Superquinn, have achieved that delicate balance. Each has elected to excel in one attribute, differentiate in a second, and maintain an acceptable level of performance in the other three. Their success hinges on building and maintaining a rock-solid relationship with consumers, one grounded in trust and mutual respect.

Wal-Mart: Theory into Practice

When you take a closer look at what consumers consider important, you begin to see an emerging pattern of basic and, one might argue, essential human values—which serves as the foundation of our new model for Consumer Relevancy. So who does it right? Our research tells us the answer is a resounding "Wal-Mart." This mega-merchant is a classic price/product retailer, with a 5, 4, 3, 3, 3 profile across price, product, service, access, and experience.

As part of our survey, we asked consumers to name their favorite retailer in five principal segments (grocery, general merchandise, drug and convenience, specialty, and consumer direct). We also asked them to vote for the best overall retailer in America. It shouldn't be much of a surprise that Wal-Mart dominated the general merchandise channel, but what was most interesting was the chain's ranking in other segments. Wal-Mart placed first in three categories—grocery, general merchandise, and overall—second in the specialty retailer category, and third in the drug and convenience segment. The votes weren't even close in the overall category, with Wal-Mart outdistancing its nearest competitor by nearly 400 votes.

There are many potential reasons for Wal-Mart's dominance in our survey, not to mention the real world. One could credit its highly effective supply chain, the breadth and depth of its databases, or its phenomenal clout and buying power, to name a few. Of course, the consumer doesn't see most of those things, and since we asked *them* to rank Wal-Mart, we believe the company's real "secret" is essentially quite simple. Wal-Mart has risen to the top of the retail world because it knows what today's consumers value—as reflected in the new definitions of the value attributes—and understands the implications those new definitions have for the company's operations. In other words, Wal-Mart knows that consumers don't necessarily want the *lowest* prices all the time, or the absolute highest-quality products, or a store on every corner. Wal-Mart executives know that experience is, at its essence, courteous and friendly store employees, and that service means gladly and quickly accepting merchandise returns, no questions asked.

And because the company understands these definitions, Wal-Mart has made smarter decisions that have a major impact on all facets of its operations. Put another way, because Wal-Mart understands what consumers value and why, it has succeeded—like no other retailer in history—in consciously exhibiting honesty, treating customers with respect, and gaining consumers' trust. And as a result, consumers have rewarded Wal-Mart with their fierce loyalty and rabid patronage.

And just how does Wal-Mart know these things? No secret Arkansas mojo here—it talks to its customers. This is the enduring legacy of Sam Walton, who set the tone early in his career and carried it with him until the day he died. Perhaps even more important than setting the tone, Walton ensured that everyone in the Wal-Mart organization—from the executive suite to the loading dock—understood why it was important to continually talk to customers and actually listen to what they were saying. Wesley and Jimmy Wright, brothers who spent a good portion of their careers with Wal-Mart capped off with stints as vice president of merchandising and vice president of distribution, respectively, told us how Walton led his troops quietly and by example.

"Here's a typical Sam visit to a Wal-Mart store," recalled Wesley Wright. "First off, nobody at the store even knew he was coming. He flies in—doesn't have anyone pick him up—and when he gets to the store, he just walks around and talks to the associates. It sounds amazing, but he knew everything about all of the associates in the stores. When he talked with one of the cashiers, he knew her name and how much in sales she rang last month. He'd ask her how much she did this month so far, and how things were going. He showed a genuine interest in her and her job. And when it was time for lunch, he'd just grab a can of tuna and some crackers and sit in the employee lounge and talk with the associates. After lunch, he often would get on the PA and announce to the store, 'Folks, this is Sam Walton, founder of Wal-Mart. Could I get all of you to come up to the front of the store for a second—even the customers?' Then he'd sit on the floor and ask everyone, 'Tell me what's going on in the store. If this was your store, what would you do to improve it?' And he'd be there with his yellow pad, taking notes. And you know that he would make sure that what was on that notepad got taken care of, whether it was the responsibility of the store manager, merchandising, distribution, or HR."

Added Jimmy Wright: "Sam never lost touch with the consumers and the associates, no matter how big Wal-Mart got. He created a culture of unity, support, and alignment—everyone from top to bottom had the same goals. Because of the commitment to employee training and Sam's leadership, that culture continues to this day. Sam's focus was on three things—take care of the customers, take care of the associates, and have name-brand products at everyday low prices—and that focus never wavered in the twenty years I worked for him."

CHAPTER 3

Would I Lie to You?

The Overrated Importance of Lowest *Price*

ROCHELLE PUSHED BACK FROM her computer and surveyed the tiny office created by the hasty imposition of some sheets of drywall and a few two-by-fours to what would have been extra backroom space in a Speedway gas station in Eastpointe, Michigan. We thought she would be the poster child for the model "price shopper," and in some ways we were right, but in at least one critical respect we could not have been more wrong. After all, the Detroit native is a single mother of eight children, ranging in age from five to twenty, and works as a Speedway service-station manager. And with nine mouths to feed on a regular basis, not to mention a small but growing army of grandchildren and assorted relatives dropping in, price is clearly important to Rochelle. What surprised us, though, is that price is not always her primary shopping motivation.

"If the product is good quality, I will pay the price," Rochelle said. "If it is poor quality, I don't care what the price is. I won't buy it. If I get bad meat, you can guarantee I won't go back again."

What does matter to Rochelle—and to plenty of the other consumers to whom we spoke—is honesty and fairness when it comes to price and pricing policies. She related a story to us that is representative of the kind of frustration many shoppers expressed. "I went clothes shopping to buy uniforms, and they had the price in the store marked as one amount, and the advertised price was a different amount," Rochelle said. "It was advertised at $9.99 and the price marked was $14.99, and when you are buying two uniforms each for five kids, that is a lot of money. And I'm arguing with the cashier, saying this is your advertised price and you have to sell it at that, it's the law. We argued for about ten minutes before she got her boss."

What finally happened? "Her boss said, 'This is what it says in the paper, evidently it was overlooked, so give it to her at that price,'" said Rochelle. "But I won't go back to that store."

Price is perhaps the attribute most commonly abused by companies chasing the myth of excellence. Believing that price is the ultimate consumer siren song, too many businesses offer gratuitous discounts on items or services that consumers would be happy to pay full margin for. Often these unexpected—and fundamentally unwanted—price reductions come into direct conflict with fundamental customer values. Customers trust prices they believe are fair and honest, often distrusting promises of "lowest possible cost." A Neiman Marcus shopper, for example, is looking for both superior products and superior service. Offering those products or services at "40 percent off" appears disingenuous. The same holds true for mass offerings from supermarkets to drugstores. Consumers routinely told us they thought that this week's "special" was either being subsidized by other products or would result in an inflated price being charged for the discounted product when it went off sale.

As we worked our way through the research data, we encountered what at first appeared to be a paradox: Price is seemingly the easiest attribute to define and yet the hardest to accurately describe. This paradox makes price the easiest attribute to mis-define. It's all too tempting to fall into the trap of defining price in a traditional way—as the absolute cost (generally low) charged for a good or service. But the message from consumers is clear: Dominating on price doesn't necessarily mean having the absolutely lowest cost—it means consistently offering customers fair and honest prices.

This new definition ought to shatter some very basic beliefs about what it means to be a price operator and serve as a wake-up call for many, if not most, companies. While most consumer businesses appear happy to compete ferociously on the basis of cost of goods or services, content that consumers really want the lowest prices available, they're just flat wrong!

Time and time again, in our phone surveys and face-to-face interviews, consumers—regardless of income level, geographic location, and/or education—said they were much less concerned with getting the lowest price than they were with getting a fair and honest price. What does that mean? It means they want a price that is easily visible and consistent and that doesn't appear to have been artificially increased or decreased at the expense of other, related items they need to purchase. You don't have to offer these consumers a sale, but if you do, it had better be a real sale, not some predictable, inventory-reduction marketing ploy. If an item is advertised at a particular price, you'd better honor that price at the point of sale. The topic of "lowest prices" never even surfaced in the face-to-face interviews unless we brought it up, and, in most cases, the whole topic of pricing tended to take a back seat to discussions of product quality, shopping ease, and service.

Fundamental societal change has taken place when it comes to price. Absolute lowest price may continue to be important to some segment of the population, but it will be just one factor in the purchase-decision process for the vast majority of consumers. And, in many cases, price will actually be a less significant factor than it has been, because people today—and tomorrow—are more rushed and more time-starved than ever before.

Most consumers told us that they value honest pricing because they don't have time to comparison shop. Time-strapped consumers hurrying down the aisles of the local Kmart store are less likely to question whether the price of a 100-ounce bottle of Tide liquid detergent is higher or lower than what they might find at the local Winn-Dixie, Kroger, or Target store—because it would be impractical to drive to all four to find out and too time-consuming to compare prices in ad circulars.

At the same time, however, our research indicated that there is a crucial difference between price and the other four attributes, because price is the one that requires the consumer to give up something—namely, money. A business can provide access, create the experience, and offer the product and service. But, ultimately, a company can only set the price; it's the consumer who provides the cash.

Which may help explain why consumers are particularly suspicious when it comes to prices. Today's sophisticated shoppers know that each pair of hands that touches an item means an increase in the price to them. But how much of a markup is taken? Are the manufacturers' discounts really passed on to consumers, or is the company taking a big cut for itself? The real problem with the traditional high-low method of pricing is that consumers simply don't trust it. They don't feel they're being rewarded at the lower sale price but, rather, that they're being screwed at the higher regular price.

The seeds for such suspicion were sown in the 1960s, when retailers of all sorts, but chiefly department stores and grocery chains, developed a pricing strategy they hoped could help them take advantage of new or seasonal items by selling them at high prices. Seeing the latest fashion or encountering an item for the first time, consumers, who were not particularly price-conscious, would buy the item without questioning its price. It was not so much a matter of socioeconomic status as a mind-set: The very wealthy as well as the poor sometimes ignored a price tag if the item carried a lot of value and dependability for them. If a new fashion didn't sell immediately, a company could always lower the price later in the season to draw price-sensitive customers into the store. Then, through promotions and special sales, merchandise could be sold even at a loss if that meant customers bought other items at their regular high prices. This high-low pricing strategy, moreover, could take some of the worry out of inventory control, because a "hot" item would sell out in a hurry whereas a less popular one might be sold during a special promotion.

Wal-Mart changed all that when it popularized the EDLP philosophy—everyday low prices. With EDLP, the company could sell in large enough volume to have firm control over suppliers, keep prices low, and still clear a sizable profit without having to worry about sales and promotions. Moreover, the EDLP strategy would enable the company to defuse some of the distrust and confusion that high-low had engendered among consumers. With EDLP, the thinking went, consumers would understand that they get one low price consistently—maybe not the *lowest* price, but a fair price on the items they want, when they want them, without having to clip coupons or drive all over town searching for the best bargains.

What Wal-Mart understands—but most consumer businesses don't—is that price has become a multidimensional attribute that goes far beyond the simple notion of lowest price. Those dimensions consist of honesty, consistency, fairness, reliability, a range of acceptable prices, and price impression.

As we spoke with individual consumers, the following three price-related issues (listed in descending order of importance) emerged as the most critical to consumers of all demographics who shop primarily in physical stores:

- They feel that they are getting an honest price, one that hasn't been artificially inflated.
- During sales, they save significant money on their purchases.
- The companies they frequent offer leading brands at lower prices.

Few people we spoke to stressed the need for the lowest prices they could find. And when they did discuss price, most consumers listed it second or third—behind product quality and physical plant access—when identifying what makes them want to buy. "I shop at Banana Republic because they have decent prices, but also great-quality clothing," said twenty-five-year-old Oscar. Similarly, Vickie, a twenty-seven-year-old consultant, said, "The quality of the products determines where and what I buy. The price should match the quality." And Mary, fifty, noted, "I do look at prices, but that's not always the best gauge of the value of the product. It's not critical that the price is really cheap; it's just got to be reasonable."

It's this last notion—that prices just have to be reasonable—that came up again and again in our face-to-face interviews with consumers. This led us to conclude that there are many effective ways to compete against strict lowest-price businesses, a valuable lesson for companies without the size, operating scale, or margins to compete on lowest price. Prices that fall within an acceptable range tend to be viewed as "honest" by consumers, keeping in mind, of course, that this range will vary depending on factors such as product category and region of the country.

What does this mean for consumer businesses? It's very simple: High-low pricing growth strategies are dead-end streets. Price plays *might* work in the short term by increasing sales and share. But based on what consumers told us, it's a position that can't help any company create either a loyal customer base or a sustainable competitive advantage over the long haul or at scale. Why? The high-low strategy fails because it teaches consumers to distrust the business, and, ultimately, causes a business to lose share of mind and share of consumer.

In fairness, the Internet appears to be an interesting exception to the new definition of price. Online shoppers don't mind spending extra time surfing the Web for the best bargains, as evidenced by the fact that the top price-related issue among our cybershopper respondents was "Feel you are getting the lowest price available." For the time being at least, the online shopper sees the Internet as one big global bazaar. Priceline.com and its "name your own price" mantra, eBay with its frenzied auctions, and the promotional din of Web booksellers like Amazon, Barnes & Noble, and Borders have conditioned online shoppers not to settle for "paying retail." This conditioning, combined with consumers' knowledge that comparison shopping was just a few clicks away and that shipping costs would bump up the final price made the Internet a free-fire zone for low-price operators—until the second- and third-round financing fell through.

Lowest price might be the key price-related factor in the wired world, but in the physical world, a consumer business attempting to dominate on price today must recognize the multidimensional aspects of price. Even operators that intrinsically appear to be only about flat-out lowest prices understand that, in fact, it takes more to attract customers. Consider the dollar-store retailers, for example. There is a temptation to classify these stores as a channel unto themselves, with different rules than would apply to other types of consumer businesses. After all, lowest prices is what they're all about—and it's *all* they're about, right? Don't their names say it all? Dollar General, Todo a Peso, The Dollar Store, Family Dollar. You can't get much cheaper than a buck.

But, in fact, the different dimensions of the price attribute apply to these businesses as well. Consider Dollar General Corp., a Nashville-based retailer that caters to low- and fixed-income consumers. While the company's stores clearly dominate on price, they are also a paragon of pricing consistency. "There's way too much inconsistency in pricing out there today," Bob Carpenter, the company's president and chief operating officer, told us. "Our customers need to know that they can count on us every day to give them the value for their dollar that they need. So we don't have sales or specials—just consistent, honest prices on everything in the store, no matter which store you're in, no matter when you shop."

These pricing attributes don't appeal just to lower-income consumers. Dollar-type stores also populate the landscape of suburban malls, for instance, where income levels can run the gamut. "I buy arts-and-crafts supplies for two hundred kids in the Just a Buck store because I know I won't get screwed on the prices," said Barbara, who runs a suburban Connecticut day-care center.

Perhaps no consumer business understands the new definition of the price attribute better than Wal-Mart. Through its consistent, honest pricing, the giant retailer has succeeded in setting the lowest-price impression among consumers and has become a trusted purchasing agent for those shoppers. In other words, people automatically think of Wal-Mart as the price leader.

But is the impression of lowest prices reality? While most consumers believe that Wal-Mart always has the lowest prices, a market-basket comparison that we conducted proved otherwise. Our research, in which we compared the prices charged by Wal-Mart and its three major competitors in eighteen U.S. markets on a list of common items, showed that Wal-Mart was not always the lowest-priced player (Table 3.1).

On average, Wal-Mart's prices were higher than those of its competitors on one-third of the items checked. On those items for which its prices were lower, consumers could expect to save anywhere from $0.14 to $1.62 per item, although the average savings were about $0.37 per item. However, in about a third of the instances where Wal-Mart's prices were lower, the savings amounted to only $0.02 or less.

TABLE 3.1

Market-Basket Comparison of Wal-Mart Versus Major Competitors

MARKET	NUMBER OF ITEMS WHERE WAL-MART IS LESS EXPENSIVE	AVERAGE SAVINGS	TOTAL NUMBER OF ITEMS COMPARED	PERCENT OF ITEMS WHERE WAL-MART IS LESS EXPENSIVE	WHERE WAL-MART IS LESS EXPEN-SIVE, PERCENT OF ITEMS WHERE SAVINGS IS $0.02 OR LESS
Houston	11	$0.22	18	61%	36.4%
Chicago	16	0.20	22	73	37.5
Detroit	8	0.19	23	35	14.0
Salt Lake City	10	0.44	16	63	40.0
Philadelphia	13	0.45	18	72	30.8
Washington, D.C.	11	1.62	13	85	9.0
Tampa	13	0.25	22	59	30.8
Overland Park, Kan.	13	0.24	20	65	23.1
Richmond, Va.	17	0.59	19	89	6.0
Seattle	12	0.25	19	63	41.7
Charlotte	14	0.41	20	70	17.0
Phoenix	14	0.22	20	70	28.6
Denver	12	0.14	18	67	33.3
Dallas	12	0.18	18	67	25.0
Los Angeles	16	0.21	22	73	25.0
North Brunswick, N.J.	7	0.56	11	64	14.0
Atlanta	8	0.17	14	57	50.0
Minneapolis	11	0.33	19	58	18.2
Average	12	$0.37	18	66%	32.3%

In some cases, we found a wide disparity in the prices that Wal-Mart charged for the same product in different areas of the country. A Wal-Mart store in Houston, for example, sold a 100-ounce bottle of Tide detergent for $7.32. The same product went for $6.27 at a Wal-Mart in Chicago, $5.62 in Salt Lake City, and $4.48 in Detroit. But the critical point is that consumers have come to *perceive* the prices at Wal-Mart to be the "lowest," even when that is often not the case. Wal-Mart has done such a good job of winning the consumer's trust that the company has become, in effect, the pricing authority, because its EDLP focus reassures customers that no pricing games are being played. And it's not just consumers who have this impression. Time and again, groups of business executives to whom we've presented our research said that when they think of lowest prices, they think of Wal-Mart.

Now, this doesn't mean the company has high prices. You have to have *low* prices to create the impression of *lowest* price. But the bottom line is that consumers simply feel they won't get ripped off in Wal-Mart, lending credence to our belief that price impression is, in fact, more important than price itself. How did Wal-Mart get to that place in consumers' minds? It didn't get there with price—at least, not initially. After all, Sam Walton started off with just one Ben Franklin store in the middle of Bentonville, Arkansas—no scale, no way to leverage price. Instead, the company listened to consumers, delivered what they wanted, and, in the process, established a relationship based on trust. Only then was Wal-Mart able to leverage that relationship to become viewed as the price leader.

Applying the Conceptual Model to Price

Because every company's position in its industry is unique, each having operations and processes that demand a solution tailored to the company, we cannot offer a generic, cookbook approach to building a successful strategy for competing on price (or any other attribute, for that matter). Rather, the model in Figure 3.1 is based on what we believe represents a realistic response to consumers' concerns.

FIGURE **3.1**

Competing on Price

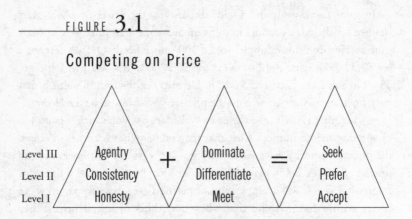

Level III	Agentry		Dominate		Seek	
Level II	Consistency	+	Differentiate	=	Prefer	
Level I	Honesty		Meet		Accept	

In our conceptual model of the consumer-company relationship, Level I represents the threshold of competing by offering honest, fair prices—the level at which consumers will *accept* you. Those prices must be viewed as competitive in the market, leading a consumer to say: *"If you don't shock me with your prices, I'll shop you."* This is the least you can offer if you want to compete on the attribute of price. Remember that customers at a brick-and-mortar store, as opposed to those shopping online, are likely to have a wider "bandwidth" of acceptable prices that they are willing to pay for a given item, but that proposition should not be construed as a license to soak customers on price. A 4.6-ounce tube of Colgate toothpaste, for instance, might range from $1.25 to $2.25, depending on the retailer, but even the most price-clueless shopper might interpret anything above that as greedy and unfair.

The success of companies such as Men's Wearhouse speaks volumes about consumers' interest in honest pricing. Men's Wearhouse, which features well-known name-brand men's apparel and accessories at prices 20 percent to 30 percent below those found on the same items at specialty and department stores, has been on a roll. The company's annual revenues have more than doubled in the past few years, to $1.187 billion in fiscal 1999. Patrons of Men's Wearhouse are not necessarily standard-issue price shoppers; rather, they are generally fairly affluent professionals who believe that department-store and boutique markups on suits, sport coats, and sweaters are unreasonable, and that Men's Wearhouse prices more accurately reflect the "real" prices of such garments.

If you are an online business, however, you have to offer prices that are lowest as well as honest. Internet-savvy consumers have too much power at their fingers to let a company get away with charging anything less than the lowest price. Such power, in fact, has gone a long way toward transforming a number of industry segments, perhaps none more so than the auto industry. Never before have consumers had the kind of pricing information at their disposal that they do now through websites such as Edmonds.com, Autobytel, and others. In the past, the sales rep at the car dealership held all the cards, but today a click of a few buttons on the Edmonds site can give car buyers complete information on what the dealer paid for the car and its options. If a dealer chooses to inflate the price of the car or an option, consumers know the percentage of inflation and can make their own decision about whether it's a reasonable profit for the dealer or blatant gouging.

At Level II, a company has to offer not only honest and competitive prices but also consistency. If you're perceived as having consistently competitive prices, consumers will *prefer* you. Consistency is the feature consumers said was more important than deep cuts in prices one week and a return to high pricing the next. Pricing consistency is a hallmark of online brokerages such as E*Trade, Schwab.com, and Quick & Reilly.com, where the price of buying or selling stock is a flat fee.

In essence, the assurance that prices will remain stable and predictable is enough to bring consumers back to your company when they need your products and services. If you offer consistent prices, consumers will come to see you as their preferred retailer.

We call Level III "agentry" to indicate that if a company goes beyond honest, consistent pricing and establishes a lasting price impression and a relationship with consumers based on trust, then consumers may abdicate to that company all responsibility for making purchases. In such a situation, consumers' faith runs so deep that they are willing, in effect, to say to the company, *"I trust you to anticipate my needs and make for me the pur-*

chases I need in your category." From the consumer's point of view, the relationship goes beyond the mere preference of Level II and assumes the quality of *this company and no other.* A company operating at Level III becomes the *pricing authority,* the company that essentially sets the price standard for its industry or segment.

If a company is perceived as the standard for low prices, consumers will *seek* out that company. This can occur even when there may be empirical evidence to prove that another company, in fact, offers lower prices. It's clear that when it comes to price, consumer behavior does not necessarily follow linearly across the attribute. As discussed earlier, Wal-Mart does not have the lowest prices on all items it carries. However, the company's customers believe that the Wal-Mart price is the *real* price, and that anything lower is just a short-term ploy by another company to entice shoppers and that ultimately it won't be sustainable.

Similarly, Dollar General has assumed the status of trusted agent among its customer base. "We've been in business for sixty years—we invented the dollar-store concept," said Bob Carpenter of Dollar General. "Our customers trust us because we have proved day in and day out that we will strive to bring them value. They know that the price we offer on an item is the absolute best we can do. And we try to never violate that trust."

The success of Dollar General offers a powerful argument for the EDLP strategy. Like Wal-Mart, Dollar General can trace its success to low and consistent prices. But, while Wal-Mart emphasizes *product* as its secondary attribute, Dollar General focuses on *access* to help differentiate its stores from the 100,000-square-foot-plus facilities operated by the Arkansas giant and other discounters. As you will see in the following case study, the results have been stellar: Revenue, gross profit, net income, and earnings per share are all up substantially since 1997, due in large part to the company's in-depth understanding of what its customers want and unwavering commitment to meeting those needs.

Case Study

Dollar General: "Value for Your Dollar"

Flannel shirt: $5. Bottle of dishwashing detergent: $1. Cotton khakis: $10. Box of presweetened cereal: $2.50.

Unbelievably low prices? You bet. Poor quality? Not at all. The flannel shirt is all-cotton and well-constructed. The dishwashing liquid is Dawn, one of the best-selling and best-known brands in the world. The cereal? Kellogg's Frosted Flakes. And the khakis? All-cotton as well, and made to the exact specifications of Levi's popular Dockers brand chinos. For most retailers, prices like these are unheard of even during sales with the deepest discounts. But for Dollar General, it's business as usual.

"You could say that we're a retailer focused on low prices, but that's really not the whole story," said president and COO Bob Carpenter. "A low price doesn't mean a thing if what you bought is cheaply made. Our customers can't afford to buy cheap things. They have to make their dollars stretch better than anybody else, so they need things that last. And that's what we give them: good quality at low prices, which we think equals value for your dollar."

It's a message reinforced by Dollar General's mission: to use its position to create a better life for everyone, many of whom rely heavily on Dollar General's ability to get them life's basics at prices that are within their budgets. "There's a real ministry when you're dedicated to selling toilet paper and bleach cheaper than anyone else in the business," said the company's CEO, Cal Turner Jr.[1]

Dollar General's growth in the past five years has been nothing short of phenomenal. Targeting the largest segment of the U.S. population—consumers with annual incomes of less than $25,000 and seniors on fixed incomes—the chain has more than doubled its number of stores since 1995 and has grown at an average rate of 20 percent to 25 percent a year. Now operating more than 5,000 outlets in twenty-four states, Dollar General generated more than $4 billion in sales in 1999—up from $2.6 billion in 1997. This would be considered a strong performance for any business, but it's especially impressive for a company that sells half its products for $1 or less and whose average register ring is $8.

The prospects for continued growth look positive, given the state of the company's target market. In fact, Carpenter believes that Dollar General has only scratched the surface of its potential customer base. "More and more people are living paycheck to paycheck these days," he said. "And it doesn't matter what the size of the paycheck is. Whether you're making $25,000 or $40,000, if you don't have a lot of extra money, you have to get real value for your dollar. Plus, as everyone knows, America's population is getting older, they're living longer, and people are retiring earlier. That means there will be more people on fixed incomes—for a longer period of time—who have to really stretch their incomes."

That's not the only factor in the company's success, however. Dollar General succeeds, first of all, because it is highly tuned to what its customers really need and operates predominantly in areas that are off the radar screen of other retailers—namely, small cities and towns in rural America. Approximately 75 percent of the company's stores are in towns with populations of fewer than 25,000 people—too small, according to Carpenter, to support the large discount chains such as Wal-Mart and Kmart. (The remainder of its stores are in urban neighborhoods that many of the major mass discounters ignore.) But most important, the company owes its success primarily to its combination of price leadership and accessibility. Dollar General dominates like no other on the value attribute of price and supports its pricing authority with a strong secondary emphasis on access.

Dollar General operates at par in terms of service and experience largely because labor cost in the channel is a significant leveler. However, the company is positioned slightly above par on product. Most of the players in what's come to be known as the "price-defined" channel have natural restrictions in the products they offer. They must be able to sell items at $1 and still maintain an acceptable margin. Of course, within that band of products, there are items with higher margin potential than others. Dollar General operates at the top end of that band due to its strong emphasis on product quality.

Consistency and Honesty in Pricing

DOLLAR GENERAL'S FORMULA FOR SUCCESS

PRIMARY ATTRIBUTE: PRICE

- Accepts only cash to eliminate credit-card fees and technology expenses.
- Does not advertise regularly, except to announce the opening of a new store.
- Features limited price points to make shopping easier for customers and accounting and inventory easy for employees.
- Carries predominantly house and private-label brands for lowest consumer prices and maximum margins.
- Focuses on fast-turning consumables to drive inventory volume.
- Operates "no-frills" stores with inexpensive fixtures and displays.
- Uses its network of district managers to help determine where to open stores and a small cadre of real-estate professionals to close lease or sale transactions quickly.
- Signs low-rent, short-term leases to minimize real-estate costs.
- Uses only basic technologies that help boost operational efficiency.
- Locates stores as close as possible to distribution centers to minimize transportation costs and reduce replenishment time.

Nobody does consistent and honest pricing better than Dollar General. At Dollar General, you won't find sales. In fact, Carpenter said, the company embraced the concept of everyday low prices well before Wal-Mart did. "We don't believe in sales," he said. "We believe in integrity in pricing, and that means that we'll guarantee that we'll offer you an item for the best price we can, given our margins—which are very small—and that every time you come into the store, you're going to get that price. Period."

What's more, he noted, "We don't play the $0.99 game with our customers. We go with even dollar price points. Our customers are smart enough not to be fooled by the sound of a supposedly cheaper price."

By taking the guesswork out of buying and, in the process, earning customers' complete trust, Dollar General has become the purchasing agent for many of its shoppers. In fact, the company considers its buyers "customer representatives" whose job it is to wrestle with suppliers for the best-quality products that the company's customers really need.[2]

Dollar General's price philosophy is rooted in ten crucial factors:

1. **Cash and carry.** Dollar General operates on a strict "cash and carry" basis, which means the company doesn't have to pay the 2 percent to 6 percent fees charged by credit-card companies. This policy also eliminates the need for credit-card verification systems (not an incidental expense when you're talking about two or three registers in each of its 5,000 stores). Besides, with an average ring of $8, there's no real need to accept credit cards.

2. **No advertising.** You'll never see a Dollar General sales circular in your mailbox or a product-oriented ad in your local newspaper. That's because the company limits its promotional spending to one special occasion: the opening of a new store. "For many retailers, their promotions account for 3 percent of their overhead costs," said Carpenter. "Not us. The only time you'll ever see an ad from Dollar General in your newspaper is when we do a grand opening for a store, to let people know that we're going to be open in a certain town at a certain location. That's it. We don't do TV, we don't do radio, and we don't advertise our products."

3. **Limited price points.** To keep things simple for customers, and for the company, Dollar General features only fourteen price points. This practice greatly reduces accounting and inventory time, not to mention headaches.

4. **Mixing of brands.** In its early days, Dollar General served as a clearinghouse for closeouts and "irregulars" from regular-price

retailers. Then, in the mid-1980s, seeking more consistency in its assortment, the company moved to only first-quality closeouts. But that still didn't allow the company to operate with the consistency it desired, and the model was changed to only first-quality items at everyday low prices.

Today, Dollar General features a mix of brands that enables the company to provide consistently good quality while keeping prices as low as possible. Approximately 10 percent to 15 percent of its items are well-known national brands, primarily in the grocery and health and beauty areas. According to Carpenter, these brands are essential to the store's mix because for certain items—toothpaste and laundry detergent, for example—consumers clearly prefer a recognized brand.

An equal portion of Dollar General's assortment consists of the DG Signature label. This is the company's house brand, and it appears primarily on grocery goods for which a national brand is not critical. The remainder of the products—about 70 percent—consist of various labels exclusive to Dollar General that, while not carrying the signature guarantee of the DG brand, still meet the company's high standards for quality. The all-cotton khakis, for instance, are sold under the Crossbow label.

The bulk of the company's private-label goods are bought directly from the manufacturer to eliminate the costs associated with distributors. Carpenter said that nearly 30 percent of these goods are sourced from outside the United States, particularly China. "With the volume we do, we can be very aggressive on pricing and specifications with our suppliers," he said.

Interestingly, the merchandising of the three brand types in the store does not follow the usual retail philosophy. "We don't set up private labels right next to every one of our national brands just to make the private label's price look better," said Carpenter. "That's how 90 percent of retailers operate, but not us. We just put the private label in where we think consumers will be accepting of something that may not be a household name, but the quality is good and it's a good value. We want to be honest with our customers, and when we think we have found a great value for them, we put it out there."

5. **Tight focus on assortments.** Carpenter notes that Dollar General features an assortment geared toward fast-moving consumables: food, health and beauty supplies, household goods—things that people use up and must replenish. This is critical in a business where volume is relied on to offset low margins. Dollar General avoids heavy exposure in apparel—it turns too slowly—but when it does offer soft lines, it sticks to the basics.

6. **Simple, no-glitz stores.** No one would mistake a Dollar General store for Neiman Marcus or even Target. But the decidedly unglamorous stores suit Dollar General customers just fine. "Our customer doesn't come to us because we have an upscale place," Carpenter noted. And keeping in-store displays and fixtures simple makes it easy for the company to outfit its locations without disrupting its margins.

7. **Quality labor force.** Like any retailer today, Dollar General is continually challenged to find the best employees it can at the most reasonable wages. Earl Weissert, the company's executive vice president of operations, said that one of the keys to getting solid employees is tapping the company's own customer base and leveraging its stores' locales. "We're primarily in rural, small-town America, and there are a lot of people in the towns we serve who need a good job," he said. "Single mothers in their thirties and forties, in particular, are a good fit for us, especially in the store-manager position. They're used to running a home, cleaning up after the kids, balancing budgets—doing all the basics around the house. Our business is so simple that it's just like running a home."

Unlike other retailers, which typically have a variety of levels of store employees, everyone working a Dollar General store "does windows." There's no sense of hierarchy; rather, everyone pitches in

Would I Lie to You?

to do what needs to be done—whether it's ringing the register, unloading the truck, or cleaning the storeroom. This enables the company to operate a busy store with an average of just seven to nine people and, in the process, keep its labor overhead low.

8. **Innovative real-estate operations.** Most, if not all, $4 billion retailers have a large real-estate department with scores of highly paid professionals who use elaborate formulas to determine site selection. Not Dollar General. While the company has approximately twenty full-time real-estate professionals who consummate building-purchase and lease transactions, the bulk of the work in choosing store locations rests in the hands of Dollar General's 250 district managers (DMs). "If I'm a DM, and I grew up in the town, then I know the people, the population, the best streets in town," Weissert explained. "Since I'm on site, I'll know when a certain store might be going out of business and when its location would be available. And all of our DMs know the criteria we look for in locations— like being near a supermarket and being on the key roads in the city or town. The DMs are our field people in real estate, and they send us only the best leads to check out. So when our real-estate people go out to follow up, they're not wasting their time looking at dozens of places that wouldn't be appropriate for us."

Because the company is not looking for a huge footprint, it can be flexible in the types of spaces it takes on. While 7,000 square feet is ideal, Dollar General can be effective in a location between 5,000 and 8,000 square feet, because its planograms can accommodate numerous sizes and configurations. In one instance in West Virginia, the company converted an old school gymnasium into a store. "We didn't change the floor. We just put in some ceiling tiles and some fixtures, then brought in our merchandise," Weissert said. And, he noted, in the markets Dollar General is interested in, turnover in sites of the appropriate size is continual, providing a substantial supply of potential locations.

When a site is decided upon, the deal is closed quickly. Dollar

General usually signs leases for three to five years to keep the terms simple and to avoid locking the company into a long-term obligation on a site that may not pan out.

9. **Judicious use of technology.** For many retailers, the Internet represents a huge opportunity to reach new markets and enhance the way they interact with their customers. In the halls of Dollar General's corporate headquarters, however, e-business—at least the business-to-consumer variety—garners little excitement. "Our customers buy at the moment of need," noted Bruce Ash, vice president of information services. "They can't wait two or three days for toilet paper or cereal to be delivered to them." Instead, the company focuses on what some may characterize as mundane technologies but what Ash considers keys to Dollar General's ability to accomplish its mission. "We have to keep our investments in IS really in line with the business model, to make sure it's relevant and appropriate to our business concept," he explained. "We don't have huge margins, so we're very conscious of costs. We only invest in what we really need to run the business."

For example, the company uses a basic technology infrastructure that features a main data-processing facility at headquarters connected to the company's six distribution centers (DCs) via a wide area network (WAN). The WAN enables headquarters to have online access to all the operations in the DCs to keep tabs on the heart of the business. To keep the business running smoothly, Dollar General uses a few basic systems: warehouse management, transportation scheduling, merchandising, and financial. "The combination of these systems really ensures that the whole cycle of goods moving from the vendors, through the DCs, and to the stores works," Ash said.

The warehouse-management application plays a particularly critical role in Dollar General's operations, as it ensures that the company maintains maximum velocity of its products. Using the data captured by the warehouse system, the company's merchants can understand such things as what products are available, where they're located, and what's being damaged in shipment. And the company's checkout scanners feed critical product-movement data into the merchandising systems, giving decision-makers detailed information on what products are selling, how often, and in which stores.

Interestingly, there are a few applications missing from Dollar General's technology portfolio that most retailers today couldn't live without—namely, those used for customer data collection and forecasting. Because Dollar General does not run specials or sales, and because most of the company's customers are "regulars" who live within two or three miles of the store, there's no reason to collect in-depth shopper information. "We're not like a department store, which wants to use your purchase data to give you preferred notification of sales or special offers," Ash said. "It's only important for us to know that an item was sold; we really don't need to know who bought it. I can't think of anything that we would do differently if we had that kind of information. We certainly wouldn't give them offers to buy goods at a lower price. We're doing that already."

Similarly, because the company stocks only fast-turning basics, there's no need for a sophisticated forecasting system to help predict trends and buying patterns. There's little variability in sales profiles from store to store, and there's not much volatility in the company's product mix. "We're not in a highly seasonal, fashion-oriented business," Ash noted. "If we make a mistake and buy too much soap, yeah, it's wrong, and it's an inventory bulge. But we won't have to mark it down, because eventually it will sell. While a mistake like that on sweaters in a department store might be trouble, in our model it's not the end of the world."

In addition to being frugal in its technology investments, Dollar General employs a lean staff of technology professionals. There are only seventy-five full-time professionals at the company—forty-five of whom are focused on applications (programmers, systems analysts, and project managers) and thirty of whom are responsible for

IS operations, keeping the computers running, monitoring the networks, etc.

10. **Highly efficient distribution.** Without a doubt, a major contributor to Dollar General's ability to offer consistently low and honest
pricing is its efficient distribution operation. The company operates
six highly automated DCs—ranging in size from 850,000 square
feet to 1 million square feet. Each DC serves approximately 700
stores, shipping more than 1 million cartons a week. Emulating
Wal-Mart's early hub-and-spoke strategy, Dollar General concentrates on opening stores close to existing DCs to minimize transportation costs. For instance, in 1995 the average distance between
a store and a DC was 600 miles. It's now about 300 miles, and is
expected to drop to 250 miles in a few years.[3]

To increase DC efficiency, Dollar General recently embarked on
an ambitious measurement program designed to help the management team identify areas in which the company can improve its performance—and, along the way, take more costs out of the system.
Jeff Sims, vice president of logistics, said the company now is "basically measuring everything that moves. We're getting into quantified
measurements in a big way, looking at things like carrier stock out,
vendor stock out, DC stock out, imports per day, bills processed per
hour. Some of our measurements are ugly. But that's the only way
we're going to be able to understand where we need to improve."

The company's logistics strategy has helped fuel its growth to this
point. But, according to Sims, Dollar General has only scratched the
surface of what it can do in the future. "These DCs, as constructed,
can serve well beyond 1,000 stores each," he explained. "Today, they
do about 700. We've got top-notch material-handling and IT systems that can handle much more throughput and that we really have
to leverage. It's like having a high-performance engine in a sports car
with a single-barrel carburetor. It's not the size of the engine that
determines how fast you go. It's the controls. It's the precision with
which you flow the fuel through the engine that wins the race."

Easy Access Brings the Traffic

DOLLAR GENERAL'S FORMULA FOR SUCCESS

SECONDARY ATTRIBUTE: ACCESS

- Store size makes it easy for customers to get in, around, and out quickly.
- Displays nothing above eye level, so customers can see the entire store.
- Uses high-speed laser scanners and avoids overmerchandising the checkout counter to speed customer processing.
- Has item prices preprinted or labeled by the manufacturer directly on each product to eliminate consumer searching for prices.
- Features the same layout, flow, and product mix in each of its 5,000 stores.
- Holds its SKUs to 4,500 to avoid crowding the stores and confusing customers as they shop.
- Locates stores on major roads in the heart of small towns or on major public-transit lines in urban neighborhoods.

To ensure that its value proposition is impossible to beat, Dollar General pairs price with a secondary focus on ease of access. As Bob Carpenter puts it, the size and layout of the company's stores give Dollar General an additional leg up on the competition and help strongly differentiate the company's stores from those of the larger discount chains. "We don't mind Wal-Mart—in fact, we try to locate near them as much as possible," he explained. "Our customers don't have the time, or physically don't have the energy, to wade through a 200,000-square-foot store. They want to come in, find what they're looking for quickly, and get out and on their way. That's not possible at Wal-Mart, and our customers know it. In reality, we're a convenience store without the higher prices."

Dollar General has identified seven factors that help keep its stores accessible to busy families and older customers alike:

1. **Small footprint.** At about 7,000 square feet, the typical Dollar General store is smaller than competitors' outlets.

2. **Eye-level focus.** In every Dollar General store, nothing—fixtures, signs, merchandise—is above eye level. This, according to Carpenter, is a crucial element of the company's store layout. The uncluttered "airspace" enables customers to stand at the store entrance and have an unobstructed view of every area of the store— thus making it easy for them to see where everything is without wandering around the building.

3. **Streamlined checkout.** To keep the checkout lines moving, Dollar General has installed new flatbed laser scanners that allow cashiers to ring up items more quickly than with the previous handheld models. In addition, the company recently removed impulse-buy items such as gum, candy, and tabloids from the front-end area. "Our buyers are giving us a hard time about that, but we think that we're right in the long run because our customers will appreciate our help in getting them out more quickly," said Carpenter.

4. **Clearly marked prices.** One of the basic tenets for competing on access is clarity and visibility of item prices. At Dollar General, the price of every product is clearly marked right on the item. In some cases, the manufacturer preprints the price on the label; in others, it's printed on a sticker that the manufacturer affixes to the label before shipping. With this program, there's no need for large price signs either on the shelves or hanging from the ceiling.

5. **Clean and well-arranged stores.** Dollar General also excels in making it as easy as possible for shoppers to navigate its stores. All the stores are clean and well-maintained, with no dirty floors or boxes

or crates strewn in the aisles. Furthermore, every store features the same layout and traffic flow: food on the left, household products and apparel in the back, and health and beauty products on the right. And, as a further nod to consistency, approximately 95 percent of the products are carried in every store (in the same location in each store), with the remaining 5 percent comprising geographically specific add-ins (such as suntan lotion and floats in a beach town or more health-care items geared toward older consumers in a store near a retirement community).

6. **Limited choices.** The company keeps a tight rein on its SKUs, limiting itself to just 4,500 (compared with about 35,000 SKUs offered by Wal-Mart). For one thing, the size of the average Dollar General store simply can't accommodate a large number of items. Second, adding more SKUs would crowd the look of the stores, making them feel less inviting and accessible. In addition, most of the company's customers really don't want—or have the time—to wade through fifteen different types of a single item (like toothpaste). Carpenter said the company knows what 75 percent of Americans buy, and sticks to those items for its stores.

7. **Convenient location.** Although access today is more about internal navigation, a nice store means nothing if consumers can't get to it. That's why Dollar General tries to locate its units in the heart of small towns or on major public-transit lines in larger cities.

Driving It All: Simplicity and Values

Dollar General's success seems amazingly simple. And, in fact, it is. *Simplicity* is one of the two critical success factors that the company's management point to over and over. In the stores, for instance, a store employee with a simple, handheld scanner does replenishment ordering: Scan the items that you need, indicate how many of each you want, and it's done. The consistent layout of the stores makes it easy for store employees to stock the shelves when inventory comes off the truck. And the cash-only policy makes running the register a breeze: Scan the items and take the money. "Our stores are so simple and easy to learn," said Earl Weissert. "So compared to other retailers, who have a bunch of policies and procedures that tell everyone how to work the store, we have almost nothing. Just some basic notes about attendance, vacations, and holidays."

According to Weissert, the simplicity of the company's operations also makes it easier to find employees to do the job, and employees are happier because they are empowered to make decisions for themselves. "Keep the work simple, the tasks easy, have a plan, and people will perform based on the guidelines we've given them," he said. Plus, the company doesn't have to spend a lot of time and money on training. Weissert noted that a person can learn how to run a Dollar General store in up to four weeks. "It is easy to teach anyone how to count the money, order the merchandise, unload merchandise from the truck, and put it out following the planogram," he said.

The other bedrock of the company's operation is its strong emphasis on values put into action. Each employee carries a card imprinted with the company's guiding mission and principles. Among the values:

- Building a company with people who are committed to moral integrity
- Leadership that encourages team spirit and empowered employees
- The dignity of work and others
- Emphasizing strengths in a positive environment
- Mutual gain

Company executives believe that these values distinguish Dollar General from any other company and provide a competitive advantage. "Our operations at Dollar General are nothing special," Weissert noted. "The only things unique to Dollar General are our culture and the values of our people. Our CEO tells our competition all the time what we do, and he knows that they can't duplicate our success because it's based on having the right values. Everyone just smiles and says, 'Right.' But it's true."

Added Jeff Sims: "I've heard a lot of lip service about culture and values in my career, but I hadn't actually seen it. Here, the positive attitude and culture literally ooze around the hallways in the company."

These values drive Dollar General's hiring policies. The belief is that if you hire someone with the right values, the rest will take care of itself. "When hiring, we certainly look at a person's morals and values," said Weissert. "That's critical, because we can teach people the technical stuff, but we can't teach values. If we see someone who has pride in their work, wants to treat coworkers and customers fairly, and understands that we are truly going to treat them fairly, they'll be a great fit."

From a management perspective, the emphasis on values has a major impact on problem resolution. According to Weissert, if there's a problem at hand, the typical reaction in most companies is to affix blame. At Dollar General, however, the underlying belief is that no one intentionally comes to work trying to figure out how she can mess things up. So, instead of pointing out what somebody did wrong, Dollar General management strives to always help the person understand what she needs to know to do it right.

"At Dollar General, it's okay to make a mistake," said Weissert. "We applaud people making mistakes, because you learn from your mistakes. But it's not okay to break one of the values. The only thing that will get you in trouble at Dollar General is breaking one of the values."

Challenges for the Future

The company's management believes the future is bright for Dollar General, as its target customer base is growing exponentially. But, they note, there remain a few issues that must be addressed. First and foremost, the company must maintain the culture and values that make it unique. Remarkably, Dollar General has been able to keep its sense of values as it has grown from a few hundred stores to more than 5,000. But, as we have learned in our research, culture is difficult to scale. Will Dollar General look and feel the same when it reaches 7,000, 9,000, or 10,000 stores? Time will tell.

Second, to maintain its leadership position in the industry, the company must remain nimble and able to respond to the advances of new competitors. No one at Dollar General is naive enough to believe that the company can't be beat. Weissert, in particular, sees the potential for someone to come along attempting to become the "new" Dollar General.

"We all know that competition changes," he said. "We don't expect it to be this easy forever. As people see the success we've had, some will try to figure out what we've done and try to duplicate it. As the old saying goes, 'Imitation is the sincerest form of flattery.' "

SELF-DIAGNOSTIC: PRICE

- If you choose to dominate on price, does your customer communication on pricing stress fairness and honesty?
- If you're not competing on price, are you meeting the prices of the competition, or are you just blindly matching the lowest prices in your category or market?
- Consistency matters, no matter what price strategy you adopt. Would a customer conducting business with you today recognize your pricing policies from six months ago or six months in the future?
- Ask your friends if your company's pricing claims appear to them to be clear, simple, and intuitively correct, given your products and/or services.
- If you aren't chasing the bottom of your market but rather trying to match competition, how often—and objectively—do you review your competitors' pricing positions?

CHAPTER 4

I Can't Get No Satisfaction

Service with a Smile?

It was the kind of July afternoon anyone who knows Detroit knows too well—too hot, too humid. The westbound traffic on I-94, which on a good weekday afternoon flows through the city like blood circulating through the veins of an eighty-year-old cholesterol junkie, had come to a stop, thanks to an impromptu exercise in spontaneous highway closing by the Michigan State Police. Then the rain came, making visibility difficult and traffic impossible. Hundreds of people fought their fellow travelers for a car-length advantage in the crawl to the airport.

A lot of people were late to Metro Airport that day, and maybe the man in seat 1C was one of them, maybe not. At any rate, the inbound equipment was delayed, so that if you were late, you could still make the flight to Atlanta—assuming, of course, that it ever took off. Eventually the plane began to load, but even as the clouds lifted off the fields, new storm clouds began forming in the cabin. The rain hadn't helped either the temperature or the humidity. By now, the passengers, who half an hour ago would have missed the flight if it hadn't been delayed, were cursing the airline for the delay in takeoff.

Mr. 1C made a fatal mistake for first-class passengers out of Detroit: He showed up five minutes into the boarding, which meant he sacrificed any hope that both he and his bags would be flying in first. "But I have a first-class ticket," he said, wandering from overstuffed overhead to overstuffed overhead. "Sorry, sir," the attendant said, "but since you're in a bulkhead row, you'll just have to stow your bags in the back of the plane." "But that means I'll have to wait for the whole plane to empty out before I can get my bag," Mr. 1C said. "I'll be happy to check it for you, sir," the attendant said. Mr. 1C then uttered a spew of unintelligible words in what may or may not have been some Eastern European dialect. The tone was generally pleasant enough, but the meaning seemed clear. "Look," the attendant said, "I don't know what you said, but you can't say that to me."

Mumbling, Mr. 1C wandered back to the exile of coach to find a place for his blue cloth backpack. Returning to his seat, he fell into his chair with a motion clearly intended to convey his world-weariness and radical ennui. Almost immediately, he leapt out of the seat, screaming a word clearly understandable, albeit inappropriate in a business book. "I've ripped my pants," he bellowed, and indeed he had. Thanks to an errant seat spring, a fierce, ugly rip had separated the attractive green microfibers from roughly mid-pocket to mid-calf, settling (for any or all interested) the boxers-or-briefs question once and for all. "I demand to see a customer-service agent at once," Mr. 1C said, his voice suddenly as ragged as his trousers.

His fellow passengers issued a collective sigh. If 1C got his wish, the flight, already an hour late, might be postponed indefinitely, if its departure depended on the airline's historically demonstrated pattern of customer service. But less than ten minutes later, a vision of command-and-control strolled into the first-class cabin with the élan of Mike Tyson leaving his corner to answer the first-round bell. Customer Service was an imposing woman, well over 6 feet tall and well north of 225 pounds. She towered over 1C, glaring down at him. "Yes, sir, I heard you've got a problem," she barked. 1C's own bark had become a tremulous whisper. "I ripped my pants," he said, like a naughty schoolboy confessing to an evil stepmother. "Where did you rip them?" Customer Service demanded. "You want to see?" 1C asked submissively. "Of course I don't want to see,"

Customer Service countered. "I don't care where they are ripped, just where you ripped them." "I tore them sitting down," the contrite 1C answered. "That would be on the plane?" Customer Service said. "Yes," 1C confessed. "Well then, I can't help you—you'll have to file a complaint in Atlanta." "But my pants are torn," 1C moaned. "But I just told you I can't help you. Customer service in Detroit doesn't have anything to do with anything that happens once you get on a plane," she said. "But my pants are torn," 1C repeated. "Sir, did you understand me?" Customer Service asked. "This plane is going to Atlanta. You ripped your pants on the plane; therefore, you have to file a claim in Atlanta."

1C stared at the floor. "But I don't understand," he stammered. "I'm sure you can see I just want someone to help me." Customer Service swelled to her full height and stared right through 1C, speaking in clipped, measured, deliberate tones. "Look, I think I've explained this to you, sir," she said. "I'm a customer-service agent. What exactly do you expect me to do for you?"

As our unfortunate fellow passenger discovered, service is all about people. In fact, it is the element of human-to-human interaction that most clearly defines the service attribute. Unlike product or price, service is a living, breathing dynamic, characterized largely by emotion. Service is experienced in a very personal way, and, therefore, the mechanisms that companies use to motivate their employees are a critical part of how their customers experience service.

But with the right motivation, employees can make a huge difference. Consider the case of Continental Airlines, which underwent an astounding turnaround in the 1990s. In the late 1980s, when the U.S. Department of Transportation began keeping score of the airlines' performance, Continental ranked at the bottom of the list on matters such as on-time departures and arrivals, lost luggage, passenger comfort, cancellations, and overall customer service. When Gordon Bethune took over as president and COO of Continental in 1994, he inherited a company deep in the doldrums. Employee morale was at a low point, flights were assigned to unprofitable routes, and customers were complaining louder every day. As CEO (also since 1994), Bethune has reenergized the company by rewriting the rules of its culture, improving employee relationships, and satisfying both customers and stockholders.

In its study of airline passengers' satisfaction, J. D. Power and Associates and *Frequent Flyer* magazine have ranked Continental first in customer service for three of the last four years.[1] Moreover, Continental was selected by *Fortune* in 1999 as one of the 100 best employers in America to work for. And the company's frequent-flier program, OnePass, is routinely held up as the model of what a loyalty program should be.

In describing the new corporate culture, Bethune likes to use a football analogy: "It's not really all that complex. Eleven guys get a ball across that goal line. That's pretty much the whole strategy. How come so many people don't score? Because they don't have a clue how to get those eleven guys to want to do it better than those other guys. How do you get 48,000 people in one company to want to be a good airline? Knowing what a good airline is, is not the same as knowing how to get people to do it."[2]

The key, according to Bethune, is to get everybody to agree on what "success" means. Otherwise, the enterprise suffers from dysfunctional pushing and pulling toward myriad goals, which ultimately results in customer dissatisfaction. In addition to surprise meetings with employees at every level, from baggage handlers to ticket agents and airline pilots, Bethune believes in the power of teamwork and rewards. Since 1995, the company has offered employees $65 a month in bonuses every time they meet their on-time goals, and $100 in bonuses each time Continental scores a first-place finish ahead of the other airlines. Expenditures for the rewards program total approximately $3 million to date.[3]

Ideas on better customer service are welcome everywhere in the company, Bethune says. As the top U.S. carrier in Mexico and the second-largest U.S. carrier in Latin America, for instance, Continental has assigned Spanish-speaking employees to those flights and has instituted regional food rather than the universal bag of peanuts. According to Bethune, Continental is "a company of multi functions that has value when we all work cooperatively—pilots, flight attendants, gate agents, airport agents, mechanics, reservation agents. And not to understand that about doing business means you're going to fail. Lots of people failed because they don't get it."[4]

As Bethune sees it, great service means giving the customers what they want: "Customers don't measure winning or losing by our income statement or earnings per share," he says. "They measure us by how we get them to where they want to go with their underwear on time."[5]

As evidenced by Continental's success, employees—and accompanying issues like selection, hiring, rewards, measures, and training—represent a vital investment for any business that hopes to dominate on the attribute of service. Yet even with that investment, service can be the most difficult attribute to execute against consistently, for the very reason that a company must rely on people to perform that service—and the bottom line is that no business can truly control its people, certainly not the way it can control product or price, for instance. Human beings, after all, have good days and bad days; they have varying moods and are subject to the fact that the world around them is a highly variable, emotional, and, at times, difficult place. So while a company can train its employees to say "Hello," "Thank you," and "Have a nice day," it can't control *how* they say it or how a customer perceives the employee.

There's no question that today's tight skilled-labor market, with some of the lowest unemployment levels ever seen, presents obvious challenges to executives leading service-oriented companies. But even so, superior service can be achieved with hard work, great leadership, and a company culture that is dedicated, above all else, to serving customers—as the case studies later in this chapter demonstrate.

The critical role played by employees in the service equation was pointed to over and over again by executives we spoke with in the course of our research. Cathy Baum, executive vice president of Stanley Martin, a Washington, D.C., home-builder, emphasized the importance of the human element in the hypercompetitive residential home-building industry. "Why do people buy a home from one company rather than another? It all comes down to the salesperson," she told us. "It's about having the right information at the right time; knowing what to say when a question is asked; understanding human nature; and having a certain sixth sense about how to handle a customer when they walk in the door. It's a quality that goes beyond the price or the location of the property."

It's also a quality that carries over to many types of businesses in many countries. "Our customers really have an attachment to our butchers and fishmongers," said Cormac Tobin, a business manager at Superquinn, an Irish grocery retailer. "They love coming to the counter because the butcher can say, 'Oh, you're having the boss over for dinner? Well, here's the cut you need, here's how to slice and prepare it, here are some good spices for it.' A lot of the next generation coming up really like to cook, but it hasn't been taught how to do it. So we're helping to educate them and give them the confidence to try new things."

It became clear that there was another key difference between service and the other attributes. In most instances, a company builds the attributes and the consumer responds. A company can set price, a company can select products, and a company can establish access (we'll get to experience later). Service, however, is a highly subjective attribute, varying not just from person to person but often from day to day or even hour to hour.

One thing that's clear: While an absolute definition of the service attribute may be subjective, consumers are objectively growing increasingly dissatisfied. The 2000 American Customer Satisfaction Index conducted by the National Quality Research Center at the University of Michigan Business School found that customer-satisfaction rates for industries such as airlines, retailing, restaurants/fast food, gas stations, and banks have fallen to some of the lowest levels since the survey began in 1994. Service tales of woe are hardly restricted to the physical realm. By some accounts, as many as one-quarter of online shoppers during the 1999 Christmas shopping season said they would never shop on some websites again because of the poor customer service they encountered.

Clearly, service is not what it used to be—in conception or in practice. Moreover, consumers have come to redefine what service means or should mean, creating a disconnect: Consumers and companies often do not see eye to eye on this attribute. Many businesses, for example, believe that packing their offerings with what they consider to be "value-added services" will attract customers. This explains why dry cleaning and banking are available in grocery stores, and why coffee bars can be found in bookstores. The problem is that for most consumers, these services really take a back seat to some very basic competencies that many businesses have failed to master. Consumers made it clear that they are looking for fewer gimmicks and more delivery when it comes to service. If the service provided at the moment of interaction is deficient, all the value-added services in the world aren't going to help a business hang on to that customer. This suggests that businesses seeking to dominate on service would do better taking the money they have been putting into all those extra services and putting it into employee screening, training, measuring, and rewarding in an effort to provide better point-of-interaction value to the customer.

Service shortcomings haven't always been par for the course. Many can remember the "good old days" when service *was* important, when consumers' expectations for individualized attention was not considered out of the ordinary. In the late nineteenth and early twentieth centuries, "full service" dominated the business landscape. At the dry-goods store, a clerk cut the cloth to customers' specifications. The owner of the general store climbed a ladder and measured out however much flour or dried peas people asked for. The storeowner knew his customers and the needs of their families. These merchants had a degree of "perfect knowledge" of their customers, and could predict their buying habits and needs with relative ease.

But the notion of what constitutes service has changed over time. Take gas stations, which, you may remember, used to be called *service* stations, complete with human beings who would check your oil, wash your windshield, and pump your gas. Today self-service has become the service norm in the gas-station business.

In fact, lower levels of service have become the standard in numerous industries. In the airline business, for example, the hub concept has served to reduce competition and, in the process, has resulted in a lower service standard. If you live in Memphis or Minneapolis, you're a Northwest customer; if you live in Cleveland, you're a Continental customer; if you're in Atlanta, you're a Delta customer. It's possible to fly other airlines, but it's not nearly as convenient, so frequent fliers to or from hub cities tend to fly hub airlines whether service levels are excellent or poor.

The paradox is that at the same time that service levels have been dropping, consumers' expectations have been rising, due to their increased awareness resulting from access to media, technology, information, and knowledge of lifestyles and products. Consider, for example, the amount of information that some consumers bring to the home-buying decision. "Five years ago, no information about home building was on the Internet that people could easily access or understand," Baum told us. "Today there are dozens of sites that list homes. People research product information and appliances. We tell them we're using XYZ insulation, and they research whether there are any medical hazards related to the insulation. Or they go into a house and see some sap coming out of a piece of wood, and they'll go and research the structural integrity of wood and what the sap means."

Understanding consumers' expectations as they relate to a particular business is the key to creating a service formula that matches that level of expectations. Take the restaurant business. Let's say you have four kinds of restaurants: a buffet, fast food, a neighborhood place, and an upscale white-tablecloth establishment. What's the correct service formula for the buffet? None, with the exception of back-end service such as making sure the food is hot and in plentiful supply at the buffet line. In that case, a consumer wouldn't—and shouldn't—have high expectations for personalized service. With a fast-food restaurant, there should be a bit more service expected and delivered. Someone takes the order, assembles it, and hands it over to the consumer. In a neighborhood restaurant, the service expectations would be a little higher. Perhaps the owner comes by and says hello. Finally, in the case of a white-tablecloth restaurant where a consumer is spending $100 or more, a considerably higher level of service is expected.

As long as an establishment delivers what the consumer expects and lets customers know up front what level of service will be delivered, and assuming, of course, the company delivers against those expectations consistently, each service formula is successful for its particular business. But if a consumer spends $100 in an upscale restaurant and is treated as if he were in a McDonald's, then the company's got a problem. It all comes down to managing expectations and delivering against the ones you manage.

If it's true—and we believe it is—that lower service has become the accepted norm, what's the incentive for businesses to change? In the most practical sense, competition—or the threat of competition—can be a key driver of change. For instance, if enough consumers begin to use online grocery companies because of the convenience and service they provide, supermarket operators may be forced to rethink their service equations.

But there's an even greater incentive for businesses to take stock of their service offering. Based on our research, it's clear that service may actually offer businesses the greatest potential return on investment of any of the five attributes, simply because most companies are doing so poorly at providing good service. In fact, service may represent the richest untapped area for differentiation in the entire consumer goods and services industry. If you're a price or product operator, another company can come along and copy your price or product offering. But it's much more difficult to copy a service offering, as so much depends on employees and company culture. For that reason, service may actually provide a better measure of competitive insulation than the other attributes. So while clearly there are costs involved in terms of employee hiring and training, the potential benefit is significant.

What Consumers *Really* Want

Historically, companies have thought of service as something they offered to consumers. However, we posit a very different view of how consumers view service: as something a business *is* or something it *embodies*. Viewed through this lens, an element as seemingly simple as a hassle-free return policy takes on new meaning. For today's consumer, the return policy is an acid test of authenticity. It offers evidence that a business walks its talk. Consumers also made it clear to us that it's not enough to have the policy; it's the action that surrounds the policy that really counts. After all, everybody makes the same claim when it comes to their return policy, assuring consumers that returning an item won't be a problem. But when customers actually try to return something, they often find themselves crawling a mile on their hands and knees over broken glass with little hope of satisfaction.

For most consumers, the ability to return merchandise unconditionally, without hassles from rude or incompetent service representatives, seemed to be a baseline for acceptable service. This speaks to the importance of providing a warranty for your products and, by extension, your business. It also provides additional evidence that consumers today tend to be distrustful, wary, and cynical. If customers don't believe that a business stands behind its products, they will view that as an egregious, irrevocable service failure that will cause them to flee from the company.

Roberta, a forty-five-year-old accountant from Cleveland, told us about a shopping experience that left her seeing red: "I purchased an outfit that I thought was in good shape, but when I got home, I discovered it had a rip in it," she recalled. "Although I had just made the purchase thirty minutes earlier, I had to fight with the clerks to see if they could either take something off the price or let me exchange the damaged item. Even the supervisor wasn't really cooperative, and from that point I didn't want to go back to that store to shop. Eventually, I had to take it to the tailor and have it sewn up."

The survey responses left us with a question: If all consumers are really looking for is to return merchandise easily and not have their goods damaged, why do so many seem so unhappy? What we learned in our one-to-one conversations is that service really isn't quite as simple as those survey responses might indicate. In fact, it became clear to us that service is, in fact, a complex attribute.

Consumers differentiated among various kinds of service that a company can offer. They spoke about *pre-sale service,* signaled by a pleasant and sincere "May I help you?" and characterized by a knowledgeable salesperson capable of answering customers' questions. Then there's *transaction-level service,* which occurs at the time of sale and includes packing or gift wrapping as well as intelligent, helpful suggestions about compatible items on sale, special discounts, or company-sponsored perks. And, finally, consumers pointed to *post-sale service,* which usually takes the form of sincere and knowledgeable people who are committed to helping customers resolve various problems they may have with their purchases (e.g., defective or unwanted merchandise, product repairs, and product-usage assistance). Businesses seeking to dominate on the service attribute must master all three types of service.

Consider, for example, how important post-sale service can be for a service-oriented home-builder such as Stanley Martin. Cathy Baum related a story about a fire that burned a just-completed house nearly to the ground. "The house had been finished and, with the land, was worth about $1.3 million," she said. "The homeowners were due to move in to the house in about two weeks. When the fire occurred, we were on the site within twenty minutes. Did we have to be there? Maybe not. The people— not us—owned the house and the lot. But we're their builder. We believe it's our responsibility to take care of them. We talked with the fire marshal; we called the lender and the insurance company. My salespeople helped them find a place to stay, stopped the moving company, stopped the telephone service. We handled all those details. It was simply the right thing to do. Most companies might start to panic more about the cause of the fire and their legal liability rather than taking care of the human beings involved. For us, the service cycle starts from the time the consumer first calls us and then continues for years."

There's also an element of customer reward that enters into the service equation—something that industries like the airlines and supermarkets have failed to understand. In both cases, the "worst" customers are often the ones being rewarded while the "best" customers are punished. Consider the high cost of a ticket for the business traveler who has logged hundreds of thousands of miles on a particular airline but who needs to get from New York to Chicago tomorrow. Meanwhile, the vacation travelers who booked their flight two months in advance but fly from New York to Chicago just once a year got their ticket for what amounts to the tax on the business traveler's fare.

Now translate this to the grocery business. The cherry-picker who grabs a few of the below-cost loss leaders gets to zip through the express lane, while the loyal shopper who spends $200 every week in the store waits in line for half an hour to check out.

Signs of the instavidual we described in Chapter 1 cropped up frequently as we examined the dimensions of service. It became clear that the same consumer may receive an identical delivery of service in different ways. For instance, a person who's in a hurry one day may be perfectly happy to pick up a cup of coffee and hand over his money without worrying about whether the person on the other side of the counter said thank you. On that day, the consumer's perception may be that the service was fine. However, the following day that same consumer may not be so rushed, and the identical service may seem less than adequate because of the lack of human interaction. Same consumer, same employee, same product, same price, same delivery of service—but under a very different perception on the part of the consumer.

There is a close relationship between service and experience, in part because both are somewhat less tangible than the other three attributes. Access, price, and product are more about *what* you offer, while experience and service are about *how* you offer it. In fact, it's possible for the attributes of service and experience to be so closely intertwined that each becomes a part of the other. We experienced that intertwining one brutal February day when we were scheduled to fly from Detroit to Chicago on Southwest Airlines. Winter storms were raging at both ends, and the flying windows were minimal, but small windows out of Detroit and into Chicago were opening and closing seemingly without warning. The gate agent told us a takeoff might be possible, but only if the first person to board took the last seat on the plane. In other words, we were asked to forget our pre-assigned boarding order (there's no assigned seating on Southwest flights) and board as quickly as possible from back to front. As you might imagine, there was plenty of grumbling. The agent apologized and said that as a small token of appreciation they'd have some refreshments for everyone. No sooner had she said that when carts were rolled in filled with doughnuts, bagels, coffee, and tea. People were starting to feel better.

But Southwest wasn't done yet. The agent offered to give anyone a $50 travel voucher if they sang some karaoke over the gate microphone while we waited. People started to line up quickly, singing five or six bars, on average, before falling apart laughing. And, as promised, a flight window mysteriously opened. "Now," the gate agent urged us. Before you knew it, everyone had obediently boarded as instructed—back to front—without pushing, shoving, or complaining. The plane was soon on its way to Chicago.

Southwest could have simply offered the minimal level of service: "We'll get you to Chicago." But instead, the company said: "We'll get you to

Chicago, and we'll make sure that you're happy when you get there." It took the level of service up a notch, treated the customers as human beings, and made the whole thing part of the overall experience of flying with Southwest.

How does the service attribute play out in the online world? Our survey responses indicated that there are some differences but also some similarities between service in the physical space and in the consumer-direct space. Online shoppers identified credit-card security as their chief service issue, followed by quick and hassle-free merchandise returns and an unconditional-return policy. While security concerns remain paramount in the minds of consumers, many retailers don't seem to view this as a key issue. It's likely that consumers will become more comfortable using their credit cards online as time goes on, but at this point e-tailers should not underestimate the importance of these security concerns.

Applying the Conceptual Model to Service

Businesses that want to compete on service as their primary attribute, or even those that wish to simply bring their service component up to industry standards, must listen carefully to the voice of the consumer (see Figure 4.1).

FIGURE 4.1

Competing on Service

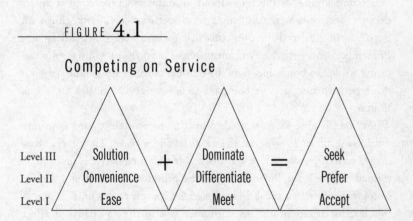

Level III	Solution		Dominate		Seek
Level II	Convenience	+	Differentiate	=	Prefer
Level I	Ease		Meet		Accept

The first level for service is *accommodation*—meeting consumers' fundamental expectations. For instance, customers expect that they should rarely have to wait in line or on the telephone for answers to their questions, and that they should be able to unconditionally return merchandise with which they are unhappy—for whatever reason—and that the returns should be quick and hassle-free. In the case of an e-commerce operator, consumers expect the website to use a natural-language service agent that is able to respond to nearly all questions, however obscure, without sending them along a dead-end path. In other words, *"If you accommodate me, then I'll accept you, and you will be a choice that I may make."* Catalog retailers such as L.L. Bean have set the standard in this regard. Stories abound of consumers who have returned items used for several months or years, hoping to get them repaired, only to have the company send them a new replacement, free of charge.

To be accommodated, consumers must feel as if they are respected and treated fairly by the company's personnel, and that the employees take seriously their discomfort or dissatisfaction with a purchase. Civility must be the hallmark of the business relationship. Companies that excel at accommodating consumers' wishes must focus on hiring and training salespeople and customer-service representatives who are committed to serving customers first and making sales quotas second. This has important ramifications for the reward-and-measurement program a company deploys. Service-centric companies avoid metrics that reward "churn and burn," opting instead for programs that focus on customer satisfaction. Remember, you get what you measure, so if you're providing your call-center workers a bonus based on the number of calls they handle per hour, don't be surprised if your company gets low service ratings from customers.

At Level II of service-oriented competition, consumers want *education:* They want information about the products and services. They expect their questions to be answered by knowledgeable staff members, people who are trained to speak intelligently about the products they sell and service. Employees must also speak in language the consumer can understand. At this level of competition, the consumer says to the company, in effect:

"Educate me and I will prefer you—all else being equal—to other companies that sell or provide similar products and services."

Consider the example of Geiger's Clothing and Sports, a small, family-run store in the Cleveland suburb of Lakewood, Ohio. The company faces numerous challenges in remaining relevant to consumers. The store is located downtown, not in a suburban mall, and it sells items that are commonly found in numerous retail formats, ranging from department stores, sporting-goods chains, and discounters to specialty stores and the Internet. It's clearly a product-focused company, specializing in sports and outdoor apparel for the active person. But it also has determined that a strong secondary focus on service can spell the difference between maintaining a solid customer base and losing sales to the Internet. To that end, the company hires salespeople who have specific areas of expertise so that they can help customers sort through the myriad styles and types of gear.

Bob, a Geiger's customer, told us a story about a visit to the store when he was looking for a high-performance parka. The young woman helping Bob turned out to be a ski instructor who knew a great deal about the performance attributes of the coats the company carries. She spent more than an hour educating Bob on the features and benefits of each coat, explaining which brand or style would be most appropriate for his needs. "It's hard to know which features are really important for what you want to do and which are just 'bells and whistles' that don't mean much in the way of performance," said Bob, who bought a $140 coat—and felt much more confident doing so as a result of the service he received.

At Level III, a business aiming for a 5 on the service attribute must offer the consumer individualized *customization* of the product or service. If that effort is successful, the consumer can say, *"If you continue to treat me as an individual, I will continue to seek you out as my company of choice for the products or services you carry."*

But what does customization really mean? Companies dominate on service by customizing or tailoring merchandise—for example, selling one item from a prepackaged set, placing special orders, cutting, trimming, or refashioning products to meet a customer's special needs. Customization and personalization take on particular significance in a business such as home building. "Consumers are looking for us to help them satisfy a vision," said Cathy Baum of Stanley Martin. "Everybody who is buying a house, whether it is their first or last home, has a vision of how they live and how they want to live, and they want the house they buy to satisfy that vision and to feel good to them."

Customization can be a tricky proposition, however. Consider the amount of seemingly customized and personalized direct mail you get from businesses like banks and airlines—mail that is addressed to you, but with your name misspelled. Such attempts at customized service reveal just how fragile a strategy this can be and demonstrate how easy it is for personalized service that's executed poorly to have a negative effect on a company's relationships with its customers.

One company that has experienced tremendous success because of its customization capabilities is St. Louis–based Build-A-Bear. This company, the brainchild of former May Department Stores executive Maxine Clark, is a classic example of a new spin on an old idea. It's debatable whether the world really needed another teddy-bear store. But each Build-A-Bear store offers customers the opportunity to create their very own personalized teddy bear—complete with a given name, birth certificate, and appropriate attire. Working with the store's staff, a customer chooses the desired "skin," has it stuffed to his or her specifications, and dresses it in the outfit of his or her choice. The finishing touch is a "Cub Condo" box in which to take the bear home.

Dell has set the standard for service in the high-tech area. Dell's website offers not only a selection of prepackaged computers that include the most popular features but also an option that allows consumers to choose from a menu of components and thus design the computer of their choice. At the end of the selection process, the Dell site presents a summary of the consumer's choices, totals the price, and allows the customer to keep the configuration on tap for later review and changes. An 800 number allows a consumer to contact the help desk at Dell to talk with a human being who can answer any questions. But the service doesn't end with the purchase. All Dell customers have access to live customer-service technicians around the clock, every day of the year, in the event they're faced with a problem that they can't solve on their own. What is the additional cost to the customer of such service? Not one penny.

Customization is something that many Internet companies mastered—so much so that what's par for personalization and customization online became significantly higher than in the physical world. The major Web portals or search engines such as Yahoo!, Excite, and Alta Vista offered visitors the ability to tailor the site's presentation and content to their own needs. Amazon.com pioneered and popularized the recommending of new books, music, and other items to customers upon their signing on, giving at least the appearance that "somebody knows me in there." And most online retailers allow customers to track the status of their orders on their own.

Technology such as the Internet will alter the service equation. As consumers become increasingly used to the level of customization that most online businesses offer, they are likely to make similar demands of physical-world operators. As that happens, will human-based service become less important? We think that depends on whether a business chooses to be at par, to differentiate, or to dominate on the service attribute. If a company is attempting to be a 3 (par) in service, it may make sense to use some technology-enabled solutions; but to be a 4 (differentiate) or a 5 (dominate), people will remain the key—as you'll see in the case studies that follow.

Case Study

How Superquinn Keeps Customers Coming Back

Superquinn isn't just an Irish supermarket chain. In the words of one blissed-out meat-department employee, it's a cult. Every employee, and most of the customers, are fervent cult members and Feargal Quinn, the company's founder and CEO, is Ireland's universally acknowledged and revered Pope of Customer Service. Quinn, the quintessential Irishman, with perpetually dancing eyes and more stories than an errant teenager, is a modern Irish institution. He served as the country's postmaster, turning the Irish Post Office into a profit-making entity, and currently serves in the Irish Senate.

Superquinn is a company conceived and executed in its founder's image. Everything inside Superquinn's stores exists to enhance the customer's service experience. Every detail—from the largest to the smallest—is almost obsessively customer-centric. Scissors are positioned near the broccoli display so shoppers can trim the hard stalks and pay only for what they will actually eat. A picture of each produce supplier hangs above the product they supply so consumers know who's really responsible for the food they're about to buy. All perishable products are fresh to a point that would drive most American supermarket managers mad. And Quinn is the head cheerleader of his own parade, regularly bagging groceries and moving from customer to employee and back in what seems like one long, dizzying, uninterrupted conversation focused on delivering ever-increasingly improved levels of service.

A visit to a Superquinn store is a life-altering experience, not in the metaphysical or theological sense but, rather, in how one views the way a retail operation—grocery or otherwise—should be run. The seventeen-store chain in and around Dublin competes first and foremost on the attribute of service, backed up by some of the freshest and highest-quality products around.

Feargal Quinn opened the first Superquinn in 1960 as a small grocery shop in Dundalk, a town north of Dublin. Quinn's father—also a grocer—instilled in him early in life that the key to building a good business was to satisfy your customers so completely that they always returned. Quinn took the advice to heart and has built Superquinn into one of the most successful and respected retail companies in the world. Today, Superquinn employs more than 4,000 people, commands a 20 percent share of the Dublin grocery market, and has racked up an impressive list of industry awards. But most important to Quinn is the fact that Superquinn's customers wouldn't dream of shopping anyplace else.

Service and More Service: The Boomerang Principle

SUPERQUINN'S FORMULA FOR SUCCESS

PRIMARY ATTRIBUTE: SERVICE

- Posts a greeter at the door to welcome people, help them get a cart, offer coffee, or fetch a wheelchair.
- Pays close attention to packaging of products to ensure that quality is not being sacrificed for low cost.
- Promotes visibility of store managers in the store instead of in their offices.
- Offers food sampling throughout the store.
- Provides umbrella and carryout service to customers' cars.
- Posts signs around the store explaining the nutritional content of fruits and vegetables to help customers make more informed choices.
- Positions a customer-service counter near the entrance of every store to help customers with questions or complaints.
- Will stock special items—even those carried only by a competitor—for customers, to eliminate the need for them to make special trips for one or two items.
- Employs aisle monitors in charge of specific areas of the store to whom customers can go with questions.
- Trains fishmongers and butchers in culinary skills so they can help recommend cuts and preparation ideas to customers.
- Operates a child-care center, staffed by trained professionals, where customers can leave their children to play while they shop.
- Uses its loyalty program not just to collect data but also to create new services.
- Has formed a joint venture with a respected bank to provide financial services in its stores.

Superquinn's success can be traced to "The Boomerang Principle," which Quinn describes in his book *Crowning the Customer: How to Become Customer Driven* as a simple philosophy of doing everything to keep customers coming back—which often means looking past a short-term expense to long-term customer loyalty. Indeed, Quinn and his management team offer numerous examples of programs or services that, from an immediate bottom-line standpoint, might not have made sense to adopt, but that have generated thousands of dollars of additional business in the long run. Store staffing is one example. Quinn staffs the stores with more than 300 employees even though they could run with 200. The additional employees focus on customer service. There's even a concierge, who can recommend restaurants and organize parties. These services may not contribute to the bottom-line profit, but they set the company apart from other supermarkets.

How does Superquinn do it? How does it embody the essence of Consumer Relevancy? In three ways:

1. **Do the simple things right.** As mentioned earlier in this chapter, many companies offer all kinds of value-added services yet forget about the simple things that customers really appreciate. A large measure of Superquinn's success can be traced to the fact that the company *never* forgets the little things. For example, all of its stores have a greeter posted at the store entrance whose job it is to not only make a good first impression but also to help customers get situated in the store so they can go about their business. The Superquinn greeter looks after shopping carts, offers a cup of coffee or soup to shoppers, helps a mother seat her children in the cart, or fetches a wheelchair for a disabled shopper. The greeter is also responsible for recognizing new customers and explaining what they will find as they make their way around the store.

   Packaging of products is a big deal at Superquinn as well. For example, the company introduced a special type of air- and water-tight insulated bag for fish and meats. The bags not only help seal in the freshness of the products (they maintain a chill for an hour longer than plastic bags), but they also prevent the products' smells from intruding on other items in the shopping cart. And they eliminate customers' need to repackage the products for refrigerator or freezer storage. "The bags are more expensive, certainly," noted Cormac Tobin, a business manager at Superquinn. "But it's a better service for our customers. They value it, and it's a real point of difference for us."

Another small, but noticeable, difference at Superquinn is the constant presence of the store managers and supervisors on the floor. Early on, Feargal Quinn made it a policy that all managers do their work on the shop floor. Managers can frequently be found doing their paperwork at empty registers, on a box of wine, on a shelf— all in the name of remaining accessible to customers and employees.

Also on the list of little things that count for a lot is an umbrella service for unprepared shoppers who get caught in a sudden downpour, package carryout to customers' cars, and a delivery service to consumers' homes. There's also a variety of in-store food sampling— from the fresh-made pancakes in the bakery section to the myriad domestic and imported cheeses.

Is that bag of potatoes too heavy to lift? No problem. Simply put the special laminated tag in your cart indicating which potatoes you want, and the bag will be brought to you as you pass through the checkout lane. Are you unsure of which fruits and vegetables are best for specific dietary requirements? Just look for the dozens of signs and brochures around the produce department that spell out vitamin content and other nutritional information for every item carried. Are you tired after an hour of shopping? Don't worry. There's a chair at the checkout lane (and a complimentary glass of champagne if you wish).

2. **Go the extra mile.** Superquinn also does a lot of big things right. One of these is the customer-service counter. While many retailers hide their "complaint department" on the top floor or way back in the store (right next to the restrooms), Superquinn places its service

counter right at the entrance of the store. In doing so, it subtly but powerfully communicates the idea that the company values service and that it takes customer input and complaints seriously. These counters are staffed by one or two employees who are responsible for dealing with a variety of questions, issues, and problems, and also for answering the store telephones. In most cases, the customer-service counter representatives can resolve any issue on the spot as they see fit (only in rare cases will they get the store manager involved). This helps defuse any problems quickly and gets the customers back on their way. The customer-service employees will often phone a customer in a few days to ensure that everything has been resolved to the customer's satisfaction.

Another example of going the extra mile is Superquinn's willingness to stock special items for specific customers—even if only a competitor carries that item. Niall Brougham, manager of the Balinteer store in Dublin's southern suburbs, says this service is just good business. "We recognize that we can't carry everything for everybody in the store—it's just not possible," he told us. "However, we do have a spot in the storeroom where we keep special items for customers who have requested them. For example, there's one woman who really prefers a certain brand of juice that's carried only by our competitor Tesco down the street. This customer would do all of her shopping with us, and drive to Tesco just for the juice. So what we do now is go down to Tesco ourselves and buy that juice, bring it back to our store, and keep it here for her. That not only saves her an extra trip, but it also keeps her out of a competitor's store."

Superquinn pays close attention to the types of people it hires and how those people are positioned in the stores. For example, every aisle in the store has an "aisle monitor," whose job is to make sure that the aisle is properly stocked, clean, and free of obstacles. Each aisle has a sign posted with the aisle monitor's name and photograph so that customers know whom to ask for help. In addition, trained cheese and wine specialists can guide customers through a sampling and purchase and tell shoppers anything they need to know about a specific vintage or cheese. And all Superquinn butchers and fishmongers are trained in culinary skills as well as the art of sausage-making or filleting, so they can help recommend cuts and preparation ideas to customers.

Sometimes, going the extra mile means, literally, *going the extra mile.* A case in point involved Jerry Twomey, a project manager with Superquinn who used to manage one of the company's stores. "One time, something got out of hand with a customer while I was away," he recalled. "When I returned, I was made aware of it, and I immediately jumped in my car and drove out to the customer's house to apologize for our error and see if there was anything we could do to make up for it. I ended up spending two hours there, talking about all sorts of things. I think we spent only fifteen minutes discussing the problem; the rest of the time we talked about the weather, their children. Sure, we resolved the problem, and they appreciated it. But we also made them feel that we really cared about them and, in the process, learned a lot about what was important to them."

3. **Exceed customers' expectations.** While there are many points of difference between Superquinn and its competitors, some programs are clearly light-years ahead of anything most other retailers are doing for their customers. One such program is the company's child-care service. Every Superquinn store is equipped with a playhouse area—staffed by trained child-care specialists—where customers can leave their children to play, free of charge, while they shop. The program, the brainchild of Superquinn Customer and Human Resource Adviser Margaret Jones, was started twenty-five years ago and has grown to be one of the principal draws for mothers. "We truly believe that our child-care centers remove the burden of grocery shopping for our customers with kids," Jones said. "The kids actually look forward to 'going shopping,' and the mothers can shop without hassles and without the worry about what their kids are doing."

Interestingly, Jones pointed out, there has been a tremendous unexpected benefit to the program. "Because we don't have pre-school in Ireland, Superquinn has become, in effect, schools that help children learn and land in the community," she said. "I can't tell you how many times we've gotten comments from schools in the area that say they can tell within six months that a Superquinn store has opened nearby because of the difference in the entry class to junior school. The children are completely socialized, they under-stand the rules, they know how to share and generally how to play together."

The child-care centers are not cheap. According to Jones, Superquinn invests $1 million a year in the program. But, she noted, the program more than pays for itself in the goodwill and loyalty it engenders. "Yes, they're expensive, and they don't take in any money on their own, but they're an example of what you do because it feels right," she said. "We've had lots of women in our customer panels tell us that they came to us initially for the playhouse, and they're still shopping here even though their kids are sixteen. And we know that a lot of people drive past our competitors to shop with us just because of the playhouse."

Superquinn has also reaped major benefits from its SuperClub customer-loyalty program. Ireland's first such program in the retail industry, SuperClub is managed by SuperClub Target Marketing (which is wholly owned by Superquinn) and includes more than twenty partner companies. Customers enrolled in SuperClub accu-mulate points based on various interactions with partner compa-nies—most often, buying specific products or services. Customers can then cash in their points to buy gifts from the SuperClub cata-log or receive discounts for purchases at partner companies.

In and of itself, the program may not seem special. Many com-panies offer customer-loyalty programs. What makes SuperClub unusual is how Superquinn uses the program to create services val-ued by customers (which helps explain why 80 percent of the com-pany's customers use their SuperClub cards). For instance, the company's famous "goof points" program rewards customers with additional SuperClub points for finding and pointing out problems in the stores—such as a wobbly shopping cart, an out-of-date product, a depleted supply of plastic produce bags, etc. The idea is sheer genius: It turns the company's entire customer base into troubleshooters, it infuses an element of fun into the shopping experience, and it keeps the store's employees on their toes.

The SuperClub program also makes it possible for Superquinn to understand its customer base more fully. First, the card clearly identifies customers as members of a particular household, which gives Superquinn the ability to garner information not only on specific transactions but also on the purchases of entire households over the course of time. Furthermore, when a customer presents his or her SuperClub card at checkout, the cashier—by swiping the card into the point-of-sale system—can display some very useful information on the POS screen. On the cashier's side of the screen, for example, the customer's name appears, which enables the cashier to appropriately address the customer. On the customer's screen, a running tally of SuperClub points is displayed, thus giving instant feedback on where he or she stands.

"Many companies make the mistake of making loyalty the game," said Tobin. "Loyalty isn't the game. It's the result of a well-played game."

A third program that is gaining in popularity is Tusa Bank, the joint venture between Superquinn and Trustee Savings Bank. Tusa not only offers customers the convenience of doing their banking while grocery shopping but also enables consumers to enjoy in a financial institution all of the high-service qualities that Superquinn embodies. "The challenge with Tusa was really to design a bank that is on the customers' side," noted Jerry Twomey, who was Superquinn's point person in the joint venture. Added Tobin: "Tusa is really a good point of difference for us. Customers will enjoy a nice interaction, good service, personal attention, longer hours, and SuperClub points as well." And with Tusa tied into customers'

SuperClub cards, the service and cross-marketing possibilities for Superquinn are endless.

Bringing Quality Products to Market

SUPERQUINN'S FORMULA FOR SUCCESS

SECONDARY ATTRIBUTE: PRODUCT

- Has an in-store bakery that produces fresh bread every four hours.
- Offers a high-quality salad bar and home meal-replacement items for time-pressed customers.
- Insists on twice-daily deliveries of produce, meat, and seafood to guarantee freshness.
- Works with a select group of suppliers on an exclusive basis to ensure product quality and innovation.
- Offers its own private-label program of products that meet even higher standards for quality and freshness.
- Cuts most seafood and meat to order to further promote the freshness notion.

For Feargal Quinn and his team, the most important thing next to service is having consistently good products unlike those you can get anywhere else in the country. Or, as Twomey said, "Of course we want to completely wow customers with our service. But if the food's not fresh, of excellent quality, why would they come back?"

Indeed, Superquinn has made a name for itself on the basis of its innovative approaches to sourcing, handling, and merchandising grocery products—whether it's produce, meat, seafood, or baked goods.

1. **A baker's dozen.** Immediately upon entering a Superquinn store, shoppers are treated to the smell of freshly baked breads. And it's not

just a marketing gimmick. With six to ten bakers working the ovens in each store, Superquinn lays claim to being the largest bakery in Ireland (the stores of the company's competitors are all served by a central bakery, according to Niall Brougham). Because of the company's policy to never sell bread that's more than four hours old, customers can be sure that the loaf they're buying is fresh.

2. **Salad days.** Although common in many North American grocery stores, the fresh salad bar is a concept in its infancy in Irish supermarkets. Each Superquinn store has a beautiful display of vegetables and salad items that are replenished throughout the day. A salad-bar "manager" is responsible for ensuring the quality and presentation of the salad bar. Brougham explained that a store policy currently in place helps the salad-bar manager keep the products looking good while keeping the managers of the fruit and vegetable displays elsewhere in the store on their toes. "In my store, Carl is responsible for quality control of the salad bar," he said. "When Carl thinks something needs to be upgraded on his bar, he's free to scout out the fruit and vegetable displays for an item that may not meet our standards for selling to customers, but would be fine for a salad. If he finds such a piece, he's free to take it from the display. Of course, this will affect the margins of the guy in charge of the fruit and veg display, so it encourages him to only put out the best."

Complementing the salad bar is Superquinn's successful "home meal-replacement" (HMR) program, which offers customers a variety of high-quality prepared foods ready to be taken home, warmed up, and eaten by hungry, time-pressed consumers. Again, although HMR has taken hold in many U.S. supermarkets, it's still a novelty in Ireland. But, judging from the positive response to Superquinn's HMR offerings, that's likely to change soon.

3. **Freshness and safety count.** Superquinn insists on twice-daily deliveries—at 7 A.M. and in the early afternoon—of all its fruits, vegetables, meats, and fish. To encourage the practice, each store

sports only a very small cooling room—no more than a few hundred square feet. When a delivery arrives, employees must discard product that is either on the shelves or in the cases—a policy that would seem wasteful. But, according to Tobin, Superquinn stores have been able to master the forecasting necessary to make such a practice work. "Our waste on fruits and vegetables is between 1 percent and 3 percent," he explained. "And while no one is happy about throwing products away, we encourage our colleagues to have some waste. Because if they don't, they're understocking. To make sure that we're in that range, we have a really tight infrastructure with our suppliers, good communications, so that we can adjust the forecast easily if we have to."

To further demonstrate product freshness to customers, Superquinn posts signs above each produce display that indicate exactly when each batch was picked. In the meat and fish sections, the staff avoids pre-cutting large quantities of product in favor of cutting to order. "Customers want to see their meat or fish being cut just for them," Tobin said. "It really helps drive home the idea of freshness for them."

Meat safety is always a concern, but it has become particularly important in recent years following the mad cow disease scare in Britain. To reassure customers that its meats have been properly handled, the temperature of each display is checked, recorded, and posted every fifteen minutes. And to reassure shoppers that the meat is safe, Superquinn maintains 100 percent DNA traceability of every piece of meat it sells. In other words, if a customer has a problem with a chop or steak, the store can trace the cut back to the exact animal from which it was taken. "Certainly, this is retrospective," noted Tobin. "But it does reassure customers, because they feel confident that we would never take any chances with our meat, given all these safety checks."

For customers seeking the highest standards of food quality, Superquinn offers the private label "Superquinn Select." Products bearing the Select label are subject to strict standards relating to food safety, taste, tenderness, freshness, animal welfare, and "Irishness" (which is particularly important to a small country whose industries rely upon strong support of residents for survival).

4. **Innovative products.** Superquinn is roundly recognized for its innovation in bringing new products to the tables of the Irish people. One of the best-known items is its sausage. The Irish are "mad about sausage," said Tobin. With only eleven stores in Dublin, Superquinn controls about 32 percent of the city's sausage market (about 15 percent countrywide). Unfortunately for foreigners, the sausages can be bought only in Ireland, as Superquinn has no intention of selling them anywhere but in its stores. "People come from all over for our sausages—it's one of the big things that get people in the stores," Tobin said. "If we sold them elsewhere, we couldn't control the quality, and we wouldn't be getting people into our stores." That's not to say that foreign visitors haven't tried to bring them home. According to Tobin, Americans routinely try to smuggle them back into the States—mostly to no avail. "The customs guys at JFK [Airport] love our sausages," he said, laughing.

Tobin pointed out that the ingredients—and the fact that the sausage is made fresh every day in the store—set Superquinn's sausage apart. Most sausages have about 30 percent meat, with the rest made up of cereal fillers. Superquinn sausages are 65 percent meat and 35 percent fillers. This, combined with the Superquinn proprietary seasoning, gives the company a true destination product.

Perhaps the only other food that the Irish eat more of than sausage is potatoes. Tobin pointed out that the Irish are extremely demanding when it comes to potatoes, and that Superquinn had a tough time getting potatoes that pleased its customers. So the company decided to develop its own potato that would exhibit all the characteristics that customers wanted. "We worked with a company in Germany to develop the seeds, and then partnered with a farm here in Ireland to grow the potatoes," said Brougham. "It's our best-selling potato—it's superb. And none of our competitors would ever put themselves through that trouble just over a potato."

The potato story is reflective of a larger philosophy at Super-quinn that governs its relationships with suppliers. To ensure prod-uct freshness, safety, quality, and innovation, Superquinn works with a select group of suppliers—the company calls them "partners"—on an exclusive basis. "We're going to do business with the most inno-vative beef supplier, the one with the best hygiene and DNA trace-ability," said Tobin. "The best seafood supplier. The best produce supplier. And our relationship will be exclusive in Ireland, so that although our suppliers can work with anyone outside the country, here they work only with us."

What makes these arrangements work, said Tobin, is the fact that there is complete pricing transparency throughout each relation-ship—a rarity in the grocery industry. "They know how much we make on an item, we know how much they make, and we work as a team," he explained. "Our partners are free to go around the store and make comments to me—negative or positive—and I will make comments to them. We want to work with partners who will help us drive business for both of us."

Empowerment Is the Key to Great Service

A few minutes spent with any Superquinn employee—"colleagues" in company parlance—are enough to convince anyone that these people love their jobs, and that this enthusiasm transfers to how the employees treat each other and customers. The root of that enthusiasm is the empower-ment that all employees feel to do what they think is right—and that empowerment starts at the top.

Jerry Twomey recalled several instances in which he helped out col-leagues reporting to him as a store manager—not because there was a pol-icy on how to do it, but because he felt that the company supported him in his decisions. One day, he discovered that a colleague's husband had been out of work for two months, and that the couple were having trouble mak-ing their rent payment. So he cut a check for that month's rent from the company checkbook and helped organize two job interviews for her husband. The following week, the woman's husband was working. "That is something that I feel we as a company have to do for our colleagues," Twomey said. "If they feel that they are wanted and look forward to coming to work, they are going to make my job so much easier."

But empowerment doesn't mean that employees have free rein. "The difficulty in our model is determining how you can empower people and still let everyone know that they can't do something that is against the culture of the company," explained Feargal Quinn. "So we try to always communicate to our colleagues that they are allowed to do what they think is right as long as their actions add to our services. For instance, if you think something is good but can be better, great. But you can't take a particular sign down because you don't like the color—that's not adding to the service."

In the end, service can mean many things to many people. For Twomey, service—from a customer point of view—is pretty simple. "I think our customers define service this way," he said. "They can come in and get everything they want to get, and can be looked after in the process. They're made to feel a part of the company, and they come out happy. If a customer comes out of our store frustrated, we haven't delivered our service."

From our point of view, Superquinn represents a Consumer Relevancy paradox. The company clearly dominates on service, but its product differentiation is so great that one could claim it has also achieved a 5 in product. And since Quinn is so monomaniacally dedicated to serving customers in every way possible, his company is aggressive on price (though not a price leader), seeks to create an intimate bond with its customers, and rates highly even on access. Can't shop because your spouse has called and informed you she is bringing an important client home? No problem. The Superquinn team will be happy to special-deliver your groceries to you. In fact, Superquinn managers are given incentives depending on how well they manage their business to certain households. As for access, if you want anything in a Superquinn, the tenets of the cult of service dictate that someone will stop whatever he's doing (unless, of course, he's already assisting a customer) to either help you find it or actually get it for you.

The company does overextend a bit in terms of creating an experience for shoppers, suggesting to us that it may be leaving a few gross margin points on the table. Earlier in this book, we said Superquinn practiced unconscious Relevancy. It is simply one of the finest companies we've seen. No company is perfect, however, and if Superquinn were to try to expand dramatically, it would have to either sacrifice some of its slavish devotion to customers or really put pressure on its bottom line.

Case Study

Tremor: Whole Lot of Shakin' Goin' On

Claudia Kotchka carries two business cards, an appropriate gesture for someone whose life and passions span two unique cultures, each—perhaps ironically—contained within the solid, tradition-bound walls of Procter & Gamble. Her "Procter" card reads "Claudia Kotchka, Vice President, eBusiness Ventures, Procter & Gamble." Her second card reads "Claudia Kotchka, CEO and Chief Barrier Buster, Tremor." Between the two cards lies the story beneath this case study, a story not about how a manufacturer can use Consumer Relevancy to sell a product but, rather, about how a manufacturer sells when Relevancy *is* the product. "The whole business-card thing was interesting," Kotchka told us. "They came around and asked me what I wanted on my business cards, and I said, 'CEO, Tremor,' and they said, 'No, how about something else?' So, I said, 'Okay, how about Chief Barrier Buster?' and they said, 'Well, no.' So, we settled on Vice President, eBusiness, and I got a Tremor business card too." That spirit of understanding the importance of working both inside and outside the P&G system has served Kotchka well and helps at least partially explain how she moved Tremor from idea to project to product in less than a year.

Tremor is a unique venture for Procter & Gamble. For one thing, it's an almost pure service offering—that is, the product is a service. For another, Tremor actually encourages the solicitation of business from direct P&G competitors. The Tremor team's organizational model has no parallel inside Procter, and if all that's not enough, Tremor violates the Holiest of Holy P&G principles—it recruits members from the outside of an organization that, until now, has always promoted from within rather than recruit specialists from the outside.

Even as you read this, Tremor is very much a work in progress, and the ultimate design and manifestation on the Internet is almost certain to change based on consumer leanings. In fact, based on continual customer feedback, the Tremor site will be changing constantly. So, before we explain its business model, let's look back at its brief history. "It started when I was in fem care [feminine care] at P&G," Kotchka explained. "One of our most important target audiences was teenage girls, and so we were always trying to find ways to connect with teenage girls and to offer them things that were new and different. And we knew it was important to try to get their input."

That input, however, proved elusive. "We just couldn't find anyplace on the Internet to get it," Kotchka remembered. "So we thought, maybe we should start a place [website] for teenage girls. Teenagers in particular are a difficult group to reach, and from the beginning we understood that it was important to have a two-way conversation rather than 'shouting' at teenage girls. We actually were thinking about starting an e-commerce site, but we realized pretty quickly it wouldn't represent a good business proposition for the company. Not enough teenage girls have credit cards of their own or spend a lot of money online."

Kotchka knew she had the beginning of a great idea and used Procter's traditional process model to help it germinate. "At P&G we're always thinking about what it is the consumer really wants and using those insights to put more definition around the product idea," she said. "So we started talking to teenage boys and girls. We found out they felt lots of things were missing on the Internet, like the chance to be really heard and access to opportunity. When we asked about existing teen sites, we heard things like: 'A lot of the sites designed for teenagers assume we're stupid'; 'They act like all we care about is the latest teen celebrity'; 'We'd like to be able to talk to other teens—people our own age'; 'We'd like a chance to be heard by adults'; and 'We don't get respect.'"

Kotchka and her coconspirators created an Internet hierarchy of teenage needs and decided that there was a white-space opportunity. Teens have many needs, a variety of which could be met by the Internet but weren't. "What we found was that there weren't any sites that teens felt were at the next level—operating a site where teens could get personalized information, had the opportunity not just to speak but to be heard, and go to get access to opportunity—the doors open, if you will," Kotchka said. "Our issue was whether the Web could help them or if a company could help them. We knew there was a big white-space opportunity there, one that fit nicely P&G's core mission of improving the lives of the consumer. We have a visual metaphor for our brand—your first set of car keys—because to a teenager those keys mean they're independent, they can spend time with their friends, and there's a real sense of responsibility."

There's no question that Tremor began as a website idea, but Kotchka is quick to point out that it's not just another dot-com. "We want to be a brand teens trust online *and* offline," she said. "And outside the United States, the Internet isn't as important as cell phones and those kinds of things. As a marketer, you want to be a brand that stands for something to consumers, a brand they can trust in a variety of mediums."

That said, Tremor's original incarnation was as a Web-based presence. The problem, of course, was how to build a site that didn't suffer from the faults of other teen-oriented sites. "We instinctively knew the best thing to do was to have teens develop this site, not us," Kotchka said. "We certainly aren't cool, so we decided to recruit teen 'MVPs'—teens who are early adopters, thought leaders, mobile, very social, connected, online, and very passionate about something."

The landscape of cyberspace is so littered with dazzling business prospectuses and abandoned PowerPoint presentations genteelly begging for venture capital that it's easy to believe that the road to digital hell is paved with good ideas. Kotchka got the idea that eventually became Tremor in January 2000. She went to her boss in the feminine-care business, only to be told there was no funding available. She then took it to A. G. Lafley, currently Procter's president and CEO but then the head of the company's Health and Beauty Care division. Lafley (who was largely responsible for the company's Reflect.com consumer-direct beauty site) was sympathetic but, like Kotchka's direct boss, didn't have any funding.

That left only one place in the P&G pantheon to turn—then-chairman, president, and CEO Durk Jager. "It was A. G.'s idea," Kotchka explained. "He said, 'I don't have any money; go see Durk.' So I did. I said, 'I want to get venture capital for this idea,' and he said, 'No, *I* want to be your venture capitalist.' So he sent me away, and when I came back with my plan, he asked me a question, a really great question: 'Are you set up for success?' he asked. 'If you stay in one of our business units, you'll run into all of our corporate problems, and I should know because I'm the biggest bureaucrat, but I'd be interested in testing a new culture in P&G.' "

Tremor is the result of that experiment in "new culture." "Like any dot-com, we've got our pot of money and our burn-rate calculations," Kotchka said. "And unlike other P&G entities, we have an entirely different compensation system. You get a bonus if you hit milestones, and if you don't hit them you don't, and the whole team gets bonuses—it's all or nothing, which is very different from the traditional P&G model that recognizes and rewards individual excellence. We have our own profit center, funded by the CEO. We have separate office space. All Durk insisted on when he agreed to fund us was that we adhere to two rules: We must follow the company's purpose, values, and principles; and second, we have to be funded internally. That's it. We've hired from the outside. We don't have functions. We have key staffers who live in San Francisco and Los Angeles. You'd think, given our setup, it would be easy to break the rules, but we still have to get people paid, and that means we have to have the right function codes, and our people don't have specific functions, so it's sometimes very hard to get some things done."

Jager's predictions about the problem of being an entrepreneur trapped inside a labyrinthine bureaucracy proved uncannily accurate. The CEO left the company following a dramatic downturn in market capitalization, but the good news for Kotchka and Tremor was that he was succeeded by Lafley, who was a believer. "So we put together a plan and a team and asked ourselves, 'What is it going to take to pull this off?' We built an answer using good, solid P&G strategy work—looking at where we could play, how we could win, and in general challenging ourselves to think about whether or not we had a business that would 'work' in P&G terms,"

Kotchka said. "That's where we came up to the B2B side model. We knew we were marketers who needed something like Tremor, so it was logical to assume it might also be useful to other marketers. We're a B2B marketing-service model, and that's just very different from anything else that P&G has ever done. We're used to selling products here."

Tremor was conceived before business-to-consumer dot-coms began to fall from the NASDAQ stratosphere, losing both their allure and market capitalization in the process. "We actually did all this before the B2Cs crashed," Kotchka said. "But I had taken a hard look at them, and their business models didn't make any sense. Most of them were selling advertising, and we were a huge buyer of that advertising, so we knew they weren't working all that well as advertising vehicles. I mean, here you had all these companies getting all this venture capital, and they had no plans for profitability. It was all so anti-P&G, because we believe that as a company you've always got to be in it for the consumer, and if you're not, whatever you're doing isn't going to work. So we tested the notion of a B2B model with Cover Girl, which is the one big teenage brand we have. We leveraged personal connections in other businesses to float the idea and got an extremely enthusiastic response. Finally, we told ourselves, 'Hey, this looks like it will fly. Let's see if we can put all the pieces together.' "

Those pieces can be roughly grouped into three buckets: the consumer offering, the business model, and future directions. Kotchka began by explaining the consumer offering: "Our mission is to empower teens. But you can't tell teens you're going to empower them, because they don't get it and they don't like it. So you tell them you're offering them an opportunity to speak out and be heard and have doors opened," she said. "Of course, you also have to connect them to other teens and have some relevant content—those are the minimums to play. One of the things our ad agency came up with to describe all this is captured in the phrase 'Type Louder!' And teens understand what that means. When you log on to the site, you hit our home page, which is basically like the front cover of a magazine, with headline stories you can personalize. Once you're on the home page, you might type in that you're interested in, say, salsa dancing in the Midwest, or safe sex, or relationships, politics—all kinds of topics—and you'll be taken to all types of sites that relate to your interest, sites that are actually put together by a teenager who's passionate and knowledgeable about the area. You can go to that site and become a member, and if you do, you get access to the site's bulletin boards and chats. Naturally, you don't have to be a member. Let's say you're a high school soccer player. You might go to a site featuring an online chat with a college coach explaining what it takes to play at the college level. Or you might go to another site where one of our authors has reviewed a concert or interviewed the band, and what you're reading is what a teen thought, not what some adult thought. And there's a product-and-service model that might let you test a new lipstick by clicking on and receiving a free sample before the product gets to market."

Kotchka said Tremor's goal is to recruit 8,000 domestic "MVPs"—teens who are mobile, visible, and passionate—into the site's corps of participants. "Being an MVP doesn't necessarily mean being the captain of the cheerleading squad—it means being thought of as a leader by your peers," she explained. "That's one of the comments we received from our initial research. Teens believe everybody thinks they're all the same, when the truth is, we've got a really diverse set of teens with really diverse sets of interests." The Tremor team and a marketing service went to places where teens hang out, like malls, in the top twenty-five U.S. cities. Potential participants were screened and then interviewed. The Tremor value proposition and opportunities are explained to those who pass through the selection process. Those who accept the offer are signed up, unless they're under eighteen, in which case a parental waiver is required. "The only glitch is that they have to have access to the Internet, and we prefer home access," Kotchka explained. "Other than that, they just have to be willing and be early adopters and thought leaders."

For P&G, the Tremor business model is a bit out of the box. "Our charge was to 'go forth and find revenue,'" Kotchka joked. "A. G. [Lafley] asked us if we thought we needed to be a separate company in order to sell to competitors, which he felt very strongly we should do. I guess one way of looking at the 'good news' is that when you look at where teens are spending their money, you find they're spending most of it in categories such as music, in which P&G doesn't currently play. So I don't have to really worry about our ability to sell our services to P&G's traditional competition to make this work. And, in terms of the B2B offering, the credibility of P&G proves immensely helpful even when you're marketing to our traditional competitors."

The model is simple. Let's say Unilever calls Tremor and says it wants to launch a new hair-care product. Kotchka and her team can do a variety of things to help Unilever design the product. "We know which teens are hair-involved and which aren't," she explained, "so we can get them feedback on the whole product idea and concept. Then there are things we can do for them from a marketing perspective. We'll find advocates for them or help them develop advocates who will recommend the product to friends. The first phase is involvement. If any teen helps design a product and/or provides feedback, they become almost automatic advocates. The second phase is that they go out and tell their friends. So the whole idea is to get them involved, let them sample, and find out who likes it. We give them incentives, from fun ways to tell their friends about the product through samples and e-mails to getting them to write about the product on their sites. The only thing is, we can't ask them to say nice things if they don't like the product. The teens like this because they like accessing products before they're in the marketplace. You could say we provide early market seeding."

What they get, she pointed out, are a lot of opportunities, such as trying products first and interviewing the people developing a product. "These kids are so smart. The first question they inevitably ask during an interview is, 'How do you make your money?' So we tell them," said Kotchka. "They tend to be very skeptical of marketing in general. If you are a shampoo manufacturer and you try to tell teenagers your product is neat and cool, they go, 'Yeah. Right.' We let teens say what they want to say. If they say a product sucks, then it sucks." One of the items beta-tested by Tremor was a food product that teens in fact did think "sucked." Even though the feedback was negative, the Tremor team made sure the product reviewers received a letter from the manufacturer whose item they trashed. "The letter said, 'Thanks for your input—here's what we're doing based on what you told us,' " Kotchka said. "In our model, they always hear from us."

Tremor's revenue stream comes not from the teens but from the companies that use the site's services. Kotchka explains that there is a wide range of pricing, although there are two basic revenue models. "For established companies, the pricing is all over the map, depending on, say, whether the company wants access to soccer girls or all teens," she said. "We track the cost of [purchasing commercial marketing] trial and awareness efforts, and we're less than those kinds of things. Then we also look at things like barter in selected cases—what a company has to offer that might be right for us. In the case of smaller companies, where they might have no money but a great idea or great product or service, we might offer to do the entire marketing campaign or handle distribution or something else for a stake in the company. In general, every pricing program is designed to meet the unique needs of a company, and, believe me, all those needs are very, very different."

Even though Tremor is barely off the drawing board, Kotchka and her team are already looking down the road. "This is Phase One of our model," she explained. "We're looking at what other kinds of things we could offer and provide to other companies and P&G. For instance, a lot of cool, neat products don't come from big companies, so maybe through Tremor P&G could help with things like distribution in exchange for taking a stake in a company or sharing in the revenue stream. The next thing we want to do— and do very quickly—is go global. We just have to prove our model first. As a teen, I want to know what's going on in Tokyo or London. I want to be able to talk to other teens on specific topics. Certainly one of the first things to do is to get an Internet site up in the top fifteen global Internet teen markets. But we also want to very quickly move past the Internet as well."

She noted that wireless applications are bigger outside the United States, particularly in Japan and Scandinavia. "We need to look at how teens are using technology, especially those technologies that eventually will get here, so we can speed up the technology transfer," said Kotchka. "There's great learning to be had about how technology moves across platforms. We really have to make sure we're on the leading edge of technology and that we're using what teens use to communicate with—not what we think they should use or what we are comfortable using. That's why we're not just a dot-com. We're using several different technologies in addition to the Internet." Beyond this, Kotchka believes the Tremor model—but perhaps not Tremor itself—could be extended to other age groups.

Authenticity is a key part of the R&D of marketing Tremor's brand of Relevancy. "The culture here is different," Kotchka explained. "Everyone here has the same size desk. Everything is open. We get this great funky furniture really cheap if we let the manufacturer use our space in their ads. We have teenage interns whose job is to hang with us. We're having teenagers decorate our whole space. Our general motto is 'Whatever it takes': We define the work and then match the work to people's experience and skill sets. We just move people around, and to work here you have to be totally flexible. Everybody on the team reports either to me or to Terry Pardue, our Chief Reality Officer. You can't come here if you want to build big hierarchies. One of the things we wanted to eliminate was the command-and-control model. We just don't have that. We've got this naive idea about flat hierarchies. We started with a group of seven, and now we're thirty-five. In the beginning, the right hand didn't know what the left hand was doing, so we had to put processes in place, not hierarchies. But we had to let people know who has decision rights. We've got a chart that says who makes decisions on what, and everybody makes decisions. Our 800-line folks [the Consumer Service group] are on our floor right next to us, which is very different for P&G. They're great. They let us know as soon as something's really right or wrong, which is easy because they're here, not five states away. Everybody here feels empowered, which at Tremor means that people know you've got work to do and you have to get it done, and if you can't, you've got to get help. We don't have politics, which is just the biggest waste of time and energy in almost any company. That said, I wish we were even more externally focused than we are."

Kotchka emphasized that everyone on the team is outside talking to teenagers. "They're the consumer; they're in charge," she said. "We try very hard to do that, but we're still not spending the amount of time doing it that we should."

Tremor is scheduled to launch in mid 2001. Given that, it's a challenge to say where Tremor will eventually end up on the Relevancy matrix. While it clearly intends to dominate on service, it's too soon to identify the attribute on which the site will eventually differentiate itself, because it has no direct competitors—yet. But what excites us about Tremor is that at the heart of its value proposition lies *our* value proposition: Listen to consumers—on their own terms—get ahead of the rest of the pack, and the market should reward you.

SELF-DIAGNOSTIC: SERVICE

- Are you willing to truly customize your product or service offering to match the needs of an individual customer?
- If you're differentiating on service, are your customers educated or informed as a result of having done business with you?
- Does every potential customer entering your business feel that you genuinely care about them, or do you herd them through like sheep?
- Do you routinely talk to your customers, trying to discover what they define as average, good, and superior service?
- Have you approached your competition as a consumer—flown their airline, purchased insurance from them, bought a seat at their stadium? How did their service levels feel to you as a person—not as their competitor?

CHAPTER 5

I Still Haven't Found What I'm Looking For

Access, Physical and Psychological

IN IRELAND, WE RAN across the "Lock Hards" of Dublin, "business-people" identified by their unique and distinctive headgear who have taken access marketing to a whole new level. The Lock Hards patrol Dublin's busy commercial districts, unsolicitously directing harried motorists into tight parking places. "Lock 'er hard, now," they yell at drivers who try to squeeze cars into spaces more appropriate for unicycles. Once an exhausted motorist has succeeded in wrestling his vehicle into the temporary safe harbor of the curb, the Lock Hards approach him. "Sure it'll be safe here, then?" they ask, the very picture of solicitousness. "I could keep my eye on it, although a man's time ought to be worth something to him. Still, you know, the old neighborhood's not what it once was." The Lock Hards have incorporated both dynamics of the access attribute—the physical (where a car can or should be parked) and the psychological (the threat that you might not be able to drive your car upon your return)—into one common market offering.

Consumer businesses could learn something from the Lock Hards. For decades, companies have defined access by the age-old real-estate adage of "location, location, location." And, in fact, access used to be all about real estate. This explains why there's a Golden Arches on every corner from Chicago to the Champs-Élysées and from Louisville to London. It's why there is a gas station on every corner and ATMs in every kind of retail setting. It explains the promiscuous parade of coffee bars, ice cream stores, and nail parlors. It also explains why every mall or public retail space from Nashville to Nice has the same set of stores—The Body Shop, Foot Locker, the Gap, and The Limited—in all their various and sundry mercantile manifestations. More recently, the gas-station/convenience-store industry modified the formula, moving into neighborhoods and central-city locations, and banks dropped branches in high-traffic areas in neighborhoods and suburbs around the country. And companies such as Starbucks, Dunkin' Donuts, CVS, and Walgreens have excelled at monopolizing space in key office buildings, strip malls, thoroughfares, and other "consumer intercept" locations, holding tightly to the belief that location is everything.

However, a new definition of access is starting to win over today's consumers, a definition that has a lot more to do with psychological access—the perception of being able to easily and successfully navigate the physical plant of a business, whether you're talking about a supermarket, bank branch, or auto dealership, and find what you're looking for—than it does with the size of a parking lot or whether you get there by making a right-hand turn.

Now, we're not suggesting that consumers want to be inconvenienced. After all, access is like the ante in a poker game. If you're not accessible, you're not in the game—you're not in business. But access today is clearly a multidimensional attribute, full of nuances that extend far beyond real estate. Location no longer is everything; it's simply one component in the mosaic of differentiation. We believe there are two primary reasons for this change. First, we are largely a mobile society—ready, willing, and able to travel some distance to get what we want. Second, the Internet allows us to reach nearly anything, anywhere, at any time.

Today access has less to do with location than with giving consumers the ability to interact with a company where or when they want with minimum interference or hassle. In the banking business, for instance, access is no longer just about building branch offices; today it's also about establishing a network of easily accessible ATMs. For a retailer, access is about providing shopability—or a mental map—for customers. It's about ease and convenience. It's about shoppers finding what they want and personalizing that store to their individual needs.

This new and emergent class of access is being driven by such developments as the resurgence of mail order, the popularity of QVC and the Home Shopping Network, and the steady rise of Internet shopping. Among the most mainstream of the new access-dominant businesses is Amazon.com. The company's website is easy to locate and navigate and includes myriad value-added services, demonstrating that the new definition of access encompasses more than just shopping. Amazon doesn't simply provide access to books or CDs; it provides access to community, through such services as book reviews by other consumers.

In the physical world, Dollar General, while dominating on price, also has successfully captured this new notion of access by focusing on ease of internal navigation in its almost 5,000 stores. "We need to be quick in and quick out," said Bob Carpenter, the company's chief administrative officer. "Our stores have to be about 6,500 to 7,500 square feet, and the reason we want that size is because when you walk in the store, you need to be able to stand in the door and see every part of the store—nothing to block you, so that you can see what you want and get it and come out. That means that I can't have any counters that go above eye level. In a small store, if the counters go above eye level it feels very crowded to a customer. They can't see what they want, and they have to go around and search everywhere and try to find it."

Understanding that access is about shoppers finding what they're looking for, Dollar General has established a consistent "map" for all of its stores. "We put nonperishable food items immediately on the left when you walk in," said Carpenter. "Those are items that people pick up quickly, and they usually come in to grab one of those. And when they do, they also generally want to grab some detergent or some housecleaning chemical or paper towels, so we put those on the back wall. And then you might need to pick up deodorant and toothpaste, so we put those on the right side up toward the front, so that then you've got to walk past some of our basic soft lines in order to get the toothpaste on the way to the door. Now, if you really just wanted to get the two main things, you could get them easily at the front—that would be the nonperishable food on the left and the tooth-paste on the right. The point is that you can walk into any one of the stores, and everything will be in exactly the same place, so that you know where they are and you can see it the second you walk in."

With a very different type of model, Amway also has made access a point of differentiation. Consumers can buy almost anything they need—insurance, autos, appliances, furniture, food, and other packaged goods—and have it delivered without ever leaving their homes. And it's all done with a model that is based on a consumer-to-consumer, neighbor-to-neighbor community.

Known for face-to-face encounters with potential customers, Amway distributors come from the ranks of ordinary citizens looking for ways to increase their monthly incomes and find new careers. The company has built its reputation as a convenient, easily accessible retail source for house-hold detergents, cleansers, and personal-care items. Along with other home-delivery retailers, Amway has helped define the attribute of access for millions of Americans, as well as consumers in other parts of the world.

And the company is expanding its model of access with its new Internet site, called Quixtar. Established in 1999, Quixtar is both an online shop-ping arena and a place to recruit new distributors. Consumers can buy the traditional home and health-care products—soaps, detergents, vitamin-powered drinks, and water-treatment items. But the new site also offers a range of electronics, jewelry, and personal items—more than 10,000 prod-ucts from over 1,500 companies.[1] A customer can purchase a Sharp televi-sion/VCR combo, a Seiko watch, or hundreds of other products without ever knowing that the site is a branch of the Amway Co. According to Ken McDonald, the Amway executive heading up the e-commerce venture, the Internet site seeks to distinguish itself by offering a wide range of non-Amway products. "We're convinced," he said, "we can make more money . . . by building two businesses that are different than just by tweak-ing one business."[2]

The sense of community these businesses create is a form of psychological access, in contrast to the physical access of an actual building, website, or interior store layout. This psychological access is often tightly linked to the attribute of experience. In this sense, access serves as a portal—an open door, figurative in some instances, literal in others—to the consumer experience that is tied to a particular business. Consider a city block with four bars across the street from one another, each attracting a completely different crowd. The physical access is the same for all four, but the psychological access is very different.

Starbucks also serves as an example. The coffee chain's ubiquitous units are placed in high-traffic locations, and therefore are accessible in a physical sense. However, the psychological accessibility associated with an individual unit has as much to do with the company's success as does ubiquity. In one neighborhood, the Starbucks shop might have a sleek, upscale feel, appropriate for that area's consumers. In another, oversized couches and funky lighting might better fit the community. Such an approach transcends physical access. Consumers enter not so much for the cup of coffee but because they're looking for access to a community of people like themselves.

During the course of our research for this book, we began to notice examples of this in our own experience. On a visit to Los Angeles, Fred was struck by how different the crowds were as one moved down the block from Rande Gerber's Skybar, with its sophisticated and hip California crowd, to a bleeding-edge bar full of the tattooed, branded, ritually scarified, and pierced set, and on to a Starbucks where PIBs (people in black) mumbled earnestly into their cell phones. Fred, the epitome of Midwestern chic despite his own fashionable Manhattan address, noted that all of the establishments operating on one of L.A.'s hottest strips used access as a way of creating a sense of affiliation, which in turn was leveraged into community building, which was then leveraged into a commercial model.

Back in New York, recalling his experience in the L.A. Starbucks, Fred complained that the PIBs didn't seem particularly interested in a customer who didn't know a latte from a chai, let alone a grande from a venti. Could it be that he was right? Was Starbucks really trying to chase out business if it didn't come swathed in black? We decided to put it to a test, a little participant anthropology done in the name of Relevancy.

Fred's office sits next door to a Starbucks in midtown Manhattan. You have to pass by one of New York's thousands of street vendors selling coffee for a dollar or less to get to the Starbucks, where you can get the same size coffee for almost $4. Waiting until the morning rush was over, we entered the Starbucks—Fred dressed in his Midwestern best and Ryan bearded and clothed head to toe in black. The clerk watched us enter and must have noticed us talking to each other, since we were the only customers in the store. "I'd like a coffee," Fred said. The clerk rolled his eyes and, with a sigh as palpable as the wind off a Jamaican Blue Mountain top, asked, "What kind of coffee?" "You know," Fred said, "a regular coffee." "You want a Colombian supremo?" the clerk asked. "Sure, I guess so," Fred responded. "What size do you want?" the clerk asked, by now avoiding any eye contact. "A large," Fred said. "Grande?" the clerk suggested. "Is that a large?" Fred asked. With a look of disgust, the clerk spit out, "We have four sizes: short, tall, grande, and venti." Fred, now completely confused, offered, "How large is tall?" This prompted a snort from the clerk as he grabbed and displayed a tall cup. "That's pretty small for a tall" was Fred's reaction. "Can I have the biggest one?" "Venti?" the clerk asked. "If that's a large!" Fred retorted, feeling his Detroit upbringing rising in his throat. Thankfully, Ryan intervened, and the process was mercifully completed.

The clerk turned to Ryan, smiled and, with a look that said, "Sorry you're encumbered by a philistine," asked, "What can I get for you, sir?" "I'd like a grande misto," Ryan replied. "Certainly, sir," the clerk said, producing a perfect café au lait. "See you again," he said, pointedly ignoring Fred. On the way out, Fred asked, "So what's a misto? It's not on the menu." "It's a café au lait, and the Starbucks menu is a little like the prices at Tiffany—if you have to ask, it's not for you," Ryan responded.

Fred pondered the point for a moment, walked over to a trash container, and dumped his venti Colombian supremo. "What's up, brother?" he asked, approaching a street vendor. "Doin' good," the vendor replied. "Whatcha need?" "How 'bout a large coffee, my man?" Fred answered.

"Hey, no problem," the vendor said, taking his dollar. "That feels better," Fred said, and it did.

The search for a certain comfort level, community affiliation, and sense of connection is crucial for consumers in today's world, where people rush through their lives, where they have numerous acquaintances but few friends, and where Internet chat rooms sometimes serve as the only relief from an otherwise disconnected existence. What's the lesson for consumer businesses? There is a pot of gold for the retailer or service provider that can create a sense of connectivity and community—that is, psychological access—as a means of differentiation.

The concept of access as a portal extends to other attributes as well. The insurance maverick Progressive Corp.'s accessibility is the starting point for the service that it provides. Access begins at the scene of an accident when a claims adjuster pulls up in a white SUV bearing the Progressive logo. Damage assessment is done on the spot, followed by the company's Immediate Response claims service. Access—both physical and psychological—acting as a portal to service.

The potential power of converging access and price spurred the establishment of Priceline.com and its Internet-based, name-your-own-price formula. While the notion of haggling over price is as old as commerce itself, it has rarely been a scalable model in the modern world of business-to-consumer transactions, with the possible exception of auto purchases. Clearly, Priceline sought to dominate on price, yet even from the beginning its business model depended on accessibility provided by the Internet. The fact that Priceline's initial success in areas such as food and gasoline purchasing didn't continue doesn't negate the potential of how Internet access can be leveraged by price operators. In fact, it can be argued that the Internet adds an entirely new meaning to the term *access*.

"All of society is reengineering the information layer of what it is that we do," said Jay Walker, founder of Priceline.com.[3] "Inasmuch as things are information, they are going to change. What brand you want to buy is information; what price you want to pay is information; what substitutions you might be willing to take is information; what store you want to go to is information; what you're buying this week is information. All these information components were always frozen in a very specific configuration, which is: Store advertises products; consumer looks at ad; consumer makes decisions; consumer writes decisions down; consumer goes to store; consumer tries to execute decisions. We said, Guess what, that information architecture is probably not the winning architecture in an age where information can be processed in new and different ways. We set about saying what the information architecture would really look like in a world in which new architecture not only could be created but also could be designed very specifically to deliver value to all players in the market. So that's what we did—we designed a new information architecture."

Of course, as with any of the consumer-value attributes, there are exceptions to the rule of access. In fact, there are some consumer businesses, such as Strand Book Store and Filene's Basement, which have succeeded in part by hindering easy access. Sometimes, it seems, the thrill is in the hunt.

Strand Book Store, at the corner of Broadway and Twelfth Street in New York's Greenwich Village, is renowned for its vast inventory of new and used books, hundreds of thousands of them stacked on shelves that rise to the ceiling. There is a semblance of order—books are arranged by subject, then by author—but the sheer scale makes finding a particular book a daunting experience. And for those customers without acrophobia, the store provides ladders for reaching the tops of the stacks.

The Strand has successfully made browsing and its quirky layout essential elements of its identity, and the store appeals to thousands of tourists and loyal locals. But such an operation is unique and rarely if ever scalable.

Need proof? Consider Filene's Basement. Housed in the basement of the landmark Filene's department store in downtown Boston, the original Filene's Basement served as a clearinghouse for merchandise and was a pioneer of off-price retailing. It was a bargain-hunter's paradise, where one could score a past-season name-brand suit for half the original price. Part of the store's "charm" was its chaos. Items—mostly clothing—were packed on shelves and in bins wherever there was room, and shoppers would squeeze through the narrow pathways, vying with each other for a particularly valuable item. Pricing seemed simple: Items went on sale at a given percentage depending on how long they had been on the shelf. In practice, however, the process was anything but simple. Customers would dig through a pile of clothes, look for a date on the tag, then check the discount list to determine the actual sale price. If an item had been on the shelf for a week, say, it was 25 percent off; two to three weeks, 50 percent off; more than three weeks, 75 percent off. Consumers would come dressed for the occasion, knowing they would have to try on clothing in the aisle, as there were no fitting rooms.

The format worked for years; Filene's Basement even became a tourist destination. Seeking to replicate the formula elsewhere, Filene's began opening discount stores in select cities around the country. In a leveraged buyout, company management took the Filene's Basement unit public and opened more stores. But the uniqueness of the original outlet was missing in the new stores, and, after several years of expansion and mounting losses, Filene's Basement Corp. filed for bankruptcy protection. In February 2000, Filene's was purchased by Value City Department Stores.

Other companies, like Coors beer and Krispy Kreme doughnuts, created a sense of exclusivity through their inaccessibility. Like the Strand or Filene's Basement, these businesses turned lack of access into a point of competitive differentiation. However, again, the model is rarely scalable, or, once it is expanded, the mystique associated with its former inaccessibility is lost.

There are also cases where apparent access is, in fact, no access at all. Take automated telephone menus, which were designed to simplify the customer-service process but often succeed only in frustrating consumers by limiting their access to a live human being.

Companies pursuing the myth of excellence are often tempted to think of access in traditional, highly one-dimensional terms, opening as many physical distribution points as possible. Years ago, the management of 7-Eleven took this path, with the result that shuttered 7-Elevens became a routine feature of the urban landscape across the United States. The manufacturing equivalent of this folly would be to open plants wherever any significant customer was located, rather than as pieces of an integrated supply chain. There are exceptions, of course. In industries like commercial paper, mill location can be a critical element of total strategy. But for most businesses this simply isn't true.

Applying the Conceptual Model to Access

It's clear, then, that physical access alone will not be a viable strategy going forward for businesses that choose to dominate or differentiate on access. To succeed, they must take the concept of access to a far higher level. When our conceptual model (Figure 5.1) for Consumer Relevancy is applied to access, here's what happens:

FIGURE 5.1

Competing on Access

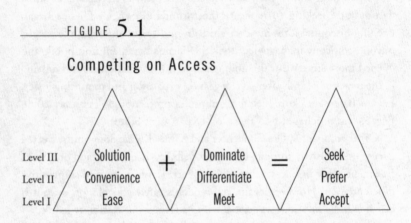

Level III	Solution	Dominate	Seek
Level II	Convenience	Differentiate	Prefer
Level I	Ease	Meet	Accept

At the basic threshold of competing on access (Level I), consumers are saying, "Make it *easy* for me to find what I need, and to get in and out of your store or location in a hurry." At the level of consumer preference (Level II), consumers are telling businesses to make the experience *convenient* for them. At the highest level, in which they actively seek a company (Level III), consumers define access not only in terms of ease and convenience but also in terms of whether that business provides *solutions* to their lifestyle problems or offers that psychological sense of connectivity and community. For instance, some consumer-direct companies such as Hallmark and Blue Mountain will remind customers about birthdays and anniversaries by sending an e-mail a few days in advance. The companies can then deliver a card or a floral bouquet in time for the special day, thus providing consumers with an easy solution.

Our consumer research helps clarify how this conceptual model of access applies in the real world. For one thing, location placed very low on the list of responses among those related to access, shattering the long-established notion that location is everything. The elements of access that mattered most to consumers exist inside the four walls of a building or inside the computer screen, rather than in the ease of getting there. Brick-and-mortar businesses hoping to compete on access should focus on four key areas: facility cleanliness, price visibility, convenient hours, and facility organization and layout. Two similar factors were considered important for online businesses: clearly stated charges such as shipping (the virtual equivalent of price visibility) and the ability to quickly find what you're looking for (organization and layout). A third key factor in the wired world was the ability to rely on the company when consumers were in a bind and needed something quickly or unexpectedly.

1. **Cleanliness.** First and foremost, consumers focus on a facility's physical appearance: Is it well-maintained and free of trash, clutter, and obstacles such as unpacked boxes, portable shelving, racks of merchandise or literature, ladders, buckets, and items that have fallen off the shelf? Do customers have to go out of their way to find or retrieve an item (such as film, which is often stocked behind the customer-service desk at supermarkets and drugstores)? Accessibility applies to both the physical and the psychological space—particularly in the case of grocery stores and drug and convenience stores, where consumers pointed to a clean, well-maintained store as the aspect of access that they considered most important.

2. **Price visibility.** The second factor in the access equation is clear and visible prices. Consumers want the prices clearly marked on the bin, the shelf, or the item itself, so that when they arrive at the checkout counter they don't have to wait for a price check. Many people say they feel embarrassed in these situations, as customers waiting in line behind them grow increasingly irritated. While grocery stores have implemented unit pricing—a helpful service to those consumers

who comparison-shop—the majority of shoppers don't understand its function or are confused by the numbers.

Clear, visible prices are particularly important to online shoppers. Consumers repeatedly told us they wanted to see all charges—especially shipping and handling fees—stated up front, not hidden in the small print at the end of an order. Successful Internet retailers like Amazon.com state such charges clearly, taking some of the anxiety out of the ordering experience. Consumers configuring a new computer at Dell Computer's website receive an updated price for the total package clearly marked and stated both as a onetime price and as a monthly charge for a business lease.

3. **Convenient hours.** Today, businesses from convenience stores to restaurants operate on the "always-open" model—twenty-four hours a day, seven days a week. Yet, a 24/7 strategy is not the best solution for every company. Considerations such as product offerings, consumer demographics, and physical location must be taken into account. For businesses that serve the very young or very old, for instance, such a strategy is likely to be fruitless, because those target consumers rarely venture out of their houses after dinner.

Of course, in the case of the Internet, a business is open throughout the day and night, ready to take an order, begin a delivery process, and compete with physical outlets for sales to certain consumers. In some instances, a company with both a physical store and a website may discover that the two ventures are competing for the *same* consumer. In others, the two can exist and even profit side by side, as appears to be the case with Amway and its Internet site, Quixtar.

In the end, it is important that companies focus on operating hours that are convenient for their target consumers, not hours that simply keep facilities open on the off chance that someone might come in at any time. Clearly, the return on investment (ROI) of the latter is questionable at best.

4. **Organization and layout.** To succeed on access, businesses must make it possible for customers to find exactly what they're looking for,

even on a first visit. One of the biggest gripes among the consumers we spoke with is the difficulty they encounter finding their way around a facility. Ekow, a thirty-two-year-old university administrator, summed up most consumers' feelings: "So many places I go, stuff is just randomly thrown up, and you really have to dig for what you're looking for. A lot of times, there are no signs telling you where things are, and the aisles are so small that two people can't even pass in them."

One key point of contention related to access today is the size of a facility, particularly in the case of discount and grocery stores. Many of these retailers continue to expand the size of their outlets in the belief that consumers want more of everything in one place. Grocery retailer Winn-Dixie, for instance, which operates nearly 1,200 stores in the Southeast, increased the average square footage per store to almost 44,000 square feet in 1999, up from 36,000 square feet in 1995. In 1999, while closing or remodeling smaller stores, the company built or acquired an additional seventy-nine stores averaging 51,000 square feet.[4] The average supermarket operated by Pittsburgh-based Giant Eagle tops out at nearly 100,000 square feet.[5] And Meijer, the mass merchant/supermarket superstore chain headquartered in Grand Rapids, Michigan, builds stores comprising more than 200,000 square feet of selling space.

So, is bigger better? Not really, according to consumers. The shoppers we spoke with are looking for less imposing structures that are easier to navigate. While they like the *idea* of one-stop shopping, the reality is not particularly appealing. "Stores are getting so large that there's no personal relationship between the customer and the store," noted Osomo, a twenty-five-year-old state government policy analyst. Tony, thirty-six, a university administrator, agreed: "We have these huge supermarkets that have every service you can imagine. But they're so impersonal, the crowds are overbearing, and the lines are so long. If you're there just to get a gallon of milk, you're in trouble. I tend to avoid them because I don't want to have to fight for a parking spot and stand in line for fifteen minutes."

Sometimes consumer concerns blend with corporate convenience. The building of smaller formats allows companies to gain strategic advantage while addressing the latent consumer desire for more easily accessible retail spaces. Wal-Mart, for example, while continuing to build more of its large supercenters, is also rolling out a number of Neighborhood Market stores, which typically are 50 percent smaller than the company's traditional units.[6] Similarly, The Home Depot, whose average store is approximately 130,000 square feet and carries between 40,000 and 50,000 products, is test-marketing its 39,000-square-foot Villager's Hardware format.[7]

Tops Markets, the Buffalo, New York–based division of Dutch grocery giant Royal Ahold N.V., is dramatically downsizing its future stores, citing the need to "shorten the amount of time tired consumers must spend shopping for groceries," according to Brad Bacon, a company executive. The new formats will average 55,000 square feet—down from the 65,000 to 90,000 square feet the company's traditional stores comprise. In addition, the new Tops format will have wider, shorter aisles to promote "quicker access to check-out lines anywhere in the supermarket," said Bacon. Conversely, Giant Eagle continues to add more footage and services "to extend the time customers spend in the store."[8] We're betting on the Tops strategy.

Winning on Access

The key to reaching the level at which consumers seek out your business lies in consistently delivering better than your competitors on one of the five value attributes. Companies that choose access as their primary focus must first make it easy for consumers to find what they need and to get in and out in a hurry. The same holds true for online shopping. No one wants to waste time "leafing" through Web pages in search of an item.

For a company to dominate on this attribute, however, it must move beyond a basic level of accessibility and make its operation increasingly convenient for consumers. That can include something as simple as having an adequate number of checkouts open during the busiest hours. After all, why should a supermarket's best customers—those whose baskets are overflowing—have to wait to check out while shoppers with just a few items are able to move quickly through the express lanes?

While the definition of access today has shifted to internal navigation, location is still critical if you want to dominate on access in certain businesses, including hotels, restaurants, and airlines. Unfortunately, a great location usually comes at a steep price. Take, for example, the hotel business. Anyone who's tried to book a room in New York's Times Square, Miami Beach, or the central business district of any major city has encountered some degree of sticker shock. So why can't somebody build a decent hotel near everything at a price that's affordable?

Well, somebody has: Jurys Doyle Hotel Group in Ireland. The company's highly successful Jurys Inns prove that it is, indeed, possible to have both a good location and an attractive price.

Jurys Doyle launched Jurys Inns in 1993 in Ireland, with the opening of Jurys Christchurch Inn (Dublin) and Jurys Galway Inn. While most hotels typically charged a wide range of rates—depending on the type of customer, how many people were staying in a room, and what amenities the hotel offered—Jurys Inns came on the scene as a three-star property with a fixed price and limited amenities (for example, no porterage or room service). At the same time, the company was committed to being in the heart of the key cities it serves. Today, its nine Jurys Inn properties are located in Dublin, Belfast, Galway, Cork, and Limerick (Ireland's largest cities); and in London, Edinburgh, Belfast, and Manchester in the United Kingdom.

Edward Stephenson, general manager of the Jurys Christchurch Inn in Dublin, explains how the company was able to secure its prime locations without breaking the bank. "To encourage reinvestment in the cities, the government introduced an urban-renewal scheme, which provided incentives and capital allowances to companies that built in the city," he told us. "So we had a great opportunity to put hotels into key city-center locations. The places we built in are now prime locations in the heart of the city center. The renewal scheme and capital allowances have been very successful in transforming these areas, and now we're in some of the best spots in the country. This really has been the key to our success."

The two sites that Jurys Inns occupy in Dublin would be the envy of any hotel operator: The Christchurch location is within walking distance of Dublin's popular Temple Bar entertainment district and Grafton Street shopping area; the Custom House site is adjacent to the Irish Financial Services Center (IFSC) and a five-minute walk from many large office buildings. Jurys Christchurch Inn has achieved some staggering results: Stephenson said that his property had an occupancy rate of 97.7 percent for 1999, with 100 percent occupancy from May through October, the height of tourist season. Jurys Custom House Inn, which also does a brisk year-round trade, serves both business travelers who need quick and easy access to the IFSC and leisure travelers seeking a key city-center location.

For corporate customers, easy access also means getting in and out of the hotel itself in a timely manner, as Derek McDonagh noted. "The ease of access, the location, and the convenience are very important to our business customers," said McDonagh, deputy general manager of the Custom House Inn. "They have to be able to check in quickly, eat breakfast quickly, and be on their way quickly, so they can get on with their business. We can't have them waiting behind a tour group of fifty people."

Jurys caters to a psychological aspect of access as well. Customers know there are no secret charges to be avoided—that what they've bargained for is what they get. The customer offering is clear and transparent.

The company can do all this while maintaining reasonable prices. Depending on the property, a clean, well-equipped room can be had for between $60 and $85 a night—a bargain by any big-city standard. To keep its prices low, Jurys eschews the services that the full-service hotels offer. "This is what our customers want," said Jennifer Lee, group human-resources manager. "They don't want to pay a higher price for a desk of porters when they can carry their bags to the room themselves, or pay for a room-service facility that they may not use."

The company also ensures a high degree of standardization and consistency in its operations (all the rooms are identical, whether you're in Belfast, Cork, or Manchester), to make employee training and physical maintenance easier and to ensure brand consistency in the consumer's mind. "Our inns concept is very simple for customers—one price, that's what you pay, no hidden charges," said Stephenson. To maintain its access/affordable-price model, the company must guard against "amenity creep." "We don't need more amenities," Stephenson explained. "We need to keep things at this level, make sure it's well-maintained, and keep the three-star rating. We do, however, listen to our customers and to our staff, and we respond to their changing requirements."

The notion of access isn't important just in the business-to-consumer market. It works equally well or even better in the business-to-business space, as evidenced by companies as large as Dell and as (relatively) small as Circles.

Case Study

Circles: Where Access *Is* the Product

CIRCLES: SELLING SOLUTIONS 24/7

PRIMARY ATTRIBUTE: ACCESS

- Offers total travel, entertainment, and lifestyle solutions to customers.
- Allows customers to extend solutions to their customers.
- Rounds out employee recruitment, hiring, and retention package.
- Helps customers achieve functional work/life balance.

SECONDARY ATTRIBUTE: SERVICE

- Customers can count on Circles delivering service to their clients effectively 100 percent of the time.
- Ability to consistently make customers "look good" to their clients.
- Ability to reduce stress and strain on key employees.
- Ability to create employee peace of mind about domestic crises.

You could think of Circles as a mother's dream come true, if, of course, you're talking about Janet Kraus's mother (more on that in a moment). At Circles, access is not only the most important product—it's also the only product. Cofounded in Boston in 1997 by CEO Kraus and Chief Growth Officer Kathy Sherbrooke, who met while studying at the Stanford Graduate School of Business, Circles defines itself as "an innovative personal services provider that reliably completes simple, complex and unique tasks by integrating leading-edge technology and proprietary knowledge with high touch assistance." We'd define it as a business-to-business cyber-concierge service that will find for its clients' employees or customers anything they want—from a reliable dog-walker in Des Moines to a rare Ashkenazi dictionary.

The company offers services to about seventy-five corporations and, through them, more than 300,000 people. Circles will find you a restaurant or spa; plan a party; buy, sell, or rent a car; plan a vacation or arrange for a passport; shop for you; organize your money matters; buy, sell, or rent a condo, apartment, or house, as well as find somebody to clean it; and generally do any kind of shopping you could conceivably want done. You can't access Circles' services as an individual consumer, but you can if you're an employee or customer of one of the client companies, which include Razorfish, Cap Gemini Ernst & Young, American Semiconductor, First Data, Hyperion, Millennium Pharmaceutical, and Natural Microsystems Inc. Circles is venture-backed by TL Ventures, Trident Capital, and GE Capital.

Contracting with a personal-services company is becoming an increasingly popular perk for corporate employers interested in strategic employee acquisitions or retentions. And, in a commercial environment in which U.S. corporations, on average, lose half their employees in five years, a growing number of companies believe they should tie into a personal-services company as an effective way to build employee loyalty.

In a sense, the idea behind Circles first surfaced in Kraus's mind when she was twelve years old. "My mother entered the paid workforce when I was twelve and my brother was two," Kraus told us. "She had her child care covered, and she had everything as programmed as possible, but at the same time there were a million and one things she would look at and say, 'I would pay to have someone do these things if I could find someone who could think and do it.' And I remember I used to say to her, 'You could pay *me*,' but, of course, I was just twelve. But it stuck in my mind. That's what people want—a solution that covers a broad array of things, nothing specific. This week I might want someone to cook my meals, and next week I might say, 'Oh, my gosh! My trip to Florida got messed up, and I need somebody to fix it.' It's really what my mother was asking for—having smart people on call to do what's required."

At Stanford, Kraus and Sherbrooke studied under Jim Collins, author of *Built to Last: Successful Habits of Visionary Companies.* "He was trying to distill the essence of what distinguishes great companies from good companies," Kraus said. "And it didn't come down to mission, it didn't come down to vision, and it didn't come down to objectives. What it did come down to were values—and values described broadly—the question of 'What is it you value; what's at the core of what you're doing?' "

It was also at Stanford that Kraus and Sherbrooke decided they were going to form a company together. The only problem was that they had no idea what kind of business they wanted to be in. "We got in a car and drove across the country for five days," Kraus recalled. "And for five days, we talked about what kind of company we wanted to build and what were the values we wanted to build into our company. We looked at doggie day-care centers and wellness centers with massage therapy, but it really wasn't about a specific business at all. It was about what kind of company it should be and what needs were out there in the community that we could address."

Eventually, the Circles cofounders quit their jobs and devoted themselves in earnest to the project. "When we started, we had two rules," Kraus said. "Work started every day at 8:30, regardless of the fact that there was nothing to do. The second rule was that I had to wear my shoes to work, which actually meant I had to walk from my bedroom to my extra bedroom fully dressed." The name "Circles" was agreed on before Kraus and Sherbrooke knew what the company was going to do. "Think of the names of some great companies," Kraus explained, "names like Sony, Apple, and Disney. They are all words people find generally likable, even if they don't know why. They are names that can be filled with all sorts of subtle messages. 'Circles' seemed to fit our values philosophy: The world works in circles; it's hard to break a circle; there are circles of power—it's a powerful symbol. And since we didn't have a business, the name didn't have to stack up to anything."

So with the name chosen and the two work rules firmly established, all that remained was to decide what kind of business Circles was going to be. "We began by basically doing all sorts of consumer research, secondary research, looking at things like Yankelovich data, trying to identify the trends we thought we had the strengths and ability to address," Kraus said. "What hit us were issues like time stress, the issue of work-life balance, and how to use technology to deliver services. So we looked seriously at our original ideas like doggie day care and massage/wellness centers. We studied Streamline and Peapod [two different Internet-based food-centric home-delivery services]. We loved the service. I wanted to be a customer, but we had no interest in running that kind of business. We were looking for something that took less hands-on capability and was more scalable."

Kraus and Sherbrooke conducted consumer focus groups and asked people what they wanted and needed most. "Overwhelmingly what we heard was 'I need help with my "to do" list.' When we asked them what was on that list, we heard so many people say so many different things that at first we were stumped," said Kraus. "We told ourselves that we couldn't possibly do all these different things. We also realized it would be hard to get individual consumers to pay us to do what we'd have to do to provide all these services. Then we realized there were other possible 'customers'—big companies that might want to provide a variety of services to employees and/or clients. So we shaped our possible offering list from everything to a set of things. Not too surprisingly, 80 percent of the requests fall into the same categories: getting tickets to shows, arranging limos, selecting gifts, locating a dog walker, picking a house cleaner. But there's also stuff that's pretty unusual. We were once asked to find a three-and-a-half-inch-wide staircase for a dollhouse; we had to find an Ashkenazi dictionary that had been printed only in Argentina; and once we had to have a chain saw delivered to a hotel when a Cap Gemini Ernst & Young consultant built his trade-show exhibit in his hotel room and then couldn't get it out the door. We were also once asked to find a suit that a client had seen in a magazine three years ago. He knew it had been an Armani suit, but he had no idea what magazine he had seen it in. We found the magazine, but that suit was no longer made. We were also once asked to find glass slippers for somebody's daughter's birthday."

Paradoxically perhaps for a company whose product is access, part of Circles' strategy is to deliberately limit access to its offerings, thereby making access to it more valuable. "Since you aren't able to get this as a consumer, when you see it as an offer from a company you have a relationship with, it triggers that old notion of something that's somehow even more special," Kraus said. Circles' clients offer services to employees and/or customers. In most cases, companies fully subsidize the Circles cost ($30 to $100 per employee or customer, depending on what range of services is contracted for by the client company, plus a $10 to $40 additional hourly charge per actual use). Kraus noted that some clients choose to offer Circles' services free for a while and then sign up customers on a subscription basis. The actual cost per person also varies by the degree of personalization requested. Having anyone at Circles service a request is one cost; a personal assistant costs more; and a personal assistant permanently assigned to specific people costs even more.

Kraus believes that it isn't a problem for a Boston-based company (all Circles' 250 employees, including 150 highly trained personal assistants, work from a central office) to service accounts on a national basis. "The question is 'What is local?'" she said. "Is Wellesley, a suburb of Boston, really local to Boston? Not really. We have to use the same sort of references to service Wellesley we would have to use to service Louisville, Kentucky. Also we're currently exploring—through our relationship with a hotel chain—ways of tying into physical concierges all over the world."

There are other players operating in Circles' commercial space. LesConcierges Inc. and Two Places at One Time, for example, compete in the corporate concierge area. Circles differentiates itself from its competitors in several ways. True, companies such as Abilizer (formerly Employee Portal Perks at Work), Motivano (formerly Perks for You), and Xylo (formerly Employeesavings) all offer high-tech portal sites. However, Kraus insists that Circles' site is the only one committed to a strategy that combines high-tech (providing personal assistants with a sophisticated Internet infrastructure that taps into the best websites more accurately than generic search engines) and high-touch (employing highly trained, service-focused assistants).

There are other strategic and tactical competitive differences as well. Circles is an almost full-service concierge. The service range is deliberately fixed but still covers a staggering range and depth of categories. Where Two Places at One Time's value proposition is driven by the placement of a physical concierge on location, Circles' offering is Web-based and driven by a database. Circles also allows clients to know the name of its service-providing partners, while other services tend to keep their partners shadowed in the background.

Kraus also believes that Circles' basic vision of customer needs helps it differentiate its offering. "People have a psychographic profile that differs on different days," she said. "Some days you want to do things yourself; other days it's, 'Forget it, I just want to get rid of this thing and let somebody else do it.' We become the short cut. Service providers can't buy their way onto our portal. We're not doing the eyeballs thing. We're doing the partners thing. We are building a channel of access to the best of the best. One of our core competencies as a company is finding, accepting, sorting, and creating relationships with the 'best.' I like to think of ourselves as a short cut to your answer."

In terms of its business strategy as it applies to the Consumer Relevancy model, Circles attempts to dominate on access; differentiate on service; and stay "in range," says Kraus, on price, product, and experience. A number of concierge companies offer similar "products," and Circles is not the cheapest digital concierge, nor are its offerings universalized to the point of marginalizing profit or return on investment. In terms of the experience attribute, it's in the nature of the concierge business to respect all customers, and Circles isn't claiming that it's the only service that can, for example, walk your dog. "At the end of the day, you could say we're a relationship marketing company," Kraus said. "It's all about *you*—learning about who you really are and how we can become more relevant to you."

SELF-DIAGNOSTIC: ACCESS

- If you're involved in either the business-to-business or business-to-consumer worlds, are you offering your customers a real solution to their needs, say, arranging extra shipments or "shopping" the competition for a last-minute purchase?
- If you think you're differentiated on access, ask yourself exactly how convenient it is to do business with you. For example, if you're a manufacturer, do you do electronic data interchange? Do you encourage electronic funds transfer, facilitate order processing, or customize terms?
- If you're in a customer-facing business, how easy is it for your customers to find the goods or services they are looking for? Do you facilitate their ability to access their choices or just try to "lead" their purchasing patterns?
- If you have a website, do you respond to customer communications in real time or only once a day?
- If you want to dominate on access, are you willing to go to the customer if need be, or do you insist they somehow come to you?

CHAPTER 6

Why "Good" Is Good Enough

Choice and the Issue of *Product* Bandwidth

YEARS AGO, WE WERE invited to a dinner hosted by August Busch III, chairman and CEO of the Anheuser-Busch Co. The dinner was held at The White House, arguably at the time the finest restaurant in Anaheim, California. One entered the event by walking down an artificially created aisle that terminated at the feet of the host. "Bud or Bud Light?" Busch asked each guest in turn. If the answer was "Bud, please," Busch nodded to a barman to his left. If the answer was "Bud Light, please," the nod went to the barman on his right. "Good evening, Bud or Bud Light?" the genial Busch asked us when we had made our way to the front of the reception line. "Would you happen to have an O'Doul's?" we asked. "Get this man an O'Doul's," Busch commanded an unwary waiter. "We don't carry that—is Sharp's okay?" the poor waiter asked. (For the uninitiated, Sharp's is produced by Miller Brewing.) Not an award-winning display of service, but that's another story.

The point here—especially for manufacturers—is that what you think of your products doesn't necessarily translate directly into how those products are treated in the market. The White House thought it had an effective range of non-alcoholic beers, but the range didn't match the minimum expectations of America's most powerful brewer. On the other hand, August Busch was justifiably proud of the O'Doul's brand, but that pride didn't seem to matter much to the poor waiter, who, we're pretty sure, quickly learned the error of his ways.

The majority of consumers who don't have their names on a product have grown up in a culture where it's assumed that "Coke" or "Pepsi" really means whatever cola the establishment serves, and where non-alcoholic beers and a whole range of other products from facial tissues (Kleenex) to copiers (Xerox) are treated as generics rather than brands. In the same way that we were misguided about how consumers view price, we thought we understood what they wanted out of product. Naturally, we assumed everyone would want "the best" (recognizing that "best" is relative, subjective, and personal)—or at the very least something approximating the highest quality. After all, companies spend hundreds of millions of dollars every year advertising that their brands are "new," "improved," or "13.7 percent better" since reformulation. These claims center around the idea that what consumers want are products differentiated by their efficacy or features. What consumers told us is that they don't care about efficacy claims they can't verify in their kitchens or laundry rooms or performance claims that can be tested only in a wind tunnel or on the Autobahn.

Differentiating on product only succeeds by inspiring consumers with true product innovation, real white-space differentiation. This can happen at multiple levels of product and consumer sophistication and at various price points. Let's contrast a customer at Gander Mountain, a Midwestern sporting-goods company, with one at REI. Both customers are looking for "outdoor" equipment. The Gander Mountain shopper may be looking for a range of tents that are "good enough" to withstand a gentle summer rainstorm at a Wisconsin campsite, while the REI shopper may be looking for a tent "good enough" to withstand a storm in the Himalayas. The Gander Mountain customer may be inspired by the choices he or she sees to take their family camping, while the REI shopper may be inspired to dream of summiting K2 or Mount Everest. The same is true of someone shopping at The Home Depot versus someone wandering through Domain, a high-end home-furnishings retailer. Both may be looking for inspiration for their homes. In the case of the former, that inspiration may come in the form of a limited selection of screen doors; for the latter, it might mean a velvet sofa. Once again, what's important in all these examples is that the retailers are product-dominant; that dominance is based on offering a tight range of products, any of which will "work" for the consumer, and that, at the highest level, will inspire a customer.

As we've already stated, today's consumer is time-starved and stressed. The majority will gladly trade off a little quality that they often can't even perceive or verify to gain some time and reduce the hassle of their daily lives. The real product-related opportunity revolves around redirecting a significant portion of all those R&D, advertising, and marketing dollars away from incremental and unclear quality claims to developing true breakthrough products that have clear, unique consumer benefits. And until that happens, the majority of consumers won't care enough about these claims to pay a significant brand tariff. The message for both manufacturers and providers is clear; for the majority of consumers, "unless your product inspires me, I am immune to your performance claims." This helps explain the rise of private-label products as well as why so many shoppers switch when their favorite brand is out of stock.

This brand blurring has created new market opportunities. Witness Priceline.com, whose entire business model, whether for airline tickets or hotel rooms, is based on brand flexibility—the idea that consumers are not as loyal as manufacturers might like them to be when faced with the prospect of significant savings. "What Priceline does is say we can collect demand from consumers prior to the specification decision, before the customer specifies, and we can find out at what price the customer is willing to trade off the right to specify in return for savings," said Jay Walker, founder of Priceline. "For many people, it's like they've won something. In many ways, they have. They've traded off a little bit of their brand flexibility in return for savings, and they are the winner."[1]

While Priceline's model arguably proved successful for airline tickets, the company stumbled when, seduced by the myth of excellence, it attempted to extend its business model to a wider range of product categories such as groceries and gasoline. In the case of airline tickets, Priceline acted as a matchmaker between the corporate need to fill vacant airplane seats and the consumer desire for discounted airfares. But in the case of grocery products, the formula backfired. Priceline correctly guessed that, within reason, consumers would accept a range of good choices over the "best" choice in their favorite grocery categories. And it also correctly predicted that offering consumers a discount on products they were already going to buy would prove popular with shoppers. But here's where the problems started: To offer the Priceline discount, participating grocery retailers had to run the risk of creating the appearance they were artificially inflating their everyday prices, thus violating the principle of fair and honest pricing (see Chapter 3). In addition, with neither retailers nor manufacturers willing to permanently underwrite the discounts, the business profit model was fatally flawed. Lessons learned: Even relevant offerings need to make money, and business models need to work for every link in the value chain.

While discounting prices—especially on items that are routinely purchased—can be an effective method of temporarily stimulating sales, it's also clear that there is a distinct and viable market, both in the physical and the online world, for those consumers who want the best regardless of price. Great franchises like BMW, The Sharper Image, and the Ritz-Carlton have been built serving this market, and they prosper by inspiring their customers with greatness and charging a premium for it. We're not saying that you can't sell a Lexus to a small, if significant and profitable, market segment who see their cars as their reward for hard work or a public manifestation of their success. What we are saying is that in the mass market you'll still sell more Hondas.

One significant caveat at this point: Today, online consumers differ significantly from their peers in the physical space. Brands matter in cyberspace, where, it seems, only the best is acceptable. Nearly 80 percent of online shoppers said they want top-quality products, and close to 60 percent are concerned with online merchants' ability to maintain adequate inventory of their merchandise. There is a significant difference in the way consumers treat service-based and product-based Internet providers. They're willing to accept Web-based service brands such as Charles Schwab in their own right (albeit with concerns about credit-card security) but when it comes to the product these services (such as Amazon or Priceline) offer, they want only the best products, quality they can verify offline. Perhaps because cyberspace is still new territory for so many consumers, they are afraid to enter the murky world of reverse logistics, making known brands function as implicit warranties. This is illustrated by one of the few real missteps Wal-Mart has made in the past few years. When the company initially launched its website, it didn't allow shoppers the option of returning Internet-sourced goods to physical Wal-Mart stores. The resulting consumer fallout was at least partially responsible for causing Wal-Mart to rethink, and eventually relaunch, its online offering.

But let's go back offline for a moment. Consider the top two product-related responses from shoppers of physical stores to our original survey. Asked to rank a series of product preferences, consumers told us: "Retailer provides consistently good merchandise quality" was far and away more important to consumers than "Retailer offers top-quality products throughout the store."

A number of our direct interviews said they were unlikely to spend the extra money on top-of-the-line or branded products if they perceive that a less expensive—and, often, less well known—item is likely to be "good enough." That wasn't always the case. "It pays to go first-class" is a slogan that dominated during the 1950s, when lower-end products did not engender a feeling of confidence among consumers. But today most consumers told us that they're just looking for goods and services that are functional and do the job.

What's more, consumers have been so conditioned by out-of-stocks that they regularly trade off one item for another, making the offering of a range of good choices more important than the offering of only one best choice. Encouraging consumers to trade off is, in fact, a tried-and-true advertising technique. It's been used for years by mass merchandisers and appliance and furniture retailers, which will advertise an outstanding deal, knowing they'll have only a few units per store. Somewhere in the ad, you'll find tiny print that reads "While supplies last" or "Quantities limited." The companies know that the deal will get consumers into the store and that many of those customers will trade off to another brand or item if the deal item is

no longer available. While the topic of out-of-stocks ranked behind quality among online shoppers, it's still a critical issue for businesses attempting to dominate on product. Our research made it clear that being out of
stock in the consumer-direct world is a particularly egregious error and is
usually a deal breaker. In the physical world, switching to a different color
or style when faced with an out-of-stock item often beats getting in the car
and driving to another retailer. However, online shoppers indicated they
were more likely to switch to another retailer's website when faced with an
out-of-stock.

The Essential Elements of Product:
Quality, Depth, and Breadth

As with most of the attributes, product has a multitude of dimensions.
Chief among them are quality, depth, and breadth. Companies that choose
to compete on the basis of product (which we use to refer to services as well
as tangible items) must determine the most appropriate mix of these three
elements.

At a basic level, a company must set the quality bar for its products:
Will we always offer the most innovative products that are made to exacting specifications (and, consequently, are very expensive)? Will we go for
items that are of lower quality but are more affordable to a larger pool of
consumers? Will we shoot for somewhere in the middle? Companies must
select a product "quality range" that spans some segment of the "good, better, best" spectrum (Figure 6.1). At the high end ("best") are businesses
such as BMW and Tiffany; at the low end ("good") are companies like
Payless Shoe Source and Ames. Of course, a product's quality must be consistent with its price tag and represents the trade-off point at which consumers will opt for savings. Payless sells a staggering number of shoes
because the price point matches consumers' expectations for the product.
Consumers know they won't get the highest-quality shoes, but they will get
a reasonably fashionable product for $11 or so a pair.

Our research also pointed to a certain emotional-commitment range
associated with product quality—a range that runs from disposability on

FIGURE 6.1

Product Quality Range

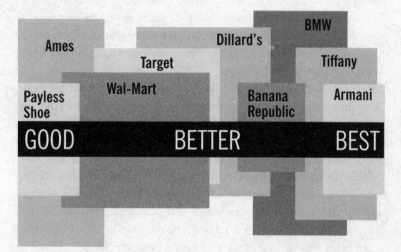

the one end to attachment on the other. Of course, the emotional commitment associated with a certain type of product varies depending on the individual. At the disposable end are products to which a consumer has little or no emotional attachment. For some, that may be cars, leading them to buy low-priced but reliable used cars; for others it may be the $11 pair of Payless shoes that they wear several times and throw away. You might call it the Bic lighter approach to products. At the other end of the spectrum are products that consumers feel strongly about and to which they feel a bond or an emotional attachment. Consumers who have an emotional commitment to cars will shop carefully and spend a considerable amount of money on a car that they'll likely wash by hand every weekend.

The notion of the instavidual that we developed in Chapter 1 became particularly critical when we talked to consumers about the product attribute. Most noted that product quality and what qualifies as good enough will vary depending upon the moment of need. If a consumer needs something fixed fast, the all-purpose wrench sold at 7-Eleven may be good enough at that particular moment. But if he's looking for a set of tools that will last over time, he's more likely to turn to Sears' Craftsman brand. Which leads to another important product distinction that emerged during our research: In the realm of "good" product, the manufacturer is the consumer's trustmark, and a shopper will search for that specific brand; in the realm of "good enough," the retailer is the trustmark, and any brand carried by that store will suffice.

Breadth and depth are also key aspects of the product attribute. Companies choosing to compete on product must decide whether they will consistently have the deepest selection of products in the category they serve, such as Toys R Us and Staples, or the broadest assortment of items for their market, like Target or The Home Depot. General Motors' Chevrolet division, for example, has chosen to compete on product breadth, offering virtually every type of vehicle possible, from sports cars (Corvette) and low-priced coupes (Cavalier) to family sedans (Malibu), pickup trucks (S-10), and sport-utility vehicles (Blazer). Ferrari, on the other hand, competes only on the tip of the high end of the premium sports-car market.

Minneapolis-based Best Buy has opted for a depth approach to product and has staked its reputation on being the country's preeminent consumer-electronics retailer. Going from the brink of extinction in 1996 to $10 billion in annual sales in 1999, Best Buy turned its fortunes around by positioning itself with a depth of product selection in the electronics category. According to Richard Schulze, the company's founder, chairman, and CEO, Best Buy has pinned its hopes for future growth on serving "technophiles and early adopters—people who have a high level of interest in adult toys, new emerging technological products."

But it's not just the product focus that sets Best Buy apart. The company's attention to its secondary attribute, experience, gives it a powerful one-two punch. Because the retailer's salespeople are on salary rather than commission, there is no high-pressure sales situation. "Best Buy's whole approach is that customers need to see, learn, and understand a product," said Schulze. "They need to feel comfortable asking for information without being pressured to buy anything."

Ultimately, we believe that, thanks to the growth of online businesses, product depth will become an increasingly more difficult strategy on which to dominate in the physical world. Let's take books. There is simply no way on earth that the biggest Borders physical store can stock one-tenth of what an online bookseller can carry. In the virtual world, then, product depth may actually increase, as it becomes the key differentiating strategy for many businesses.

Extending the Product Attribute

Beyond the three key elements of the product attribute, there are additional nuances that emerged from our research. One important consideration for product-dominant businesses is the notion of product extension. How far can they take their brand or product? That question has become particularly crucial today as companies attempt to migrate from the physical world into the online realm. A strong argument can be made that a business must be consistent with its brand promise if it is going to successfully transfer from the physical to virtual space. However, the execution of that promise may vary. Consider the case of outdoor-lifestyle retailer Eddie Bauer, a successful product-dominant company that understands the essence of Consumer Relevancy. According to Janice Gaub, the company's vice president for brand marketing, Eddie Bauer is a brand ". . . embodying values very much in sync with what [our] consumers want."

An unswerving commitment to its product lies at the core of the company's operating philosophy. The Eddie Bauer brand is universally recognized for its quality and value to consumers: a good fit, high-quality materials, and hassle-free service. "There's a physical comfort in wearing these clothes, but there's also a large emotional component," said Gaub. "Instead of cutting-edge fashions, Eddie Bauer describes a lifestyle for people who want to be authentic, make their own choices, and aspire to a higher quality of life without appearing presumptuous."

This philosophy extends to the company's many product extensions and licensing agreements, from home furnishings and eyeglasses to the Eddie Bauer Edition Ford Explorer. "Our customers are not people who sit around and let life pass them by," Gaub noted. "They're very active and like to do things. We have picked very strategic partners that have the same identification and convey the same type of lifestyle—which really helps reinforce our positioning." A cynic might note that there really aren't that many Eddie Bauer Explorers at the foot of K2 and that some of those hiking shorts shore up waistlines whose closest encounter with the wilderness was the sixth hole at Pebble Beach, but that isn't the point. Eddie Bauer markets as much to people's self-image as to their reality, and its efforts are, more often than not, right on target. The approach is so powerful that it works regardless of channel, although a different secondary attribute is used in each of the three primary channels the company sells through.

- **Physical stores (secondary attribute: service).** Since its acquisition by Spiegel Inc. in 1988, which itself is controlled by the German catalog retailer Otto Versand, Eddie Bauer has expanded the number of stores to more than 500 in fifty states, as well as various joint ventures in Japan, Germany, the United Kingdom, and Canada.

- **Catalogs (secondary attribute: access).** Well before becoming a fixture in malls, Eddie Bauer landed in the homes of millions of consumers via its catalogs. Today, that tradition continues, as the company mails more than 120 million catalogs a year, which carry products from flannel shirts to bedsheets.

- **Internet (secondary attribute: experience).** Since the fall of 1998, the division has worked on developing a popular website, eddiebauer.com, which offers visitors not only a full range of products and options but also an easy-to-navigate Internet experience that keeps people coming back. Among the innovations is a virtual dressing room, which gives consumers the opportunity to test various combinations of clothing, simply by clicking and dragging images with a mouse.

The website further cements the company's product play. "Because of the Eddie Bauer brand recognition, consumers put a lot of trust in the product—and that removes a huge obstacle to their willingness to make a purchase on the Web," said Gaub. If that purchase turns out to be the wrong size, color, or style, the consumer can return it by mail or in person, no matter which channel was used to make the purchase. Such versatility is possible only where the corporate culture supports it, both by training personnel and integrating the company's logistics systems across all three channels in order to handle such requests.

As with all the attributes, there is plenty of interplay between product and other attributes. Arguably, that interplay may be even more important with product, as it is difficult to sustain a pure product point of difference given the ubiquity of distribution today. When consumers can buy the same product virtually everywhere, a company has little ability to leverage product alone. The connection between product and price, of course, is particularly strong. In fact, consumers we spoke with rarely talked about product without talking about price. This connection helps explain the success of off-price retailers such as T.J. Maxx and Marshalls.

There's also an affinity between product and service that's particularly pronounced among specialty companies and high-end retailers that focus on product depth. These types of businesses are expected to provide a higher-quality, better-educated staff that can answer specific questions from shoppers. A consumer buying a $5,000 Sub-Zero refrigerator, for example, wants to know more than just that the fridge will keep things colder than the standard-issue GE model. The notion that the service level must be consistent with the product offering holds true at the other end of the spectrum as well. High-end service from a lower-end product retailer confuses the message to consumers and is expensive to execute.

Applying the Conceptual Model to Product

So, how do you execute a consumer-relevant product-dominant strategy? Consumers' first demand is for *credibility* in a company's products—the threshold or Level I in our model (Figure 6.2). Businesses must offer

FIGURE **6.2**

Competing on Product

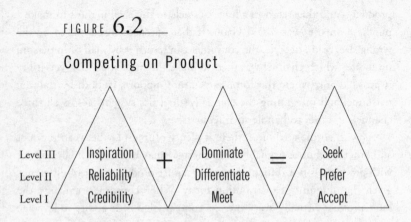

Level III	Inspiration		Dominate	Seek
Level II	Reliability	+	Differentiate	= Prefer
Level I	Credibility		Meet	Accept

product that meets basic expectations and a minimum utility threshold. In other words, even a cheap wrench should still be able to loosen a rusted nut.

Now, how do you move to Level II? At the second level, consumers demand *reliability*—that is, consistently good merchandise and a low out-of-stock condition. At this point, consumers will begin to prefer you as a provider of those goods or services. How do you achieve reliability? Whether it's a $50 Swatch watch, a $500 stockpot, or a $5,000 sofa, the product must do what it purports to do. FedEx touts its reliability with the message that the company is the choice "When it absolutely, positively has to be there overnight." Allstate Insurance does the same with its "You're in good hands" policy. Maytag, with its commercials depicting a bored repair-man with nothing to do, created one of the most famous reliability promises of all time. The perception of reliability is a principal result of successful branding and the expectation that such brands will always perform consistently.

Reliability also extends to the company that sells the product. Consumers expect their goods-and-services providers to be in stock on the items they carry—regardless of the season, holiday, or location. A common complaint among the consumers we interviewed was that companies advertise a certain product, only to underestimate the response to the promotion. Such situations, if they happen often enough, will drive shoppers elsewhere.

Businesses that achieve Level III of the product pyramid provide not only credibility and reliability but also *inspiration*. Such companies carry products that are unique, unusual, or hard to find—items that cause the consumer to aspire to a higher level of lifestyle. Consumers will seek out such providers because they have become a lifestyle choice. Companies like Williams-Sonoma, Tiffany, Rolex, Brookstone, The Sharper Image, and Ferragamo provide this level of inspiration.

But inspiration is not confined to high-end businesses. The Home Depot uses its footprint and buying power to offer everything a consumer might need to turn that weed-filled expanse of scrub brush into an immaculately manicured garden, or the musty old basement into the ultimate entertainment room. At this level of competition, product-oriented businesses can depend on loyal customers to keep coming back year after year.

Ikea International A/S, the mid-priced Swedish furniture retailer, has also achieved the level of inspiration with its bold and stylish designs that are accessible at price points well within reach of most consumers. Playing off the inspiration theme, Ikea invites consumers to "Imagine the Possibilities," while the home-furnishings section of a recent catalog was subtitled "Ideas and inspiration for every room in your home."

Even at the lower end of the price spectrum, product-focused consumer businesses are able to inspire their customers. Among discount retailers, Target Stores does this better than anyone. Through strong advertising and marketing and unusual alliances, the company has built a reputation for quality products at a reasonable price. For instance, Target has formed an exclusive relationship with Michael Graves, an award-winning architect, to design hip, Target-only products ranging from watches, clocks, and cookware to frames, home accessories, and small appliances. With these and other low-priced yet stylish items, Target communicates the notion that "discount" doesn't have to mean "average" or "boring." In the process, it has won the intense loyalty of legions of consumers who look to the company to help them stay on the cutting edge of fashion without draining their bank accounts.

Clearly, companies that want to compete on the product attribute must first understand their target consumers' product quality and price thresholds, as well as the importance that potential customers place on brands. But regardless of where on the quality and price spectrum you are operating, dominance in the product realm is defined by your ability to challenge your customers' imagination and help them paint a picture of a lifestyle in which your products play a starring role.

Case Study

Record Time: Playing to the Tune of Relevancy

Record Time's story isn't just a simple uplifting tale of how a nice Midwestern boy found true happiness played out against a rock 'n' roll beat. We didn't go to Roseville, Michigan, to find proof that youthful passion can survive into your forties (although that in itself is a comforting thought). We went there for two distinct reasons: First, Record Time is a great example of how what we call "unconscious relevancy" can be leveraged into a value proposition; and, second, because it also demonstrates that Relevancy isn't just a "big company" strategy.

We believed Consumer Relevancy worked in businesses of all sizes, and we found proof in the story of Mike Himes, a music lover who has followed popular music down the road from what's now "classic rock" to techno and beyond. Along the way, he built a modest but profitable business. But most of all, he beat the odds, and he did it by understanding what some of the biggest retailers in America don't—you have to do business with customers on their own terms, not your version of their terms. It seemed to us that too many business books offer good advice, provided you are a Cisco, Ikea, Microsoft, Nokia, or Sony. But what do business books say about more modest businesses? If we were right about the role and function of the five attributes, shouldn't we be able to demonstrate their impact in every business, regardless of size? At Record Time we found a homegrown version of Relevancy acting as a commercial juju protecting the business against deep-pocketed national competitors and the onslaught of technologies that threaten to disintermediate an entire retail channel and maybe even the entertainment conglomerates that feed it. Most important, the company's Relevancy model has helped Record Time build an operating system for staying even with "the kids."

RECORD TIME: BECOMING THE PRODUCT

PRIMARY ATTRIBUTE: PRODUCT

- Inspires customers by bringing them cutting-edge artists, particularly in the indie rock, techno, and dance music genres not available at other music retailers.
- Hires salespeople who are themselves deeply involved with music either as artists, DJs, or just devoted fans.
- Doesn't carry much depth in certain areas (say, classical and country) that are unpopular with target market.
- Has a separate "Dance Room" where customers can listen to product and "hang out" with other aficionados to get ideas about what trend-setters are listening to.
- Encourages live in-store performances by local artists.
- Has sponsored certain artists by, in effect, becoming multiple-label music distributor.

SECONDARY ATTRIBUTE: SERVICE

- Key staff members are always on hand to suggestively sell customers or give detailed explanations about artists, labels, or musical styles.
- Regular customers are often advised about the availability of favorite artists or new genre offerings.
- All new releases for the week are posted in a prime in-store location.

"Last night I actually watched C-Span for the first time," said Mike Himes, somewhat puzzled by his own admission. It was July 12, 2000, and the occasion triggering Himes's newfound concern with the affairs of state was the broadcast of the Senate Judiciary Committee hearings on digital music. It had indeed been, as Hunter S. Thompson might have said, a day full of great weirdness. Viewers were stopped by the image of songwriter and Utah Sen. Orrin Hatch (yes, he's penned more than 200 tunes, including an immortal tribute to Muhammad Ali titled "The Difference Makes a Difference") grooving to Metallica in the privacy of his own office.

But Himes's interest transcended the natural human fascination with the bizarre. As founder, sole proprietor, and one-man R&D department of Record Time, Michigan's largest-volume independent music store, Himes was worried that Napster, MP3, or another Internet-based player might succeed in their efforts to give the planet, or at least its wired population, the technology to mass-reproduce music, essentially for free. The convergence of that technology with his target market's natural sociopolitical inclinations could force him out of business, something that strong regional competitors like Harmony House and national chains from Best Buy to Borders and e-tailers from Amazon.com to CDNow have so far failed to accomplish. "They [younger customers] hate 'The Man,' " Himes told us. "And anything that seems like it hurts 'The Man' is seen as sort of cool." Himes himself walks a daily tightrope of hipness that separates being "The Man," as in, "Dude, you're the man," from being "The Man" as in "Ain't nothing like beating The Man at his own thing." Staying on the right side of that line is a full-time job.

Being Relevant is tough enough, but staying Relevant as a product-dominant business in the face of a perpetual whirlwind of changing post-adolescent trends and styles is quite another. Add to that the problem of running a business that caters equally to African-American urban youth fueled with dreams of being the next big-house, dance, techno, or hip-hop artist and disaffected blue-collar suburban white kids, searching for the latest indie bands or Goth and heavy-metal music, and you begin to understand the difficulty of crafting a Relevant offering. And all this has to be accomplished without the tricks available to big retailers—no advertising agency, no marketing department, no gigantic promotional tie-ins to major entertainment corporations. Himes's version of Consumer Relevancy is built the hard way: one customer at a time.

"The first time a kid comes in here and starts talking about a kind of music I can't understand, I'll know I'm too old for this business," he said.

"The other day, I realized I have a woman working here who wasn't even born when we opened our first store. That kind of thing could start to make you feel old if you thought about it too long." But there isn't too much danger of that happening. Music seems to be the one thing that Himes thinks about all the time.

The road to Relevancy-based entrepreneurship began modestly enough. "I had originally worked from Christmas of 1979 until May of 1981 at Musicland in Ann Arbor [Michigan]," Himes recalled. "I started as part-time Christmas help and worked myself up first to assistant manager, and then I got my own store [to manage]. It's then that I realized that everything at Musicland was so structured and corporate that all my ideas and energy couldn't be used. I was still young, so I went to Peaches." At Peaches Entertainment Corp., Himes met Mike Luzo, a store manager, who eventually became his partner. When Peaches shuttered its Michigan operation, Himes and Luzo picked up some "almost free" fixtures from their former employer and opened a 1,200-square-foot store in East Detroit (now Eastpointe, Michigan). "We used 700 square feet to sell, and a back wall we moved back as we grew. We finally got rid of the wall," Himes told us. "And a couple of years into it, I bought out my partner, who was never involved because he had a family, which meant he had to work a day job, where I was single and had no commitments. Six years later, we moved to a 4,800-square-foot spot on the corner of Gratiot and 10 Mile [a major suburban intersection], and six years after that, we moved down Gratiot to our current location."

In 1996 a second unit was opened, in upscale, suburban Rochester, which was eventually relocated in 1999 to the trendier if decidedly more proletarian suburb of Ferndale. But the flagship store is what still sets the tone for the company. It's where Eminem came in his "real" Marshall Mathers III, pre–Slim Shady days, and Kid Rock before he "made it." And it's where legions of techno musicians, ravers, and house DJs hang out, all believing that Record Time is "their" store.

Himes didn't take any money out of the operation for almost three years. "I always put more and more back in," he said. "If you special-ordered something I'd drive the next morning to a distributor in Detroit, pick it up, then rush back and call you to tell you we had gotten it in. I did whatever I could do to win over customers, and eventually it caught on. Of course, a lot of it was timing. The time we grew the fastest—sales doubling every year for five years in a row—was when CDs first gained mass acceptance. We had a huge 'vinyl' crowd coming in to buy CDs. They were bringing in piles of used records and taking CDs, and we'd double our money on the used records. Sales snowballed, and during 1985–86 until 1990–91 they were straight off the charts."

Later on, Himes developed a mission statement. "My mission was basically to make people happy, to give them a product at a price they'd pay so they'd come back," he said. "I have a little trouble saying this, because it's best to stay humble, but in those days it was just the combination of my personality and music knowledge that began to win people over. People come here because they want music, and I'm here because I know about music. I want to make sure there's an environment that they have a good time coming to, someplace they can escape the day-to-day stress. Music is an outlet. It's fun, or at least it's supposed to be fun. We all have busy lives. People don't come here to hear our problems; they come here because it's nice, bright, it's a busy place where something's going on all the time and where people either know what you're talking about or can find it for you on a computer, in a book, or somewhere, and get you on your way."

Competition has always been tough in the retail music business, but it isn't Best Buy or the Boys from Bentonville that trouble Himes the most—it's technology. "If you look at the worst-case scenario, record companies *could* just eventually skip the record stores, and artists *could* skip the record companies if they wanted to. David Bowie's doing that right now," he said. "Our biggest challenge is to get the people who work for us excited and to have the proper mix of people working here so that someone knows at least a little about rap, hip-hop, alternative rock 'n' roll, and electronic music. You try to find people in those scenes to help you. It's hard to find people who have a passion for music who also have the personality to work retail, especially with what we can afford to pay them.

"There's so much music out there right now and so many different kinds of music. We have to carry over five decades of music, from the rock 'n' roll of the 1950s right through to the more futuristic stuff. Someone will come in and want something from one of those eras, and you've got to have somebody selling who knows that we carry it, where it is, and what they're talking about. That's why I still make myself active on the sales floor and do a lot of the buying. I have to work harder than anyone else. Over the years, I've learned more imaginative management skills than 'follow the leader,' but that's still the one that seems to work the best."

Most of Himes's customers are between fifteen and thirty. "The ones who buy the most are seventeen to twenty-five," he said. "Part of why we've done well is because we've been around for a while, and we've kept customers who are now making money. They have disposable incomes, and now the record companies are catering to them by remastering the 'hair bands' and staging eighties reunion tours for bands like Poison, Warrant, and L.A. Guns the same way they've rereleased the Beatles' *Yellow Submarine* for the boomers."

And there's the issue of psychodemographics. "We're a blue-collar store in a sense," Himes said. "Blue-collar customers—from the middle class on down—party more. They spend proportionately more on music. They live more from paycheck to paycheck, and they're not as tight with their money. They're more apt to blow it. There just seems to be more passion for music in a blue-collar area."

As his business grew, Himes found it more important to spend more time on the floor. The biggest threat to his business, he believes, is if he were to wake up one day prosperous and decide he could finally afford to relax and delegate the customer-contact work to a subordinate. "There are a lot of people in this business who have been bigger than us and are gone," he said. "The reason? The people who ran them lost interest in what they were doing or got a touch of the King Midas problem. I'm at the point where I could look back and say to myself, 'I've got a huge store now and a second store that's coming along, so I think I'll go golfing all the time.' But my passion and commitment is still to the music and the customer. I'd still rather be on the floor helping a customer than in an office. In this business, you can't keep up with what's going on unless you're out on the battlefield. I still buy the trendiest stuff in the store. I'm here for the music, and I love people too, so I guess I'm in the right business."

Of course, catering to everyone means holding large amounts of certain types of inventory that doesn't turn quickly. "My philosophy is to try to make as many people happy as possible, offer special services—we can get almost anything in a week, unless it's an obscure import, and that seems to keep most people coming back," said Himes. "But we also try to not be so drastic, wild, or underground that an older person might feel awkward. You know, they come in here, and all of a sudden they notice everyone here is way younger than they are, so they run to Borders, which is like a retirement home for music buyers."

Despite his passions and philosophy, Himes delegates certain purchase decisions in areas like "aggressive rock" to employees who feel strongly about the genre. "You need feelers out there, either people on the front line who live that music, communicate with people who are buying that music, and report back to you, or people who are the buyers themselves or distributors who specialize in certain forms of music," he said. "You have to give them a budget and let them go." Himes's employees reflect the customer base and range in age from seventeen to forty-three; about 75 percent of them are men.

A good deal of Record Time's business over the years has centered around the sale of used tapes and albums and, more recently, used CDs. But offering cheap copies of *Led Zeppelin II* does not an empire make. So in what may be described as the ultimate Relevancy play, Record Time actually became several record labels at one point in its history, helping to save a whole genre of music in the process. "About 1985 or 1986, three or four guys from Detroit pretty much started a new kind of electronic dance music, which was a little more 'electronic' than house music, which became known as techno," said Himes. "The sound started catching on, and while they all had independent releases in America, they ended up being more accepted in England and Europe. They started traveling over there and got big record deals and became household names. We got involved first because I was always progressive and into new stuff, but at the time, I was mostly into hip-hop—anything that was scratchy and noisy I bought, and then these other techno bands started coming out, and I started getting into that sound."

At the time, Record Time was a distant third even in the suburban Detroit independent music-store circuit, trailing such competitors as Car City Records, Harper Woods (still the place for classical, jazz, and vinyl collectors), and Sam's Jams in Ferndale, then the state's largest independent music seller. But techno, and its devoted audience, were about to leapfrog Himes to the front of the pack, even if it meant he picked up a few enemies in the process.

"People always came to us second or third with what they had to sell," he said. "So I started to see a pattern in what they [the competitors] bought. They'd never buy dance music or abrasive alternative. So I said, 'Hey, I like this music, and I know I can't go head-to-head with those big guys.' I started to carry more and more of the product they wouldn't and developed a niche. We had one row of dance. Then we brought in a band, and then it was two bands. Then we moved to our second store, and it became a whole room inside that store with its own stereo system, and we became the first stop for local musicians. They'd bring in their stuff and drop it off because we were the only store on this side of the Atlantic that gave them the time of day. We started selling a lot of it, and then the other DJs started coming in to shop. We never advertised much, but the DJs had exposure to tons of people. Things just spread, and before you knew it, we were the biggest dance store and used store on top of it."

In the process, Himes got to know the bands and DJs. "At the time, there were only two other distributors in America that were buying their stuff, and they were shipping it all overseas," he said. "So I started a distributorship that didn't ship much overseas, just to the American market— small college stores at places like Oberlin and others. I even went to the New Music Seminar in New York and handed out flyers to other stores just to advertise and get product out there. But you don't make much wholesaling even when you sell a ton of product. We were making only a 20 percent markup, and in the last couple of years the store was basically subsidizing the distribution, and we realized the labels really didn't need us anymore. There were only five or six labels when we started, and now there are fifty or sixty out of Detroit alone. When we got going, we were actually several labels too, just to keep everything going. But it all made a name for us internationally, because we started exporting, which was really the only way to make money with techno at the time. You could maybe sell 100 total copies of a record in America, where one European account might buy the same record 300 units at a time."

While Himes always sold his dance and techno music lower than any-one else, some of the artists and DJs he essentially underwrote thought he had sold them out. But wounds heal, and today dance music accounts for 25 percent of the company's gross sales.

Dance and techno put Record Time on the map, but how does Himes make sure it doesn't get blown off, especially by price players like Best Buy and Media Play? "I think price might have been bigger two or three years ago than it is now," Himes said. "We've weathered a big storm; 30 percent to 40 percent of the independent record stores closed over the last three years because of Best Buy, Media Play, and Circuit City and the onslaught of prices at cost or below. Price was a big deal, because people were saying, 'If I'm buying three CDs and I can get them for $5 less at Best Buy, that's lunch.' Then those stores started carrying less music, and today price isn't as much an issue. People still look for price, and since we've become estab-lished, they look to us as having a competitive fair price. Of course, there are still some who shop to save a penny here or there. We match all adver-tised prices, and, believe it or not, we've got customers who don't even bring in the ads because they know the price is below our costs and they don't want to hurt us, so they'll buy that [advertised item] from, say, Best Buy and then come here to do the rest of their shopping."

Himes has also made some economic trade-offs in pursuit of Relevant product. He only reluctantly put listening stations in Record Time's stores. Music labels underwrite the stations, and Himes could have had them ear-lier, but he didn't want to be forced to agree to the kind of product that went in them. He retains total control of which CDs are featured at the stations. Again, it's hard to be "The Man" when you have to take money from "The Man."

Staying true to his customers and the product they love continues to be the key to Himes's Relevancy strategy, and so far it's working. Former cus-tomers Kid Rock and Eminem have come back to support Record Time, and Kid Rock's platinum album is displayed in a shadow box in the main store. Why have they continued to support Himes? "Well, Eminem shopped here when he was a kid, and we took care of him," Himes said. "And when you take care of people, they just keep coming back. The same thing's true of Kid Rock, who did appearances in the store before he made it. People remember they might have seen him here first, and they tell everybody else about their experience."

Himes's strong identification with the customer molds his business philosophy. Asked about his corporate culture, he told us, "I ask myself if this is a store I'd want to shop at. Are these prices I'd pay to have what I want? Is it what I think of as a nice atmosphere? These are the rules I've lived by since day one," Himes said. "If you can't say that you'd shop in your store yourself, you shouldn't be in business. You're not doing it right. I'm not a textbook business guy. I'm not even hands-on with the financials; my wife does that and then gives me the stuff I can understand. I'm just driven by the music and the customer, and I leave the other stuff to people who do it better. My part is being out there talking music."

SELF DIAGNOSTIC: PRODUCT

- If you're a manufacturer, do your customers really stock your products because consumers see them as inspirational, or do they carry them just to fill out their inventory?
- How often are you out of stock on items your best customers want?
- If you're a retailer or reseller, are all the items you offer really credible, i.e., does each offering pull its own weight in the minds of consumers?
- Do your products or services allow your customers to think of themselves in new and exciting ways?
- Do you carry items your customers don't want—even at the expense of items they do want or would find inspirational—because of some arbitrary business practice, or in order to capitalize on the availability of promotional or marketing funding?

CHAPTER 7

Do You Really Get Me?

The *Experience* Factor

THERE'S MANY A SLIP between intent and the register. We were visiting a retailer in St. Louis who was justifiably proud of his company's commitment to the city's older neighborhoods and African-American community. Dressed in typical corporate uniforms (suits and ties), we walked through the retailer's central-city unit. The store was immaculate. The product mix had been tastefully adjusted to reflect the real buying patterns of the neighborhood, but with the same attention to quality, cleanliness, and attractive merchandising that we had seen in the company's suburban units. Pricing appeared to be in line with the chain's general pricing policies, and many of the store's employees lived close to their jobs.

What we saw frankly impressed us, but we soon learned it was because we weren't looking at the store through the eyes of the consumer. Our next stop was at one of the chain's older, suburban units. The store wasn't half as attractive as the store we had just visited. The fixtures were older and somehow dingier. As we wandered through the aisles, an older African-American customer stopped us (guessing by our appearance that we were executives of the company). We learned that he actually lived just blocks away from the central-city store we had just seen but drove twenty-five miles to shop at this unit. "Why don't you shop at the other store?" we asked. "It seems much nicer." "Racism," the man replied. "Racism?" we asked. "Sure," he said. "Didn't you see that big sign explaining all of the pieces of ID you need to get a check cashed there? You don't see a sign like that here, do you? It tells me they don't trust black people, and that's what I call racism."

The truth, of course, is that while we no doubt had looked at the sign, we hadn't in fact *seen* it the same way the customer had. The next day, at a meeting with the company's executives, we started to relate the story. "One of your customers thought you discriminated against African-Americans in that store because . . . ," we started to explain. "Probably because of the check-cashing sign," one of the executives said, essentially finishing our sentence. "It's a problem, all right." Opening up a beautiful store might have succeeded in showing community members that the company cared about them, but that single check-cashing sign screamed out that they weren't trusted and therefore were not respected, a serious issue for anyone trying to trade on the attribute of experience.

A serious issue, but one that's generally missed, for the simple reason that many businesses often make the mistake of equating experience with entertainment—and entertainment alone. Entertainment can augment an already solid offer and contribute to the consumer's experience, as in the case of Southwest Airlines or grocery retailer Stew Leonard's, but it isn't a substitute for a solid offer. When entertainment is the only thing standing between a customer and an essentially inferior product or service, consumers can be counted on to tire of an offering, at least once the initial novelty wears off. Think about "eatertainment" phenoms such as Fashion Café, Planet Hollywood, All-Star Café, and the Hard Rock Café. In fact, the eatertainment industry as a whole has encountered a fairly rocky path for just this reason.

Our research led us to the conclusion that substituting entertainment for a solid business value proposition—just like high/low pricing—is not a winning strategy. But doesn't everybody want to have fun? Of course they do, and guess what? They can entertain themselves better than you can entertain them. With options like mountain biking through war zones, base jumping off skyscrapers, ocean kayaking, and a multitude of high-altitude extreme activities from which to choose, not to mention 100 channels on cable TV, the Internet, movies, cultural and sporting events, and much, much more, consumers just don't need that parking-lot petting zoo or a magician in the supermarket. Subscribers to the myth of excellence are as prone to gratuitously add entertainment to the offering as they are to promiscuously—and unnecessarily—discount prices, overlooking the fact that what experience-oriented customers really want is a sense of intimacy, not dancing bears in the soft-goods aisles.

While many business operators like to think of today's consumers as time-starved whirlwinds grateful that companies combine juggling demonstrations with picking up the dry cleaning, the truth is that today's instavidual consumers are really consummate time editors, constantly deciding what activities to edit in and out of their daily lives. You want time-starved? Talk to farmers.

There was a time when, in fact, consumers did look to retailers and other businesses to provide entertainment—a time when they didn't have the litany of leisure options available to them today. We can all point to examples from our past. Ryan remembered how his mother used to demonstrate sheet music in stores. She would play the piano and sing while customers gathered around to listen. The entertainment aspect was clearly a vital part of the experience for shoppers. Time wasn't at such a premium then, but entertainment was. Today most of us don't have that degree of gentility—or time—in our lives; we are unlikely to stand and listen to someone sing for fifteen minutes in a music store. Instead, we'll buy our CD and get out the door, or order it from Amazon or CDNow, or download it directly off the Internet from MP3.com.

It's clear, then, that entertainment alone will not keep consumers coming back. The coarsening of American society in the past twenty years, the general declining civility level and increasing feeling of isolation—a sort of social devolution—have made it more important for consumers to get respect from the companies with which they do business. Why? Because they're not getting it anyplace else. The need for respect—to be treated like a human being—shouted so loudly at us as we reviewed the research that it's hard to believe all companies don't market it along with their more traditional goods. Nearly three-quarters of consumers in our survey said that courteous and respectful employees were "most important" to their shopping relationship, and 66 percent said that having a company treat them as a valued customer was a critical component of their commercial interactions.

Over the past few years, news headlines have repeatedly told the tale of consumers enraged about the poor treatment and lack of respect they have received at the hands of businesses:

- "Why Everyone Is So Short-Tempered" (*USA Today*—7/18/00)
- "Passenger Dies in Air Rage Terror" (*The Mirror*—9/19/00)
- "Privacy Concerns Cool Holiday Spirit" (*Infoworld*—12/5/00)

Increasingly, consumers are venting that rage, whether it's aimed at airlines, retailers or other businesses, with verbal—and, occasionally, physical—assaults against employees. Take the case of Miranda Smith, a twenty-one-year-old suburban Detroit resident who was arrested for assaulting a clerk in a Hudson's department store, apparently after being dissatisfied with the service she received. And stories of airline passengers exploding in fits of air rage abound. Other angry consumers have taken their gripes to the Internet, with websites such as sucks.com providing a forum to blast offending businesses.

Of course, the need for respect works both ways. The cashier, the airline-gate agent, or other employee on the front line who becomes the target of a customer's rage is likely to respond in kind. Consider this diatribe, titled "The Helliday Season," posted on the Web by a Minnesota student and retail employee: "Then there are the customers. 'This bottle is in the wrong slot!' screams an aging woman with platinum blond hair and Sears Weatherbeater eyeliner. 'I wasted seven minutes to walk back here and check on it myself, and it's in the wrong slot. You have to give it to me for that price. You're making my daughter late. I don't have time for this.' Okay. But you do have time to scream at me for twenty minutes? I didn't put the bottle there. You know who did? A customer. Yes, a whiny, screamy, navy-blue-slacks-and-chartreuse-blouse-with-magenta-buttons customer. Not me. I have enough of my own things to worry about, lady . . . keeping the diapers full that YOU pull out and mess up; cleaning up broken bottles of perfume that YOU dropped and left . . . picking up the circle rack of sweatpants that YOUR drooling three-year-old knocked over. . . . I can only do so much. Kiss my f---ing ass. I don't say that, of course. You know how it is . . . if the customer says the blue jacket is green, well, it's green, right? Customers are NEVER WRONG!"

How's that for evidence of the breakdown in civility, human values, and communication in today's world? While the growing mutual disrespect that has developed in recent years between consumers and businesses represents a significant change in society, it also offers an opportunity for companies that can create a culture of respect. Those that do will be able to provide an experience that transcends the exchange of money for goods or services. In this sense, experience is all about the feeling a consumer has when he or she visits or shops a business—a feeling that goes far beyond simple entertainment.

Howard Schultz, CEO of Starbucks, understands the importance of this form of experience. He knows that the hundreds of thousands of consumers who stop in a Starbucks shop every day are buying more than just a cup of coffee. "Coffee has been at the center of conversation for hundreds of years," said Schultz.[1] "We are trying to create a 'third place' for our customers . . . a place between home and work where people can come to get their own personal time out . . . have a sense of gathering. . . . Starbucks has become an extension of people's front porches. There's a level of trust in what we stand for, a sense of reliability. . . . The reason that our customers come back is the quality of the experience."

In much the same way that there are two kinds of access—physical and psychological—our research indicates that there are also two types of experience: the external experience, that is, the entertainment factor, whether it's a piano player in the store or a chef demonstrating how to make shish kebab; and the internal experience, which is tied to the feeling a consumer has about doing business with a particular company—a far more personalized sense of experience. Here's how a consumer might make the distinction: "It's not the experience associated with the store that counts as much as my experience of myself in the store. How do I feel when I'm in the store? Am I treated with courtesy and respect? Am I treated as a valued customer? Are my concerns handled in a positive manner?"

Is it possible to provide both the external and internal experience? Sure. Stanley Marcus, for instance, ran Neiman Marcus as if it were a theatrical production, yet he also understood the value of providing a personal experience for consumers. Take the story he liked to tell about the time he created a "million-dollar parfait" for a particular customer. Marcus started with an expensive champagne glass, lined it with silk scarves, and added layers of diamonds, emeralds, and rubies. The finished creation resembled an ice cream parfait, sporting a price tag of a cool $1 million. Marcus turned the entertainment aspect—or external experience—of the transaction into a sort of private theater—or internal experience—for that individual shopper.

Connecticut-based Stew Leonard's also succeeds in combining the external and internal aspects of experience. The company's stores are replete with animatronics, sampling stations, and a boatload of other bells and whistles. But the entertainment factor is backed up with friendly, courteous, knowledgeable, and respectful employees, who supply the internal element of the experience equation.

The bottom line for businesses? Companies that put all their resources into entertainment—or the external experience—and forget to treat customers with respect are leaving money on the table. The yearning for respect among consumers is so great that of the five value attributes as they're defined today, experience may offer the greatest hidden treasure trove for consumer businesses.

Experience is perhaps the most difficult attribute to accurately define. Like the attribute of service, it is largely subjective, representing in effect the consumer's response to all of the attributes. People new to Consumer Relevancy often have a difficult time distinguishing between service and experience. After all, your "experience" of a commercial transaction is largely formed by your perception of the service you received in the course of that transaction.

So, where does service stop and experience start? Think of it this way: In addition to a customer's subjective analysis of a transaction, service has objective, tangible aspects that can be measured. We like to say that the bottom line of service is how you feel about a business as a result of having done a transaction, while experience is how you feel about yourself as the result of a transaction. If a business accommodates and educates its customers and customizes its offering, consumers will generally walk away with a positive service impression. Experience, by contrast, is far more internalized and infinitely more difficult to quantify, because it is dependent on my perception of whether or not I've been treated with respect, that a business *really* cared about me, and that a business displayed a sufficient level of intimacy to make me feel special but not so much that I feel invaded or compromised.

Richard Schulze, founder, chairman, and CEO of consumer-electronics retailer Best Buy, explains how his company translated this notion of experience into action. "We seized on connecting with consumers by providing them what they really wanted, which more than anything else was a fun, engaging shopping experience that was totally without pressure or intimidation," Schulze said. "One of the first wins we had with that strategy was our ability to attract female consumers, who historically had been talked down to by commission salespeople who used intimidation and took control of the transactions so aggressively that a lot of the women who were shopping opted to go to Wal-Mart, Target, Sam's, or someplace else. They'd buy whatever it was they happened to have on the shelf and say that, you know, this is good enough, rather than endure the kind of strategies that were used. Well, our strategy, which was so much more friendly, really locked on to the female marketplace. At one point, as much as 48 percent of our customer base was female versus 52 percent male. Contrast that with a more traditional consumer-electronics store that we competed with, where it was 75 percent/25 percent male/female. So we won with the American female consumer by giving them a shopping experience that was much more closely aligned to ones they were experienced with."

Clearly, the key factor for a company attempting to dominate on experience rests heavily on the interaction between customers and employees. Consumers we spoke with identified the following items as the most critical aspects of experience:

- The company's employees are courteous and respectful.
- Consumers are treated as valued customers.

- The company's staff responds to customer concerns in a positive manner.
- Salespeople promote a positive image about the products or services the company sells.
- Employees dress to reflect/complement the atmosphere of the company.
- The interior visual appearance (e.g., décor, signage, layout) of the company's bank branch, store, or showroom is pleasing to the eye.
- Music or videos that enhance the customer's experience are played in the facility.

The environmental factors—signage, music, employee dress—help set the stage for the consumer. These elements create the first impression of the company, and provide some indication of the personality of the store or business and the type of experience consumers might expect from that company. For example, Williams-Sonoma, the kitchen-supplies retailer, understands the role environmental factors can play in creating a strong first impression. There's always something brewing in the store for consumers to sample—an interesting tea, a new coffee blend, a mulled spiced cider at Christmas. The aromas are powerful draws to the store. Similarly, the loud, pounding music in a Hot Topic store, a favorite among Generation Y shoppers, is appropriate for the target market and sends a message to its customers that "this place is for you."

But while environmental factors create the first impression, the treatment that consumers receive from employees provides the *lasting* impression. Tara, a thirty-nine-year-old cosmetologist, echoes the sentiments of many consumers. "I'm sick of store clerks judging customers by the way they look," she fumed. "You could have a guy who looks like a bum off the street and not know he's a multimillionaire. Why do employees have to be so judgmental and rude?"

Conversely, a good experience can be just as memorable—and potentially profitable for the company. In fact, our research made it clear that in today's society a positive experience with a company has come to be viewed as the exception rather than the rule. "When I go into a store and the employees are pleasant and helpful and smile a lot, it's a great experience," noted one consumer. "I remember being in stores like this and thinking, 'Wow, that owner must really be on the ball.'"

This is true for Internet businesses as well as for those in the physical world. Most consumers we interviewed said that being treated as a valued customer is the most important element of creating a positive experience in consumer-direct dealings. Many also noted that the visual merchandising of a company's products on its website or in its catalog defines their experience with that firm. And even in the wired world, consumers want to be able to make contact with real people. Retailers such as REI have learned to do more with their websites than simply reproduce the company catalog. REI's site gives consumers an opportunity to ask questions of the staff, check the competition's prices, and contact other consumers who can vouch for a pair of hiking shoes or recommend a particular mountain trail in West Virginia.

As companies rush to establish an online presence or play catch-up, they may run the risk of confusing customers about the brand experience. Barnes & Noble has worked hard to create a pleasant environment in their physical stores, complete with coffee bars and armchairs. Their Internet site developed a parallel strategy, offering consumers a place to read and respond to reviews written by their peers and make connections with other readers. But the website doesn't have to worry about the inventory problems faced by the physical stores. In terms of the book-buying experience, consumers in physical stores might be told they have to wait several weeks for the same book they could order online and receive in several days. Barnes & Noble is aggressively working to integrate its online and physical markets, but other companies are struggling to blend the virtual and physical experiences.

Unresolved, the conflict, or the perception of one, between a company's physical stores and its website has the potential to eventually destroy the sense of experience that a business is trying to develop. Companies must ensure that the experience delivered by their websites is the same as—or complementary to—what consumers would find in the physical environment, unless they are creating an entirely different company and brand on the Internet.

Applying the Conceptual Model to Experience

So what must businesses do to compete successfully on experience? Applying the conceptual model for Consumer Relevancy provides a picture of the implications for experience (Figure 7.1). At the threshold level (Level I), consumers say, "*Respect* me, or I will look to your competitors for the products and services I need." Consumers simply want to be treated as human beings. "Get pleasant, helpful employees," said one consumer. "Don't make customers feel like they're pressured to buy something," noted another. Simple, basic stuff—yet largely overlooked by most businesses, judging from our research.

FIGURE 7.1

Competing on Experience

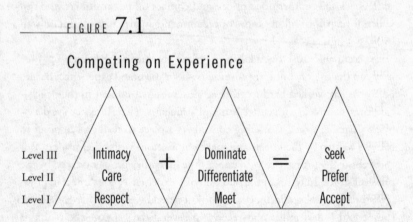

Level III	Intimacy		Dominate	Seek
Level II	Care	+	Differentiate	= Prefer
Level I	Respect		Meet	Accept

At the second level—where consumers begin to prefer a company—the relationship between consumer and business deepens to include *care*. At this level, consumers are saying, "Show me you genuinely care about me and my needs, and I will prefer you to other companies in most situations." In addition to employees' attitudes, care also encompasses environmental factors such as signage, music, and employee dress. After all, if companies don't care about the image their employees and stores convey, how can they care about their customers? But any show of care has to be sincere, or consumers won't buy it. Consider one consumer's experience at an Ann Taylor store: "The young saleslady was eager to help me," she recalled. "She was with me from the beginning to the end of my shopping trip. She suggested things to me, made honest comments, and seemed to care about what I bought. I was more eager to spend, and I thought the whole experience was worth it."

The Ritz-Carlton Hotel Co. has a tangible approach to ensuring a high level of customer care. Hotel employees—from housekeeping staff to hotel management—each have a discretionary fund of $2,500 to handle any customer problem or complaint. One night we were sitting in the bar of the Ritz in Laguna Naples, Florida. An inebriated client—on his fourteenth screwdriver—began to lecture the cocktail waitress on the wonders of the ashtray being graced by the rather sodden presence of his Macanudo. "How much can I give you for this ashtray?" our client asked more or less coherently. "Nothing, sir," she said. "But I want it. I really want it. It's beautiful," the client insisted. "That ashtray isn't for sale, sir," she said politely but firmly. "But don't go anywhere—I'll be right back." Within ten minutes, she arrived back at our table with a small, tastefully gift-wrapped box. "Here you are, sir," she said. Our client unwrapped the box, and inside rested a presumably new and certainly clean version of the ashtray that our client was currently designing his next dream home around. "But you said I couldn't buy this ashtray," he said, somewhat confused. "Well, that's right," the waitress said. "I bought this one for you, and that one is dirty, after all."

Level III is the customer-affirming experience. Here, the consumer feels a close bond with the company, a degree of *intimacy*, interaction, and trust that leads to a long-term relationship. At this level, the consumer says, "I believe you have my best interests at heart, that you will tell me the truth because you respect me as a human being and care more about me and my satisfaction than you do about making a sale." Or, as Sandra, a twenty-three-year-old department-store buyer, put it, "It's really nice when the stores I normally go to know me personally."

That aspect is not lost on cybermerchants. Many of us have gotten personalized e-mails from Amazon with book or music recommendations. In contrast, how often does a similar type of communication occur in the physical world? Ryan points to his own experience with a brick-and-mortar retailer near his office that he's shopped in since it opened a number of years ago: "I've literally spent thousands of dollars at the store, but when I walk in, nobody says hello to me, nobody knows who I am, nobody says, 'It's nice to see you again.' When I log on to Amazon, it says, 'Hi, Ryan Mathews, here are some recommendations for you.' At least the software knows who I am." The challenge for Amazon's collaborative-filtering software, which recommends books and CDs based on past purchase patterns, is to satisfy the future needs of customers with eclectic buying habits who don't establish a clear pattern.

Certainly, e-tailers aren't the only businesses that understand the value of providing a positive experience. Transportation-services company BostonCoach, for example, has made it a clear point of distinction. You don't have to take many taxi rides from La Guardia Airport in New York to experience the true meaning of anxiety and abuse. But for an increasing number of travelers across the country, BostonCoach represents a more civilized (albeit expensive) alternative for getting from the airport to their destination. A wholly owned subsidiary of Fidelity Investments, BostonCoach seeks to wrap all the amenities of its offering—safety, convenience, dependability, comfort, and, above all, respect for the customer—into a single package that the company refers to as "The BostonCoach Experience."

When traveling via BostonCoach, customers are picked up by a courteous, professional driver. He addresses you by name, opens doors, handles your luggage, makes sure you're comfortable, and can probably tell you what happened on Wall Street that day—but only if you want him to. To top it off, BostonCoach will get you where you're going when you need to be there: The company has a 99 percent on-time performance record.

Companies that succeed in dominating on experience and maintaining a high level of respect for their customers stand to gain big. Yet the experience attribute is a difficult feature to scale. It may be company policy to respect, care about, and establish trust among customers, but getting the people who work on the front lines to act on such a policy is a tough task.

While there are many companies that operate at Level I, and some that have reached Level II, there is just a small group of businesses that truly dominate the competition on experience. Among these companies are Southwest Airlines, Midwest Express, Gourmet Garage, and Ireland's Campbell Bewley Group.

Case Study

Southwest Airlines and Midwest Express: Bringing Civility to the Air

Talk to just about anyone who flies on a regular basis, and you'll hear how bad air travel has become. And it's not just the lost luggage, delayed flights, cramped quarters, and inedible food that are at issue. It's the attitude and performance of airline employees that add fuel to an already explosive situation. The bottom line: Airlines could provide a much better experience if they just made respect for the customer a higher priority.

But how do you accomplish that? Ask the folks who run Southwest Airlines and Midwest Express, two of the biggest success stories in the industry. Despite Southwest's "no-frills" approach—no assigned seating, no meals or snacks, no preferential treatment—the traveling public has consistently ranked the airline as one of the best in the United States. In the public's mind, Southwest has become a company renowned for the consumer experience it provides.

Colleen Barrett, executive vice president for customers at Southwest, attributes this response to the high level of personal and respectful treatment the company's passengers receive. "Our basic business is short-haul, point to point," Barrett said. "Ninety percent of our business is really that of a commuter carrier. Because we offer low fares for such flights, we actually get to know many of our frequent fliers by name. And they know us. I can't tell you how many calls I get from customers along the lines of 'I haven't seen Sandra Smith at Gate 3 in San Antonio for the last two weeks. Is something wrong?' Similarly, I get calls from our flight crews who say, 'Colleen, John Jones has flown with us for the past seventeen years, and we just read in the newspaper that he's had a heart attack. Can the company send him some flowers?' These are just some examples of the degree of bonding that goes on between Southwest personnel and the consumers they serve."

How does Southwest create a culture in which such bonding is recognized and rewarded? There's no formula for it, said Barrett, other than "practicing the Golden Rule inside and out every day: Do unto others as you want them to do unto you."

Southwest selects new employees largely on the basis of their "attitude profile." New recruits are expected to show an interest in people, respect them, and be eager to respond to their needs. "We hire for attitude, not for skills," Barrett said, "because we believe we can teach the skills. The attitude—the desire to help people, to care for and about them, has to already be there in the new hire. This is not to say, of course, that we don't look at a pilot's skills. Southwest has extremely stringent flying requirements. But we've turned down some top guns even though they had letters of recommendation from U.S. senators, because we felt they didn't fit our attitude profile. We've interviewed as many as fifty people for one position—a ramp agent in New York. Why? Because we're looking for those few who are servant leaders, altruistic people with a sense of humor to boot."

Milwaukee-based Midwest Express has also risen above the fray by excelling on experience. Midwest started operations in the early 1980s as the corporate shuttle for employees of Kimberly-Clark Corp. because, according to Dan Sweeney, director of business performance at Midwest, "employees were experiencing such a high level of dissatisfaction flying on commercial carriers." Within two years, the airline went commercial.

Operating under the slogan "The best care in the air," Midwest has grown to a $400 million, 3,000-employee national airline offering premium-class service. "Our foundation is based on a number of key corporate values," said Sweeney. "For instance, we always focus on the customers and try to treat them as if they are guests in our own homes. We want to always strive for honesty and integrity and being responsive to customers' needs and expectations. And respect for the individual is critical. And we do so by hiring extremely customer-conscious, friendly, and caring people."

Unlike Southwest, whose experience tends toward the "fun and zany," Midwest creates an upscale and sophisticated environment on its flights, including the in-flight dining service. "We have color pictures of each meal we serve, so that everyone in the kitchen—many of whom don't speak English—knows exactly what the meals should look like on the plate," Sweeney said. "Then we have a very complex logistics process for transporting all of the meals—which are on china and linens—from the kitchen to the aircraft without tipping or spilling. And we spend a lot of time with all of our flight attendants to help them understand all the elements that make up the dining experience: the presentation of the meal, the offering of choices, the way you hold and pour wine and champagne, the timing and flow of the service."

While Southwest competes secondarily on price with its no-frills operation, Midwest's secondary attribute is product. The company's planes feature two-by-two, leather-covered seating for more legroom and "seatroom." All travelers get complimentary newspapers and are treated to baked-on-board chocolate chip cookies.

But in the end, Midwest pins its winning formula on its people. "When we hire people, we really want to understand their value systems to see if they match up with our values," said Sweeney. "We're looking for team players who actually care about people. Once we get new employees on board, we invest heavily in training them. Everyone goes through a two-day orientation process where we talk about our strategy and philosophy, and how we work together to make it happen. After this, they go into an eight- to ten-week technical training program to learn more specific things about their jobs—for instance, flight attendants learn the aircraft equipment, CPR, first aid, etc. But even during this, there's continual reinforcement of our strategy as it relates to caring for our customers."

According to Sweeney, the greatest challenge Midwest Express faces is avoiding complacency. "When you've achieved the position we have, it's natural for people to feel like, 'We've done it—we've arrived!' But, as you know, customer expectations are continually being redefined and changing. We need to make sure that we do the things we have to so that we always have the credible, consistent, and reliable experience—the clean plane, friendly and caring people, the terrific meal—that our customers expect every time they get on the airplane."

Case Study

Campbell Bewley Group: An Authentic Experience

Bewley's coffees and teas are more to Dublin than Peet's or Seattle's Best are to Seattle. In a very real sense, Bewley's and its flagship coffeehouse on Grafton Street *is* Dublin. Walking into Bewley's is like walking back into Dublin's, and Ireland's, history. You'll find the corner where a young James Joyce came to write not marked by a bronze memorial but occupied by another Dubliner, maybe an Irish senator and maybe a street sweeper. It doesn't matter. Stay in Dublin long enough to need a good cup of coffee or tea, or maybe a morning "fry" or a superior afternoon teacake, and you'll find your way to Bewley's. The company, its products, and its stores play such a pivotal role in Dublin's self-image that when Bewley's ran into trouble in the 1980s, there was a formal debate on the floor of the Díal, the Irish parliament, as to whether the government should purchase the ailing company. The argument was simple: How could Dublin exist without Bewley's?

It seems that every Irish man, woman, and child and even most tourists are familiar with Bewley's coffees and teas, and many—if not most—Dubliners have spent more than a few hours relaxing in one of the company's famous cafés sprinkled about the city. So what makes Bewley's so special?

"Without a doubt, the most valuable element of Bewley's is its authenticity," noted Donal O'Brien, Bewley's managing director of retail and franchising. "With Ireland being a very 'cool' place at the moment, an awful lot of people are trying to create Irish authenticity. We don't have to create it—we've had it since 1840. Our cafés are where people like James Joyce and other writers came and got their inspiration. That history is still firmly in the minds of the locals and, indeed, in the minds of visitors who come looking for that quintessential Irish experience."

Bewley's was founded in 1840 by Samuel Bewley and his son, Quakers who operated the company on the principles of the Society of Friends, to bring tea to the Irish people. In 1893, the company introduced coffee to Ireland and by 1927 was operating a number of cafés, bakeries, and even a chocolate factory. The cafés quickly developed a reputation as places where people could meet, converse, eat, and possibly be inspired to poetry and prose.

The company flourished until the early to mid-1980s, when it fell on hard times, at least partially the result of the family consistently insisting on putting Quaker philosophy ahead of commercial gain. Still run by the Bewley family, the business needed financial help, and needed it fast. Enter Patrick Campbell and his Campbell Catering Ltd., which purchased Bewley's and began to reinvigorate and expand the brand. Campbell, an accomplished artist, made his money in the foodservice business, beginning by catering oil rigs in the North Sea. When a strike on one of the rigs threatened the future of his fledgling company, Campbell personally ferried food to the rig in the middle of a storm, delivering provisions and saving his contract. Campbell had been giving serious thought to leaving the world of business and pursuing his painting on a full-time basis, but the opportunity to save Bewley's put those plans on the back burner. "I felt that by getting involved with the company, I would be giving back something in payment for all my success," said Campbell. "I felt I had no other choice."

Interestingly, Campbell took over the company only after receiving several guarantees. The first was that the Bewley family members involved in the business remain in the business. The second was that under no condition was product quality to be sacrificed to improve bottom-line performance. "I told Mr. Bewley [the company's then-chairman] that he would continue to manage the product and I'd manage the bankers," said Campbell.

Today, the renamed Campbell Bewley Group—with Patrick Campbell as its chairman—runs more than thirty outlets across Ireland, the United Kingdom, and the United States (under the Bewley's name and the Rebecca's Café chain, which the company purchased in 1998). Bewley's coffees and teas are also available for purchase via the Web.

The company's primary competitive attribute is experience, and it is clearly differentiated by strong product quality. The coffeehouses themselves are competitive on price, and the retail prices on some of the coffees and teas may be slightly higher than other competitors. Bewley's coffeehouses are essentially self-service, with customers selecting their own goods and moving to a pay station. The secondary mall locations resemble Starbucks' kiosks in an airport, limiting the opportunity for truly full service. In terms of access, Bewley's has a relatively limited number of shops and is more concerned that the retail products are sold by a certain type of retailer, such as Ireland's Superquinn supermarkets, rather than seeking out ubiquitous distribution.

The Bewley's Experience

BEWLEY'S FORMULA FOR SUCCESS

PRIMARY ATTRIBUTE: EXPERIENCE

- Maintains intense attention to detail in physical plant.
- Does not offer waiter service, to encourage people to relax and linger and go at their own pace.
- Trains café staff extensively.
- Categorizes all café staff by "grade levels."
- Posts signs and table cards around the café explaining to customers the attention and services they will receive in the cafés.
- Solicits feedback from customers.
- Ties employee and management rewards and incentives to customer feedback.

While Bewley's history and authenticity are the initial attractions for customers, there's more to the Bewley's brand than a strong link to the past. The company spends a considerable amount of time, effort, and money maintaining the experience so that customers keep coming back. This is especially important today, as Dublin's renaissance has sparked the opening of a string of new, American-style coffeehouses—"cappuccino alleys," as O'Brien calls them—that are making a strong push to attract the younger crowd. By focusing on five key factors, Bewley's is staying a step ahead of its competitors and positioning itself for growth, both domestically and abroad.

1. **Maintaining attention to detail.** The physical structure of each Bewley's café is one of the most important facets of the experience. The high ceilings, stained-glass windows, mahogany walls and woodwork, open coal fire, brass trim, and red upholstery are as much a part of the Bewley's experience as the coffee and tea. For that reason, the company won't scrimp on the physical plant. For example, Bewley's is in the midst of revamping and modernizing all of its Dublin cafés while maintaining their distinctive character and details. The recent makeover of the flagship café on Dublin's chic Grafton Street cost $5 million. "We could have done it for less, and probably gotten away with it," said O'Brien. "But it would have removed some of the value of the brand."

2. **Prohibiting waiter service.** In a break from traditional practice at most food and beverage establishments, Bewley's operates without a waitstaff. The reason, O'Brien said, is to support the notion that it's okay for customers to take their time when visiting. With no one continually asking them if they need anything, customers feel more comfortable just "hanging out"—which likely plays a big role in the fact that more than 60 percent of customers come alone. Similarly, O'Brien said, women—who represent 45 percent of the cafés' business—are attracted by the atmosphere because they find it a safe place to enjoy a sandwich or coffee by themselves or to wait for a

friend. "There's still a feeling here in Ireland that women would not enter a public house on their own and sit there to meet somebody," O'Brien explained. "But in our cafés, women know they can relax there without being hit on by anyone or without being really conspicuous."

3. **Staff training.** Bricks and mortar only go so far in creating the Bewley's experience; employees play a major role as well. Café employees are categorized by one of five levels: white (initial trainee), blue, silver, gold, and diamond (shift leader). Table tents explain the code to customers. An employee must complete a series of training seminars and gain a certain amount of experience on the floor to move from one level to the next. Each move up comes with an increase in responsibilities and pay. Name tags are colored to reflect an employee's level—which, according to O'Brien, not only gives employees motivation to aspire to higher levels (and rewards those who have reached the top) but also helps customers understand the capabilities and authority of a particular employee.

   Staff training at Bewley's is driven by the concept of multitasking. This has become especially important as the pool of available labor in Dublin has virtually dried up in recent years. "Instead of hiring three or four people to do a bunch of different jobs, we try to train one person to do all of them—and then pay them a lot more money," said O'Brien.

4. **Communicating to customers.** Bewley's customers are treated to an array of subtle—and not so subtle—hints of what they can expect at a Bewley's café. For instance, there's a sign at the entrance of every café that says customers can expect the staff to be friendly and helpful toward them, that the café will be clean and pleasant, and that the staff will address any problem efficiently. The message is reinforced with similar signs on tables and

counters that "give the customer the sense that, hey, these guys really want to make this nice for me," O'Brien explained. "It's a feel-good factor."

In addition, customers are alerted a week in advance to any changes that might be taking place—something that's especially important since Bewley's has a large number of regular customers. Managers also explain any changes and solicit customer reactions. The tactic is effective not only because customers appreciate the courtesy but also because their reactions to a proposed change provide a sense of whether an idea is likely to be a winner or a loser.

5. **The feedback loop.** Bewley's management believes that the only way to keep giving people what they want is to listen to customers and do what they say. The company solicits input via comment cards in all of its cafés. These cards ask for customers' thoughts on how things can be improved and encourage patrons to provide praise when appropriate. "Most comment cards can be very negative," said O'Brien. "They only encourage people to tell you when something's wrong. We thought it would be beneficial to our staff if we gave people a way to say, 'You know, I really love this' or 'Mary treated us so well on our visit.' "

The feedback from the comment cards is taken seriously by store staff and company management. A café employee praised by name is immediately rewarded by the store manager—with, say, two tickets to the cinema. For store managers, the feedback can mean the difference between a good and bad monthly evaluation. "If there's a sudden increase in comment cards in either direction, it's noted, and it affects the manager's overall scoring and evaluation," O'Brien explained. "If your comments are overly negative, it's going to make your evaluation go down, which will affect your bonus. But if the comments are very positive, you will get a better evaluation and a bigger bonus. That's the reason for giving customers a way to relate positive experiences as well as problems."

Uncompromising Product Quality

BEWLEY'S FORMULA FOR SUCCESS

Secondary Attribute: Product

- Builds personal relationships between the coffee and tea buyer and the farmers/brokers around the world.
- Strictly controls the roasting and blending of the beans and tea leaves.
- Maintains an extensive tracking system to ensure consistency of blends.
- Provides café staff and corporate customers with comprehensive training on how to properly brew and serve coffee and tea.
- Rents, services, and maintains a variety of coffee machines to ensure that corporate customers are using the correct equipment.
- Conducts refresher training of café staff every three months.

Executives point out that the Bewley's experience would be nothing without the company's famous coffees and teas. Bewley's' reputation for great tea and coffee is the foundation upon which the business was built, and it's what sets Bewley's apart from its competitors. In fact, this reputation was the key factor in Bewley's favor when Campbell Catering purchased the firm in 1986. "When we bought Bewley's, it was hemorrhaging money very badly. It was about to go out of business," said Chairman Patrick Campbell. "There was very little value left in the business other than its reputation. But it was a great legacy that we knew we could build on and help bring back to life."

The quality of Bewley's coffees and teas begins in the fields of Africa, the Far East, and Central and South America, where the beans and leaves are grown. Paul O'Toole, Bewley's resident "buyer and blender," maintains strong relationships with his suppliers to ensure that he gets the highest-quality product. He visits the growers and the brokers around the world every few years to maintain a personal connection, and works closely with

Patrick Bewley, the great-grandson of the company's founder, who handles much of the responsibility for coffee buying.

All of the coffee beans and tea leaves arrive at the company's new facilities in suburban Dublin, where they are roasted and blended under controlled conditions. O'Toole maintains a detailed system for tracking the various coffee and tea blends from month to month to ensure consistency. "The Irish are the biggest tea drinkers in the world," he pointed out. "They don't always realize how good the quality of the tea they're drinking is, but they certainly know when that quality is compromised—even just a little bit."

A crucial element of the coffee-roasting process is the fact that the system is fully integrated and sealed. Such an arrangement is vital, O'Toole noted, because it helps trap the aromas of the beans as they are roasted, ensuring a higher flavor content. This process extends to the bags in which the coffee beans are packed. Rather than vacuum-packing their beans, Bewley's has designed a special package that enables the beans to remain surrounded by their aroma. "When you vacuum-pack, you're sucking all the air out of the bags, and with that, you're removing a lot of the flavor of the beans," O'Toole explained.

To ensure that the coffees and teas receive the same care once they leave the roasting-and-packing facility, Bewley's provides an array of services and guidelines for its corporate customers and cafés. For example, O'Toole and his staff maintain a training room in the headquarters facility in which café employees and customers are schooled in the basics of brewing and serving coffee and tea. The company also provides rental, maintenance, and refurbishment of coffee machines for its corporate customers.

For café employees, the training never ends. Each employee is trained every three months on the correct way to brew and serve coffee and tea—not as simple a procedure as you might think. To make a cappuccino, for instance, employees are schooled in exactly how to warm the coffee, the depth at which the frother must be in the cup to froth the milk to get a proper head, and the angle at which the cup is held when the coffee is poured. And tea should never be poured into a cup unless the cup is scalded first. ("Otherwise, the infusion isn't correct," explained O'Brien.)

"We are in the business of repeat customers," O'Brien said. "Therefore, we must make sure that every cup of coffee or tea is absolutely the best it can be. If you have eighty bags of tea, they represent eighty potential ways to satisfy customers or make them mad. If you have three hundred cups of coffee in a pot, and that pot wasn't made up to our standards, you'll have three hundred unhappy customers. So we can't, at any stage of the process, interfere with the core basic ingredients of the products, because our customers have come to expect a certain level of performance from Bewley's. If there's one thing our employees know, it's Don't mess with the tea or coffee."

The People Challenge

Although the café experience and superior product quality are the two most visible reasons for Bewley's success, the company's culture and people are equally vital, said Campbell. "Picking good people is the most important thing we do," he noted. "If we as managers pick good people, show them what we want done, and then don't meddle with them while they get on with it, we're going to be successful."

For instance, we were amazed at the passion Paul O'Toole brought to his job. He taught us how to slurp coffee and tea and spent half a day attempting to educate our proletarian palates on the subtle distinctions among blends of teas. After hours of slurping and spitting, we were convinced that there may not be anyone in the world who cares more about tea than O'Toole.

Later that afternoon, we sat with Patrick Campbell and told him about the crash course in tasting we'd received from O'Toole. "In America we'd take a guy like that and make him a media star," we told Campbell. "He'd be the perfect pitchman." "That he would be," Campbell laughed, "except for one small problem: Paul hates to talk to groups. Put six strangers in a room with him, and he'll mesmerize them with talk of tea. Put him in front of a room full of people where he can't build that one-on-one sense of intimacy, and he's much less comfortable." So, we asked, did that mean that O'Toole wouldn't rise higher in the organization? "Depends on what you mean," said Campbell. "He's compensated as though he were climbing the corporate ladder, because he's the best there is at what he does. On the other hand, I'm not going to force him to take any job where he won't be comfortable and where the company won't get the full benefit of his skills. It wouldn't be fair to him, it wouldn't be fair to us, and, in the end, it wouldn't be fair to the customers who place their faith in our products because Paul O'Toole is so vigilantly watching over the quality." We were impressed—a management model that really did seem to work *for* people.

Picking—and keeping—good people, however, is an ongoing challenge, especially as Ireland's labor market continues to tighten. Bewley's motivates and rewards its employees by offering shares in the company to those who reach their two-year anniversary. Management also hands out various awards in recognition of jobs well done. The efforts seem to be working. Campbell noted that Bewley's turnover is lower than that of most companies in its industry, and pointed to the fact that many employees have risen through the ranks. "We have a number of people who started out with us washing pots and are now running branches," he said.

In fact, one long-timer working in the company's Grafton Street café has become the most famous person at Bewley's, noted Campbell, and typifies what it means to excel in experience-based retailing. "She's been with us for fifty years—she's part of the institution, and also an institution in her own right," he said. "But do you know why she's so famous? It's because she always says hello or good morning, and she always says goodbye and thank you. It's simple stuff, really. But if we could get all our employees to do that, think how people would be talking."

Case Study

Gourmet Garage: The Rock 'n' Roll Supermarket

Gourmet Garage has carved out a special niche in the New York food world with its knack for discovering and promoting unusual food items. The retailer has created a unique environment as the self-described "rock 'n' roll supermarket" with stores that provide both the external and internal elements of experience.

The stores are high-energy and inviting: Tight aisles lead shoppers past the extensive gourmet cheese section, through the large produce area, to the prepared-foods counter. The accompanying soundtrack picked by the staff, which segues from classic Jimmy Cliff reggae to vintage John Mellencamp, is loud but appropriate. The stores' physical plants are as interesting as the products they carry. The facility on Sixty-fourth Street on the Upper East Side is a converted parking garage in the ground floor of a co-op; the flagship store in Soho is housed in an 1870s storefront with original tin ceilings and high windows; the Ninety-sixth Street site is shoehorned into a neighborhood-defining thirty-story tower; and the Seventh Avenue store in the heart of Greenwich Village takes up an entire block in a Bauhaus-inspired 1930s-style edifice.

Complementing the physical plant and the unusual product mix is the staff. Smiles and helpful inquiries abound. In turn, the stores' customers—a diverse group ranging from thirtysomething professionals and New York University students in the Lower Manhattan stores to older, higher-income shoppers in the Sixty-fourth Street location—appear to be having fun as well.

An emphasis on reasonable prices also helps set Gourmet Garage apart from many other specialty food retailers. The company distinguishes itself as an experience-based retailer that competes on the secondary attribute of price.

The Gourmet Garage Experience

GOURMET GARAGE'S FORMULA
FOR SUCCESS

PRIMARY ATTRIBUTE: EXPERIENCE

- Passion for the business among the company leadership.
- In-store events and promotions that enhance the company's "fun, funky, and sophisticated" image.
- Rock 'n' roll soundtrack for each store.
- Unique, offbeat physical plants and storefronts.
- Interesting visual merchandising of specialty food products.
- "Diamond-in-the-rough," friendly and engaging employees.

The emphasis on experience and price is an unusual combination that has given Gourmet Garage a true competitive edge and enabled the company to post some impressive numbers. Started in 1992 in a warehouse on Wooster Street in Soho, Gourmet Garage has grown to four locations in Manhattan that generate an estimated $35 million in annual revenue. Not bad for a nine-year-old company, with no external financing, that is the brainchild of three men with widely divergent backgrounds and job experiences: Andrew Arons, chief executive officer; John Gottfried, president; and Ned Visser, chief operating officer. Arons is one of the pioneers of the specialty gourmet-food business in the United States: He started Flying Foods International in the early 1980s and eventually sold it to Kraft Foods. Gottfried is a former banker turned food editor who served as the food and wine critic for the *Village Voice* and penned occasional columns for *The New York Times, Food & Wine,* and *Travel and Leisure.* And Visser, who is trained in architecture, is a former manager of Maxwell's Plum, a famous New York bar. What brought them together? "We're foodies, not grocers," said Gottfried. "We came to this because of our passion for food. It's like someone who loves dance."

That type of passion is the single most important quality a company that competes on experience must have if it is to succeed. "When we started out, we were something really special," Arons said. "We were a destination location because we looked great against our competition such as Dean & DeLuca, which we thought were very, very overpriced at the time. We had beautiful products at great prices. Unfortunately, we really served as a spark to those merchants that had been in the business for twenty or thirty years. So we have to operate in a very organic environment in which we are willing to change and constantly innovate."

All three founders are in the stores every day, talking to customers, in an effort to continue to clearly define what separates Gourmet Garage from its competitors and to maintain its relevance to shoppers. Arons likens the exercise to a musician jamming with other musicians: "When you're playing the guitar, you have to listen to what's entering your ears and make sure that what goes out through your fingers is relevant to what's coming in."

The passion of the founders is one thing, but having that passion rub off on employees is another. Arons admits that finding the right people is difficult due to the combination of the tight New York labor market and the wages that Gourmet Garage must pay to remain competitive. "We look for people we call 'diamonds in the rough,' " he said. "These are inner-city people who have some very important qualities but who just need the right situation for them to come through. We look for the intelligence in their eyes, their smiles, a sense of humor—things that would enable them to function well as a top executive in a corporation were it not for the fact that they didn't have the opportunities that others have had. If they have these raw characteristics, we can train them and have some amazing results."

One such success story is Martin Nunez, a store manager, who was initially a produce stocker making $6.50 an hour. Now, according to Arons, he's a "hotshot store manager who just lives for the place." Nunez, who often comes into the store on his day off—"just to make sure things are right"—now earns enough to provide a comfortable living for his family and put away money to send his children to college.

Gourmet Garage's efforts to create a strong store experience are paying off in the form of positive dynamics between employees and customers. "Because our business is very residential-oriented, we have the same people coming into the same stores all the time," said Gottfried. "As a result, the cashiers have their own favorite customers, and vice versa, and shoppers will line up for their favorite checkout person. It's amazing. But because you have the same people coming in, you have to reinvent the store every day to keep the experience fresh."

At this point, Gourmet Garage's employee-training program comprises a standard employee-training package from the Food Marketing Institute, a Washington, D.C.–based industry trade association; an employee handbook; and a walk around the store. However, Arons said that he hopes someday to open "Garage University" to bring a more formal and comprehensive approach to employee initiation.

The company also strongly relies on promotional activities to help reinforce the store experience. A key belief at Gourmet Garage is "A dollar spent on public relations is worth $1,000 of advertising." So communications with journalists is fundamental to creating the company's continuing image as a pioneer and source of information on new foods. The company's

PR activities are built around a series of in-store events that extend the "fun, funky, and sophisticated" image that the company projects and support Gourmet Garage's strong identification with the professional chefs who comprise a significant portion of the customer base. For instance, in conjunction with the local National Public Radio affiliate each year, Gottfried arranges a weeklong series of in-store cooking appearances by celebrity chefs, many of whom are nationally known.

"It's very important that we create an environment where customers feel they are getting something of value and are being cared for," Gottfried said. "It's not a one-way relationship. In the case of the chefs' series, yes, it's great PR, but it also is educational for our customers. They learn from the pros how to shop and cook like a chef, and oh, by the way, we've got the food and ingredients that the chefs use."

The Budget Gourmet

GOURMET GARAGE'S FORMULA FOR SUCCESS

SECONDARY ATTRIBUTE: PRICE

- Special relationship with Metro Agri, a wholesale food business owned by two of the owners of Gourmet Garage.
- Active and successful private-label program.
- Centralized kitchen that helps serve as a value-added clearinghouse for products that may not sell in the stores.
- "Warehouse" look of the stores.
- Focus on promotion through low-cost public relations instead of big-budget advertising campaigns.

While Gourmet Garage's primary emphasis is on crafting the rock 'n' roll experience, there is a strong secondary focus on price. The company makes a concerted effort to offer innovative, high-quality items at affordable prices. The strategy is not without its challenges. For instance, the company's size tends to limit its purchasing clout with vendors. So how does a four-store specialty food retailer compete on price against larger outlets such as A&P's Food Emporium and Fairway, whose economies of scale and mass-market appeal give them greater buying power?

Arons, Gottfried, and Visser cite a number of factors that help them maintain their price points. The first is the unique relationship that Gourmet Garage has with its primary supplier, Metropolitan Agri-business. Metro Agri is a wholesaler of meats, cheeses, produce, and ingredients to 200 New York restaurants. What makes the relationship special is the fact that Gottfried and Arons also own Metro Agri, giving Gourmet Garage affordable access to the products that many of the city's chefs use. In fact, Gourmet Garage is a direct outgrowth of Metro Agri. "John had founded Metro Agri and had a very successful wholesale business going," Arons recalled. "I approached him with the idea that we should open a retail outlet that was sort of a 'Costco meets Dean & DeLuca.' He bought into it, so we opened the doors to the public in November 1992, and 2,000 people showed up the first day. Since then, we have focused primarily on the retail side but still kept the wholesale business running as well. Wholesale is fun, but retail is COD, which means cash flow is much better."

Metro Agri is not Gourmet Garage's sole supplier. Other vendors compete with Metro Agri for the business, and each store is free to order from other vendors if a better deal is found. "If Metro Agri's price is equal to or better than another vendor's, then that's who they go with, but if the price or quality or reliability is better at another supplier, the store buys from them," said Gottfried. In the case of produce, 80 percent of the company's fruits and vegetables are bought and delivered directly from farms in California, which helps ensure quality and eliminates the middleman.

Another facet of Gourmet Garage's business that helps keep costs down is the private-label program, which is marketed under the distinctive Gourmet Garage logo. Private-label items comprise approximately 20 percent of Gourmet Garage's product mix but 50 percent of total sales, which translates into a solid profit. The company is vigilant about quality because of the important role that private label plays in its operation and the need to maintain the strong equity in the Gourmet Garage brand. Gottfried likes to think of Gourmet Garage as the "buying agent" for its customers, helping them find quality products at affordable prices. "We try to represent our customers when we look for items," Gottfried said. "We've pared down 60,000 potential SKUs to somewhere around 5,000. We preselect products for customers, and do the legwork for them. But we preselect with the best, not the mass market."

Gourmet Garage's centralized kitchen also contributes to the company's low-cost structure. The 5,000-square-foot facility, which operates sixteen hours a day and produces 3,000 to 4,000 prepared meals daily, is worth several million dollars a year in revenue. Its operation in the basement of one of the stores translates into low overhead, and its ability to serve as a value-added clearinghouse for items that may not sell in the stores helps turn what would otherwise be waste into profitable products. "Fruits and vegetables have to be ripe, but if they are too ripe—less than a day's worth of shelf life—they won't survive delivery to the home," Gottfried said.

The look and feel of Gourmet Garage's stores—essentially a warehouse-type model, featuring cut-cases and industrial fixtures and plumbing—does double duty in the company's strategy. The utilitarian design and decor contributes to the in-store experience and is less expensive than a high-end presentation. Arons believes that the stores' "complete lack of pretentiousness" is a huge strength. "Our format really reads as honesty for shoppers," he said. "People know that they're not paying for polished brass fixtures or fancy Italian marble, and they know they're not getting ripped off by our prices."

Finally, because of the focus on lower prices, Gourmet Garage doesn't run big-budget advertising campaigns. Instead, the company focuses on public relations. Gottfried notes that such a strategy is far less expensive and more effective than advertising, and capitalizes on his media relationships. The company's PR efforts result in continual mentions in food columns and articles in the New York and national press, and even helped land a gem that any business would covet: three hours as the backdrop for television's *Good Morning New York*.

Future Challenges

If Arons, Gottfried, and Visser have their way, New Yorkers won't be the only people enjoying the rock 'n' roll supermarket. The company has ambitious expansion plans, hoping to open its first stores outside Manhattan shortly, probably in neighboring New Jersey. Because its reputation and product line lend themselves to the Internet, the company plans to eventually take its concept nationwide and even worldwide via the Web. The founders recognize the myriad challenges that come with such a move, particularly ensuring that the Gourmet Garage experience translates well to other markets. Many retailers have found it difficult or even impossible to maintain a particular experience on a larger scale.

Gottfried acknowledges that understanding the different consumer bases in new markets, learning what they want, and developing the appropriate logistics infrastructure to serve those shoppers will be difficult. But he also believes that the challenges are surmountable. The most difficult challenge, and one key to the success of the company's expansion, will be finding the types of buildings that fit the Gourmet Garage philosophy and turning those spaces—an old train station, a former courthouse, or an abandoned police barracks, for example—into successful stores. It will require equal parts hard work, location, and magic, Gottfried pointed out.

"There is something about entering any physical space that makes it either sympathetic to people or not, and it cannot be totally planned," said Gottfried. "My father used to say that people enter a store and try to find a reason *not* to buy. If you can build a space that creates a positive attitude in people, sort of, 'Hey, what can I find in here?', then you've done it right. The problem is, it's not reducible to a formula. There's only one way to do it, and that's roll the dice."

SELF-DIAGNOSTIC: EXPERIENCE

- Are your employees trained to demonstrate respect in all their interactions with customers, and do your human-resource measures and metrics reinforce that training?
- How do you show your customers that you actually care about them?
- Do you have the kind of knowledge you need to be meaningfully intimate—as opposed to being intrusive or feigning intimacy—with your customers?
- Do you offer your customers something they simply can't get from anyone else?
- Do you have a sense of your customers' broader needs and concerns, or is your knowledge of their lives confined to their purchasing behavior?

CHAPTER 8

Making Consumer
Relevancy Work

As we've demonstrated, Consumer Relevancy is a process that aligns business operations and offerings to new or targeted markets and moves them forward over time. So how do you do it? What does it take to develop the Relevancy strategy and build the infrastructure that facilitates it? Every Relevancy application is unique, but the operational process remains the same across a wide range of industries and enterprises. It begins when a company—using the Relevancy framework—assesses how its offerings are defined by its customers, the mass market of potential consumers, its management, employees, and, in some cases, supply-chain partners.

If you think your company might need a little Relevancy, try this experiment: Ask your senior managers to take out a blank sheet of paper and write down which of the five attributes (access, experience, price, product, service) you dominate in. Now ask them to write down a second attribute they believe you're differentiated on. Finally, ask them to list any of the three remaining attributes on which they believe you're failing to at least meet your direct competitors. If you have perfect alignment in the responses and nobody has suggested that you're below market par in your performance on any of the attributes, conduct the same test with some of your front-line employees. Now try your spouse, your family, and your neighbors. If everyone agrees, congratulations, you're probably doing a great job. If they don't agree, you are a candidate for Relevancy.

Assuming you're prepared to concede that Relevancy *might* be for you, it's time for the next step. Start by conducting a survey of enough customers to ensure a broad base of respondents to find out how existing customers view your company and competitors, and where they would place all of the companies on a Relevancy matrix. We had one client who discovered that his customers had a much broader sense of the competitive set than he did. While he was worried about three direct competitors, our initial research discovered that his "loyal" customers regularly shopped at more than a dozen firms, nine of which he refused to even acknowledge as viable competition.

The next step is to move beyond your existing customers, taking a similar survey instrument out to consumers (who may or may not be your customers), again with enough range to ensure statistical validity. If you operate across multiple consumer bases, we advise augmenting the survey with several geographically and demographically dispersed focus groups, which will provide additional filters for understanding the survey results. As in the case of the customer survey, the objective is to plot a matrix of how consumers see you and your competitors.

The next step is to conduct a similar internal survey asking your key managers to identify your company's, and your competition's, primary and secondary Relevancy attributes. Once again, this exercise should be followed up with interviews to help round out management's perspective. Similar surveys and interviews should be conducted with a wide cross-section of employees, from the corporate office to field locations. In some cases, it may also help to conduct the exercise with vendors and other trading partners.

Once you've gathered all these perspectives, the combined results should be mapped on a Relevancy matrix. This provides a quick visual representation of your key stakeholders' alignment—or lack thereof.

There is tremendous power in this exercise, which large businesses can perform in six weeks, smaller businesses in two. This power comes from identifying gaps between various constituents. A business that does not have alignment experiences value leakage, which occurs anytime a business system under-delivers against a corporate value proposition.

Invariably, our client work surfaces these misalignments, even among members of the key executive team. We've actually refereed some near-fistfights in executive boardrooms—these discussions can be very emotional as the functional heads of a business champion the dominance and importance of their area of responsibility.

This isn't to say that you don't want your HR director to be world-class in his or her recruitment practices or your CFO to exercise world-class financial modeling, but it is to say that you don't want them to think that labor-cost control is the most critical element in a company attempting to dominate on service.

Letting departmental responsibility get confused with market offering is the first step on the slippery path to the myth of excellence. The effective leader of new product development may be doing an excellent job running his or her department while being at industry par in product. The same holds true for the store-operations executive who keeps labor costs way below industry average while remaining at par in service. All executives need to understand that a disproportionate amount of corporate resources should be devoted to the functional areas that reinforce the company's dominant or differentiating attributes in the consumers' minds. This requires the entire executive team to be on the same page, which is rarely the case. As individuals, most good executives strive to be world-class in their functional area, often confusing functionality with market positioning, and will fight tooth and nail for resources and capital. Many executive "teams" operate this way, with the predictable outcome being that the company ends up world-class at nothing—poorly differentiated and therefore not thought of by consumers at the moment of need. These teams have been seduced by the myth of excellence, and their lack of alignment sends mixed signals to employees and customers.

The results of this misalignment are never pretty. "I'd say our real strength is pricing," one CEO told us. "We used to have a price-impression problem years ago, but we've fixed all that." The next day, the company's

HR director told us, "I think pricing is still an issue. I make great money, and I'm loyal, but I still shop the competition for some of the items we carry. Money or no money, loyalty or no loyalty, I just can't bring myself to pay these kinds of prices." We secured that job, and when our work was finished, it was clear the target market sided more with the head of HR than with the CEO.

Once an executive team comes to alignment on its primary and secondary attributes, it can compare how various stakeholders perceive it versus how it would like to be perceived. If executives have one perspective and store management and/or store employees another, the firm may have both a communications and a reward-and-measurement problem. If there is misalignment between management and potential customers, advertising and marketing problems exist. Store operations and advertising are suspects if there isn't agreement between current customers and potential customers. We are reminded of a very successful client that had a wonderful market position as a product/experience company. Butchers in the meat department, fresh sushi made in the store, a wonderful wine selection complete with a sommelier, a humidor stocked with expensive cigars, and gourmet cooking classes. Yet every week, the front cover of the store's advertising circular screamed:

Coca-Cola twelve-packs
$1.89
Limit three
or
Tropicana Pure Premium 64 oz.
$2.49
Limit two

Clearly, a disconnect existed between the company's perceived value proposition and its customer communications. Disconnects between executives and store employees are indicative of training and education problems, while gaps between management and supplier assessments always mean there is value being lost in the supply chain.

Suppliers have the ability to adjust their offer—whether in terms of pricing, promotion, advertising, replenishment, or physical distribution— to align with channel partners' consumer-value propositions. Dollar General understands this. It approached Procter & Gamble to see if P&G could find a way to offer Dawn dishwashing liquid at a price point consistent with the retailer's "extreme value" proposition. That inquiry resulted in P&G (which has a strict policy of offering transparent and equivalent pricing to all its customers) creating a special smaller package of its non-concentrated formula that could be sold at a price point consistent with Dollar General's market position. The bottom line: With the exception of Wal-Mart, Dollar General is the world's largest Dawn retailer.

Asking suppliers to hit precise price points, even when it requires modifications in standard package sizes or formulation, allows Dollar General to remain true to its business model. At the same time, its partnership and alignment with manufacturers adds real consumer value while increasing sales for all trading partners.

Substantial differences between self-perception and market perception foster individual executive rationalization, which in turn leads to collective corporate denial. Brand degradation and loss of market share inevitably follow. It's a pattern of corporate behavior practiced by American automakers in the 1970s, organized labor in the 1980s, and regional mass merchandisers in the 1990s.

Recently, we worked with a company whose market share had been in steady decline for five straight years. Puzzled by the steady loss of customers and sales, we performed a Consumer Relevancy assessment and found significant misalignments around the price and product attributes between management on one side and employees, customers, and consumers on the other. Given the company's historical market position, we weren't too surprised by the misalignment on the pricing attribute, but the product finding surprised all of us. After all, this company had just expanded its in-store inventory by more than 100 percent and offered what was objectively the highest quality and greatest product variety and selection available. Further assessment revealed several critical problems. First, many customers were overwhelmed and confused by the increased variety. Second, the new products were drowning out the local products customers knew and loved. And finally, while the new products were of high quality, in many cases they simply weren't appropriate or relevant to the existing customer base. The result: Customers told us they no longer felt comfortable in the stores. Our client has taken steps to address both the price and product perception issues, and is regaining customers.

The alignment assessment also gives companies a chance to measure their progress with respect to any attribute as often as they like with any or all constituents. Consumer Relevancy is modular. It should be used holistically to set strategy, but it can also be exercised in pieces when attempting to measure tactical progress.

Conducting an alignment assessment inevitably forces companies to face a series of critical decisions, beginning with the reinforcement or reselection of primary and secondary market attributes, decisions with far-reaching impacts on the business. You may find you're well positioned—competing on attributes that your customers and consumers in general value. If that's the case, the prospects for future success are solid, and you should focus your attention on prioritizing and implementing operational improvements that support your current position. However, if instead you're watching customers defect to competitors, direct or indirect, and your prospects for future success are questionable, it's time to consider competing on different primary or secondary attributes.

A word of caution here: The decision to change a primary attribute is risky and should only be undertaken with great caution. Over time, brands such as Kmart, Holiday Inn, Buick, Sears, TWA, JCPenney, and dozens of others have struggled because consumers didn't adjust to their changing value propositions. It is easier, and less risky, to change your differentiating attribute, especially when your dominant attribute remains constant. A product-dominant retailer can change its differentiating emphasis from price to experience, as Best Buy did, or a product-dominant company can move its differentiation point from price to service, as Home Depot did.

Switching your dominant attribute is hard, for several reasons. First, today's consumers are extremely skeptical and cautious, requiring constant communication, relentless policy execution, and patience. Second, the operational implications of switching are hard on employees, who, like the population at large, are generally change-averse. Third, such a move almost always involves a short-term decline in financial performance, as both the market and the organization adjust. For all public companies and most others, this is increasingly hard to do.

Still, there are times when shifting your dominance attribute is exactly the right thing to do. Gordon Bethune changed the fortunes of Continental by reorienting the company to focus on service. Evian became one of the dominant brands in the bottled-water category when it focused on making its product more accessible. RadioShack has successfully migrated from a price-dominant to a product-dominant retailer, probably—given the strong growth in Internet electronics retailing—just in the nick of time.

The hard work begins once these kinds of macro-decisions have been made. Consumer Relevancy is not a magic bullet. It involves making the strategic choices we've outlined and then moving into highly customized implementations. That said, there are a couple of general rules that apply.

First, when making priority tradeoffs, emphasize those activities that bring all your attribute activities at least to par. Every day that you are not meeting customers' minimum criteria on all five attributes, your brand is being damaged. Second, you have to know both what you're not and what you are. Consumer Relevancy is all about making choices. No organization can be great at everything; all executives must be aligned; and resource decisions must be made in a manner that ensures that the majority of resources, time, and effort go to those areas that will strengthen an agreed-upon value proposition.

Dollar General doesn't have a frequent-shopper program, nor does it advertise—these are expensive activities inconsistent with its price/access position. Wal-Mart doesn't attempt to create an industry-leading experience for its customers; instead, it invests in supply-chain systems and infrastructure that allow it to relentlessly drive down net landed cost. Orvis isn't trying to gain mass distribution, and if it did, it would dilute its products' cachet among fly fishermen. And we doubt you'll see VF Corp.'s Wrangler brand on the high-fashion runways of Paris anytime soon.

That's the top-line look at Consumer Relevancy, but every senior-level executive knows that process maps and theory rarely translate directly into results. In fact, we've added more qualitative elements to most of the Relevancy applications, our own participant anthropology—everything from shopping with customers to actually "becoming" customers by anonymously using an offering. We've discussed businesses over drinks and dinner and spent untold numbers of hours just walking around. We've struck up conversations on airplanes and at ball games, and the results have verified what the research told us. Alignment is the critical first step in moving from offering transactions to establishing relationships, from value addition to the addition of values.

The Human Side of Relevancy

As we stated earlier, there isn't a standard approach to Consumer Relevancy. Like a mechanic's toolbox, Relevancy contains a set of tools and methods for tuning up a business. And the most important of those are human resources. Human resources are the secret weapon in the Relevancy war: Companies whose human-resource pools "get" the Relevancy message are companies that win. In an age characterized by regulatory human-resource constraints and employee free agentry, when loyalty often counts for little to nothing, human resources are critical to domination on any attribute. In fact, without the right people in place, it's all but impossible to effectively differentiate your business on any attribute.

For instance, a business competing on experience needs to hire people with a passion for its mission. The success of experience-oriented companies as diverse as Southwest Airlines, BMW, and the Ritz-Carlton Hotel Co. hinges in large part on positive interaction between employees and customers. Employees in an experience-dominant business are responsible for executing the company's culture, since they have a direct impact on customers' impressions and memories. In these companies, compensation and performance measures generally emphasize feedback from customers, as well as observations by management on how employees handle customer interactions—both positive and contentious.

By contrast, companies competing on product must have employees who can intelligently speak about those products: what they are, how they're used, and how they work. This characterizes firms like Williams-Sonoma, The Home Depot, and Best Buy and is most critical for businesses whose products are complex (consumer electronics), expensive (automobiles), or trendy (recorded music and fashion). Compensation should be based on work experience with related products, and should reward continuing education. Rewards and performance measures generally are based on demonstrated merchandise knowledge and customer feedback.

It's generally true that price-dominant companies from Dollar General to Red Roof Inn need to expend fewer absolute dollars per unit of sale than, say, service- or experience-dominant companies. As a result, they often focus on recruiting "diamonds in the rough," smart individuals with good people skills who can be easily trained and motivated. Often these individuals are recruited for part-time work from specific hiring pools (working mothers, housewives, teenagers, and retirees). Price-dominant players are looking for disciplined individuals comfortable with working in an environment of standardized processes and procedures.

Of course, there are exceptions to this model. We remember spending time with the head of a night-stocking crew of a major Canadian retailer. The crew boss was retiring after almost thirty years of service, and his average crew member had more than twenty years with the company. Needless to say, with that much seniority, the crew was at the top of the employer's pay scale for hourly workers. But they also were the most productive stocking crew (measured in terms of standard performance and the absence of negatives such as absenteeism and shrink) in the company, clearly providing good labor dollar value even at a fairly high price.

But such exceptions aside, as a general rule of thumb most price operators' reward-and-measurement systems should be based on a handful of relatively simple and easily understood measures, focused on compliance to a clearly communicated, repetition-based standard of performance. This emphasis on process and repetition is a hallmark of most well-run, large price-dominant companies. Employees who thrive in a price-dominant company might not feel comfortable in a product or experience culture, and vice versa. Again, we need to invoke the earlier caveat about employees like seniors and housewives who may be drawn to price-dominant companies because of flexible hours, liberal hiring policies, and frequent hiring cycles (retention often being a problem in such companies). The psychology and success model of price-dominant companies is unique, and so they must develop the ability to understand the success predictors of their model, and hire against them.

Access-dominant companies make things easy and convenient for their customers, as well as solving problems and creating solutions for them. This requires employees who are sensitive to the specific sales and service demands of their environment, with the interest and ability to resolve problems and suggest total solutions. Tide, Gerber, and Gatorade's call centers are staffed with people trained to easily answer consumer questions regarding product usage and suggest solutions to customers having a crisis related to fabric care, infant nutrition, or hydration. Kozmo.com and Circles' employees need a passion for making deadlines and derive satisfaction from solving their customers' problems—whether it's a late-night beer delivery, finding low-fat grocery products, or booking a hotel room in New York during Christmas week. Access-dominant companies need to find reward and recognition metrics that encourage independence, creativity, and an eye for deadlines and details.

Service-dominant companies face perhaps the most critical hiring, training, and retention challenges, because they need people with great interaction and communication skills. Working on this book, we often marveled at how service-dominant companies from Lands' End and Allstate to Citibank and Dell—which draw from exactly the same labor pool other companies do—manage to find people who apparently love what they do. Their employees communicate enthusiasm and seem to adjust their companies' offering on the fly at the point of customer interaction. Employees at service-dominant companies must be accommodating, not intrusive; capable of learning and communicating their learning; and capable of crafting real-time, customized decisions. Their reward-and-measurement systems should be grounded in continuing education on product or service, as well as direct customer feedback and satisfaction measures. Great employees at service-dominant companies are often higher-paid than their peers at price- or access-dominant companies. But like workers at product- and experience-dominant companies, best-of-class service workers must share a passion for their company's mission and vision and may forgo some direct compensation in favor of "psychic income."

Where Leadership Comes In

Of course, no army—no matter how skilled or well-equipped—can win without a strong general. As in all corporate change initiatives, the importance of the role of the leader simply can't be overestimated. Understanding Consumer Relevancy's importance, continuing to emphasize its importance, and being able to command the resources necessary to ensure its success aren't the same thing. If you as a leader don't deliver a clear Relevancy message, live the implications of that message, and make sure all your employees understand how they help deliver on that message, your company will never become Relevant.

Good leaders are hard to find. Consider this story about Joe Antonini, the former chairman, president, and CEO of Kmart. Several years ago, at a student-sponsored business forum at Western Michigan University, Antonini gave a presentation full of excitement about Kmart's future, punctuated at about every third sentence with a reference to Wal-Mart. During the question-and-answer portion of the presentation, a little gray-haired lady stood up in the back of the room and said, "Mr. Antonini, I thought you were the chairman of Kmart." He laughed and replied, "I am, madam. I'm the chairman, president, CEO, and COO." Looking a bit confused, the lady said, "Well, all through your speech, you talked about Wal-Mart." Antonini shot back, "Yes, that's right. I compared us to them because they're our biggest competitor." Without hesitating, the lady pressed on: "Exactly what is it that makes Wal-Mart so effective at competing against you?" The room suddenly fell into total silence. No one seemed to breathe as Antonini took two full minutes—an eternity on a stage—to respond. "I'd say that Wal-Mart's greatest asset is the fact that we're their biggest competitor."

Clearly, Joe didn't get what the little old lady intuitively understood. Wal-Mart was doing something different, starting with Sam Walton's true genius—getting ordinary people to do extraordinary things. Under Antonini, Kmart believed it was doing the right things and refused to change, while Walton always said, "This is okay. This is great for what we're doing this year. But we need to do it differently next year." Indeed, to Joe Antonini's detriment, Sam Walton succeeded in getting his company to refine its execution against its basic strategy, year after year.

Walton did everything possible to push the company in the right direction. He believed in consistency, so everyone knew what Wal-Mart was supposed to deliver to its customers, and everyone delivered. He believed in accountability, so everyone was on the spot to deliver on Wal-Mart's promises, and he checked up on them. He believed in communication, so (before the rise of the Internet) a satellite system brought the news to the organization in real time, and everyone knew what the management team knew. He believed in profit sharing, so all employees had an opportunity to share in the company's success.

Wal-Mart's management know it is not enough to dictate goals—you have to teach every single employee how his job and responsibility align with the company's goals. This requires an obsession with, and command of, the details of the operation and an ability to deliver a clear, consistent message and philosophy to the entire company over and over again.

Above all, it's vital that corporate leaders understand that Consumer Relevancy can be sustained and transferred from one leader to another and from one part of the company to another. Wal-Mart has successfully exported its philosophy to Mexico and other places around the globe.

Making Better Pancakes

One last point about putting Consumer Relevancy into practice. We were in Amsterdam working with a group of senior executives. It was our first real work session utilizing Consumer Relevancy, and we were struggling to articulate the principles and get complete, mutual understanding. It had been a hard day and with jet lag, language barrier challenges, the heat in the room, and the difficulty of achieving alignment, everyone was tired and a little frustrated.

At around 6 P.M., a senior executive sat back in his chair and said, "I now understand Consumer Relevancy. I get the difference between product value and human values, between content and context. My problem is that I agree with everything you say, because all of this stuff has been around since the dawn of commerce. If I get you right, the ingredients haven't changed, it's the recipe. We're still using the same stuff, but we need to emphasize some things more and some things less. It's like making pancakes. Sometimes you use a little more egg to make them rise; sometimes you use a little more milk to make them thin. You always use the same stuff, but the mixture changes depending on what you're trying to achieve. Do I get it?"

He did.

CHAPTER 9

Supply-Chain Realities

Sometimes myths collide, and when they do, gods who have been worshiped for generations are often unceremoniously dumped from their heavenly perches. It happened when the Greek gods clashed and fell to the gods of the Romans, and it happens every day to less divine presences in the marketplace when the myths of excellence of suppliers come face to face with those of the distributors.

The difficulties that manufacturers or resellers experience trying to align against real consumer values are compounded when their offering is directly influenced by trading partners' business practices. More often than not, the values of either side of a transaction are overshadowed by some quality of the other side's market positioning. Resellers of high-end goods—from luxury-car dealerships to specialty electronics retailers—would have inherent difficulty trying to dominate their market spaces on price-oriented values. By the same token, the temptation to at least attempt to differentiate their businesses around product-oriented value claims might prove all but impossible to resist. On the other hand, manufacturers of fast-moving consumer packaged-goods from paper towels to canned vegetables often find their products positioned on the basis of price and/or access value propositions, regardless of product quality or efficacy.

The final outcomes of the subtle and delicate relationship between a product, brand, or service and its resellers or channels of distribution are critical to forming consumers' value and Relevancy perceptions. This relationship is brokered every day in the streets, with manufacturers pressing product efficacy and marketing information on one side and retailers and other resellers leveraging their direct interface with the consumer and shelf space on the other. While manufacturers remain the primary authors of the content aspect of a transaction, it is the retailer who, more often than not, exerts dominant influence over its context.

This isn't particularly good news for manufacturers targeting mass distribution markets. By virtue of their control of the point-of-sale interface, reselling channels hold more and more sway with consumers. Therefore, it becomes increasingly more important for manufacturers to find ways to build effective relationships directly with consumers. This is easier said than done, since resellers want to retain exclusive ownership of the consumer relationship and the data associated with that relationship. Still, some manufacturers such as Krispy Kreme, Patagonia, and Gateway are having success as hybrids, acting in effect as both supplier and retailer. But more branded giants are struggling with slow real growth, market-share declines, and capital flight to more attractive sectors.

We know consumers value simplicity, clarity, speed, and ease of transaction over disorienting efficacy claims, warring marketing slogans, and exploding line extensions. These consumer values are inherently difficult for manufacturers to build directly into a piece of furniture, a diaper, or an engine. It is much easier for resellers to build and express these values into the context in which products are sold.

This helps explain the rise of private-label products in the consumer packaged-goods industry. Today, store brands are a $50 billion business in the food, drug, and mass-merchandising channels, up from $30 billion in 1996, according to the Private Label Manufacturers Association and Information Resources Inc. Their market share has also grown. Store brands accounted for more than 20 percent of unit sales and almost 16 percent of dollar volume in supermarkets in 1999, compared with 18.6 percent of units and about 14 percent of dollars in 1995.

This isn't to say that brands aren't still a big business across the planet. Even in China, which operates under controlled market rules, the Haier Group's Haier brand of household appliances increased in value by $1.58 billion from 1994 to 1999, paralleling similar growth among other Chinese brands. Lianxiang Group's Legend brand of computers increased in value by $1.55 billion during the period; TCL Group's TCL brand of televisions increased $1.31 billion; Sichuan Changhong Electronic Group's Changhong (electronics goods) brand increased $98 million; and Konka Group's Konka brand of televisions appreciated $75 million over the five years.

The competitive advantages of controlling both sides of a transaction help explain the success of retailer-controlled brands such as the Gap's denim lines, and Gateway going direct to consumers, and exclusive marketing agreements between a manufacturer and reseller such as Kmart and Martha Stewart. Branded manufacturers that ignore the power of vertical integration do so at great peril.

Conventional supply-chain wisdom relies on tools that simply fail to address the realities of the modern market—especially the reality of who the new consumers are and what they want and demand from business. For example, longitudinal demographic and sales data have historically formed the basis of many companies' short- and long-range marketing, merchandising, and advertising plans. But Consumer Relevancy demands more. It requires another layer of information, one that provides context in addition to traditional content and that allows us to look at end users not in the traditional demographic terms we've always used to measure them, but in new ways—grouped by values and their affinity toward one of the five Relevancy attributes.

The lessons learned from Consumer Relevancy ought to force all supply-chain partners to look beyond transactions to motivation and behavior. For example, one project we worked on ultimately grouped seniors and teenagers as a cohort for a reseller of multimedia entertainment products and other durable goods. Both age groups were looking for the same set of characteristics (not being rushed, a comfortable place to meet friends, coffee and snacks, easy-to-find information on artists), yet they obviously wanted very different products and a very different environmental look and feel. And somewhat ironically, both cohorts wanted something installed in that environment the retailer hadn't thought of—couches! We assume teenagers and senior citizens use couches in different ways, but both cohorts felt couches would have improved their total experience with the retailer. Ultimately, this work impacted the layout and design of the store, with a central snacking area that served both ends of the store, one of which was configured for Generation Y, the other for the sixtysomething set. Sadly, to date at least, there still aren't any couches in the stores. In this case, we discovered not just what products consumers wanted but the kind of environment in which they wanted to make their purchases. This approach has profound implications for issues as diverse as trading-partner selection and allocation of marketing and promotional dollars, advertising, and consumer services. Our families, forced to endure more than two years of nonstop badgering about what they and their friends think about this advertisement or that service, now actually laugh out loud at the stream of product feature and function advertising. "What about service?" they ask. "Why is it that if I call the 800 number before 9 A.M. or after 4 P.M. I get a recording?" "I called to ask about a product of theirs and where to buy it, and their only response was to tell me to ask the manager at the store where I shop to order it." From our perspective, most companies spend way too much on advertising and way too little on consumer services.

In 1999 advertisers in the United States spent $215 billion trying to influence consumer opinion through messages placed everywhere from the Yellow Pages to public restrooms, a 6.8 percent increase over 1998 spending levels, according to Robert J. Coen, senior vice president and director of forecasting for Interpublic's Universal McCann. And as this book was going to press, it was estimated that advertising spending might increase an additional 8.3 percent by the end of the year 2000, reaching the $233 billion level. Yet by any objective measure, that spending is increasingly less and less effective. Why? Because the core message of most advertising is focused on price and product features and functions, rather than the development of a balanced message of content and context. Too much advertising is concerned with creating transactions rather than building relationships and emphasizes value over values. In short, it mirrors all of the mistakes being made by most businesses.

This mistake is multiplied by every step a business is removed from the ultimate consumer. As a result, almost all manufacturers and suppliers run the risk of becoming less and less relevant to consumers over time. Consumer Relevancy ought to drive manufacturers to do two things: first, to adjust the message of their advertising to reflect a better balance between content and context; and second, to focus more resources and effort on building consumer-defined values-based relationships with target customers.

This is clearly seen in the area of new-product development. Endless added features, new and improved formulations, concentrates and blends, functions added just because they can be, and the other tricks of covering a lack of real innovation with the veneer of newness aren't appreciated by consumers and often contribute to their confusion. Companies are well advised to confine their new-product development to concepts that offer true—consumer-defined—innovation, address real consumer needs, or offer perceptible consumer benefits. For Dell, RadioShack, Compaq, or Acer, this might mean offering consumer training courses.

Some manufacturers intuitively recognize this principle. BMW clearly understands the power of marrying content and context. The company offers its best customers the opportunity to put their high-end cars—and equivalent models from other manufacturers—through a series of high-performance tests. These tests serve two purposes. First, from a content point of view, they establish BMW as world-class, high-performance vehicles. And second, from the standpoint of context, pre-qualified car enthusiasts get to spend a day doing controlled spinouts, bending the cars through obstacle courses, going into full lock-ups at 70 miles per hour, and testing the limits of their skills, clearly adding to the "BMW experience."

For food companies like Kraft, Kellogg's, Kroger, Ahold, and Del Monte, this might mean offering nutritional counseling or sponsoring mobile cooking schools. Many companies attempt to use the Internet as a vehicle for blending content and context. Kraft's website (www.

kraftfoods.com) attempts to establish a form of online community for harried mothers and other people interested in simple, quick meal preparation. Procter & Gamble's Tide website (www.tide.com) helps consumers find the closest Tide retailer to their homes as well as solve individual fabric-care problems. As of this writing, neither site offers the opportunity to join a chat room, but we think both could be improved—from a context point of view—by creating an opportunity for consumer interaction.

Consumer Relevancy can also be used to help organizations move past new-product development into areas as diverse as brand strategic positioning to enterprise-level brand portfolio management.

The same questions haunt all companies, whether in Asia, Europe, or the Americas. For manufacturers, these questions include "Should the spending on either a high-end or low-end brand be discontinued, allowing for the development of value-added services for the brands that are relevant for a larger market?" and "Is a given high-potential brand deserving of more resources than a so-called corporate heritage brand long associated with the company but failing for several years?" In other words, should Procter & Gamble have supported Pringles during decades of underwhelming sales, or should Kraft have retained ownership of its Kraft Caramel brand? The answers aren't always obvious.

In our first example, Pringles has finally become a robust and profitable brand, largely because consumers' attitudes toward snacking have changed—in no small part thanks to the existence of brands like Pringles. In the Kraft example, as much as consumers loved those little caramels, they loved them only at certain times of the year, making it difficult for Kraft to justify keeping them in its brand portfolio. In a parallel example, should a global company like DaimlerChrysler keep the majority of its R&D funding tied up developing new fuel-efficient minicars for the developing world rather than designing expensive high-performance sports cars for luxury buyers?

Retailers face questions such as "Should I trade promotional allowances for more effective, consumer-friendly, in-store assortment?" and "How do I match the brands I offer to the consumers I serve?" So should Wal-Mart, for example, promote its own laundry detergent and make better gross margins, or should it promote Tide? Should Williams-Sonoma stock Calphalon cookware only, or should it also stock Revere Ware?

Consumer Relevancy also has broad impact in the area of trading-partner selection, especially at a time when the environment in which a product is offered is at least as important as the product itself. As we noted in Chapter 1, Gitano jeans were once moderately high-fashion wear prior to being introduced into Kmart. Maybe channel selection wasn't the only cause of Gitano's fall from fashion grace, but June 12, 2000, when VF Corp. paid a bankrupt Fruit of the Loom $18 million for Gitano's trademarks and inventory, had to be a sad day for brand watchers with long memories.

When you look at categories as diverse as carbonated beverages and moderately priced pens and pencils, ubiquitous distribution, or at least near-ubiquitous distribution, is clearly important. But for manufacturers, not all channels are equal. Some are inherently more profitable. Others drive volume, but only at the expense of short-term profitability and long-term brand degradation. Given this, do Sony's high-end phones belong in RadioShack? If the answer to this question is "yes," then how much support should Sony give RadioShack versus a high-end electronics retailer? Should Sony segment its brands, or manufacture lower-end private-label items for RadioShack? Is the relationship best maintained at a rigid, standardized level, or should Sony engage in joint product development in order to offer products unique to RadioShack that are more closely aligned to its customers' needs? How much should Sony invest in training RadioShack employees about its products? Ideally, every manufacturer would like to enjoy both the benefits of widespread distribution and the advantages of customizing against specific consumer target groups. Trading partners can maximize their profitability over time by aligning with companies whose Relevancy attributes are consistent with their own.

Consumer Relevancy forces a redefinition of competition to include companies that aren't—at first blush—directly competitive. If Barnes & Noble had defined competition in terms of broadening consumer access—and defined access as something other than the number of physical locations—it might have anticipated an Amazon. The pattern holds true in any industry where traditional companies suddenly face the threat of a new competitor. Sam Walton redefined competitive pricing to mean not just low prices but fair and honest pricing and ultimately ended up globally dominating in a category (food and beverage products) in which he initially didn't even compete. The mass marketing of consumer fax machines by Sharp, Panasonic, Brother, and other manufacturers almost instantly redefined part of the competitive environment for delivery companies like Federal Express and UPS, reshaping how customers thought of access and service.

Sometimes the threat is more oblique. The surveying companies that helped lay out what became the interstate highway system probably weren't conscious of the fact that they were delivering a body blow to the power of the railroads, but they were. Similarly, Dell's and Gateway's offers of computer customization and functional next-day delivery were initially hard for traditionally retail-dependent computer companies to counter.

Consumer Relevancy is even more critical in the business-to-consumer Internet space, where the context-dominance lines still aren't firmly established. It is clear that the Internet represents a great opportunity for manufacturers to directly interact with consumers and build and strengthen relationships. But direct fulfillment costs aside, as with so much related to Consumer Relevancy, a manufacturer's Internet positioning—from site design and content to navigational mechanisms, to the opportunity to build and define community, to actual goods and services offered, ought to be shaped by what consumers—not the companies themselves—think is important.

Consumer Relevancy also impacts a manufacturer's alliance and acquisition strategy. Generally, we advocate manufacturers getting more involved in channels that directly interact with consumers, whether this means setting up consumer-direct operations, vertically integrating, or creating other strategic alliances. The closer a manufacturer can get to doing business directly with consumers, the more Relevant they should become, assuming they know how to pay attention. However, we recognize that commerce doesn't occur in a vacuum and that traditional channel partners—particularly large-scale retail distributors—aren't likely to applaud any move by their suppliers to get closer to the end user. The Home Depot, for example, will not allow any suppliers to use their websites to directly sell any of the products the chain carries. At the same time, the alliances between Amazon and a variety of publishers, including the publisher of this book, haven't seemed to damage the relationship of those publishers with Borders and Barnes & Noble. Procter & Gamble, which birthed Reflect.com, a customized beauty website, spun off that business and now enjoys a new relationship with some of its fiercest physical-world competitors—a relationship that benefits Reflect users, P&G, and its "competitors." Ahold USA, the American arm of the Netherlands-based international retailer, purchased Peapod and significant assets of Streamline (before its final collapse) as a way of getting closer to consumers.

At the end of the day, most manufacturers are dependent upon their distribution channels for determining consumer perceptions of access, experience, service, and price, a fact that can sometimes place them at odds with their customers. David Nichol launched the President's Choice line of consumer packaged goods at Canada's Loblaw supermarket chain around the value proposition that consumers shouldn't pay a "brand tax" when private-label brands are "as good or better" than national brands. Chips Ahoy found itself used (in a negative light) to promote the efficacy of President's Choice Decadent Chocolate Chip cookies. The choice facing the Chips Ahoy brand manager was simple—let his brand get attacked by a customer or lose distribution in Canada's largest supermarket chain, not exactly a "Lady and the Tiger" choice since there was a hungry tiger behind both doors.

Think of a foodservice company providing a superior-quality product, say, Kobe beef, to a dirty restaurant with rude service and high prices. The danger is that Kobe beef can become associated with those negatives in the consumer's mind. In today's society, the old adage of "Build a better mousetrap, and the world will beat a path to your door" is generally untrue. Access is dependent largely on the channel, whether that channel is owned by the manufacturer or a third party. Even the Internet, with its promise of ubiquitous distribution, is suspiciously dependent on such decidedly old-economy concepts as supply chains and reverse logistics.

Frito-Lay and Coca-Cola both acknowledge that their distribution infrastructures are key to their competitive domination of their categories. Yet for some brands, domination on the access attribute can, ironically, cause damage. For generations of college students east of the Mississippi, Coors was once considered the Holy Grail of hops-based beverages, commanding a premium bootleg price and high social-status points. Coors' popularity continued despite the fact the beer wasn't pasteurized, and as a result the taste of many of those brews so carefully transported across the country by Volkswagen vans was, to put it charitably, sub-optimized. It didn't matter. But once Coors expanded its distribution and began to compete nationally, it became just another beer, and its price point and cachet suffered accordingly. There are dozens of other examples.

Indie bands that sign deals with major labels—gaining significantly improved distribution—are often attacked by their most rabid fans for "selling out." Vernor's ginger ale, once the pride of Detroit, lost its sense of uniqueness—even in the Motor City—once it went into broader distribution. And a growing number of people have discovered that they don't really need to go to Orlando to experience Disney World or Universal Studios when they can buy souvenirs at the local mall.

Service also is often reliant on the channel. Custom-mixing paint, tailoring suits, and automotive detailing are all examples of real channel-dependent customization. Differentiation can be achieved in several ways: by directly reaching out to consumers after a purchase; by analyzing purchases made by individuals or households; through customized product communication; affinity marketing; and even new-product development. The Internet can play an important role in helping manufacturers dominate on experience or service, while simultaneously reducing their reliance on the channel. If a manufacturer's website provides interesting and helpful information, allows for order-status checking, in-stock availability, meaningful interaction, and community development, it has the potential to raise its grades on these two attributes.

This is a lesson profitably learned by brands and companies like Tide, Pampers, General Mills' Quisp, and CNN, which have managed to improve their grade on service or experience by creating positive direct interactions with consumers on the Web. It will become increasingly more and more important for manufacturers to focus on this as the next generation of consumers comes of age, unless they're prepared to cede context in cyberspace to their trading partners in the same way they have in the physical world.

SELF-DIAGNOSTIC: SUPPLY CHAIN

- Do your trading partners mirror your primary and secondary value propositions, or do their offerings stress attributes that conflict with those on which you go to market?
- If you're a manufacturer, are you concerned with losing control of the context in which consumers see your products, and, if so, what are you doing about it?
- If you're a retailer, what position do you take when your trading partners go direct to consumer, i.e., do you see their efforts as brand building or an attempt to pirate sales?
- If you're a reseller, have you thought through your Relevancy positioning and, if so, how have you communicated it to your trading partners?
- If you're a manufacturer, have you established clear and coherent strategies for developing effective context that addresses the values of the current—and upcoming (wired)—generations of consumers?

CHAPTER 10

Consumer Relevancy
and the Future

As William A. Sherden pointed out in *The Fortune Sellers: The Big Business of Buying and Selling Predictions,* prediction is the world's second-oldest profession, in spite of the fact that it lacks the moral integrity, intellectual acceptability, and general social respectability of the first. So why bother talking about the future at all? There are several reasons. First, because whatever else we believe about the future, most of us would agree in principle that it will be different from what we know today, and that difference may be accompanied by either opportunity, or threat, or both. Second, because with any luck, the future is inevitable. And finally, because in the rapidly changing world and business climate in which we find ourselves, none of the old rules that most of us learned during the course of our careers seem to work quite as well as they used to, assuming they work at all.

As Jasper Kunde, cofounder of Denmark's Kunde & Co., one of Scandinavia's largest integrated advertising agencies, noted in his book *Corporate Religion: Building a Strong Company Through Personality and Corporate Soul,* "The problem for all international companies is that budgetary controls based on forecast sales are technical, dead mechanisms.

Most management tools have their roots in the past, when the only interesting thing is the future. I've heard people say, quite seriously, that there is no point in trying to predict the future. But if you don't have ideas about it, or really want to be part of it, you have already lost."

Exercise

Here are two examples designed to demonstrate both the opportunity offered by thinking about the future and the dangers inherent in that opportunity. Imagine for a minute that you are in charge of strategic planning for your company. You're charged with creating a ten-year plan to help your company leapfrog its competition, dominate its market, and even expand into totally new offerings. Fair enough? All right, now let's add an increased level of difficulty. Close your eyes for a moment and imagine that it's 1957. Ozzie and Harriet are the symbols for the perfect lifestyle, the happily married suburban couple with two impish but obedient children. Everyone on the block drives the same kind of car; everyone on the block eats together and serves their families Campbell's soup; all the houses look alike; everyone (who's anyone) shops at the same stores for the same products; everyone watches the same three television stations.

Now, fast-forward ten years to the Summer of Love. Those impish kids are openly taking drugs, scoffing at all authority figures, having sex in public, and questioning the same corporations their parents identified with so strongly. Think for a minute. Was the "future" of 1967 visible from 1957? The right answer is "yes and no." Certain elements of what became the future were already in place—elements such as television and all those baby-boomer hormones just waiting for the opportunity to manifest themselves. The civil rights movement was tracing the template of mass protest in the South. And around the world, in a place most Americans couldn't find on a map, a Southeast Asian freedom fighter named Ho Chi Minh was battling to free his nation from the French. So connections could have been drawn, inferences could have been made, and maybe somebody could have crafted a story anticipating "the sixties," but it's still doubtful anyone could have sold the potential of marketing a social revolution to a corporate audience.

Let's take an example that might be more familiar to a contemporary audience: the Internet and the revolution that has followed in its wake. Close your eyes again, and imagine that it's now 1989. The smartest corporate minds are gathered together in a remote location, thinking about the decade to come and attempting to map out successful future business strategies. The ARPANET (Advanced Research Projects Agency Network), a sophisticated system of linked computers, had been created in 1969 as a way of protecting the U.S. Department of Defense's computer system against nuclear attack. The French had demonstrated the commercial viability of a mini-Internet (Minitel, launched in 1981), and writers such as theologian Pierre Teilhard de Chardin (*The Phenomenon of Man,* 1955) had, with considerable amounts of poetic license, imagined a global communications network uniting the planet, later described by novelist William Gibson (*Neuromancer,* 1993) as "cyberspace."

But the truth is that when the digital market hit (as had happened in France with Minitel), the pornography industry was the only commercial enterprise that really seemed to have figured out how to make money through online commerce. Perhaps no surprise, then, that most of the attendees at our hypothetical 1989 meeting would have failed to include the Internet, the World Wide Web, cyberspace, e-commerce, or any similar idea in their ten-year plan. And yet what did the Internet change? Why, just about everything, of course. Yet, from the point of view of 1989, the future—in this case a future already partially developed and at most only four years away—was inconceivable except to a handful of computer whizzes. But if you were around then, you shouldn't feel too bad. After all, even Bill Gates, the whizzes' whiz, managed to miss the call.

In all fairness, it isn't that easy to draw linear connections even in retrospect. One can see how the intersection of, say, all those boomer hormones and the invention of the birth-control pill helped bring passion to the Summer of Love, but keep in mind that the existence of guns and trigger fingers at the same time didn't result in a Summer of Slaughter. You could fill volumes with people's foolish predictions about the future, so why should we think about the future at all? Perhaps that's a question best addressed to the railroad industry, network television, etc.

The Case for the Future and the Future of Relevancy

At the beginning of this book, we suggested that while the attribute elements (price, service, access, product, and experience) of Consumer Relevancy have remained unchanged since the days of commercial prehistory, their specific definitions have changed radically at any given period. Now, if we believe the future is—at least in any significantly meaningful sense—unpredictable, or difficult to predict at best, how can we be so sure the attributes will continue to be present in whatever digital or physical markets may emerge, or have any sense of what their meaning might be? The simplest, but perhaps least satisfying, answer relies on a historical approach. We believe it is impossible to find an example of free, or at least quasi-free, market conditions in which the Relevancy attributes aren't present. Of course, this alone isn't enough to guarantee that the Relevancy model will hold true in the future.

While this isn't a social-anthropology textbook, we'd like to go out on a limb and suggest that the attributes are somehow inherently integral to the way people go about commerce. We're not positing some form of commercial "law" here but, rather, suggesting that the attributes emerge as almost preconditions to commercial relationships. In all relationships, there is some form of buyer, some form of seller, some object or service being bartered for, and some medium of exchange, all of which intersect at some point in time and space. Whether the exchange occurs in the digital boundaries of cyberspace or at the corner deli, we can expect to find the same ingredients present. The cornerstones of the Relevancy theory are quarried out of our sense of self-awareness, our awareness of the ability of others to positively and negatively influence us, and the necessity for a common set of values on which to base exchanges. We can't conceive of a world in which something of a perceived value isn't exchanged for something else with its own perceived value. And if such a world is possible, you won't need business books to prosper in it.

What We Can (Tentatively) Know for Sure About the Future

In Chapter 1 we cited Jonas Ridderstråle and Kjell Nordström, the shaved-headed bad boys of the Stockholm School of Economics, who end their *Funky Business: Talent Makes Capital Dance* by noting, "People expect good stuff. They have become used to great value for money. And they can get that from almost all companies around the world. So, being great is no longer enough. . . . By focusing only on the hardcore aspects of business we risk becoming irrelevant. And, trust us, irrelevancy is a much greater problem than inefficiency." We couldn't agree more, but for significantly different reasons. Ridderstråle and Nordström believe that "[t]he only way to create real profit is to attract the emotional rather than the rational consumer and colleague by appealing to their feelings and fantasy." While we agree that Relevancy is the key to building a strong business today, and will be mandatory to even being in business in the future, we strongly believe it is the customer rather than the enterprise who increasingly defines Relevancy. And while we also agree that emotions are important across all of the attributes, we're not prepared to throw out the rational aspects of transactions quite so quickly. So, let's take a look at why it's Consumer Relevancy rather than, say, Corporate Relevancy.

We think the supremacy of the enterprise, the once near-sovereign right of a business to arbitrarily define its commercial terms of engagement with the consumer, is a casualty of the transition from the Industrial Age to the Information and Post-information eras. Consumer Relevancy isn't something businesses can unilaterally offer—it is something they must research, understand, and incorporate into their goods and/or services. Consumers alone know how they define the attributes. One way to think about how Relevancy might work in the future is to think about why we have found it so easy to divide the past into ages, eras, epochs, or other linguistic pigeonholes. Put another way, an easy way to think about the future is to consider how we think about the past. Some methods of dividing up history rely on dominant socioeconomic activities—Hunter/Gatherer, Agrarian, Industrial, Information ages. Others look at the dominant technology or invention of the time—Iron Age, Bronze Age, etc. Still others look at history along military or governance lines—the Age of Charlemagne, the Roman Empire, the Cold War Era, and so on. There are, of course, those who attempt to divide history by activity—the Renaissance, the Age of Exploration, the Atomic Age.

We have looked at all these classification systems and decided they essentially come down to a matter of resonance—what seemed to make sense to the people of the period (or at least what we can impose as making sense to the people of the period). We believe that the rate of social change has accelerated to the point that we no longer have the luxury of having a generation to absorb the convergence of social forces, discontinuities, and technological innovations that typically characterize an age. In fact, we believe that we have already moved out of the Information Age, even though most of you may still feel a bit frustrated as you try to cope with its impact. Rather than worry about what to call this Post-information Age, we've opted for describing how to recognize it. Every "age" generates its own language, symbols, and metaphors, which in turn are incorporated into the language of commerce. We've looked at the most recent three ages and what we see as the dominant metaphors and how those metaphors have been translated into business, advertising claims, and commercial opportunities (see Table 10.1).

Clearly, in order to be Relevant to the consumers living through an "age," business must learn how to effectively translate its language, goods, and services into offerings that resonate with the contemporary consumers. For example, one could argue that part of the problem Monsanto encountered in marketing genetically modified food in Europe was that it couched the offering in essentially Industrial Age language. The concentration on issues of crop yield, pest reduction, etc., would have resonated well in the Industrial Age, when consumers were in awe of chemistry-based claims. But they were perceived as threatening to the Post-information Age audience, with its concerns about corporate pollution and environmental toxicity. A more appropriate campaign might have started with advertising

TABLE **10.1**

The Science of Commerce

SOCIOHISTORICAL "AGE"	DOMINANT SCIENTIFIC METAPHOR	DOMINANT BUSINESS CLAIM	TYPICAL ADVERTISING CLAIM	DOMINANT BUSINESS OPPORTUNITY
Industrial	Chemistry	Product efficacy	"Better living through chemistry" (DuPont)	Improve measurable product functionalities
Information	Physics	Fusion of product and services	"Unleashing the power of connectivity" (Intersil)	Extend value through network of providers
Post-information	Biology	Coevolution of business and consumer ecosystems	"Growing to meet your changing needs"	Appreciation and reverence for life

focusing on the problems of world hunger, especially in terms of its impact on children and the opportunity to prevent needless death and disease. The product would have been identical in both scenarios, but the reception might have been a bit different.

Industrial Age claims still abound ("Wonderclean makes your clothes 75 percent whiter, brighter, or whatever"), but they lose their Relevance to contemporary audiences. Are we supposed to rush out, for example, and buy a car because it isn't like the one our fathers drove? What kind of Relevancy is that? In a world where many products seem to perform with the same level of efficacy (outside a laboratory), what good are claims that can be verified only by a chemist? These are more than just academic questions.

To be successful in the future (and, we'd argue, the present), corporations need to learn how to address consumers on their own terms. Product efficacy is great, but it may not be Relevant to an environmentally aware consumer if it comes at the cost of air, land, and/or water pollution. Right-hand-turn access into a parking lot is important, but not as important to a working single mother who has just picked up her children from day care as the ability to find what she needs and get out of a store with a minimum of chaos. Price is clearly important, but to the upscale couple with no children, a high price tag might be more attractive than a low one. Service and experience are almost entirely subjective even by rigid Industrial Age measures. So what's a company to do?

Well, let's begin with the notion of being open to new possibilities, new language, and new ideas. One literally has to learn how to speak the language of the consumer. Recently we flew back from New York with a woman who worked for an advertising agency specializing in "ethnic marketing." Her company had just been bought by a New York–based company that wanted the Detroit-based firm's knowledge but was wrestling to understand why. "They just don't get it," she complained. "They want to do more business in the African-American community, but when they look at a product they don't see the same thing we see. For example, when they look at a Jeep, their mental image is a guy in climbing boots standing on the top of a mountain staring at a sunset. When an African-American urban consumer looks at that same vehicle, they see an upscale luxury vehicle. And when we try to explain this to New York, they just don't seem to understand how urban consumers relate to their vehicles."

The problem was obvious. We had encountered the same issue years ago when we had suggested to a car company that it market fully "tricked out" sport utility vehicles complete with interiors by FUBU and Phat Farm and sound systems whose bass ranges could create potholes. We were told these kinds of cars would be "appropriate" only in urban areas. How, then, we asked, do you account for the fact that hip-hop sells so well in the suburbs of Minneapolis and Des Moines and that for one fateful week in 2000 two very Caucasian Detroit "home boys"—Eminem and Kid Rock—had the number one and two best-selling albums in the country with their respective versions of a sound "only African-American audiences can understand"?

The point here is that different things have different meanings to different people at different times. We know it's a little tough to think about, so we prepared Table 10.2, which shows alternative imaging across the three most recent historical ages:

TABLE **10.2**

The Transformation of Symbols, Meanings, and Conventional Practices—from the Industrial to Post-information Ages

AREAS/OBJECT	INDUSTRIAL	INFORMATION	POST-INFORMATION
Computation	Slide rule	Computer	DNA computation
Medicine	Scalpel	Laser surgery	Genomic manipulation
Communication	FedEx	E-mail	Sentient software
Business presentation	Overheads	PowerPoint	Virtual reality
Ideal employment model	"For life"	"For now"	"Free agent"
Sources of insights on the consumer	Traditional longitudinal demographic models; focus groups	Scan data; Internet cookies	Only what the consumer lets you see
Products	Built to last	Inherently obsolete	Evolve with user
Organizational model	Hierarchical	Team	Ad hoc
Automobile	Transportation	Status	Mobile environment
Educational model	Learning	Continuing education	Unlearning, relearning
Community	Physical	Virtual	Physical/Virtual
Retail	House products	Sell products	Educate consumers
B2B trading models	Linear supply chains	Non-linear value chains; networks	Economic webs
Air travel	Luxury	Necessity	Selective necessity
Dominant financial expert	Bank	Broker	Individual
Social goal	To belong	To excel	To be fully realized
Consumer attitude toward business	Implicit faith and evolving skepticism	Cynicism	Selective faith based on information
Medicine	To cure disease	To prevent disease	To extend both quality and duration of life
Dominant learning tool	Print	Screen	Streaming multimedia
Marketing tools	Mass marketing	Mass customization	User demand
Enterprise goal	Growth and profit	Survival	Evolution and learning
Artifact	The factory	The chip	The idea

Into the Ether: Consumer Relevancy Online

Some might argue that in the commercial world of the future, the world of e-commerce, whether business-to-business or business-to-consumer or both, some of the Consumer Relevancy attributes begin to lose their luster. Of course, that's not our position. We believe the attributes will endure, taking on different specific meanings appropriate to the times. Table 10.3 suggests what this change of definition might look like:

TABLE 10.3

The Future Face of Commerce

ATTRIBUTE	COMMERCE TODAY	FUTURE COMMERCE
Access	Location and ability to navigate through a location	Link to portals
Experience	My response to your environment	Your ability to customize an environment for me
Price	Unit cost	Total costs
Product	Inherent features	Upgrades
Service	You recognize me	You represent me

Of course, this is only one set of possibilities. We don't suggest that we can actually predict the future, but we do think it's important for every business to find ways to think about how its future may be different from its present and the implications of that change on its offerings. One way to get at this is through one of the oldest communication devices known to human beings: the story. We're big believers in the power of the story and what we see as an increasing future role for corporate storytellers. The case for storytelling has been documented in any number of books, from Rolf Jensen's *The Dream Society: How the Coming Shift from Information to Imagination Will Transform Your Business* to Jim Taylor's and Watts Wacker's *The 500-Year Delta: What Happens After What Comes Next* and *The Visionary's Handbook: Nine Paradoxes That Will Shape the Future of Your Business.*

But as we think about the future of Consumer Relevancy, we're intrigued by the use of a very special kind of story, the scenario. Scenario planning is a mainstay in the toolboxes of most futurists, and appropriately so. Every scenario planner has a unique methodology he or she claims to be "the" way to do scenario planning. We're not interested in weighing in on whose method is best. In fact, we're about to offer an exercise that combines some of the best features of all the methodologies—bottom-line scenario planning for the Consumer Relevancy set.

Basically, the idea is this: Since the future is unknowable, is there a method that can help you anticipate what might happen, help you think about what might happen in a different way, or test your readiness to cope with several alternative futures? The answer for scenario planners is a decided "yes." The construction of scenarios involves a fairly comprehensive process of identifying trends and uncertainties that might impact a business, an industry, or even a government. But again, we're not as interested in the methodology as the output—the scenario itself is really nothing more than a story about what life might look like in a future or several futures. We've saved you the methodological heavy lifting and cut to the bottom line. So here are the results, five stories about the future that examine whether or not our five attributes—price, service, access, product, and experience—will survive in the increasingly complex world of the third millennium. Here we go:

Price: The Price Was Right . . . and Wrong

Luke's finger paused millimeters above the garage-door digipad. In his mind he knew what sat behind the door: his Global Motors' Rocketbike, the XTRM16 model, sitting on its stand, a gleaming black-and-chrome vision of speed and power and a perpetual reminder of how much he still had to learn about the world. His parents had warned him that any deal that seemed too good to be true probably was, or some such Information Age cliché, but what did they know? They had grown up before people even had personal bots programmed to find them goods and services that they weren't even aware they wanted, all at price points that were—at least marginally—affordable.

His bot had found the bike on Lama Line, the Sino-Tibetan cyber-exchange. It was a classic, built in 2025. Luke was so excited that he made the mistake of telling his father about the bike, only to hear a thousand paternal reasons he shouldn't get it, ranging from "It isn't safe" to some story about losing credits on Lama Line years ago. His parents' "bots" were programmed not to shop on bootleg exchanges, but all the kids knew cybershops like Lama Line were where the really "evo" stuff could be found. Besides, he had been making his own money on his website since he was nine, and his bot wouldn't have suggested it if he couldn't afford it.

So Luke had ordered the bike, which came exactly as advertised. Even his parents had to know that misrepresentation of products on any exchange could result in permanent unplugging, thanks to the Universal Consumer Protection Act of 2015, which regulated commerce on what Luke called the Exchange but what his parents, with their terminally retro flair, still insisted on calling the Web. Even Luke had to admit the sale price seemed too good to be true, but that's why you jacked into places like Lama Line in the first place. It seemed like a bargain, such a deal, that he had never bothered to check the service agreement, which—he quickly learned—compelled him to ship the bike back to Lhasa every 10,000 miles for service at the only authorized dealer on the planet. And while the bike itself was a steal, the shipping and service fees were plain old-fashioned robbery. Without service the bike couldn't be certified road safe, and without certification it couldn't be insured. No insurance, no plates; and no plates, no riding.

The deal of a lifetime proved too expensive, and so the bike sat on its stand, a silent reminder of how he had been cheated. Luke had been so mad he had deleted his bot's central memory, in a programming maneuver known as a LoBOTomy, turning it into a cybersquash. But it didn't help—his credits were still irretrievably gone. What's worse, he had to admit Dad was right—a higher honest price was better than a lower-priced "deal."

Service: Don't Worry About a Thing, Sir, I'll Take Care of It

Adam flew through his bills with an enviable economy of keystrokes, until he came to his monthly Walworldmarket invoice. Pausing, he stopped to consider how much easier the company made his life. When his firm had transferred him to Scandinavia, Adam had felt more than a little apprehensive. There were all the language and logistics issues, but working in another country didn't mean you really *belonged* there.

Feeling a little sadder and less confident than he would have wanted to admit, Adam had walked to his "neighborhood" Walworldmarket on his second day in Stockholm. Swiping his "Guest" card on his way in the door, he shuffled down the first aisle. "Good afternoon, Adam," he heard a voice boom behind him. Startled, Adam turned to see whom the voice belonged to. "Oh, I'm so sorry," a smiling giant of a man said. "Perhaps I startled you, or perhaps your profile needs updating. Is it still permitted to call you by your first name? Oh, I'm being so stupid! My name is Jonas, and I have the very great privilege of managing this store. Tell me, er, Adam, what brings you to Stockholm, and how can I assist you?"

Almost despite himself, Adam began to relax. He had, it seemed, unwittingly caused the only person he had really "met" in his adopted city to feel off balance, which was exactly how he felt. "No, no, Adam's fine, and you didn't startle me—it's just that I wasn't planning on anyone recognizing me. Actually, I moved here yesterday. My company transferred me to oversee the Digicom business, but, well, how did you know I was me?" Relaxing a bit, Jonas said, "I didn't, until your card swipe triggered a radio-frequency signal to be sent to my pager containing a brief profile—where you're from, what you preferred to be called, and so on. Please, may I offer you a coffee or tea?" Adam liked Jonas's openness and honesty. "That'd be fine," he said, "but I don't quite remember this kind of treatment back home."

Smiling, the Swede pointed Adam toward the dining room. "That's because at Walworldmarket, we pride ourselves on not just identifying our customers but, in effect, acting as their full-service representatives. Your profile indicates that when you're at home—well, your old home, that is—

you preferred to use our automated ordering service, our digital shopping list, and other fairly passive services," said Jonas. "Naturally, we respect your preferences and concentrate on making sure those systems get you what you really want. We screen out advertising messages and new product offerings we know you wouldn't like, for example. However, it's been our experience that when one of our guests is so far from home, they often need slightly different service. So when I knew you were in the store, I appeared, frightened you, and then generally made a fool of myself, all in the name of good service."

For the first time since he had found out he was being transferred, Adam laughed out loud. "Jonas, you're great. I was beginning to think I'd never meet anybody besides the people I work with. I'm glad you recognized me for what I am—a stranger very far away from home and grateful for a friendly face." Now it was the Swede's turn to smile. "Well, to tell you the truth, the store really speaks for itself. The aisle scanners offer automatic translation of package graphics and convert the price into any of the world's twelve currencies. Outside of a few items, you'll find much of the inventory remarkably like what you would see in the States. And I'll assign a shopping assistant to help you program your shopping profile to reflect the difference in selection and introduce you to some of our fine domestic products. We're happy to have you as 'our' customer now." Adam thought for a moment. "Jonas, if it's all right with you, could you walk me through that profile, and do you know of any good restaurants in the neighborhood? I'm not really much of a cook, even with a quantum oven." "It would be my pleasure to help you with the profile, Adam," Jonas said. "But I'll only recommend a restaurant if you allow me the pleasure of taking you out to dinner this evening—if, of course, it would be convenient, er, I mean . . ." "It would be more than convenient," Adam said. "You know, I'm really pretty hungry. I'm starting to feel like my old self again. I must have just had a touch of jet lag."

Access: Flying the Friendly Ties

Gabriel sank back in the seat of the Virgin Transglobal 878 and gathered his thoughts. He logged on to the screen that had, just seconds before, been concealed under his left armrest, choosing from a keypad menu ranging from "Somatic Options" to "Entertainment," "Shopping," and the rather innocently labeled "Commerce." Reluctantly, Gabriel pressed "Commerce," noting that it seemed the most-used key on the pad. He entered his secure user code and watched as the screen before him hiccuped into life. Using the screen's visual monitor to guide the mouse, he selected the "Expenses" icon. Using the built-in scanner, Gabriel entered his last two hotel bills and his airplane-ticket receipts. The data were immediately integrated into his corporate expense portfolio. Gabriel sipped his mineral water, waiting for the polite but firm digital red flag he knew the airline ticket would trigger. A few seconds later, it appeared—a small blinking message that read, "The firm thanks you for your prompt expense download and wishes to remind you that coach class on planes in the 867 series or below is recommended for all trips of less than 2.5 hours between continents."

Huffing to himself, Gabriel reached for the digital keyboard. "Integrate this expense entry against the secured reason for this trip," he typed. And, he thought to himself, *when you do you'll notice that traveling on Virgin's 878 series allows me to access the company's Executive Class service portal, which connects me to its Advanced Translation desk, which comes in handy when one is preparing a presentation for a company in Ulan Bator and doesn't speak any Mongolian dialect!* There were other benefits as well. Virgin's alliance partner in central Asia ran the only decent hotels south of Lake Baikal, east of Turkey, and west of central China. No ticket on Virgin, no access to the hotel. In addition, the hotel chain was linked to the only reliable transit company in the region, and staying there also gave you access to a translator-guide, although Gabriel didn't need that service this trip. And, if that weren't enough, his medical provider had a Medlink agreement with the hotel's Wellness Network, which guaranteed that should a runaway pony run over his foot, Gabriel could receive adequate medical care until he could get home.

These not-so-subtle benefits were probably lost on the firm's accountants who, rumor had it, were really sentient software programs that had overpowered the people who had been chained to them years ago and were now exacting revenge on any carbon-based life form they could coerce. "The integration you requested has been completed, and your

incremental travel expenditure has been approved. You're reminded, however, that under normal conditions coach class on planes in the 867 series
or below is recommended for all trips of less than 2.5 hours between continents." Smiling to himself in spite of his impatience with policy, Gabriel
hit the "Shopping" icon on the keypad and scrolled through a list of
Virgin's exclusive trading partners' newest offerings. "Yeah," he thought,
"and if I wasn't on an 878, it might be just a tad more difficult to have
this beluga caviar airlifted to my hotel room. Oh, well, anything for
the firm."

Product: Mirror, Mirror in My Hand

Sierra stared in amazement at the pocket-size Life Minder sitting in the box
before her. She was nearly 45, and some form of the Life Minder had been
with her since her father bought her first unit when she had graduated from
college. That model had come with a Retro graphics hologram case that,
whenever it was in use, downloaded antique digital footage of classic oldies
singers like the Backstreet Boys, Boyzone, and Ricky Martin from one of
the 460 MTVSONY Media Stations orbiting the earth.

Most Life Minders offered the same basic functions. Essentially digital
diaries, the machines allowed users to record their impressions of life, sample music and video, and capture digipics or holographic representations
of important life events. The text, music, or video images could be recalled
any number of ways, from a straight chronological report (what was I
thinking when I was twenty-seven?) to events (birthdays, etc.), general sub-
jects (jobs, school, and so on) to more intimate issues (from loves to fears).
Advanced models like Sierra's would even trace the development of a user's
thoughts on specific issues from global trade to political philosophy, allowing the owner to retrace the development of what Sierra grudgingly had to
admit were young adult (thirty-five to fifty-five) biases. And given the competitive nature of the global personal-communications industry, almost
every company producing Life Minders offered the same service agreement: twenty-five years parts and labor, covering everything except for
direct user abuse (this happened a lot when people referenced former

spouses and employers); free upgrade downloads for the lifetime of the original owner (policed by retinal scans); and free translation services for the lifetime of the machine if the original owner willed it to a direct descendant living in a different Language Zone.

But Sierra's father had paid a little extra for a feature she hadn't appreciated at the time. Her version of the Life Minder actually "learned" from her entries and ordered new cases when it deemed appropriate. At first, Sierra was a bit disconcerted whenever the Life Minder ordered itself a new cover. "I haven't changed," she'd whisper to herself. "I'm not getting older." Acceptance came in waves. It was easy, for example, to get rid of the Backstreet Boys but a little harder when the high-resolution mirror case was replaced by what the manufacturer called the "Soft Focus" case. Eventually, though, Sierra understood that her Life Minder was like all great products—it morphed into something better whenever something better was really useful. She smiled at the new case that would house the memories of her lifetime, until, of course, a better model came along.

Experience: Color My World

Zack had been looking forward to going to the gym all day. His muscles ached from the tension of simultaneously trying to coordinate procurement bids from 186 corporate nation-states. The actual tracking of the bidding was all done digitally, of course, but even in 2045 no machine could detect the subtle differences between a microsecond market fluctuation, which could be caused by anything from viral progressions through any given workforce on any given day, to the increasingly frequent transmission errors and what Zack liked to call "the Blink" in an obscure homage to an old Information Age business phrase his mother had explained to him when he was younger. Zack had amassed a fortune in credits by sensing the difference, hedging the market, and buying or selling accordingly. "Yes," he thought to himself, "you blink, and I buy or sell, and you sit and wonder how I knew you were sweating through the climate control when I'm two thousand or three thousand miles away from you."

Any number of increasingly sophisticated infinite-regression complexity programs had been developed that attempted to do what Zack seemed to intuit, but in the long run, they weren't any more successful than the early chaos analyzers that people had tried to use to predict fluctuation patterns in the old stock exchanges. In fact, Zack didn't know how he did what he did—he just knew that it worked and it was profitable.

With all his success, Zack could have joined any health club in the city. A number of them had actually solicited his business, offering to waive his fees in exchange for having the city's most successful and sought-out financial adviser as a member. But Zack liked the Jungle Club, insisting, in fact, on paying a full membership. It wasn't that the Jungle Club offered anything that different from a product or service standpoint, as most of the major clubs offered the same equipment, from pools to personalized digital trainers who tracked every calorie burned and, unfortunately for some, apparently every one ingested. Almost every club analyzed a variety of factors, from age to weight to performance profiles, and then ordered specifically designed menus for the following week. And most of the better clubs sent abbreviated weekly or monthly reports to a designated health-care provider.

In most respects, the Jungle Club was like all other comparable clubs, but it was significantly different in one critical—at least for Zack—respect. The club's Mood Rooms were actually modified to reflect a customer's daily mood. Entering the club, Zack was greeted (by name, of course) by his health concierge. "Good evening, sir," the concierge said. "Would you care for the Custom Environment as usual?" "Yes," Zack said. "Very well," the concierge said. "Let's just step up on the machine for a moment." "The machine" was really a sophisticated health meter that sampled a variety of things, from pulse rate to skin temperature to retinal reaction to a series of varied images, and calibrated a subject's mood. That information was then fed into the club's central memory unit, which compared it with past data, searched through an active and passively constructed (user) data bank, and modeled the appropriate environment.

No matter how many times Zack went to the club, he never experienced quite the same environment. The music was by the same group but from a different year; the visuals might be similar, but the perspective was subtly different; and programmed environmental elements (smells, humidity, wind) differed ever so slightly, even between days when Zack would have sworn he felt exactly as he had the day before. The concierge had told him that some people's environments never changed. "But yours, sir, always has to change," he said. "After all, you're always trying to feel that difference in things, aren't you? Give you exactly what you are comfortable with, and you'll be vaguely uncomfortable. You're happy only when you're looking for that little difference." And that, Zack had to agree, was exactly why he kept coming back to this place, even with so many new places bidding for his business. At the Jungle Club, they recognized a hunter when they saw one.

We hope these stories help you see both how the attributes might survive and how their definitions might change. As we said earlier, we can't predict what the future will really look like, but we do know one thing: From the time the first person traded a shiny stone for some brightly colored feathers, all commercial transactions have had certain things in common, and those things are our five attributes. Markets are changing daily. Industries are consolidating. E-commerce is fighting for its rightful place in the commercial tableau. Consumers have climbed out of the convenient demographic boxes we've forced them into and burned those boxes behind them. The complexity of the speed, breadth, and depth of change we face today will pale into insignificance in the face of the change we believe will come. Technology will extend ubiquitously into every corner of our lives. Our search for values will become ever more complex and, in all probability, more difficult. But in this sea of change, we believe there are four beacons whose convergence will define what our future will become:

1. As long as there are people, they will collectively engage in some form of commerce and individually seek out some form of personal-value reinforcement.

2. As long as there are transactions, the five attributes will be present.

3. As long as those attributes are present, they will be measurable.

4. And as long as they are measurable, it will be possible to craft successful, competitive, and profitable market offerings around them, provided those offerings incorporate the contemporary values of the times.

Around the industrialized world, consumers have learned to recognize the power of their own voice, and that voice will not—and cannot—be silenced. It's not difficult to hear that voice, but the real business advantage will fall to those companies that not only hear it but also listen to it and shape their offerings accordingly. And based on what we've found in our work on Consumer Relevancy, that's something much easier said than done.

Notes

1: Field Notes from the Commercial Wilderness

1. Kalle Lasn, *Culture Jam: The Uncooling of America*™ (New York: William Morrow, 1999), p. 40.

2. Based on Robert D. Putnam's analysis of poll data archived at the University of North Carolina and quoted in *Bowling Alone: The Collapse and Revival of American Community* (New York: Simon & Schuster, 2000), p. 47.

3. George Bishop, "What Americans Really Believe: And Why Faith Isn't as Universal as They Think," *Free Inquiry*, July 1, 1999, p. 41.

4. Ronan McGreevy, "Church Invites Whole Nation in for Supper," *The Evening Standard*, March 2, 2000, p. 5.

5. Huston Smith, *Cleansing the Doors of Perception: The Religious Significance of Entheogenic Plants and Chemicals* (New York: Jeremy P. Tarcher/Putnam, 2000), p. 146.

6. "America's Education Choice," *The Economist*, April 1, 2000, p. 17.

7. "1 in 3 of Poor Aren't Covered," snapshot, U.S. Census Bureau data, *USA Today*, July 7, 2000, p. 1a.

8. Steven Greenhouse, "Running on Empty: So Much Work, So Little Time," *The Journal Record*, Dolan Media, November 10, 1999.

9. Cherry Norton, "Stressed Managers Complain of E-mail Overload," *The Independent*, February 24, 2000, p. 9.

10. Results of 1999 symposium, sponsored by the WHO, "Culture, Society, and Depression"; results reported on the World Health Organization website, www.who.org.

11. "Rise in Antidepressant Use at UW–Madison," as reported by the Associated Press, AP Newswire, October 4, 1997.

12. *Foreign Policy*, p. 70, April 1, 2000.

13. "Zenith Media Publication's Advertising Expenditure Forecast, 1990–2000," Zenith Media, 2000.

[14] Zenith Media.

[15] Kalle Lasn, p. 23.

[16] *Ibid.,* p. 24.

2: The New Model for Consumer Relevancy

[1] Calmetta Coleman, "Lands' End Warns on Sales, Sinking Stock," *The Wall Street Journal,* November 12, 1999, p. B8.

[2] Valerie Seckler, "Target's Successful Formula: Upscale Trends with Discounts," *Women's Wear Daily,* November 11, 1998, p. 2.

3: Would I Lie to You?: The Overrated Importance of Lowest Price

[1] Debbie Howell, "The Right Reverend of EDLP," *Discount Store News,* May 24, 1999, p. 46.

[2] Laura Heller, "Leigh Stelmach, Dollar General: A Singular Sense of Mission," *Discount Store News,* December 8, 1997, p. 49.

[3] Jennifer Negley, "Dollar General Is Poised to Grow," *Discount Store News,* November 3, 1997, p. 13.

4: I Can't Get No Satisfaction: Service with a Smile?

[1] Sheila M. Puffer, "Continental Airlines's CEO Gordon Bethune on Teams and New Product Development," *Academy of Management Executive,* August 1999, pp. 28–35.

[2] *Ibid.*

[3] *Ibid.*

[4] *Ibid.*

[5] *Ibid.*

5: I Still Haven't Found What I'm Looking For: Access, Physical and Psychological

[1] Todd Lapin, "Get Rich . . . Quixtar!", *Business 2.0,* August 1, 1999, pp. 135–44.

[2] Lisa Singhania, "Selling-Giant Amway Makes Leap Online," *Cincinnati Enquirer,* September 24, 1999.

[3] Priscilla Donegan, "Wired for Sales," *Grocery Headquarters,* April 2000, p. 44.

4 Winn-Dixie Stores Inc., 1999 Annual Report, p. 8.

5 Angela Hardin, "Tops Sizes Up Smaller Store Format," *Crain's Cleveland Business,* November 15–21, 1999, p. 1.

6 "Wal-Mart Announces Expansion Plans," company news release, October 5, 1999.

7 "Saddle Brook Named Third Villager's Hardware Site in the Garden State," company news release, December 8, 1999.

8 *Ibid.,* p. 4.

6: Why "Good" Is Good Enough: Choice and the Issue of Product *Bandwidth*

1 Priscilla Donegan, p. 44.

7: Do You Really Get Me?: The Experience *Factor*

1 Howard Schultz, as quoted in "Interview with Howard Schultz: Sharing Success," *Executive Excellence,* November 1999, p. 16.

Index

About the Authors

FRED CRAWFORD is an executive vice president with Cap Gemini Ernst & Young (CGEY), the major international management consulting and systems integration firm. He is an internationally recognized strategist who has worked with a wide variety of global companies.

In his current role as managing director of the consumer products, retail, and distribution practice at CGEY, he works with some of the firm's largest and most important clients. He is a sought-after speaker for industry events and a frequent contributor to business and trade publications.

RYAN MATHEWS is a Detroit-based futurist and author, noted for providing creative and innovative business solutions. A popular international speaker and consultant, he is recognized for his expertise and understanding of consumer goods, as well as demographic and lifestyle analysis, and for his work in the areas of e-commerce and the information economy. He has provided consulting services and advice to a variety of international companies, including Cap Gemini, Ernst & Young, Coca-Cola, Unilever, General Motors, and Procter & Gamble.